Common Core State Standards Edition

Everyday Mathematics®

The University of Chicago School Mathematics Project

Teacher's Lesson Guide
Volume 2

Grade 3

Chicago, IL • Columbus, OH • New York, NY

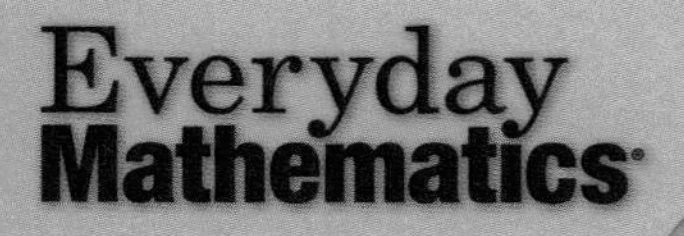

The University of Chicago School Mathematics Project (UCSMP)

Max Bell, Director, UCSMP Elementary Materials Component; Director, *Everyday Mathematics* First Edition; James McBride, Director, *Everyday Mathematics* Second Edition; Andy Isaacs, Director, *Everyday Mathematics* Third Edition; Amy Dillard, Associate Director, *Everyday Mathematics* Third Edition; Rachel Malpass McCall, Associate Director, *Everyday Mathematics* Common Core State Standards Edition

Authors
Max Bell, John Bretzlauf, Amy Dillard, Andy Isaacs, Kathleen Pitvorec, Jean Bell, Mary Ellen Dairyko, Robert Hartfield, James McBride, Peter Saecker

Technical Art
Diana Barrie

Third Edition Teachers in Residence
Lisa Bernstein, Carole Skalinder

Mathematics and Technology Advisor
James Flanders

UCSMP Editorial
Jamie Montague Callister, Don Reneau

ELL Consultant
Kathryn B. Chval

Contributors
Regina Littleton (Office Manager), Kriszta Miner (Project Manager), Carol Arkin, Robert Balfanz, Sharlean Brooks, Mary Dominguez, David Garcia, Rita Gronbach, Mikhail Guzowski, Serena Hohmann, Carla LaRochelle, Deborah Arron Leslie, Curtis Lieneck, Diana Marino, Mary Moley, William D. Pattison, William Salvato, Rebecca A. Schneider, Sheila Sconiers, Sandra Siebert, Kathleen Snook, David B. Spangler, Jean Marie Sweigart, Carolyn Wais, Leeann Wille

Photo Credits
Cover (l)Stockdisc/PunchStock/Getty Images, (r bkgd)Tim Flach/Stone+/Getty Images; **Back Cover** Stockdisc/PunchStock/Getty Images; **iii** (t)The McGraw-Hill Companies, (b) Brian Hagiwara/Brand X/CORBIS; **iv** (t to b)The McGraw-Hill Companies, (2)Comstock/Alamy; **v** The McGraw-Hill Companies; **vi** (t)The McGraw-Hill Companies, (b)Steve Allen/Brand X Pictures/Getty Images; **vii** (t c)The McGraw-Hill Companies, (b)Ryan McVay/Photodisc/Getty Images; **562** (t)Carl Steif/SuperStock, (b)f 1.2/Alamy; **563** Brian MacDonald Photography/FoodPix/Getty Images; **573** Stockbyte/Getty Images; **575** The McGraw-Hill Companies; **634** The McGraw-Hill Companies; **635** Burke/Triolo Productions/Getty Images; **646 647 683** The McGraw-Hill Companies; **698** (t)The McGraw-Hill Companies, (b)Dorling Kindersley/Getty Images; **709** The McGraw-Hill Companies; **711** Blue Line Pictures/Photographer's Choice/Getty Images; **794** The McGraw-Hill Companies; **795** bluemagenta/Alamy; **806 847** The McGraw-Hill Companies; **866** Lawrence Manning/Spirit/CORBIS; **867** Kennan Ward/CORBIS; **877** Dr. Robert Muntefering/The Image Bank/Getty Images; **919 926 938 945** The McGraw-Hill Companies; **Icons** (NCTM l-r)Sharon Hoogstraten/Courtesy of Dave Wyman, Jules Frazier/Photodisc/Getty Images, Comstock/PunchStock, Sundell Larsen/Getty Images, PhotoAlto/PunchStock, Four Elements/V262/CORBIS, Juan Silva/Stockbyte/Getty Images, Digital Vision/Getty Images; (iTLG)C Squared Studios/Getty Images; (Online Content Support)Image Source; (Objective)Brand X Pictures/PunchStock/Getty Images.

Illustration
Liz Allen and Steve Karp

everyday**math**.com

 **Education**

Send all inquiries to:
McGraw-Hill Education
STEM Learning Solutions Center
P.O. Box 812960
Chicago, IL 60681

ISBN: 978-0-07-657689-0
MHID: 0-07-657689-2

Printed in the United States of America.

4 5 6 7 8 9 RMN 17 16 15 14 13 12

McGraw-Hill is committed to providing instructional materials in Science, Technology, Engineering, and Mathematics (STEM) that give all students a solid foundation, one that prepares them for college and careers in the 21st century.

Contents

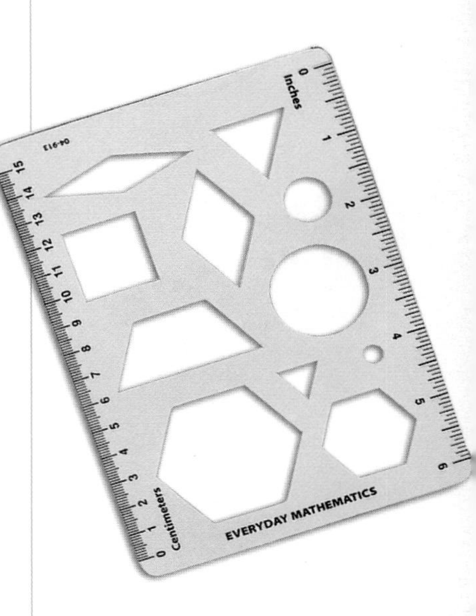

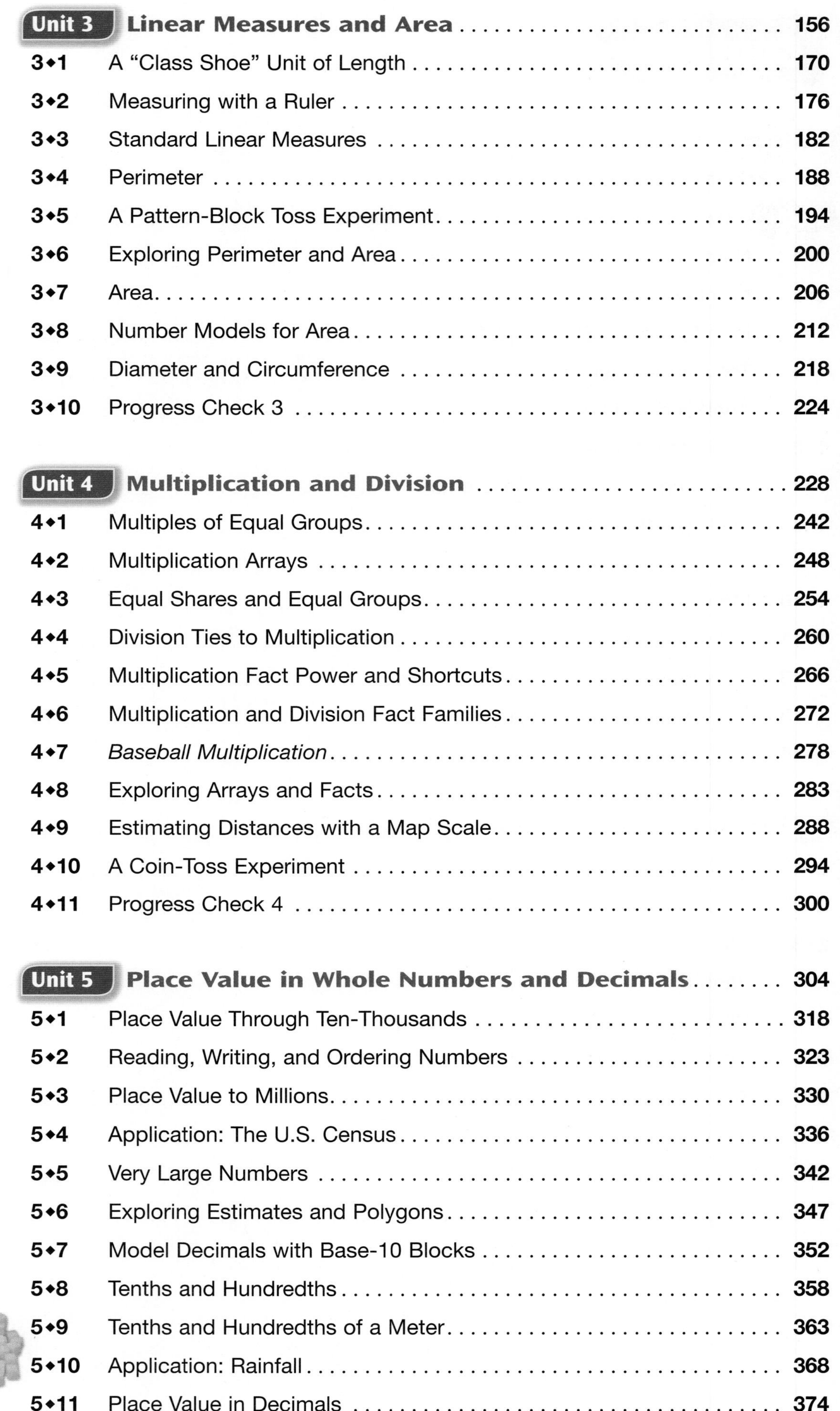

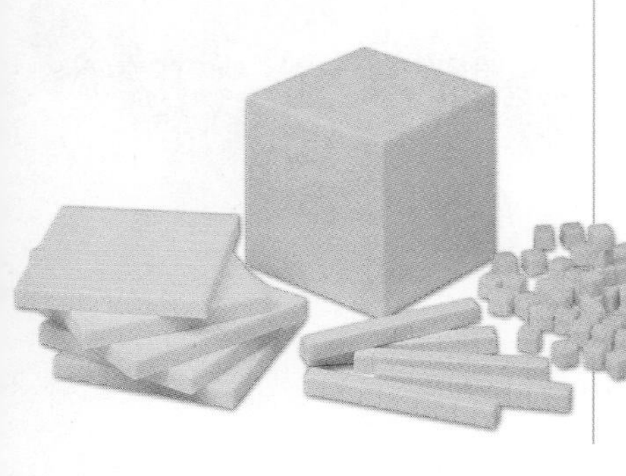

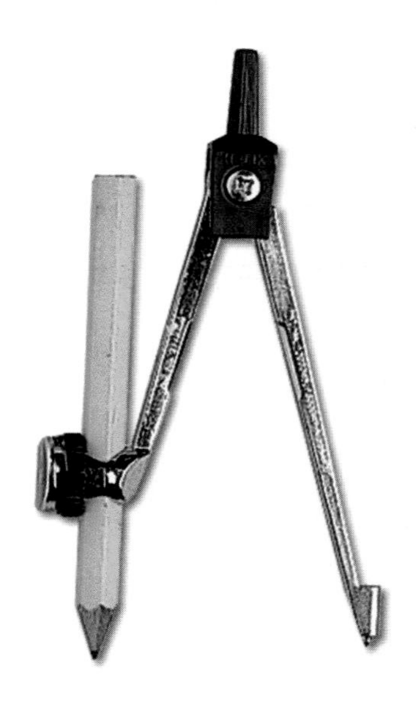

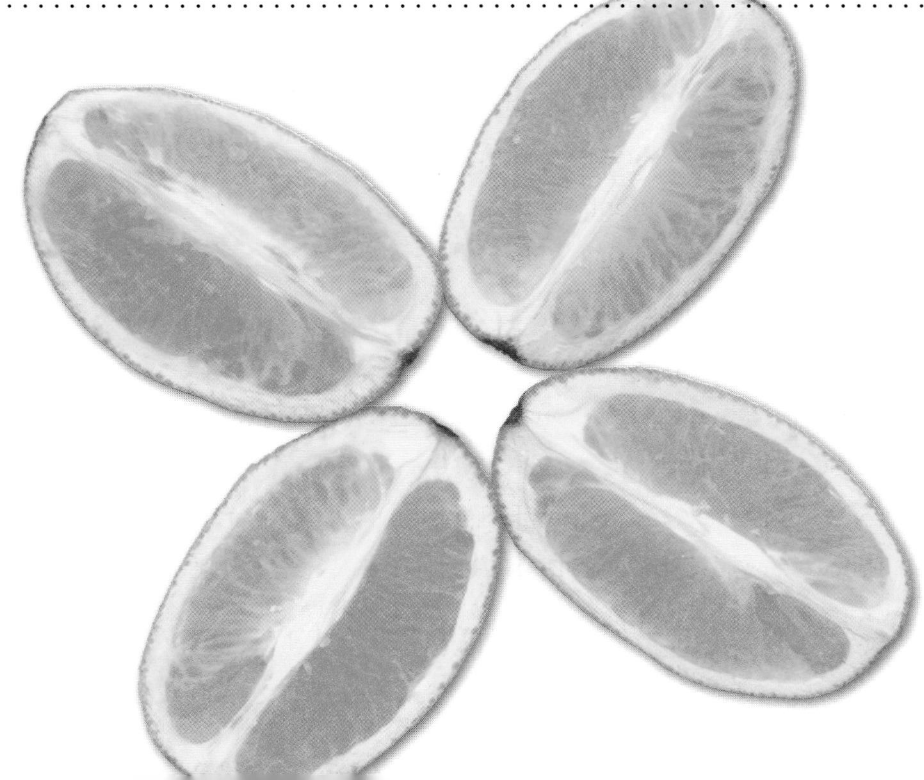

Volume 2

50
40
30
20
10
0
-10
-20
-30
-40
°C
120
100
80
60
40
20
0
-20
-40
°F

12
1
2
3
4
5
6
7
8
9
10
11
WED 7

Unit 7 Organizer

Multiplication and Division

Overview

Unit 7 extends the basic multiplication and division skills children learned in the first half of the year. The skills developed in this unit are useful in their own right, but are also important requisites for the use of estimation and calculators and for the development of multiplication and division algorithms. Unit 7 has four main areas of focus:

- To review multiplication and division patterns,
- To extend basic multiplication facts,
- To practice making estimates of costs, and
- To explore ratios and geometric figures.

Linking to the Common Core State Standards

The content of Unit 7 addresses the Common Core State Standards for Mathematics in *Operations and Algebraic Thinking* and *Number and Operations in Base Ten.* The correlation of the Common Core State Standards to the *Everyday Mathematics* Grade 3 lessons begins on page CS1.

Contents

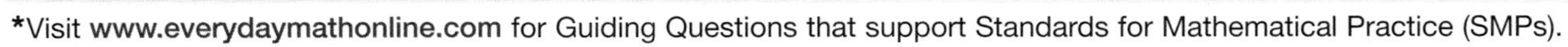
*Visit www.everydaymathonline.com for Guiding Questions that support Standards for Mathematical Practice (SMPs).

Learning In Perspective

	Lesson Objectives	Links to the Past	Links to the Future
7•1	To review square-number facts, multiplication, and division patterns.	Children are introduced to square products when using the Multiplication/Division Facts Table in second grade.	Work with square numbers continues beyond third grade. Children use exponential notation and create square arrays.
7•2	To guide children as they determine which multiplication facts they still need to learn.	Multiplication facts are formally introduced in second grade.	Throughout third grade, children practice multiplication facts through games and in a variety of problem-solving situations. Unit 9 also focuses on multiplication and division.
7•3	To guide children as they practice multiplication and division facts.	Multiplication facts are formally introduced in second grade.	By the end of third grade, children are expected to demonstrate automaticity with multiplication facts through 10×10. By the end of fourth grade, children are expected to demonstrate proficiency with related division facts.
7•4	To introduce parentheses in number sentences.	Children are exposed to the use of parentheses in number sentences in second grade, through the use of parentheses puzzles.	In fourth grade, children review the use of parentheses in number sentences involving more than one operation.
7•5	To provide opportunities to express numbers as sums of products using number models that contain parentheses.	Children are exposed to the use of parentheses in number sentences in second grade, through the use of parentheses puzzles.	In fourth grade, children review the use of parentheses in number sentences involving more than one operation.
7•6	To guide children as they multiply 1-digit numbers by multiples of 10, 100, and 1,000 and divide such multiples by 1-digit numbers.	In second grade, children work with extensions of addition and subtraction facts.	Children continue to work with fact extensions throughout the grades.
7•7	To guide children as they determine when an estimate is appropriate and as they practice making estimates.	In second grade, children estimate costs and use estimation to check the reasonableness of answers.	Estimation and mental arithmetic are found throughout *Everyday Mathematics.*
7•8	To guide children as they multiply multiples of 10 by multiples of 10.	In second grade, children are introduced to the multiplication facts.	Children continue to work with fact extensions throughout the grades.
7•9	To provide experiences with exploring similar polygons, solving ratio problems, and exploring geometric configurations.	In second and third grade, children solve comparison number stories. Children explore geometric configurations and polygons starting in Kindergarten.	In fourth grade, children construct geometric figures with a straightedge and compass. In fourth through sixth grades, they solve rate and ratio problems.

	Key Concepts and Skills	Grade 3 Goals*
7•1	Identify factors, products, square numbers, and patterns in the Multiplication/Division Facts Table.	Operations and Computation Goal 3
	Use the Multiplication/Division Facts Table to generate fact families.	Operations and Computation Goal 3
	Use arrays to find square products.	Operations and Computation Goal 6
	Use the turn-around rule (Commutative Property of Multiplication) to generate multiplication facts.	Patterns, Functions, and Algebra Goal 4
7•2	Identify square products.	Operations and Computation Goal 3
	Describe patterns in factors and products.	Patterns, Functions, and Algebra Goal 1
	Describe and apply the turn-around rule (Commutative Property of Multiplication) to generate multiplication facts.	Patterns, Functions, and Algebra Goal 4
7•3	Use multiplication facts to play *Multiplication Bingo.*	Operations and Computation Goal 3
	Use multiplication facts to solve division facts.	Operations and Computation Goal 3
	Solve "What's My Rule?" problems.	Patterns, Functions, and Algebra Goal 1
7•4	Use basic and extended addition and subtraction facts to solve number sentences.	Operations and Computation Goal 1
	Use multiplication facts to solve number sentences.	Operations and Computation Goal 3
	Write number models with parentheses to match number stories.	Patterns, Functions, and Algebra Goal 3
7•5	Write equivalent names for 10.	Number and Numeration Goal 4
	Use multiplication facts.	Operations and Computation Goal 3
	Write number models with parentheses to match number stories.	Patterns, Functions, and Algebra Goal 3
	Apply properties of multiplication and addition to solve problems.	Patterns, Functions, and Algebra Goal 4
7•6	Recognize multiples of 10.	Number and Numeration Goal 3
	Use multiplication facts to solve problems.	Operations and Computation Goal 3
	Use multiplication facts to solve division problems.	Operations and Computation Goal 3
	Share solution strategies for solving number stories.	Operations and Computation Goal 4
	Use relationships between units of time to solve number stories.	Measurement and Reference Frames Goal 3
7•7	Calculate the cost of an item.	Operations and Computation Goal 2
	Discuss situations where it is sensible to make an estimate and those where it is sensible to compute an exact answer.	Operations and Computation Goal 5
	Use estimation strategies to solve number stories.	Operations and Computation Goal 5
7•8	Find multiples of 10.	Number and Numeration Goal 3
	Find products of multiples of 10.	Operations and Computation Goal 3
	Explore strategies to solve multiplication number stories.	Operations and Computation Goal 4
7•9	Use equal groups to solve problems.	Operations and Computation Goal 6
	Construct 2- and 3-dimensional shapes from straws and twist-ties.	Geometry Goal 2
	Use pattern blocks to explore similar polygons.	Geometry Goal 2

*See the Appendix for a complete list of Grade 3 Goals.

A Balanced Curriculum

Ongoing Practice

Everyday Mathematics provides numerous opportunities for ongoing practice. These activities are embedded throughout the lessons:

Mental Math and Reflexes activities promote speed and accuracy in mental computation.

Math Boxes offer mixed practice and are paired across lessons as shown in the brackets below. This makes them useful as assessment tools. The last one or two boxes on each page preview the next unit's content.

Mixed practice	[7•1, 7•3], [7•2, 7•4], [7•5, 7•7, 7•9], [7•6, 7•8]
Mixed practice with multiple choice	7•1, 7•2, 7•5, 7•8
Mixed practice with writing/reasoning opportunity	7•3, 7•4, 7•6, 7•7

Home Links are daily homework assignments that review the content of the lesson and often contain ongoing facts practice or computation practice.

Minute Math+ problems are offered for additional practice in Lessons 7•6 and 7•9.

EM Facts Workshop Game provides online practice of basic facts and computation.

EXTRA PRACTICE **Extra Practice** activities are included in Lessons 7•6, 7•8, and 7•9.

Practice through Games

Games are an essential component of practice in the *Everyday Mathematics* program. Games offer skills practice and promote strategic thinking. See the *Differentiation Handbook* for ways to adapt games to meet children's needs.

Lesson	Game	Skill Practiced
7•1, 7•4	*Name That Number*	Finding equivalent names for numbers [NN Goal 4 and OC Goals 1–4]
7•3	*Multiplication Bingo*	Multiplication facts [OC Goal 3]
7•6	*Beat the Calculator* (Multiplication)	Multiplication facts [OC Goal 3]
7•8	*Baseball Multiplication*	Multiplication facts [OC Goal 3]
7•9	*Roll to 100*	Mental computation [OC Goal 1]

[NN] Number and Numeration
[MRF] Measurement and Reference Frames
[OC] Operations and Computation
[GEO] Geometry
[DC] Data and Chance
[PFA] Patterns, Functions, and Algebra

Problem Solving 

Good problem solvers use a variety of strategies, including the following:

- Draw a picture.
- Act out the problem.
- Make a table, chart, or list.
- Look for a pattern.
- Try a simpler version of the problem.
- Make a guess and try it out.

The table below lists some of the opportunities in this unit for children to practice these strategies.

Lessons that teach *through* problem solving, not just *about* problem solving

Lesson	Activity
7•1	Find patterns in the Multiplication/Division Table.
7•2	Find an even/odd pattern in products when factors are both even, both odd, one even, and one odd.
7•3	Complete "What's My Rule?" tables.
7•5	Determine how many different ways 10 points can be scored in basketball.
7•7	Solve stories by estimation and calculation.
7•8	Analyze line graph data for patterns in high/low temperatures.

See Chapter 18: Problem Solving in the *Teacher's Reference Manual* for more information.

The Language of Mathematics

Everyday Mathematics provides lesson-specific suggestions to help all children acquire, process, and express mathematical ideas. Throughout Unit 7, there are lesson-specific language development notes that address the needs of English language learners, indicated by ELL.

ELL SUPPORT Activities to support English language learners are in Part 3 of Lessons 7•1, 7•4, and 7•7.

The *English Learners Handbook* and the *Differentiation Handbook* have suggestions for promoting language development and acquisition of mathematics vocabulary. See Unit 7 in each handbook.

Unit 7 Vocabulary

estimate
extended facts
factor
parentheses
product
similar figures
square number
square product

Literacy Connection

Betcha!, by Stuart J. Murphy, Scholastic Inc., 1997

Sea Squares, by Joy N. Hulme, Hyperion Books for Children, 1999

The King's Chessboard, by David Birch, Puffin Books, 1993

The Best of Times, by Gregory Tang, Scholastic Inc., 2002

If You Hopped Like a Frog, by David M. Schwartz, Scholastic Inc., 1999

Anno's Mysterious Multiplying Jar, by Mitsumasa Anno and Masaichiro Anno, Putnam Juvenile, 1999

For more literacy connections, see the *Home Connection Handbook,* Grades 1–3.

Balanced Assessment

Daily Assessments

- **Recognizing Student Achievement** – A daily assessment that is included in every lesson to evaluate children's progress toward the Grade 3 Grade-Level Goals.
- **Informing Instruction** – Notes that appear throughout the unit to help anticipate children's common errors and suggest appropriate problem-solving strategies.

Lesson	Recognizing Student Achievement	Informing Instruction
7•1	Compute multiplication facts. [OC Goal 3]	
7•2	Use arrays to model multiplication. [OC Goal 6]	
7•3	Find and use rules to solve multiplication and division problems. [PFA Goal 1]	
7•4	Recognize that parentheses affect the order of operations. [PFA Goal 3]	Solve a number sentence with parentheses.
7•5	Recognize that the operation inside the parentheses is carried out first. [PFA Goal 3]	Use a systematic way to find solutions.
7•6	Use relationships between units of time to solve number stories. [MRF Goal 3]	Use arrays to show magnitude increases. Write multiplication expressions for products.
7•7	Explain how an estimate was obtained. [OC Goal 5]	Determine when to estimate.
7•8	Multiply 2-digit numbers by a 1-digit number. [OC Goal 4]	
7•9	Identify and describe solid figures. [GEO Goal 2]	

[NN] Number and Numeration
[MRF] Measurement and Reference Frames
[OC] Operations and Computation
[GEO] Geometry
[DC] Data and Chance
[PFA] Patterns, Functions, and Algebra

Portfolio Opportunities

The following lessons provide opportunities to gather samples of children's mathematical writings, drawings, and creations to add balance to the assessment process: Lessons 7•2, 7•3, 7•4, 7•5, 7•6, 7•7, 7•9, and 7•10.

See pages 16 and 17 in the *Assessment Handbook* for more information about portfolios and how to use them.

Unit Assessment

Progress Check 7 – A cumulative assessment of concepts and skills taught in Unit 7 and in previous units, providing information for evaluating children's progress and planning for future instruction. These assessments include oral/slate, written, and open-response activities, as shown below in the sample Progress Check lesson opener.

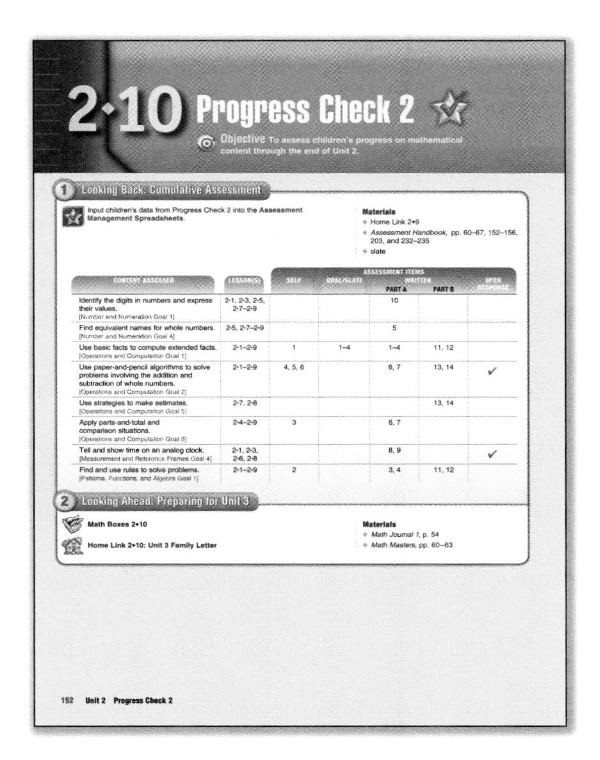

2•10 Progress Check 2

Objective To assess children's progress on mathematical content through the end of Unit 2.

1 Looking Back: Cumulative Assessment

Input children's data from Progress Check 2 into the **Assessment Management Spreadsheets.**

Materials
- Home Link 2•9
- *Assessment Handbook,* pp. 60–67, 152–156, 203, and 232–235
- slate

Content Assessed	Lesson(s)	Assessment Items: Self	Oral/Slate	Written: Part A	Written: Part B	Open Response
Identify the digits in numbers and express their values. [Number and Numeration Goal 1]	2•1, 2•3, 2•5, 2•7–2•9			10		
Find equivalent names for whole numbers. [Number and Numeration Goal 4]	2•5, 2•7–2•9			5		
Use basic facts to compute extended facts. [Operations and Computation Goal 1]	2•1–2•9	1	1–4	1–4	11, 12	
Use paper-and-pencil algorithms to solve problems involving the addition and subtraction of whole numbers. [Operations and Computation Goal 2]	2•1–2•9	4, 5, 6		6, 7	13, 14	✓
Use strategies to make estimates. [Operations and Computation Goal 5]	2•7, 2•8				13, 14	
Apply parts-and-total and comparison situations. [Operations and Computation Goal 6]	2•4–2•9	3		6, 7		
Tell and show time on an analog clock. [Measurement and Reference Frames Goal 4]	2•1, 2•3, 2•6, 2•8			8, 9		✓
Find and use rules to solve problems. [Patterns, Functions, and Algebra Goal 1]	2•1–2•9	2		3, 4	11, 12	

2 Looking Ahead: Preparing for Unit 3

Math Boxes 2•10

Home Link 2•10: Unit 3 Family Letter

Materials
- *Math Journal 1,* p. 54
- *Math Masters,* pp. 60–63

152 Unit 2 Progress Check 2

Core Assessment Resources

Assessment Handbook

- **Unit 7 Assessment Overview,** pages 102–109
- **Unit 7 Assessment Masters,** pages 177–181
- **Unit 7 Individual Profiles of Progress,** pages 252, 253, and 280
- **Unit 7 Class Checklists,** pages 254, 255, and 281
- **Math Logs,** pages 286–288
- **Exit Slip,** page 283
- **Other Student Assessment Forms,** pages 284, 285, 289, and 290

Assessment Management Spreadsheets

The Assessment Management Spreadsheets consist of the Digital Class Checklists and Individual Profile of Progress Checklists. Use them to monitor, record, and report children's progress.

Addressing All Needs

Differentiated Instruction

Adjusting the Activity – suggests adaptations that target advanced learners, English language learners, or learners who need additional instructional support.

ELL SUPPORT / ELL – provides lesson-specific suggestions to help English language learners understand and process the mathematical content.

READINESS – accesses children's prior knowledge or previews content that prepares children to engage in the lesson's Part 1 activities.

EXTRA PRACTICE – provides additional opportunities to apply the mathematical content of the lesson.

ENRICHMENT – enables children to apply or further explore the mathematical content of the lesson.

Lesson	Adjusting the Activity	ELL Support/ ELL	Readiness	Extra Practice	Enrichment
7•1	•	•	•		•
7•2	•		•		•
7•3	•		•		•
7•4	•	•	•		•
7•5	•	•	•		•
7•6	•		•	•	
7•7	•	•	•		•
7•8	•	•	•	•	•
7•9	•	•		•	•

Additional Resources

Differentiation Handbook
Provides ideas and strategies for differentiating instruction.
Pages 90–96

English Learners Handbook
Contains lesson-specific comprehension strategies.
Pages 66–74

Multilingual Handbook
Previews concepts and vocabulary. It is written in six languages.
Pages 131–148

Planning Tips

Multiage Classroom

Companion Lessons from Grades 2 and 4 can help you meet instructional needs of a multiage classroom. The full Scope and Sequence can be found in the Appendix.

Grade 2	7•1, 7•4, 11•7	11•6, 11•9, 12•4	11•6–11•9, 12•4	10•11	7•3, 10•11	7•2, 10•8, 11•9	4•5, 4•6, 10•5	7•2, 10•8, 11•9	5•1, 8•2, 10•7
Grade 3	**7•1**	**7•2**	**7•3**	**7•4**	**7•5**	**7•6**	**7•7**	**7•8**	**7•9**
Grade 4	3•5, 5•1	3•1–3•4	3•3, 3•4	3•10	3•10	5•1, 5•9	4•4	5•9	1•3, 1•5

Pacing for Success

Pacing depends on a number of factors, such as children's individual needs and how long your school has been using *Everyday Mathematics*. At the beginning of Unit 7, you may want to use tools available at www.everydaymathonline.com to help you set your pace.

Home Support

Unit 7 Family Letter (English/Spanish) provides families with an overview, Do-Anytime Activities, Building Skills through Games, a list of vocabulary, and answers to the daily homework (Home Links). Family Letters in English, Spanish, and seven other languages are also available online.

Home Links are the daily homework assignments. They consist of active projects and ongoing review problems.

Home Support Resources

Home Connection Handbook
Offers ideas and reproducible masters for communicating with families. See Table of Contents for unit information.

Student Reference Book
Provides a resource for children and parents.

Pages 52, 191, 194, 198, 199, 216, 217, 236, 237, 274, 275, 279, 293–295, 299, 300, 307, 308

Technology Resources

Unit 7 Organizer

Materials

Technology Resources www.everydaymathonline.com

ePresentations | eToolkit | Algorithms Practice | EM Facts Workshop Game™ | Family Letters | Assessment Management | Common Core State Standards | Curriculum Focal Points | Interactive Teacher's Lesson Guide

Lesson	Masters	Manipulative Kit	Other Items
7•1	Home Link Master, p. 206 Teaching Masters, pp. 207 and 208 *Differentiation Handbook,* p. 132	4 each of number cards 0–10 and 1 each of number cards 11–20; slate	centimeter cubes
7•2	Transparency of *Math Masters,* p. 206 Home Link Master, p. 209 Teaching Aid Masters, pp. 431–434, 438A, 438B*, and 438C* Teaching Master, p. 210		half-sheets of paper; colored pencil or crayon; scissors; ×, ÷ Fact Triangles; paper; envelopes
7•3	Game Master, p. 449 Home Link Masters, pp. 211 and 212 Teaching Masters, pp. 213 and 214	4 each of number cards 1–6 and 10	8 pennies or other counters; half-sheets of paper; red and blue crayons; calculator*
7•4	Teaching Masters, pp. 216 and 406* Home Link Master, p. 215 Game Master, p. 451 *Differentiation Handbook,* p. 132	4 each of number cards 0–10 and 1 each of number cards 11–20; slate	3" by 5" index cards; ×, ÷ Fact Triangles; stick-on notes*
7•5	Teaching Aid Master, p. 398 Home Link Master, p. 217 Teaching Masters, pp. 218 and 219	slate	counters*; 10 pennies; calculator*
7•6	Home Link Master, p. 220 Teaching Master, p. 221	4 each of number cards 1–10; base-10 blocks; slate	calculator
7•7	Teaching Aid Master, p. 398 Home Link Master, p. 222 Teaching Masters, pp. 21, 223, and 224	2 each of number cards 1–9; slate	paper; calculator; markers or crayons
7•8	Home Link Master, p. 225 Teaching Masters, pp. 48, 226, and 227 Game Master, p. 445	base-10 blocks; dice; slate	play money*; ruler or straightedge; 4 pennies or counters; calculator*
7•9	Teaching Masters, pp. 228–230 and 232 Home Link Master, p. 231 Game Master, p. 456	pattern blocks (at least 16 of each shape); dice; 9 short straws of equal length and 20 twist-ties	Pattern-Block Template; paper; calculator*; counters*; straightedge*
7•10	Assessment Masters, pp. 177–181 Home Link Masters, pp. 233–236	slate	straightedge; counters*

*Denotes optional materials

Mathematical Background

The discussion below highlights the major content ideas presented in Unit 7 and helps establish instructional priorities.

"Automaticity" and Proficiency with Basic Number Facts

(Lessons 7•1–7•3)

Everyday Mathematics believes that knowing the basic facts as reflexes, without having to figure them out, is an essential prerequisite for mental math, estimation, the use of calculators, and paper-and-pencil computation. A program goal for *Third Grade Everyday Mathematics* is for children to demonstrate automaticity with multiplication facts through 10×10. By the end of fourth grade, children are expected to demonstrate automaticity with multiplication facts through 10×10, proficiency with related division facts, and to use basic facts to compute fact extensions such as 30×60.

In third grade, children use a variety of strategies to assist them as they learn the facts: shortcuts, fact families, drills with Fact Triangles, finding facts and observing patterns and relationships on the Multiplication/Division Fact Table, and games. Fact families and Fact Triangles have the added advantage of highlighting the important links between multiplication and division.

Games are a wonderful way to take the tedium out of learning the facts. Because children enjoy playing games, they are more likely to "volunteer" for facts practice. At times, you may find it beneficial to have children figure out how to play a game by reading the rules on their own. You can also provide them with the needed materials so they may play during free-choice time or take the games home to play with siblings, friends, or parents.

See the *Teacher's Reference Manual,* Sections 16.3.2 and 16.3.3 for additional information on basic facts and fact practice.

Patterns in Products (Lesson 7•1)

Certain numbers, called figurate numbers, may be represented by arrangements of dots that form geometric shapes. Square numbers are examples of such numbers.

square numbers

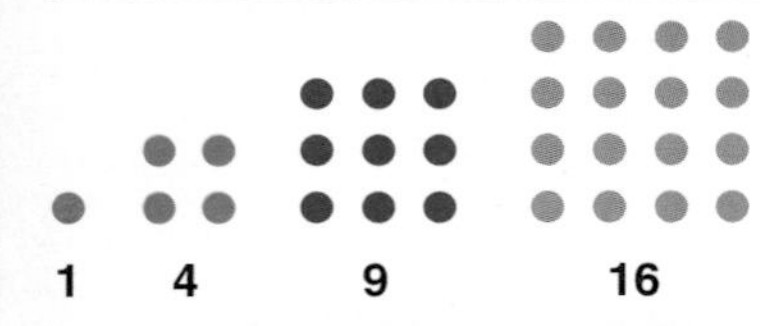

Square numbers are numbers raised to the second power. The power of a number is the number of times the same factor is multiplied; it may be represented in exponential notation, where the exponent shows the number of times the factor is used. You need not teach powers and exponents at this time; these concepts will be taken up in grades 4–6. Some children may know of them from people at home or ask about them as something they have seen but don't yet understand.

Sequences of figurate numbers exhibit patterns that obey definite rules. In this lesson, children explore such patterns for square numbers and rectangular numbers (numbers of the form $n \times (n + 1)$).

rectangular numbers

Parentheses (Lessons 7•4 and 7•5)

Commas, periods, and other punctuation marks are needed to make printed text easier to read and to make its meaning clear. Similarly, grouping symbols, such as parentheses and brackets, are used in number models in order to eliminate any possible ambiguities.

$(3 + 6) \times 5 = 45$

$3 + (6 \times 5) = 33$

Children use parentheses to clarify number models

The standard (binary) operations are performed on two numbers at a time; as long as just two numbers and one operation are involved, there is no need for inserting grouping symbols in number models. One simply proceeds from left to right. Similarly, no grouping symbols are needed in number models that involve either adding or multiplying several numbers; these operations may be performed in any order. However, in number models involving subtraction, division, or a mixture of operations with several numbers, one may obtain different results depending on the order in which the operations are performed. It becomes necessary to insert parentheses to indicate the order of the operations.

The use of parentheses in number models is introduced in Lesson 7-4. In Lesson 7-5, point scores in basketball are used to provide practice with parentheses. Include brief exercises with number models that contain parentheses throughout the rest of the school year. Such exercises also provide drills with basic number facts and extensions, reminders of the effects of multiplying by or adding zero, and practice in expressing solutions (in games such as *Name That Number*).

Project Note

Use Project 7, Order of Operations, to introduce the rules for order of operations.

Additional information on parentheses can be found in the *Teacher's Reference Manual,* Section 10.1.2.

Extended Facts (Lessons 7◆6 and 7◆8)

Once the basic multiplication facts have been learned, it is easy to solve problems involving multiples of 10, 100, and 1,000 (extended facts). When asked to solve a problem, such as 30×600, most adults probably multiply the leading digits ($3 \times 6 = 18$) and attach as many zeros to the product as there are zeros in both factors (3 zeros; $30 \times 600 = 18{,}000$).

If this method or a similar shortcut is taught to children, there is a danger that they will not apply the shortcut correctly, because they do not understand what is involved in finding such a product, especially when it involves decimals. For this reason, it is recommended that, at least at this stage, children be encouraged to reason their way to the solutions of such problems; at some point, they will discover a shortcut that they can make their own.

Estimation and Mental Math with Multiples (Lesson 7◆7)

In Lesson 7-7, children are asked to find closer and closer estimates for the cost of buying several of the same item. The closest estimate, of course, is the exact value. Some children may get exact answers with mental (informal) math, and that's fine, but they should not be expected to do so. Estimates serve well in most situations—if an exact answer is essential, one can do the computation with paper and pencil. Children's mental math strategies often anticipate useful algorithmic procedures. Mental math also helps children develop a better feel for the magnitude of products and partial products.

Refer to the *Teacher's Reference Manual,* Sections 16.1 and 16.3, for additional information on estimation and mental arithmetic.

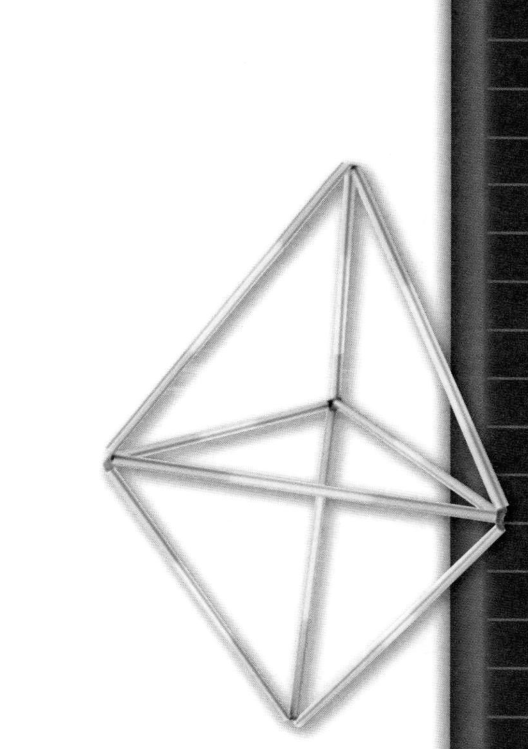

Ratios and Geometric Figures (Lesson 7◆9)

In Exploration A, children arrange various pattern blocks to construct similar but larger polygons. They form a large square from four pattern-block squares, a large triangle from four triangles, a large rhombus from four rhombuses, and a large trapezoid from four trapezoids. In Exploration B, children solve number stories based on a ratio of one farm animal to another farm animal. In Exploration C, children use straws and twist-ties to try to build a certain number of triangles with a given number of straws.

7•1 Patterns in Products

Objective To review square-number facts, multiplication, and division patterns.

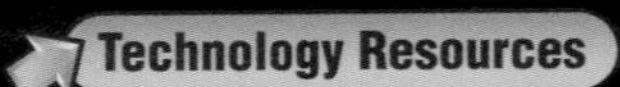

www.everydaymathonline.com

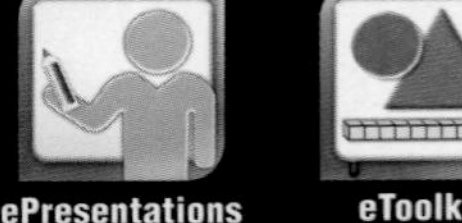

ePresentations | eToolkit | Algorithms Practice | EM Facts Workshop Game™ | Family Letters | Assessment Management | Common Core State Standards | Curriculum Focal Points | Interactive Teacher's Lesson Guide

1 Teaching the Lesson

Key Concepts and Skills

- Identify factors, products, square numbers, and patterns in the Multiplication/Division Facts Table.
  [Operations and Computation Goal 3]
- Use the Multiplication/Division Facts Table to generate fact families.
  [Operations and Computation Goal 3]
- Use arrays to find square products.
  [Operations and Computation Goal 6]
- Use the turn-around rule (Commutative Property of Multiplication) to generate multiplication facts.
  [Patterns, Functions, and Algebra Goal 4]

Key Activities

Children identify patterns in a sequence of square numbers and in the Multiplication/Division Facts Table.

Ongoing Assessment: Recognizing Student Achievement
Use journal page 157.
[Operations and Computation Goal 3]

Key Vocabulary

product ◆ square product ◆ square number ◆ factor

Materials

Math Journal 2, p. 157
Student Reference Book, p. 52
slate

2 Ongoing Learning & Practice

Playing *Name That Number*
Student Reference Book, pp. 299 and 300
per partnership: 4 each of number cards 0–10 and 1 each of number cards 11–20 (from the Everything Math Deck, if available).
Children practice finding equivalent names for a number.

Math Boxes 7•1
Math Journal 2, p. 158
Children practice and maintain skills through Math Box problems.

Home Link 7•1
Math Masters, p. 206
Children practice and maintain skills through Home Link activities.

3 Differentiation Options

READINESS

Building Square and Rectangular Arrays
Math Masters, p. 207
cm cubes
Children build square and rectangular arrays and look for patterns.

ENRICHMENT

Exploring a Pattern in a Sequence of Products
Math Masters, p. 208
Student Reference Book, pp. 198 and 199
Children look for patterns in a sequence of rectangular arrays and in the products they represent.

ELL SUPPORT

Building a Math Word Bank
Differentiation Handbook, p. 132
Children add the terms *product* and *factor* to their Math Word Banks.

Advance Preparation

***Teacher's Reference Manual,* Grades 1–3** pp. 204, 205

Getting Started

Mathematical Practices
SMP1, SMP2, SMP5, SMP6, **SMP7**
Content Standards
3.OA.1, 3.OA.4, 3.OA.7, **3.OA.9**

Mental Math and Reflexes

Have children practice quick recall of basic multiplication facts. *Suggestions:*

●○○ 2 × 4 8 3 × 4 12 3 × 5 15 4 × 5 20
●●○ 3 × 6 18 4 × 6 24 4 × 7 28 5 × 7 35
●●● 3 × 8 24 3 × 9 27 4 × 8 32 6 × 6 36

Math Message

Turn to page 157 in your new journal. Find the ***products*** *in Problems 1 through 10.*

1 Teaching the Lesson

Interactive whiteboard-ready ePresentations are available at www.everydaymathonline.com to help you teach the lesson.

▶ Math Message Follow-Up

(*Math Journal 2,* p. 157)

Review answers to the Math Message problems. Ask children to share how they found answers to facts they have not yet memorized. Some children may suggest a count-by strategy: for example, for 5 × 5, count by 5s five times. 5, 10, 15, 20, 25

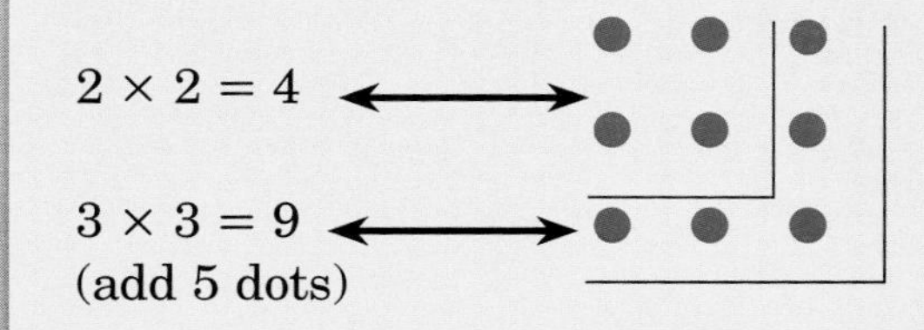

Array showing square products

Ongoing Assessment: Recognizing Student Achievement

Journal Page 157 

Use **journal page 157, Part A** to assess children's progress toward learning the multiplication facts. Children are making adequate progress if they use strategies to correctly complete the facts in Problems 1 through 10. Some children will demonstrate automaticity with the facts.

[Operations and Computation Goal 3]

Point out how the array diagram highlights the number of dots that are added to an array to obtain the next array. For example, 5 dots are added to the 2-by-2 array to obtain the 3-by-3 array. This shows that 3 × 3 = 9 is 5 more than 2 × 2 = 4.

Adjusting the Activity

ELL

Draw square arrays for 4, 9, and 16 on the board without lines. Ask children to imagine what a 5-by-5 array looks like. Have a volunteer draw the 5-by-5 array on the board.

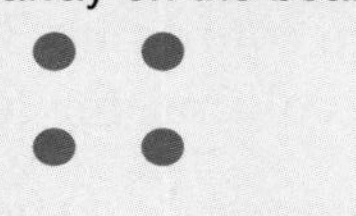
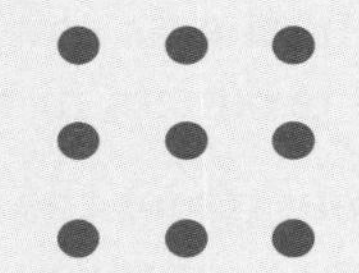
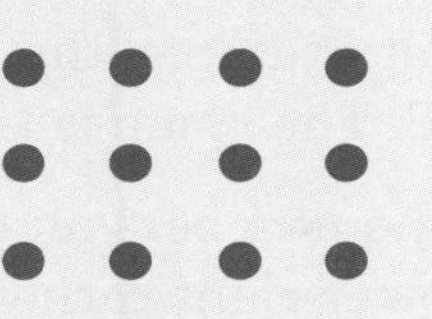

4, 9, and 16 are square products

AUDITORY ◆ KINESTHETIC ◆ TACTILE ◆ VISUAL

Student Page

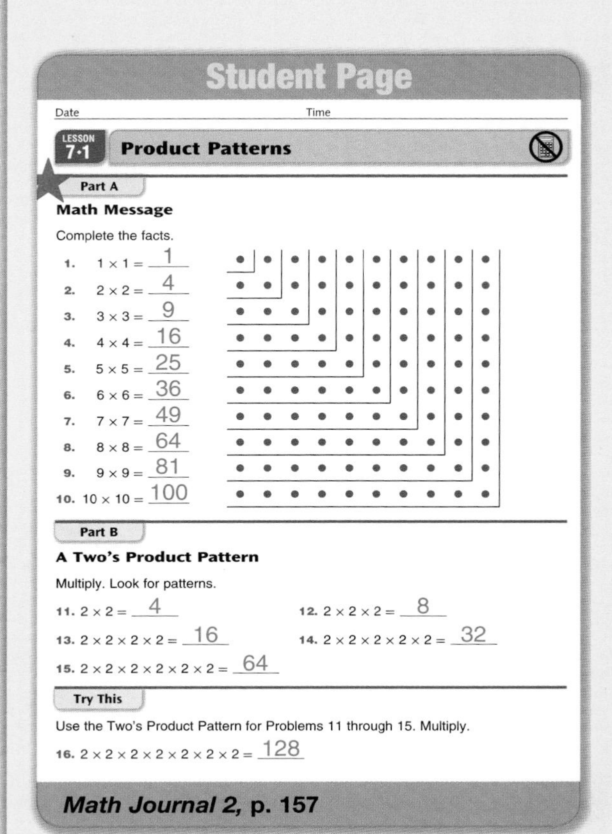

Date Time

LESSON 7·1 **Product Patterns**

Part A

Math Message

Complete the facts.

1. 1 × 1 = 1
2. 2 × 2 = 4
3. 3 × 3 = 9
4. 4 × 4 = 16
5. 5 × 5 = 25
6. 6 × 6 = 36
7. 7 × 7 = 49
8. 8 × 8 = 64
9. 9 × 9 = 81
10. 10 × 10 = 100

Part B

A Two's Product Pattern

Multiply. Look for patterns.

11. 2 × 2 = 4
12. 2 × 2 × 2 = 8
13. 2 × 2 × 2 × 2 = 16
14. 2 × 2 × 2 × 2 × 2 = 32
15. 2 × 2 × 2 × 2 × 2 × 2 = 64

Try This

Use the Two's Product Pattern for Problems 11 through 15. Multiply.

16. 2 × 2 × 2 × 2 × 2 × 2 × 2 = 128

Math Journal 2, p. 157

With the help of the children, list the number that is added to each square product to obtain the next square product. The numbers below the arrows name the number of dots that are added to each succeeding array. Point out this pattern on the dot array on journal page 157.

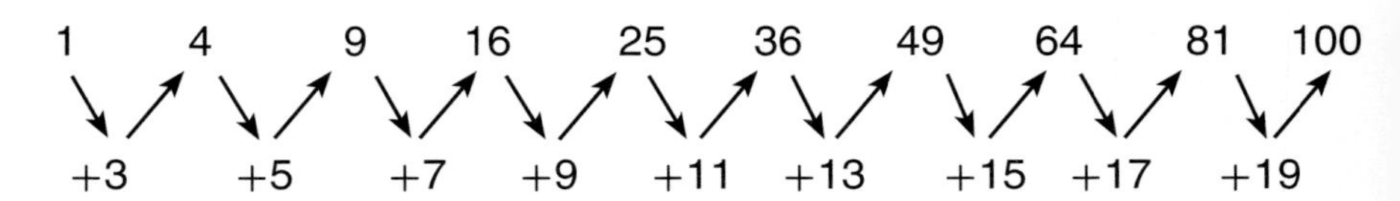

Write a list of square products on the board. Remind children that these are called **square products** or **square numbers.** Draw arrays to illustrate the square numbers. Then ask why these numbers might be called *square numbers.* Starting with 2×2, each product can be represented by a square array.

Adjusting the Activity

Find 11×11 without using a calculator. Add 21 to continue the pattern shown above. $11 \times 11 = 10 \times 10 + 21 = 100 + 21 = 121$

AUDITORY • KINESTHETIC • TACTILE • VISUAL

▶ Finding Patterns in the Multiplication/Division Facts Table

(*Student Reference Book*, p. 52)

Algebraic Thinking Divide the class into small groups and ask children to turn to the Multiplication/Division Facts Table on page 52 in their *Student Reference Book*. Remind them that the shaded numbers across the top and down the left side of the table are called **factors** and that the rest of the numbers are the products of the factors. Ask each group to look for patterns in the table and record them on a sheet of paper. After a few minutes, bring the class together to share the patterns they found. To support English language learners, write the patterns on the board as the children describe them.

Examples:

- The products in the row for a factor are counts by that factor. For example, the products in the 3s row are counts by 3: 3, 6, 9, 12. The same is true of the products in the column for a factor.
- The numbers on the diagonal (from the upper-left to the lower-right corner) are square numbers.
- The square numbers divide the table into two parts that are mirror images of each other.
- All products in even-factor rows and columns are even numbers.
- Products in odd-factor rows and columns alternate between even and odd numbers.

NOTE In Lesson 4-6, children used the Multiplication/Division Facts Table to generate fact families. They looked for patterns in the table with teacher guidance. In this activity, expect that children will be able to describe many of the patterns on their own.

Student Page

Operations and Computation

Basic Facts for Multiplication and Division

Solving problems is easier when you know the basic number facts. Here are some examples of basic multiplication and division facts:

Basic multiplication facts:
$6 \times 4 = 24$, $10 \times 7 = 70$, $1 \times 8 = 8$, $3 \times 9 = 27$

Basic division facts:
$24 \div 6 = 4$, $70 \div 10 = 7$, $8 \div 1 = 8$, $27 \div 3 = 9$

The **facts table** shown below is a chart with rows and columns. It can be used to find *all* of the basic multiplication and division facts.

Multiplication/Division Facts Table

×,÷	1	2	3	4	5	6	7	8	9	10
1	1	2	3	4	5	6	7	8	9	10
2	2	4	6	8	10	12	14	16	18	20
3	3	6	9	12	15	18	21	24	27	30
4	4	8	12	16	20	24	28	32	36	40
5	5	10	15	20	25	30	35	40	45	50
6	6	12	18	24	30	36	42	48	54	60
7	7	14	21	28	35	42	49	56	63	70
8	8	16	24	32	40	48	56	64	72	80
9	9	18	27	36	45	54	63	72	81	90
10	10	20	30	40	50	60	70	80	90	100

fifty-two

Student Reference Book, p. 52

- The 1s products are consecutive counting numbers.
- The 2s products end in 2, 4, 6, 8, or 0.
- The 5s products end in 0 or 5.
- The 10s products end in 0.
- The sum of the digits in each of the 9s products is 9. For example, $4 \times 9 = 36$, and $3 + 6 = 9$.

NOTE Zero can be divided by any nonzero number, but no number can be divided by zero. Because this table is also used for division, the zero facts are omitted from it.

▶ Exploring Multiplication Patterns

INDEPENDENT ACTIVITY

(*Math Journal 2,* p. 157)

Algebraic Thinking Have children work for about 5 minutes to solve the problems in Part B on journal page 157. Bring the class together to share solution strategies. Mention that each product is twice as much as the product before it. To find the product in the Try This problem, children can double 64 (or add $64 + 64$).

2 Ongoing Learning & Practice

▶ Playing *Name That Number*

PARTNER ACTIVITY

(*Student Reference Book*, pp. 299 and 300)

Children practice finding equivalent names for a number as they play *Name That Number*. Encourage them to use as many operations as they can to name numbers. See Lesson 1-6 or pages 299 and 300 in the *Student Reference Book* for detailed instructions.

▶ Math Boxes 7•1

INDEPENDENT ACTIVITY

(*Math Journal 2,* p. 158)

Mixed Practice The Math Boxes in this lesson are paired with the Math Boxes in Lesson 7-3. The skill in Problem 6 previews Unit 8 content.

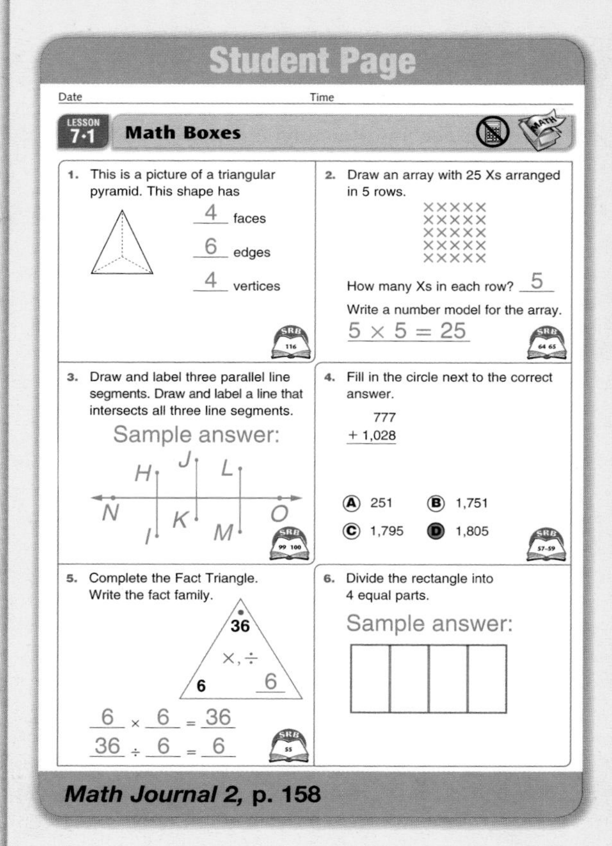

Student Page

Date Time

LESSON 7•1 **Math Boxes**

1. This is a picture of a triangular pyramid. This shape has
4 faces
6 edges
4 vertices

2. Draw an array with 25 Xs arranged in 5 rows.
How many Xs in each row? 5
Write a number model for the array.
5 × 5 = 25

3. Draw and label three parallel line segments. Draw and label a line that intersects all three line segments.
Sample answer:

4. Fill in the circle next to the correct answer.
777
+ 1,028
(A) 251 (B) 1,751
(C) 1,795 (D) 1,805

5. Complete the Fact Triangle. Write the fact family.
6 × 6 = 36
36 ÷ 6 = 6

6. Divide the rectangle into 4 equal parts.
Sample answer:

Math Journal 2, p. 158

▶ Home Link 7•1

INDEPENDENT ACTIVITY

(*Math Masters,* p. 206)

Home Connection Children read about the Greek myth of the Minotaur. They will then trace a path through a labyrinth, or maze, moving from one square product to another.

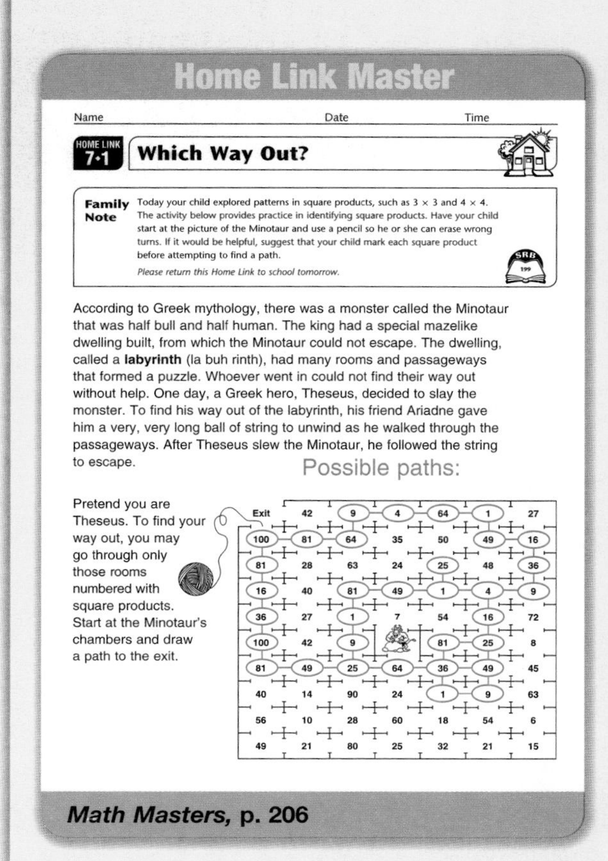

Home Link Master

Name Date Time

HOME LINK 7•1 **Which Way Out?**

Family Note Today your child explored patterns in square products, such as 3 × 3 and 4 × 4. The activity below provides practice in identifying square products. Have your child start at the picture of the Minotaur and use a pencil so he or she can erase wrong turns. If it would be helpful, suggest that your child mark each square product before attempting to find a path.

Please return this Home Link to school tomorrow.

According to Greek mythology, there was a monster called the Minotaur that was half bull and half human. The king had a special mazelike dwelling built, from which the Minotaur could not escape. The dwelling, called a **labyrinth** (la buh rinth), had many rooms and passageways that formed a puzzle. Whoever went in could not find their way out without help. One day, a Greek hero, Theseus, decided to slay the monster. To find his way out of the labyrinth, his friend Ariadne gave him a very, very long ball of string to unwind as he walked through the passageways. After Theseus slew the Minotaur, he followed the string to escape.

Possible paths:

Pretend you are Theseus. To find your way out, you may go through only those rooms numbered with square products. Start at the Minotaur's chambers and draw a path to the exit.

Math Masters, p. 206

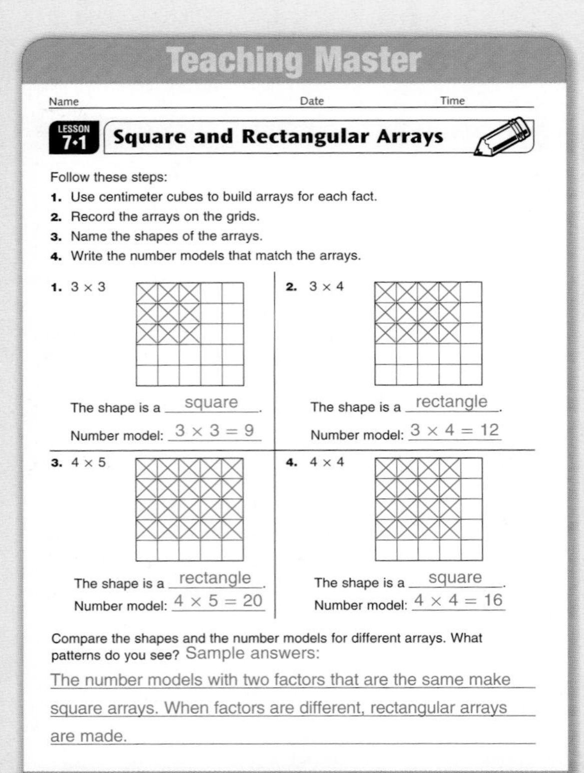

Teaching Master

Name Date Time

LESSON 7•1 **Square and Rectangular Arrays**

Follow these steps:
1. Use centimeter cubes to build arrays for each fact.
2. Record the arrays on the grids.
3. Name the shapes of the arrays.
4. Write the number models that match the arrays.

1. 3×3
The shape is a square.
Number model: $3 \times 3 = 9$

2. 3×4
The shape is a rectangle.
Number model: $3 \times 4 = 12$

3. 4×5
The shape is a rectangle
Number model: $4 \times 5 = 20$

4. 4×4
The shape is a square.
Number model: $4 \times 4 = 16$

Compare the shapes and the number models for different arrays. What patterns do you see? Sample answers:
The number models with two factors that are the same make square arrays. When factors are different, rectangular arrays are made.

Math Masters, p. 207

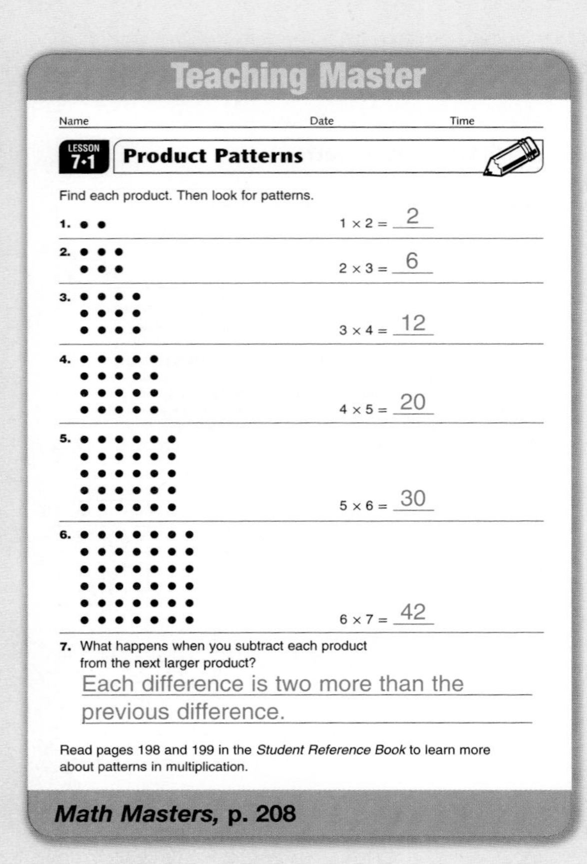

Teaching Master

Name Date Time

LESSON 7•1 **Product Patterns**

Find each product. Then look for patterns.

1. $1 \times 2 =$ 2
2. $2 \times 3 =$ 6
3. $3 \times 4 =$ 12
4. $4 \times 5 =$ 20
5. $5 \times 6 =$ 30
6. $6 \times 7 =$ 42
7. What happens when you subtract each product from the next larger product?
Each difference is two more than the previous difference.

Read pages 198 and 199 in the *Student Reference Book* to learn more about patterns in multiplication.

Math Masters, p. 208

3 Differentiation Options

READINESS

INDEPENDENT ACTIVITY

5–15 Min

▶ Building Square and Rectangular Arrays

(*Math Masters,* p. 207)

To provide experience with square and rectangular arrays, have children use centimeter cubes to build arrays for given factors. They record their work on *Math Masters,* page 207. When the children have completed the page, have them share the patterns they found.

ENRICHMENT

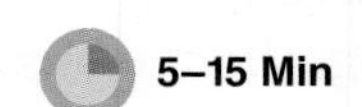

INDEPENDENT ACTIVITY

5–15 Min

▶ Exploring a Pattern in a Sequence of Products

(*Math Masters,* p. 208; *Student Reference Book,* pp. 198 and 199)

To further explore multiplication patterns, have children look for patterns in a sequence of multiplication problems in which one factor is 1 more than the other factor (1×2, 2×3, 3×4, and so on).

Possible patterns:

- Each array has one more row and one more column than the preceding array.
- Each array has one more column than a square array. Therefore, each product can be expressed in the form $n \times n + n$:

$$1 \times 2 = 1 \times 1 + 1 = 2$$
$$2 \times 3 = 2 \times 2 + 2 = 6$$
$$3 \times 4 = 3 \times 3 + 3 = 12$$
$$4 \times 5 = 4 \times 4 + 4 = 20$$
$$5 \times 6 = 5 \times 5 + 5 = 30$$
$$6 \times 7 = 6 \times 6 + 6 = 42$$

- If you subtract each product from the next larger product, each difference is 2 more than the preceding difference.

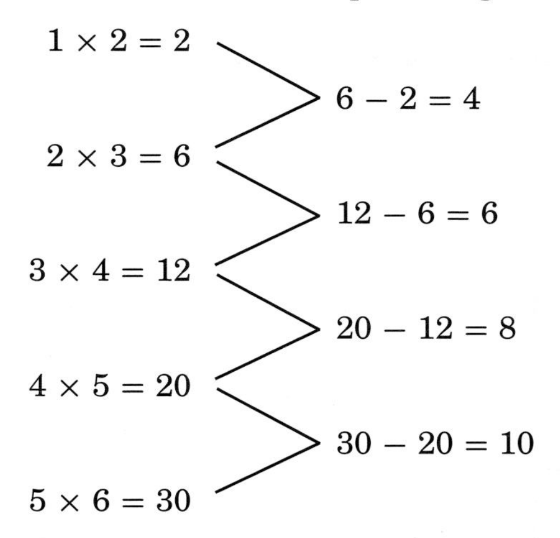

ELL SUPPORT

▶ Building a Math Word Bank

5–15 Min

(*Differentiation Handbook*, p. 132)

To provide language support for multiplication, have children use the Word Bank template found on *Differentiation Handbook,* page 132. Ask the children to write the terms *product* and *factor,* draw a picture representing each term, and write other related words. See the *Differentiation Handbook* for more information.

REMINDER Have children copy the sunrise/sunset data on journal page 125 to the graph on journal page 279.

Have children continue recording the sunrise, sunset, and length of day for your location in their new journals on pages 279–281.

Have children copy their body measures from journal page 64 onto journal page 251. They will revisit their body measures in Lesson 10-7.

NOTE The data on journal page 43 will be graphed in Lesson 7-8. You may want children to keep Journal 1 accessible until the data are used in Lesson 7-8, or you might choose to make the data available by making copies of the class record of temperature differences kept on *Math Masters,* page 48. Children will continue to record the national high and low temperatures for the rest of the year on journal page 175 as they did on journal page 43.

7•2 Multiplication Facts Survey

Objective To guide children as they determine which multiplication facts they still need to learn.

www.everydaymathonline.com

ePresentations

eToolkit

Algorithms Practice

EM Facts Workshop Game™

Family Letters

Assessment Management

Common Core State Standards

Curriculum Focal Points

Interactive Teacher's Lesson Guide

1 Teaching the Lesson

Key Concepts and Skills

- Identify square products. [Operations and Computation Goal 3]
- Describe patterns in factors and products. [Patterns, Functions, and Algebra Goal 1]
- Describe and apply the turn-around rule (Commutative Property of Multiplication) to generate multiplication facts. [Patterns, Functions, and Algebra Goal 4]

Key Activities

Children use a Multiplication/Division Facts Table to identify the facts they know and the facts they still need to learn. They take a timed multiplication facts survey.

Ongoing Assessment: Recognizing Student Achievement
Use the Math Message.
[Operations and Computation Goal 6]

Materials

Math Journal 2, p. 159
Math Journal 1, Activity Sheets 3 and 4
Math Masters, p. 438A; pp. 438B and 438C (optional)
transparency of *Math Masters,* p. 206 (Home Link 7•1) ◆ half-sheets of paper ◆ colored pencil or crayon ◆ scissors ◆ envelopes

2 Ongoing Learning & Practice

Practicing Multiplication/Division Facts with Fact Triangles

×, ÷ Fact Triangles
Children practice multiplication basic facts using the second set of Fact Triangles.

Math Boxes 7•2

Math Journal 2, p. 160
Children practice and maintain skills through Math Box problems.

Home Link 7•2

Math Masters, pp. 209 and 431–434
Children practice and maintain skills through Home Link activities.

3 Differentiation Options

READINESS

Exploring Turn-Around Facts

Math Masters, p. 210
scissors
Children identify turn-around facts on the Multiplication/Division Facts Table.

ENRICHMENT

Finding Patterns in the 9s Facts

1 sheet of paper
Children identify and describe patterns in the products for 9s facts.

Advance Preparation

For Part 1, make one copy of *Math Masters,* page 438A for every 2 children. *Math Masters,* pages 431–434 are Fact Triangles. Make copies of the Fact Triangles to send home with Home Link 7•2.

***Teacher's Reference Manual,* Grades 1–3** pp. 196–198

Getting Started

Mathematical Practices
SMP2, **SMP5,** SMP6, SMP7, **SMP8**
Content Standards
3.OA.4, 3.OA.5, 3.OA.7, 3.OA.9

Mental Math and Reflexes

Have children practice quick recall of basic multiplication facts. *Suggestions:*

Examples:

●○○ 2 × 10 20 3 × 10 30 6 × 10 60 8 × 10 80

●●○ 2 × 2 4 3 × 3 9 4 × 4 16 5 × 5 25

●●● 4 × 9 36 6 × 7 42 7 × 8 56 6 × 9 54

Home Link 7•1 Follow-Up

Ask children to demonstrate different paths for escaping the labyrinth on a transparency of Home Link 7-1. Discuss which of the paths is the shortest.

Math Message ★

Each of the following products is a square product. Complete the number sentences on a half-sheet of paper.

3 × 3 = 9

5 × 5 = 25

7 × 7 = 49

9 × 9 = 81

Sample answer:

● ● ●
● ● ●
● ● ●

Draw an array to show one of the square products.

1 Teaching the Lesson

Math Message Follow-Up

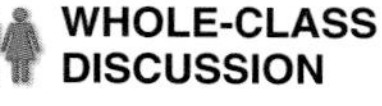

Briefly review the answers. Have children make observations about the factors and the products. Point out that all the factors and their products are odd numbers. Make a chart (see below) on the board to record examples of factors and their products. Ask:

- If both factors are odd numbers, is the product odd or even? odd
- What is the result if both factors are even numbers? even
- What is the result if one factor is even and the other odd? even

2 even factors	1 odd and 1 even factor	2 odd factors
2 × 8 = 16	3 × 6 = 18	5 × 9 = 45
6 × 2 = 12	9 × 2 = 18	3 × 3 = 9
4 × 4 = 16	7 × 4 = 28	1 × 7 = 7
8 × 6 = 48	5 × 8 = 40	9 × 7 = 63

Products for even and odd factors

Ongoing Assessment: Recognizing Student Achievement

Math Message 

Use the **Math Message** to assess children's progress toward using arrays to model multiplication. Children are making adequate progress if they are able to draw an array to show one of the square products. Some children may be able to draw an array for each of the square products and discuss their similarities.

[Operation and Computation Goal 6]

Student Page

Date Time

LESSON 7·2 **Multiplication/Division Facts Table**

×,÷	1	2	3	4	5	6	7	8	9	10
1	1	2	3	4	5	6	7	8	9	10
2	2	4	6	8	10	12	14	16	18	20
3	3	6	9	12	15	18	21	24	27	30
4	4	8	12	16	20	24	28	32	36	40
5	5	10	15	20	25	30	35	40	45	50
6	6	12	18	24	30	36	42	48	54	60
7	7	14	21	28	35	42	49	56	63	70
8	8	16	24	32	40	48	56	64	72	80
9	9	18	27	36	45	54	63	72	81	90
10	10	20	30	40	50	60	70	80	90	100

Math Journal 2, **p. 159**

NOTE To extend this activity to include basic multiplication facts through 12 × 12, go to www.everydaymathonline.com.

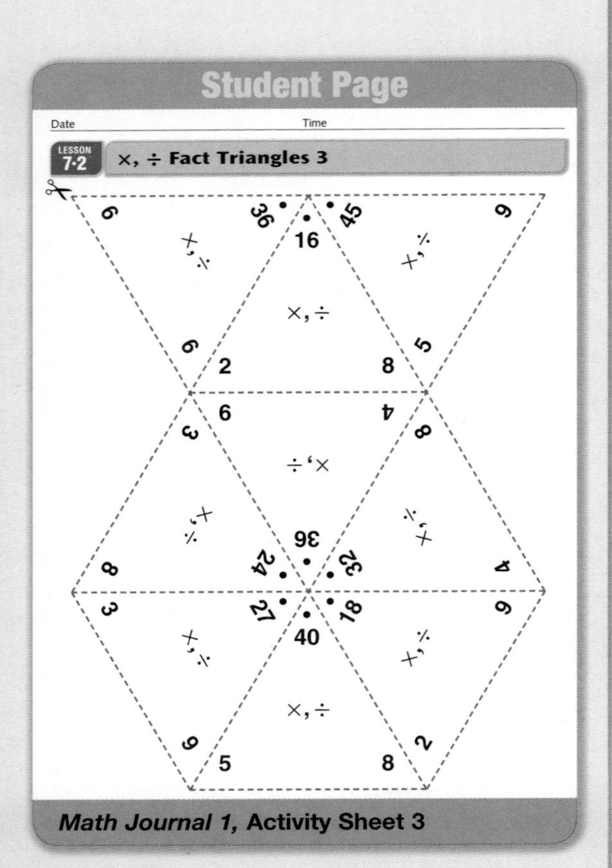

Math Journal 1, **Activity Sheet 3**

▶ Identifying the Multiplication Facts to Be Learned

WHOLE-CLASS ACTIVITY

(*Math Journal 2,* p. 159)

By now, most children know the 1s, 2s, and 10s multiplication facts. Most children should also know all of the facts on the first set of Fact Triangles from Lesson 4-6. The purpose of the activity on journal page 159 is to let children know that there are only a few facts left to learn.

Ask children to use light-colored crayons or pencils to color all the products above the square-number diagonal. Remind them that the square-number diagonal divides the table into two parts: Each product above the diagonal has a turn-around product below the diagonal.

Next, children color the products for all remaining 1-facts, 2-facts, and 10-facts. Finally, they shade the remaining products from the first set of Fact Triangles, including those *on* the square-number diagonal, even though they are pre-shaded. The pre-shading indicates square products. The *children's* shading indicates products they already know.

Ask: *How many products are left unshaded?* 16 This shows that if they know all the 1-, 2-, and 10-facts, all the facts from the first set of Fact Triangles, and the turn-around rule, they need to learn only 16 more facts. Have children examine the 16 products left unshaded. Discuss patterns they notice with the unshaded products.

Adjusting the Activity

Show children the 9s Facts-on-Fingers shortcut. Hold both hands open, palms down. To multiply a number less than 10 by 9 (for example, 7 × 9), count fingers, starting with the little finger of the left hand. If the factor is greater than 5, continue counting on the right hand, starting with the thumb. Bend down the last finger in your count. (For 7 × 9, the down finger is the right-hand index finger.) The number of fingers to the left of the down finger represents the tens digit in the product; the number of fingers to the right represents the ones digit (6 to the left and 3 to the right).

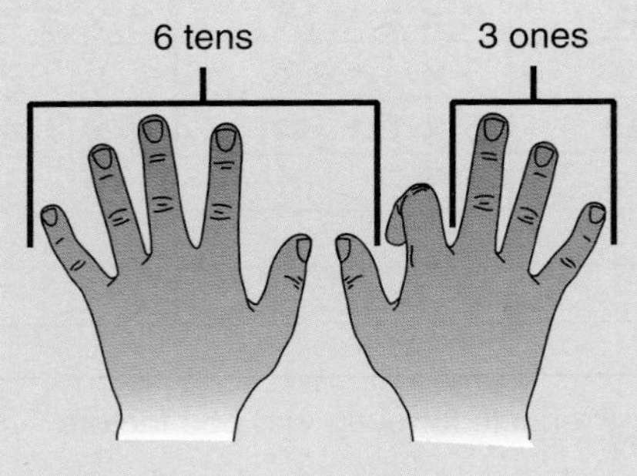

7 × 9

The last finger in the count bends to separate the 10s and the 1s in the answer.

AUDITORY • KINESTHETIC • TACTILE • VISUAL

▶ Administering a Facts Survey

(*Math Masters,* pp. 438A–438C)

Explain to children that they will find out for themselves how many of the 16 facts they already know and how many they have yet to learn.

Distribute the survey on *Math Masters,* page 438A. At your signal, children have 90 seconds (approximately 5 seconds per problem) to complete as many problems as possible. Adjust the amount of time as you see fit, but remember that children should not be given enough time to *figure out* the answers. The point is to know the answers from memory.

Decide how you would like to have the surveys corrected. Children may correct their own or you may correct them yourself. Note that the reason for administering the survey is to help children to identify the facts they still need to learn; it is not to give a grade.

Once the surveys are corrected, consider having children write the facts they still need to learn on the Notes page at the back of *Math Journal 2.* They will be able to access these facts quickly for continued practice.

Plan to assess children's progress on the Facts Survey once every couple of months. *Math Masters,* pages 438B and 438C are alternate versions of the same 16 facts.

▶ Cutting Out Fact Triangles

(*Math Journal 1,* Activity Sheets 3 and 4)

After children have cut out the Fact Triangles on the Activity Sheet card stock pages, review how to use Fact Triangles to generate fact families and to practice the multiplication and division facts.

Remind children that they need to learn the multiplication and division facts so they can solve multiplication and division problems with larger numbers. Provide children frequent opportunities to practice their facts with the Fact Triangles. The year-end goal for third grade is to demonstrate automaticity with facts through 10×10.

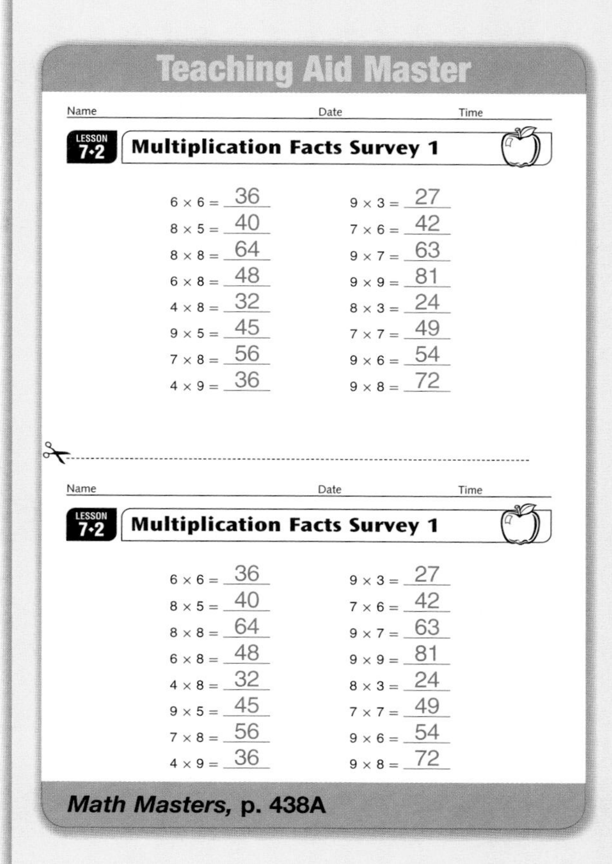

Teaching Aid Master

Name Date Time

LESSON 7·2 **Multiplication Facts Survey 1**

6 × 6 = 36	9 × 3 = 27
8 × 5 = 40	7 × 6 = 42
8 × 8 = 64	9 × 7 = 63
6 × 8 = 48	9 × 9 = 81
4 × 8 = 32	8 × 3 = 24
9 × 5 = 45	7 × 7 = 49
7 × 8 = 56	9 × 6 = 54
4 × 9 = 36	9 × 8 = 72

Name Date Time

LESSON 7·2 **Multiplication Facts Survey 1**

6 × 6 = 36	9 × 3 = 27
8 × 5 = 40	7 × 6 = 42
8 × 8 = 64	9 × 7 = 63
6 × 8 = 48	9 × 9 = 81
4 × 8 = 32	8 × 3 = 24
9 × 5 = 45	7 × 7 = 49
7 × 8 = 56	9 × 6 = 54
4 × 9 = 36	9 × 8 = 72

***Math Masters,* p. 438A**

NOTE Have children write their initials on the back of each Fact Triangle in case they misplace them.

NOTE For additional Fact Triangles for facts through 12×12, go to www.everydaymathonline.com.

Teaching Aid Master

Name Date Time

LESSON 7·2 **Multiplication Facts Survey 2**

8 × 8 = 64	8 × 5 = 40
9 × 7 = 63	6 × 8 = 48
9 × 9 = 81	4 × 8 = 32
8 × 3 = 24	6 × 6 = 36
9 × 5 = 45	7 × 7 = 49
7 × 8 = 56	9 × 3 = 27
7 × 6 = 42	9 × 6 = 54
4 × 9 = 36	9 × 8 = 72

Name Date Time

LESSON 7·2 **Multiplication Facts Survey 2**

8 × 8 = 64	8 × 5 = 40
9 × 7 = 63	6 × 8 = 48
9 × 9 = 81	4 × 8 = 32
8 × 3 = 24	6 × 6 = 36
9 × 5 = 45	7 × 7 = 49
7 × 8 = 56	9 × 3 = 27
7 × 6 = 42	9 × 6 = 54
4 × 9 = 36	9 × 8 = 72

***Math Masters,* p. 438B**

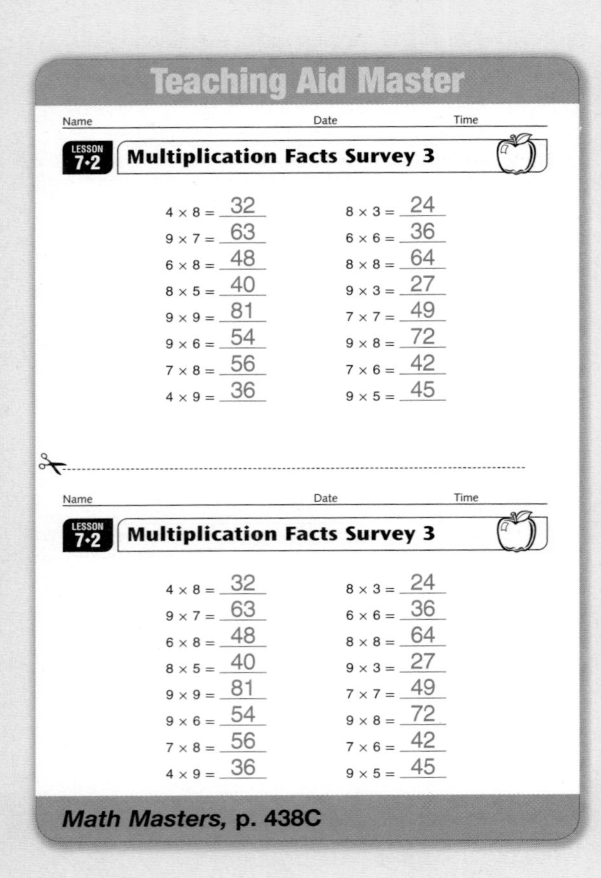
Teaching Aid Master

Name Date Time

LESSON 7•2 **Multiplication Facts Survey 3**

4 × 8 = 32	8 × 3 = 24
9 × 7 = 63	6 × 6 = 36
6 × 8 = 48	8 × 8 = 64
8 × 5 = 40	9 × 3 = 27
9 × 9 = 81	7 × 7 = 49
9 × 6 = 54	9 × 8 = 72
7 × 8 = 56	7 × 6 = 42
4 × 9 = 36	9 × 5 = 45

Name Date Time

LESSON 7•2 **Multiplication Facts Survey 3**

4 × 8 = 32	8 × 3 = 24
9 × 7 = 63	6 × 6 = 36
6 × 8 = 48	8 × 8 = 64
8 × 5 = 40	9 × 3 = 27
9 × 9 = 81	7 × 7 = 49
9 × 6 = 54	9 × 8 = 72
7 × 8 = 56	7 × 6 = 42
4 × 9 = 36	9 × 5 = 45

Math Masters, p. 438C

2 Ongoing Learning & Practice

▶ Practicing Multiplication/Division Facts with Fact Triangles

PARTNER ACTIVITY

Partners practice basic facts using their Fact Triangles. Children keep track of the facts they miss and direct their partners to focus on those facts during a second round. Encourage children to store their Fact Triangles in an envelope when they are not using them.

▶ Math Boxes 7•2

INDEPENDENT ACTIVITY

(*Math Journal 2,* p. 160)

Mixed Practice The Math Boxes in this lesson are paired with the Math Boxes from Lesson 7-4. The skill in Problem 6 previews Unit 8 content.

▶ Home Link 7•2

INDEPENDENT ACTIVITY

(*Math Masters,* pp. 209 and 431–434)

Home Connection Children share with someone at home their progress with the multiplication facts. Send home *Math Masters,* pages 431–434 (which are the same Fact Triangles as Activity Sheets 3 and 4) so children can practice multiplication facts.

3 Differentiation Options

READINESS

FACTS PRACTICE

SMALL-GROUP ACTIVITY

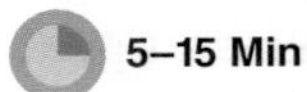
5–15 Min

▶ Exploring Turn-Around Facts

(*Math Masters,* p. 210)

To provide experience with turn-around facts, have children compare two halves of the Multiplication/Division Facts Table. They cut out the Multiplication/Division Facts Table on *Math Masters,* page 210 along the dotted lines and fold it diagonally from right to left along the blank squares. Notice that equal factors and products fold onto themselves. Ask children why this happens. The same factors are used in order along the top row as are used down the first column. The products of the turn-around facts are the same.

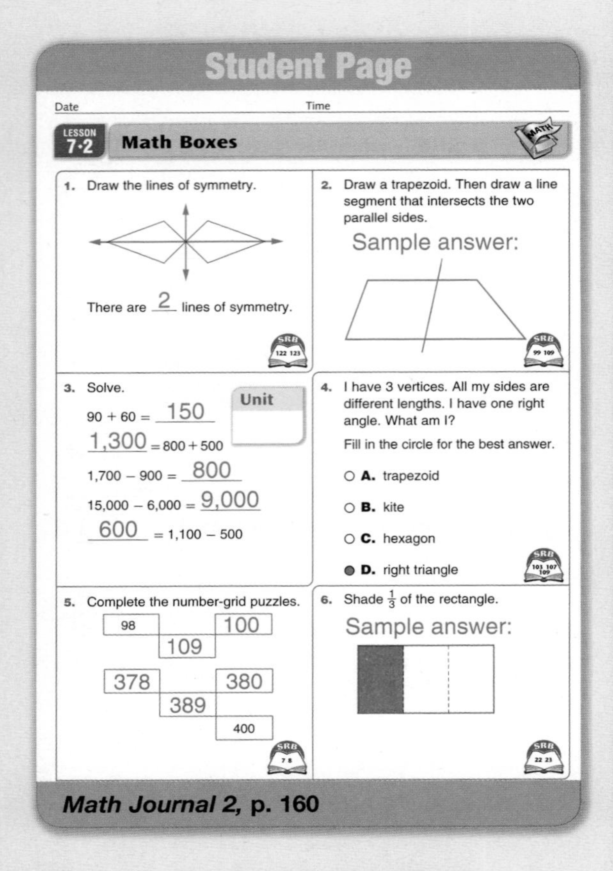
Student Page

Date Time

LESSON 7•2 **Math Boxes**

1. Draw the lines of symmetry.
There are 2 lines of symmetry.

2. Draw a trapezoid. Then draw a line segment that intersects the two parallel sides.
Sample answer:

3. Solve. Unit
90 + 60 = 150
1,300 = 800 + 500
1,700 − 900 = 800
15,000 − 6,000 = 9,000
600 = 1,100 − 500

4. I have 3 vertices. All my sides are different lengths. I have one right angle. What am I?
Fill in the circle for the best answer.
A. trapezoid
B. kite
C. hexagon
D. right triangle

5. Complete the number-grid puzzles.
98, 100, 109
378, 380, 389, 400

6. Shade $\frac{1}{3}$ of the rectangle.
Sample answer:

Math Journal 2, p. 160

Have children find a few turn-around facts on the table. Next, have children fill in the blank boxes along the diagonal fold line and share their strategies. Ask children why these numbers are not mirrored like the others. Both factors are the same number; they are square products; the turn-around fact is exactly the same.

ENRICHMENT

SMALL-GROUP ACTIVITY

15–30 Min

▶ Finding Patterns in the 9s Facts

To apply children's understanding of patterns, have them identify and describe patterns they see in the products for 9s facts. First, children write the 9s facts on paper in a column and look for patterns among the factors and products. Then, they write a description of the patterns they find. Encourage children to test their patterns by continuing to multiply 2-digit numbers by 9. Consider making a class book of the children's work.

Possible 9s facts patterns:

- The digits in the tens place (first column) of the products column are in order starting at 0, 1, 2, ... 9 and repeat as the factors get larger.
- The digits in the ones place (second column) of the products column are in backwards order starting at 9, 8, 7, ... 0 and repeat as the factors get larger.
- The sum of the digits of the products equals 9. ($3 \times 9 = 27$, $2 + 7 = 9$; $11 \times 9 = 99$, $9 + 9 = 18$, $1 + 8 = 9$)
- For 1×9 through 9×9, the product of the first factor multiplied by 10, minus that factor is the product of the first factor multiplied by 9. For example, $(4 \times 10) - 4 = 36$ and $4 \times 9 = 36$.
- For 1×9 through 9×9, digits in the product are predictable. The first factor minus 1 is the first digit in the product. The second digit of the product is 9 minus the first digit in the product. For example, 5×9: first digit of product is 4; $5 - 1 = 4$. The second digit of product is 5; $9 - 4 = 5$. Thus, $5 \times 9 = 45$.

Have children describe the patterns they see using words like *factor, product, more, less, multiplied by, larger, smaller,* and so on.

Home Link Master

Name Date Time

HOME LINK 7·2 Factors and Products

Family Note Listen to your child explain what factors and products are before he or she writes the answers in the table. Then listen as your child tells you what he or she knows about multiplying by 1, multiplying by 0, and multiplying numbers that result in square products. Fact Triangles for the remaining multiplication/division facts are included with this Home Link.

Please return this Home Link to school tomorrow.

1. Explain to someone at home what factors and products are. Find the missing products and factors in the table.
2. Write what you know about the products when you multiply by 1.
   The product is the same as the other factor.
3. Write what you know about the products when you multiply by 0.
   The product is always 0.
4. Write what you know about facts with square products.
   The factors are always the same number.

Factor	Factor	Product
3	5	15
7	2	14
4	10	40
8	8	64
9	5	45
864	1	864
10	10	100
0	999	0
1	48	48
243	0	0

Practice

Write these problems on the back of this page. Make a ballpark estimate for each. Solve. Show your work.

5. 7,201 + 6,988 = 14,189
   ballpark estimate 14,000
6. 3,623 − 457 = 3,166
   ballpark estimate 3,100

Unit

Math Masters, p. 209

Teaching Master

Name Date Time

LESSON 7·2 Turn-Around Facts

×,÷	1	2	3	4	5	6	7	8	9	10
1		2	3	4	5	6	7	8	9	10
2	2		6	8	10	12	14	16	18	20
3	3	6		12	15	18	21	24	27	30
4	4	8	12		20	24	28	32	36	40
5	5	10	15	20		30	35	40	45	50
6	6	12	18	24	30		42	48	54	60
7	7	14	21	28	35	42		56	63	70
8	8	16	24	32	40	48	56		72	80
9	9	18	27	36	45	54	63	72		90
10	10	20	30	40	50	60	70	80	90	

Math Masters, p. 210

7•3 Fact Power

Objective To guide children as they practice multiplication and division facts.

www.everydaymathonline.com

1 Teaching the Lesson

Key Concepts and Skills

- Use multiplication facts to play *Multiplication Bingo.* [Operations and Computation Goal 3]
- Use multiplication facts to solve division facts. [Operations and Computation Goal 3]
- Solve "What's My Rule?" problems. [Patterns, Functions, and Algebra Goal 1]

Key Activities

Children practice solving multiplication and division facts. They play *Multiplication Bingo.*

Ongoing Assessment: Recognizing Student Achievement Use the Math Message. [Patterns, Functions, and Algebra Goal 1]

Materials

Math Journal 2, p. 161
Student Reference Book, pp. 293–295
Home Link 7•2
Math Masters, p. 449
per group: 4 each of number cards 1–6 and 10 (from Everything Math Deck, if available) ◆ per child: 8 pennies or other counters ◆ half-sheet of paper

2 Ongoing Learning & Practice

Solving Multiplication and Division Facts
Math Journal 2, p. 162
Children write fact families and complete multiplication and division puzzles.

Math Boxes 7•3
Math Journal 2, p. 163
Children practice and maintain skills through Math Box problems.

Home Link 7•3
Math Masters, pp. 211 and 212
Children practice and maintain skills through Home Link activities.

3 Differentiation Options

READINESS

Solving Problems with Multiplication Diagrams
Math Masters, p. 213
Children solve number stories using multiplication diagrams.

ENRICHMENT

Finding Rules
Math Masters, p. 214
red and blue crayons ◆ calculator (optional)
Children identify and use multiplication and division rules to fill in Frames-and-Arrows diagrams.

Advance Preparation

***Teacher's Reference Manual,* Grades 1–3** p. 199

Getting Started

Mathematical Practices
SMP1, SMP5, SMP6, SMP7, SMP8
Content Standards
3.OA.1, **3.OA.2, 3.OA.3, 3.OA.4, 3.OA.5, 3.OA.6, 3.OA.7**

Mental Math and Reflexes

Have children practice quick recall of basic multiplication facts. *Suggestions:*

●○○ 2 × 7 14 3 × 7 21 4 × 7 28 5 × 7 35
●●○ 6 × 5 30 6 × 6 36 6 × 7 42 6 × 8 48
●●● 3 × 9 27 4 × 9 36 6 × 9 54 7 × 9 63

Math Message

Copy the tables on a half-sheet of paper. Find the missing rule for the first table. Fill in the tables.

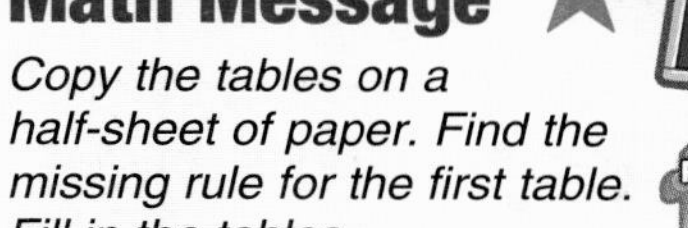

Rule
× 3

in	out
3	9
2	6
5	15
7	21
Answers vary.	

Rule
÷ 5

in	out
30	6
15	3
25	5
35	7
Answers vary.	

Home Link 7·2 Follow-Up

Invite children to share their answers to Problems 2, 3, and 4 with the class. Briefly review the × 0 and × 1 rules.

1 Teaching the Lesson

▶ Math Message Follow-Up

WHOLE-CLASS DISCUSSION

Algebraic Thinking As you discuss the answers in the Math Message, review the relationship between multiplication and division. For example, if the rule is × 3, you would *multiply* an input number by 3 to find the output. In contrast, you would *divide* an output number by 3 to find the input. To find the input, given the output 15, you could ask yourself: *How many 3s are there in 15?* or *What number multiplied by 3, equals 15?*

Ongoing Assessment: Recognizing Student Achievement

Math Message

Use the **Math Message** to assess children's progress toward finding and using rules to solve multiplication and division problems. Children are making adequate progress if they successfully find the rule for and complete the first table. Some children may be able to complete the second table successfully.

[Patterns, Functions, and Algebra Goal 1]

Student Page

Games

Multiplication Bingo (Easy Facts)

Materials
- ☐ number cards 1–6 and 10 (4 of each)
- ☐ 1 *Multiplication Bingo* game mat for each player (*Math Masters,* p. 449)
- ☐ 8 counters for each player

Players 2 or 3

Skill Mental multiplication skills

Object of the game To get 4 counters in a row, column, or diagonal; or 8 counters anywhere on the game mat.

Directions

1. The game mat is shown below. You can make your own game mat on a piece of paper. Write each of the numbers in the list in one of the squares on the grid. Don't write the numbers in order. Mix them up.

List of Numbers	
1	18
4	20
6	24
8	25
9	30
12	36
15	50
16	100

Multiplication Bingo Game Mat

2. Shuffle the number cards and place the deck number-side down on the table.

Student Reference Book, p. 293

▶ Playing *Multiplication Bingo*

(*Math Journal 2,* p. 161; *Student Reference Book,* pp. 293–295; *Math Masters,* p. 449)

As a class, read the rules for *Multiplication Bingo* on *Student Reference Book,* pages 293 and 294. Model a few rounds for the class. Remind children to use the familiar fact shortcuts that were reviewed in Lesson 4-5 to help them find products they have not yet memorized.

For the first two games they play, children will record the results in their journals. For future games, they may use *Math Masters,* page 449 or draw their own grids on a sheet of paper.

Adjusting the Activity

There are two versions of *Multiplication Bingo.* The first focuses on the 1s, 2s, 3s, 4s, 5s, 6s, and 10s multiplication facts. The second focuses on all the multiplication facts and is described on *Student Reference Book,* page 295. Have children play the appropriate version.

AUDITORY ◆ KINESTHETIC ◆ TACTILE ◆ VISUAL

Student Page

Games

3. Players take turns. When it is your turn, take the top 2 cards and call out the product of the 2 numbers. If someone does not agree with your answer, check it by using the Multiplication/Division Facts Table on page 52 in your *Student Reference Book* or the inside front cover of your journal.
   - ◆ If your answer is incorrect, you lose your turn.
   - ◆ If your answer is correct and the product is a number on your game mat, place a counter on that number. You may only place a counter on your game mat when it is your turn.
4. If you are the first player to get 4 counters in a row, column, or diagonal, call out "Bingo!" and win the game! You can also call "Bingo!" and win if you get 8 counters anywhere on your game mat.

If all the cards are used before someone wins, shuffle the cards again and keep playing.

Example A player could call out "Bingo!" with any of these game mats:

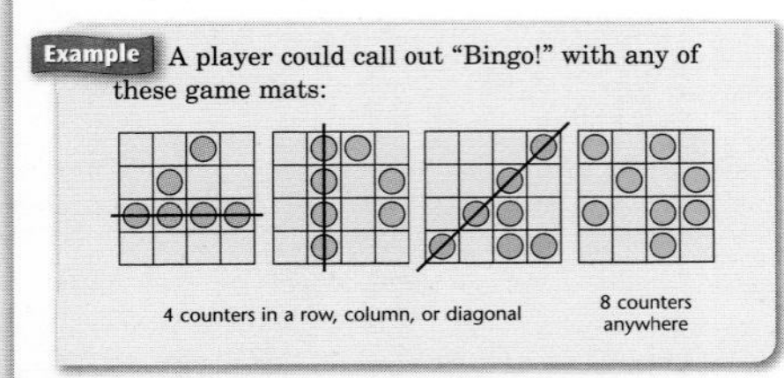

Student Reference Book, p. 294

Student Page

Date ______ Time ______

LESSON 7·3 **Multiplication Bingo**

Read the rules for *Multiplication Bingo* on pages 293 and 294 in the *Student Reference Book.*

Write the list of numbers on each grid below.

List of numbers

1	9	18	30
4	12	20	36
6	15	24	50
8	16	25	100

Record the facts you miss.
Be sure to practice them!

______
______
______
______
______
______
______

Math Journal 2, p. 161

2 Ongoing Learning & Practice

▶ Solving Multiplication and Division Facts

INDEPENDENT ACTIVITY

FACTS PRACTICE

(*Math Journal 2,* p. 162)

For Problems 1 and 2 on the journal page, children complete the Fact Triangles and write fact families for each. For Problems 3–7, explain that each puzzle is part of a multiplication and division table. In the first three puzzles, children fill in products only. In the last two puzzles, they fill in factors and products.

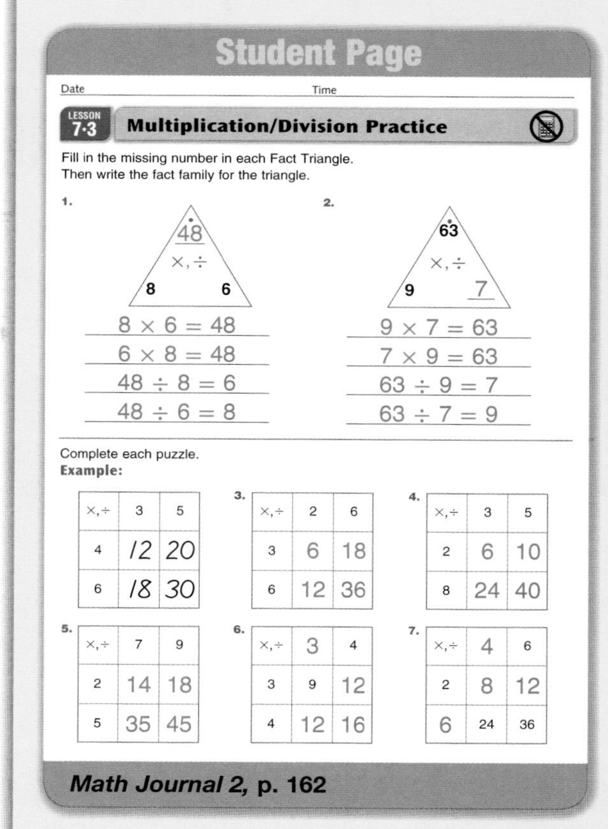

Student Page

Date Time

LESSON 7·3 **Multiplication/Division Practice**

Fill in the missing number in each Fact Triangle.
Then write the fact family for the triangle.

1. Fact Triangle: 48 (top), ×, ÷, 8 and 6

$8 \times 6 = 48$
$6 \times 8 = 48$
$48 \div 8 = 6$
$48 \div 6 = 8$

2. Fact Triangle: 63 (top), ×, ÷, 9 and 7

$9 \times 7 = 63$
$7 \times 9 = 63$
$63 \div 9 = 7$
$63 \div 7 = 9$

Complete each puzzle.
Example:

×,÷	3	5
4	12	20
6	18	30

3.

×,÷	2	6
3	6	18
6	12	36

4.

×,÷	3	5
2	6	10
8	24	40

5.

×,÷	7	9
2	14	18
5	35	45

6.

×,÷	3	4
3	9	12
4	12	16

7.

×,÷	4	6
2	8	12
6	24	36

Math Journal 2, p. 162

▶ Math Boxes 7·3

INDEPENDENT ACTIVITY

(*Math Journal 2,* p. 163)

Mixed Practice The Math Boxes in this lesson are paired with Math Boxes from Lesson 7-1. The skill in Problem 6 previews Unit 8 content.

Writing/Reasoning Have children write the answer to the following: *Look at Problem 3: Explain how rays and lines are alike and how they are different.* Sample answer: A line is a straight path that extends forever in both directions, and a ray is a straight path that extends forever in one direction. A line can be named by any 2 of its points. The name of a ray must begin with its end point.

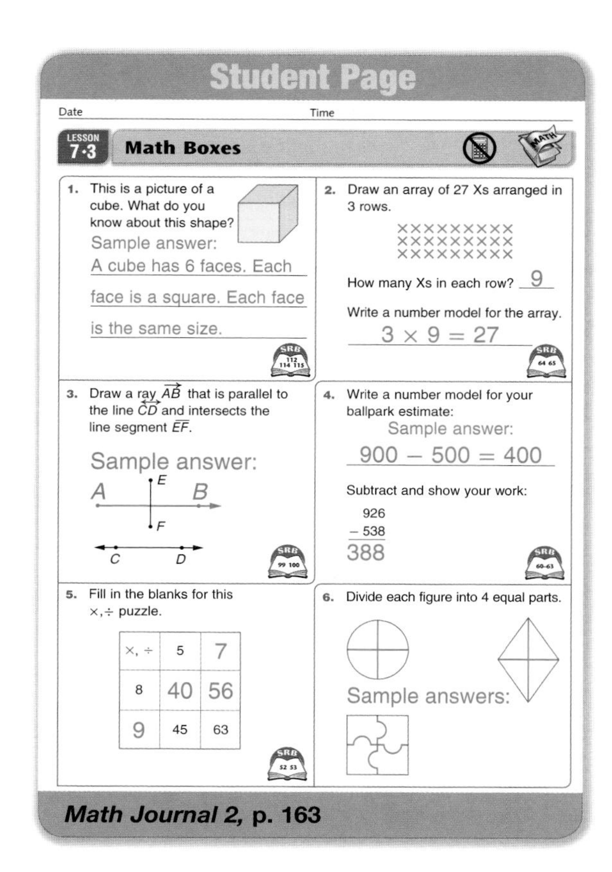

Student Page

Date Time

LESSON 7·3 **Math Boxes**

1. This is a picture of a cube. What do you know about this shape?
Sample answer: A cube has 6 faces. Each face is a square. Each face is the same size.

2. Draw an array of 27 Xs arranged in 3 rows.
XXXXXXXXX
XXXXXXXXX
XXXXXXXXX
How many Xs in each row? 9
Write a number model for the array.
$3 \times 9 = 27$

3. Draw a ray $\overrightarrow{AB}$ that is parallel to the line $\overleftrightarrow{CD}$ and intersects the line segment $\overline{EF}$.
Sample answer:

4. Write a number model for your ballpark estimate:
Sample answer: $900 - 500 = 400$
Subtract and show your work:
926
− 538
388

5. Fill in the blanks for this ×, ÷ puzzle.

×, ÷	5	7
8	40	56
9	45	63

6. Divide each figure into 4 equal parts.
Sample answers:

Math Journal 2, p. 163

▶ Home Link 7·3

(*Math Masters,* pp. 211 and 212)

Home Connection Children play *Multiplication Bingo* with someone at home. Families are not expected to return these Home Link pages to school. They should be kept at home for continued practice.

3 Differentiation Options

READINESS

▶ Solving Problems with Multiplication Diagrams

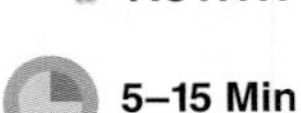

(*Math Masters,* p. 213)

Portfolio Ideas

To explore the connections between multiplication and division, have children solve number stories using multiplication diagrams. After children complete the page, have them describe how they decided whether to use multiplication or division to solve a problem.

Home Link Master

Name Date Time

HOME LINK 7·3 **Multiplication Bingo (Easy Facts)**

Family Note Today the class learned to play *Multiplication Bingo.* This game is a good way to practice the multiplication facts. Ask your child to show you how to play the game; then play a couple of games. When your child is ready to practice harder facts, use the cards and list of numbers on the next page. Encourage your child to keep a record of the facts he or she misses.

Keep this Home Link at home.

Materials
- ☐ number cards 1–6 and 10 (4 of each)
- ☐ 8 pennies or other counters for each player
- ☐ game mat for each player

Players 2 or 3

Directions

1. Write each of the following numbers in any order in one of the squares on a game mat: 1, 4, 6, 8, 9, 12, 15, 16, 18, 20, 24, 25, 30, 36, 50, 100.
2. Shuffle the number cards. Place the cards facedown on the table.
3. Take turns. When it is your turn, take the top 2 cards and call out the product of the 2 numbers. If the other players do not agree with your answer, check it using a calculator.
4. If your answer is correct and the product is a number on your grid, place a penny or a counter on that number.
5. If your answer is incorrect, you lose your turn.
6. The first player to get 4 counters in a row, column, or diagonal or 8 counters on the game mat calls out *Bingo!* and wins the game.

If all the cards are used before someone wins, shuffle the cards again and keep playing.

***Math Masters,* p. 211**

Home Link Master

Name Date Time

HOME LINK 7·3 **Multiplication Bingo (All Facts)**

Follow the same rules as for *Multiplication Bingo,* with the following exceptions:

- Use a deck of number cards with 4 cards each for the numbers 2 through 9.
- Write each of the numbers in the list in one of the squares on the grid. Don't write the numbers in order.

List of numbers

24	35	48	63
27	36	49	64
28	42	54	72
32	45	56	81

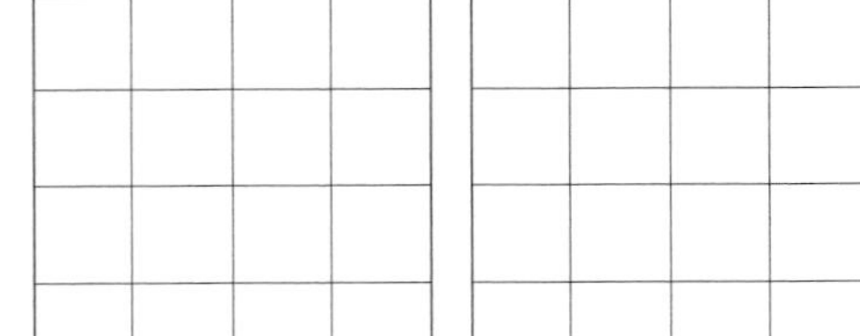

Record the facts you miss. Be sure to practice them.

______ ______ ______
______ ______ ______
______ ______ ______
______ ______ ______

***Math Masters,* p. 212**

Teaching Master

Name Date Time

LESSON 7·3 **Problems with Multiplication Diagrams**

For each problem, fill in the diagram. Use a question mark to show the unknown part in the diagram. Write a number model and solve the problem.

1. Jo had 24 markers. Markers come in boxes of 8. How many boxes did she buy?

boxes	markers per box	markers in all
?	8	24

Number model: $24 \div 8 = ?$ or $? \times 8 = 24$ Answer: 3 boxes

2. Franklin was trying to figure out how many eggs his mom bought. She bought 4 cartons with one dozen eggs in each.

cartons	eggs per carton	eggs in all
4	12	?

Number model: $4 \times 12 = ?$ or $12 \times 4 = ?$ Answer: 48 eggs

3. Mr. Lee has 25 meters of string for hanging flags from the ceiling. He needs 5 meters of string for each flag. How many flags can he hang?

flags	meters per flag	meters in all
?	5	25

Number model: $25 \div 5 = ?$ or $? \times 5 = 25$ Answer: 5 flags

***Math Masters,* p. 213**

ENRICHMENT

INDEPENDENT ACTIVITY

▶ Finding Rules

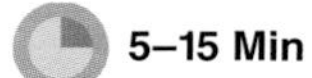

5–15 Min

(*Math Masters,* p. 214)

Algebraic Thinking To apply children's understanding of multiplication and division, have them complete two-rule Frames-and-Arrows puzzles on *Math Masters,* page 214. Note that the arrows will not always alternate *ABAB*. Have children color code their arrow rules with crayons to distinguish one from another. When children have finished the page, discuss their solution strategies.

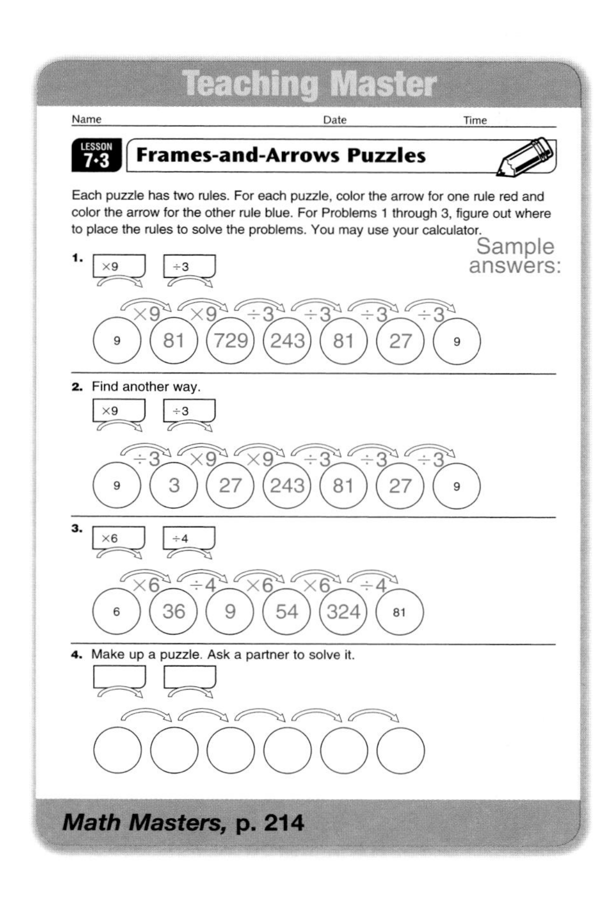

Teaching Master

Name Date Time

LESSON 7·3 **Frames-and-Arrows Puzzles**

Each puzzle has two rules. For each puzzle, color the arrow for one rule red and color the arrow for the other rule blue. For Problems 1 through 3, figure out where to place the rules to solve the problems. You may use your calculator.

Sample answers:

1. ×9 ÷3

×9, ×9, ÷3, ÷3, ÷3, ÷3

9, 81, 729, 243, 81, 27, 9

2. Find another way.

×9 ÷3

÷3, ×9, ×9, ÷3, ÷3, ÷3

9, 3, 27, 243, 81, 27, 9

3. ×6 ÷4

×6, ÷4, ×6, ×6, ÷4

6, 36, 9, 54, 324, 81

4. Make up a puzzle. Ask a partner to solve it.

Math Masters, p. 214

7·4 Number Models with Parentheses

 **Objective** To introduce parentheses in number sentences.

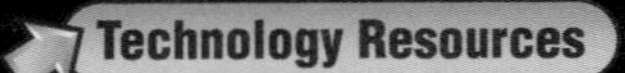

www.everydaymathonline.com

ePresentations

eToolkit

Algorithms Practice

EM Facts Workshop Game™

Family Letters

Assessment Management

Common Core State Standards

Curriculum Focal Points

Interactive Teacher's Lesson Guide

1 Teaching the Lesson

Key Concepts and Skills

- Use basic and extended addition and subtraction facts to solve number sentences.
  [Operations and Computation Goal 1]
- Use multiplication facts to solve number sentences.
  [Operations and Computation Goal 3]
- Write number models with parentheses to match number stories.
  [Patterns, Functions, and Algebra Goal 3]

Key Activities

Children compare the use of commas in word sentences to the use of parentheses in number sentences. Children use parentheses in writing number models for number stories.

 **Ongoing Assessment: Informing Instruction** See page 596.

 **Ongoing Assessment: Recognizing Student Achievement**
Use journal page 164.
[Patterns, Functions, and Algebra Goal 3]

Key Vocabulary

parentheses

Materials

Math Journal 2, p. 164
Home Link 7•3 (teacher only)
Math Masters, p. 406 (optional)
slate ◆ stick-on notes (optional)

2 Ongoing Learning & Practice

Practicing with ×, ÷ Fact Triangles

×, ÷ Fact Triangles
Children practice multiplication and division with Fact Triangles.

Math Boxes 7•4

Math Journal 2, p. 165
Children practice and maintain skills through Math Box problems.

Home Link 7•4

Math Masters, p. 215
Children practice and maintain skills through Home Link activities.

3 Differentiation Options

READINESS

Playing *Name That Number*

Math Masters, p. 451
Student Reference Book, pp. 299 and 300
per group: 4 each of number cards 0–10 and 1 each of number cards 11–20 (from the Everything Math Deck, if available), 3" by 5" labeled index cards (see Advance Preparation)
Children use at least three cards and two operations to make target numbers.

ENRICHMENT

Describing Dot Patterns with Number Models

Math Masters, p. 216
Children write number models to represent the patterns in arrays.

ELL SUPPORT

Building a Math Word Bank

Differentiation Handbook, p. 132
Children add the term *parentheses* to their Math Word Banks.

Advance Preparation

For the optional Readiness activity in Part 3, prepare 1 set of operation cards per partnership. Cut five 3" by 5" inch index cards in half. Write the following—one on each card: +, +, +, −, −, −, ×, ÷, =.

 ***Teacher's Reference Manual,* Grades 1–3** pp. 82–84

Getting Started

Mathematical Practices
SMP1, **SMP2,** SMP4, SMP6, SMP8
Content Standards
3.OA.3, 3.OA.4, **3.OA.7, 3.OA.8,** 3.NBT.2

Mental Math and Reflexes

Have children practice quick recall of basic multiplication facts. *Suggestions:*

●○○ 3 × 3 9 4 × 4 16 5 × 5 25 6 × 6 36

●●○ 2 × 9 18 3 × 9 27 4 × 9 36 5 × 9 45

●●● 7 × 7 49 8 × 8 64 9 × 9 81 9 × 8 72

Math Message

Can you find more than one meaning for each sentence?

Nancy fed Tom the big gray cat.

My sister Tess and Jimmy are going.

Discuss the meanings you found with a partner.

Home Link 7·3 Follow-Up

Remind children of the importance of frequent practice with the facts. Ask them to name their favorite activity for learning the facts. Do they set aside a certain time for facts practice with someone at home?

1 Teaching the Lesson

▶ Math Message Follow-Up

WHOLE-CLASS DISCUSSION

Although the sentences illustrate the need for punctuation marks, most children will need an explanation from you about the meanings of the sentences.

One interpretation of the first sentence is that Nancy gave Tom a big gray cat to eat! Another interpretation is that the cat's name is Tom, and Nancy gave Tom something to eat. If that is the intended meaning, a comma needs to be inserted after Tom. (Nancy fed Tom, the big gray cat.)

Without commas in the second sentence, two people are going (Tess and Jimmy—Tess is my sister.). With commas, three people are going (my sister, Tess, and Jimmy).

▶ Comparing Punctuation Marks to Parentheses

WHOLE-CLASS ACTIVITY

ELL

Algebraic Thinking Explain that just as word sentences can often be interpreted in more than one way, so can number sentences. When a number sentence may be interpreted in more than one way, **parentheses** are used to make the intended meaning clear. Parentheses indicate which part of a number sentence should be solved first. To support English language learners, write *parentheses* on the board along with the number sentences listed below.

$$(25 - 8) + 7 = ?$$

$$25 - (8 + 7) = ?$$

- In $(25 - 8) + 7 = ?$, the parentheses indicate that $25 - 8$ is to be solved first and that 7 is to be added to the result: $25 - 8 = 17$ and $17 + 7 = 24$. Replace the question mark with 24 in the first number sentence.
- In $25 - (8 + 7) = ?$, the parentheses indicate that $8 + 7$ is to be solved first and that the sum is to be subtracted from 25: $8 + 7 = 15$ and $25 - 15 = 10$. Replace the question mark with 10 in the second number sentence.

Ask children to compare both number sentences and their answers. Emphasize that the answer depends on where the parentheses are placed.

Ongoing Assessment: Informing Instruction

Watch for children who have difficulty focusing their attention on the parentheses in the number sentence. Cover the number outside the parentheses with a stick-on note. After the computation inside the parentheses is completed, remove the stick-on note so the remaining computation can be finished.

- Write the following number sentences on the board. Have children copy them onto their slates and solve them.

$53 - (17 + 13) = 23$

$27 = (17 - 8) \times 3$

$48 = 68 - (4 \times 5)$

$(12 + 38) - 15 = 35$

- Write the pairs of number sentences below on the board. Have children copy them and insert parentheses to make each answer correct.

$32 - (5 + 7) = 20$	$(38 - 14) - 9 = 15$	$40 - (5 \times 2) = 30$
$(32 - 5) + 7 = 34$	$38 - (14 - 9) = 33$	$(40 - 5) \times 2 = 70$

Discuss solution strategies. Pose additional problems as needed.

Adjusting the Activity

The problems to the right provide children with practice in using mental math strategies and parentheses. The problems may be simplified so that children are able to focus on the use of parentheses. For example, instead of $53 - (17 + 13)$, use $12 - (4 + 6)$.

AUDITORY ◆ KINESTHETIC ◆ TACTILE ◆ VISUAL

NOTE Some calculators have parentheses keys and evaluate expressions using a different order of operations than four-function calculators. *Third Grade Everyday Mathematics* does not expect children to have these more advanced calculators. If you or one of your children has a calculator with parentheses, however, you might make an exploration of how it works using some of the number sentences in this lesson. To further explore order of operations without grouping symbols, see Project 7, Order of Operations.

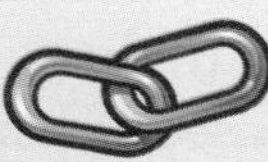

Links to the Future

The activities in this lesson provide an introduction to using parentheses to write number models for specific situations in number stories. This begins to teach the concept that continues into algebra. Recognizing that parentheses affect the order of operations is a Grade 3 Goal. Writing number sentences with parentheses to fit specific situations is a Grade 4 Goal.

▶ Writing Number Models with Parentheses

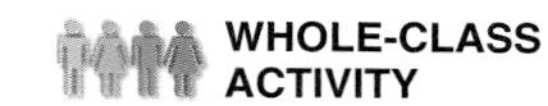

(*Math Journal 2,* p. 164; *Math Masters,* p. 406)

Algebraic Thinking Explain to children that some number stories have two steps. Number models for such stories can be written with parentheses to show which step comes first.

Ask a child to read aloud Problem 1 on journal page 164: *Alexis scored 12 points and Nehemia scored 6 points. If their team scored 41 points altogether, how many points did the rest of the team score?*

Remind children of the *Guide to Solving Number Stories* on *Math Masters,* page 406.

- What do you want to find out? The number of points the rest of the team scored

  What do you know from reading the story? Alexis scored 12 points, Nehemia scored 6 points, and 41 points were scored by the team altogether.

- Explain that two calculations can be made to solve the story. One strategy could be to first add to find the total points that Alexis and Nehemia scored. Write 12 + 6 and tell children that this expression models the first step in the solution. Add parentheses around 12 + 6 to show that this calculation is to be done first. The second calculation would then be to subtract that sum from the 41 points the team scored altogether. For step 2, write 41 − in front of (12 + 6). Remind children that a letter can be used to represent what we want to find out. Since we want to find the number of points the *rest* of the team scored, write an R in the open sentence. $41 - (12 + 6) = R$

- What is the answer? The rest of the team scored 23 points.

- Does your answer make sense? yes How can you tell? Sample answer: I knew that the rest of the team had to score fewer points than the team scored altogether. Does your answer make the open sentence true? yes

Write a summary number model on the board. $41 - (12 + 6) = 23$ Ask children if they can think of a different way to solve the number story. Some children may suggest adding 12 and 6 and then counting up to 41. $(12 + 6) + R = 41$ Others may suggest beginning with 41 and subtracting 12 and then 6. $(41 - 12) - 6 = R$ As children share their thinking, invite volunteers to write the open sentences that reflect these strategies.

Teaching Aid Master

Name Date Time

Guide to Solving Number Stories

1. **What do you understand from the story?**
   - Read the story. What do you want to find out?
   - What do you know?
2. **What will you do?**
   - Add?
   - Subtract?
   - Multiply?
   - Divide?
   - Draw a picture?
   - Make tallies?
   - Use counters or base-10 blocks?
   - Use a number grid or number line?
   - Make a table?
   - Draw a diagram?
   - Write a number model?
3. **Answer the question.**
   - Solve the problem. Record your work.
   - Write the answer with the units.
4. **Check.**
   - Does your answer make sense? How do you know?

Math Masters, p. 406

Student Page

Date Time

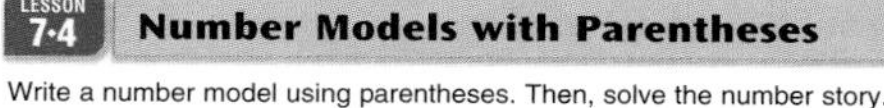

Write a number model using parentheses. Then, solve the number story.

1. Alexis scored 12 points, and Nehemie scored 6 points. If their team scored 41 points altogether, how many points did the rest of the team score?
   Possible number models:
   Number model: $41 - (12 + 6) = R$, $(12 + 6) + R = 41$, $(41 - 12) - 6 = R$
   Answer: 23 points
2. In a partner game, Quincy has 10 points, and Ellen has 14 points. They need 50 points to finish the game. How many more points are needed?
   Possible number models:
   Number model: $50 - (10 + 14) = M$, $10 + 14 + M = 50$, $(50 - 10) - 14 = M$
   Answer: 26 points
3. Quincy and Ellen earned 49 points but lost 14 points for a wrong move. They gained 10 points back. What was their score at the end of the round?
   Possible number models:
   Number model: $(49 - 14) + 10 = E$, $(49 + 10) - 14 = E$
   Answer: 45 points

Complete these number sentences.

4. $4 = 18 - (9 + 5)$
5. $(75 - 29) + 5 = 51$
6. $35 = 8 + (9 \times 3)$
7. $36 + (15 \div 3) = 41$

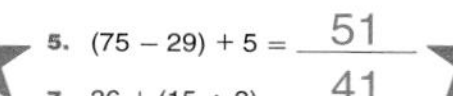

Add parentheses to complete the number models.

8. $20 - (10 + 4) = 6$
9. $(20 - 10) + 4 = 14$
10. $100 - (21 + 10) = 69$
11. $(100 - 21) + 10 = 89$
12. $(27 - 8) + 3 = 22$
13. $18 = 6 + (3 \times 4)$

Math Journal 2, p. 164

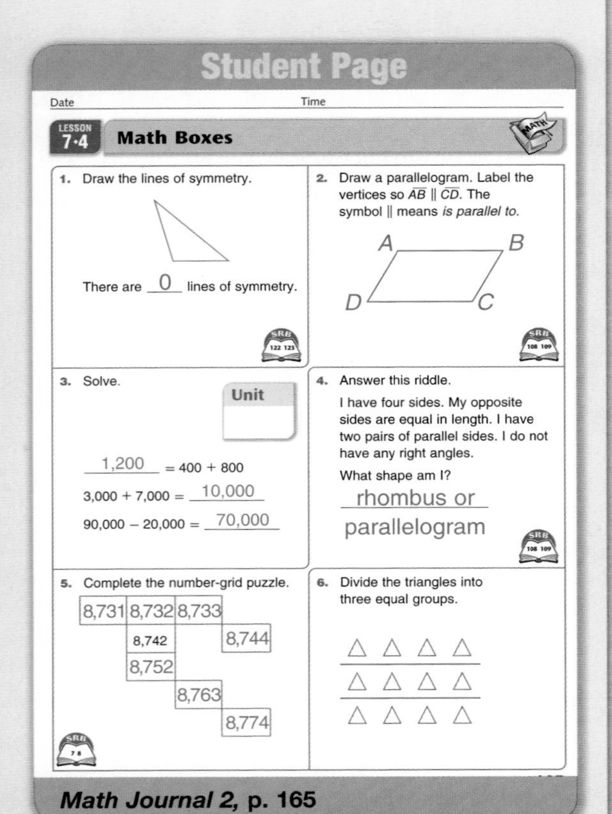
Student Page

Date Time

LESSON 7·4 **Math Boxes**

1. Draw the lines of symmetry.

There are 0 lines of symmetry.

2. Draw a parallelogram. Label the vertices so $\overline{AB} \parallel \overline{CD}$. The symbol $\parallel$ means *is parallel to.*

A B D C

3. Solve.

Unit

1,200 = 400 + 800

3,000 + 7,000 = 10,000

90,000 − 20,000 = 70,000

4. Answer this riddle.

I have four sides. My opposite sides are equal in length. I have two pairs of parallel sides. I do not have any right angles.

What shape am I?

rhombus or parallelogram

5. Complete the number-grid puzzle.

8,731 8,732 8,733

8,742 8,744

8,752

8,763

8,774

6. Divide the triangles into three equal groups.

△ △ △ △

△ △ △ △

△ △ △ △

Math Journal 2, p. 165

Home Link Master

Name Date Time

HOME LINK 7·4 **Parentheses Puzzles**

Family Note Observe as your child adds parentheses and explains what to do first in the number sentence puzzles in Problems 1 through 4. If needed, assist your child in writing a correct number model for the Try This problem. You might ask how many gifts Dalia would need to fill 8 bags and how many she would need to also take care of Denise.

Please return this Home Link to school tomorrow.

Show someone at home how to add parentheses to complete the number sentences below. Remember that the parentheses are used to show what you do first.

1 a. $(17 - 10) + 3 = 10$ **1 b.** $17 - (10 + 3) = 4$

2 a. $(26 - 7) \times 2 = 38$ **2 b.** $26 - (7 \times 2) = 12$

3 a. $(24 - 17) - 6 = 1$ **3 b.** $24 - (17 - 6) = 13$

4 a. $3 \times (6 + 13) = 57$ **4 b.** $(3 \times 6) + 13 = 31$

Make up other parentheses puzzles below. Sample answers:

5 a. $4 \times (8 - 6) = 8$ **5 b.** $(4 \times 8) - 6 = 26$

6 a. $(7 + 3) \times 4 = 40$ **6 b.** $7 + (3 \times 4) = 19$

Try This

7. Dalia made 8 party bags for her birthday party. Each bag contained 4 small gifts for her friends. When Denise said that she could come, Dalia had to make one more bag with 4 gifts. How many small gifts did Dalia need to fill her bags?

Walter wrote this number model: $8 \times (4 + 4) = 64$

Explain Walter's mistake.

The parentheses are placed incorrectly. The number model should be $(8 \times 4) + 4 = 36$.

Math Masters, p. 215

In the same manner, do the remaining two number stories on the journal page with the class. In Problem 2, since we want to find how many *more* points are needed, the letter M can be used in an open sentence to represent what we want to find out. Likewise, for Problem 3, since we want to find out the score at the *end* of the game, the letter E can be used in an open sentence to represent what we want to find out. (Of course, any letter may be used for any variable.)

Then, have children complete the rest of the problems on the page.

Journal Page 164 Problems 4 and 5

Use **journal page 164, Problems 4 and 5** to assess children's progress toward recognizing that parentheses affect the order of operations. Children are making adequate progress if they successfully complete Problems 4 and 5. Some children may successfully complete the remaining problems on the page.

[Patterns, Functions, and Algebra Goal 3]

2 Ongoing Learning & Practice

▶ Practicing with ×, ÷ Fact Triangles

PARTNER ACTIVITY

5–15 Min

Partners practice basic facts using the second set of Fact Triangles. At first, children should limit themselves to finding products. When children are well on their way to learning the products, they can cover one of the other two numbers to practice finding missing factors.

▶ Math Boxes 7·4

INDEPENDENT ACTIVITY

(*Math Journal 2,* p. 165)

Mixed Practice The Math Boxes in this lesson are paired with the Math Boxes in Lesson 7-2. The skill in Problem 6 previews Unit 8 content.

Writing/Reasoning Have children write the answer to the following: *Write your own polygon riddle similar to the one in Problem 4.* Sample answer: I have 4 sides. My opposite sides are equal in length. I have 4 right angles. What shape am I? Rectangle.

▶ Home Link 7·4

INDEPENDENT ACTIVITY

(*Math Masters,* p. 215)

Home Connection Children solve parentheses puzzles.

3 Differentiation Options

READINESS

SMALL-GROUP ACTIVITY

15–30 Min

▶ Playing *Name That Number*

(*Math Masters,* p. 451; *Student Reference Book,* pp. 299 and 300)

To provide experience with using basic facts to solve multistep problems, have children play *Name That Number*. Encourage children to work together to find solutions for the target numbers using at least 3 cards and 2 operations. Children can use the operations cards you prepared to physically model their thinking. Have partners record their best round on *Math Masters,* page 451. Have children read the number sentences they recorded.

ENRICHMENT

INDEPENDENT ACTIVITY

15–30 Min

▶ Describing Dot Patterns with Number Models

(*Math Masters*, p. 216)

To apply children's understanding of number models, have children write number models to represent the patterns in the arrays on *Math Masters*, page 216.

ELL SUPPORT

SMALL-GROUP ACTIVITY

5–15 Min

▶ Building a Math Word Bank

(*Differentiation Handbook,* p. 132)

To provide language support for number sentences, have children use the Word Bank template found on *Differentiation Handbook,* page 132. Ask the children to write the term *parentheses,* draw a picture representing the term, and write other related words. See the *Differentiation Handbook* for more information.

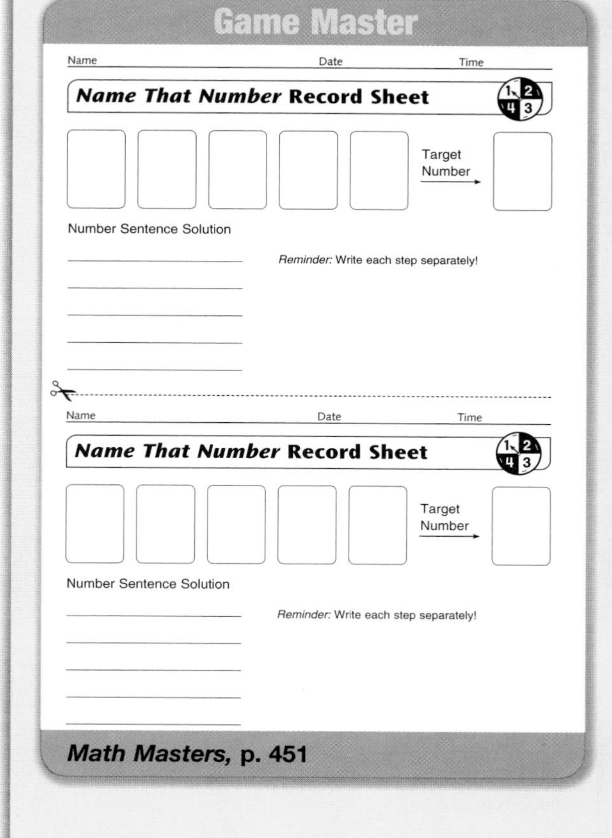

Math Masters, p. 451

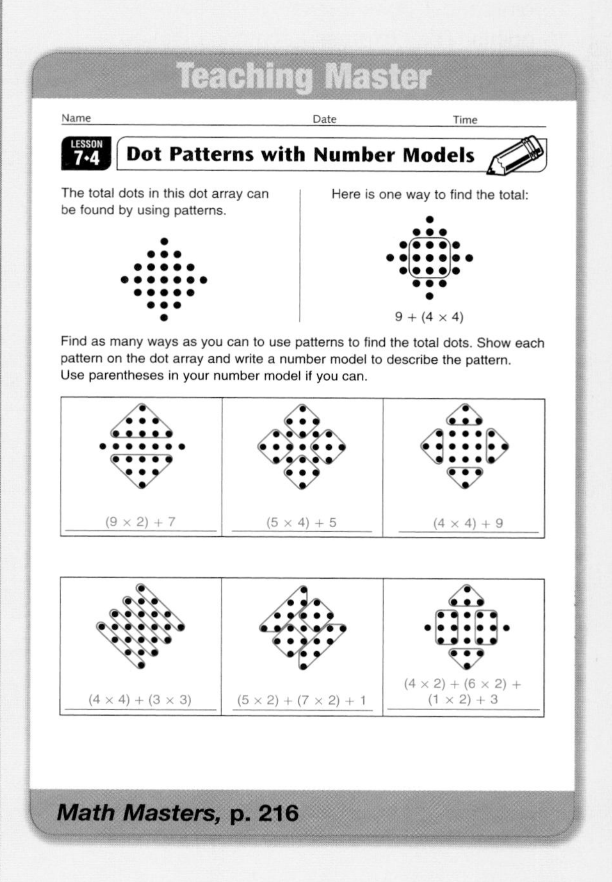

Math Masters, p. 216

7•5 Scoring in Basketball: An Application

Objective To provide opportunities to express numbers as sums of products using number models that contain parentheses.

Technology Resources www.everydaymathonline.com

ePresentations

eToolkit

Algorithms Practice

EM Facts Workshop Game™

Family Letters

Assessment Management

Common Core State Standards

Curriculum Focal Points

Interactive Teacher's Lesson Guide

1 Teaching the Lesson

Key Concepts and Skills

- Write equivalent names for 10. [Number and Numeration Goal 4]
- Use multiplication facts. [Operations and Computation Goal 3]
- Write number models with parentheses to match number stories. [Patterns, Functions, and Algebra Goal 3]
- Apply properties of multiplication and addition to solve problems. [Patterns, Functions, and Algebra Goal 4]

Key Activities

Children find various combinations of 3-point, 2-point, and 1-point baskets that add up to 10 points. They express each combination with a number model.

Ongoing Assessment: Informing Instruction See page 602.

Ongoing Assessment: Recognizing Student Achievement Use journal page 166 and an Exit Slip (*Math Masters,* page 398). [Patterns, Functions, and Algebra Goal 3]

Materials

Math Journal 2, p. 166
Home Link 7•4
Math Masters, p. 398
slate ◆ counters (optional)

2 Ongoing Learning & Practice

Solving Problems with Parentheses in Name-Collection Boxes
Math Journal 2, p. 167
Children practice using parentheses in number models by solving name-collection box problems.

Math Boxes 7•5
Math Journal 2, p. 168
Children practice and maintain skills through Math Box problems.

Home Link 7•5
Math Masters, p. 217
Children practice and maintain skills through Home Link activities.

3 Differentiation Options

READINESS

Finding Equivalent Names
Math Masters, p. 218
10 pennies per child
Children use equal groupings to find combinations for 10 pennies.

ENRICHMENT

Writing Names for Digits
Math Masters, p. 219
calculator (optional)
Children write equivalent names for digits.

Advance Preparation

For Part 1, draw the four-column chart from journal page 166 on the board.

***Teacher's Reference Manual,* Grades 1–3** p. 84

Getting Started

Mathematical Practices
SMP1, SMP2, **SMP3, SMP4,** SMP6, SMP8
Content Standards
3.OA.7, **3.OA.8**

Mental Math and Reflexes

Pose multiplication stories involving equal groups. Encourage children to use arrays, counters, or multiplication/division diagrams. Children share their solution strategies. *Suggestions:*

●○○ Claire has 3 bags of apples. Each bag has 5 apples. How many apples does Claire have in all? 15 apples

●●○ Philip collected 25 cents from himself and 5 friends so he could buy a comic book for them to share. How much money did Philip collect? \$1.50

●●● Kevin bought 2 boxes of computer disks. Each box contained 3 dozen disks. How many disks did he buy all together? 72 disks

Math Message

Sheila made two 3-point baskets and two 2-point baskets in a basketball game. How many points did she score in all? Write a number model on your slate that contains parentheses. $(2 \times 2) + (2 \times 3) = 10$; $(3 \times 2) + (2 \times 2) = 10$; $(2 \times 2) + (3 \times 2) = 10$

Home Link 7·4 Follow-Up

Have children share a few of their parentheses puzzles with the class. Discuss the Try This problem. Ask: *What did Walter do wrong?* He put the parentheses in the wrong place. A correct number model is $(8 \times 4) + 4 = 36$. The number of gifts for all children, except Denise, is represented by 8×4. Add 4 to the total for Denise's gifts.

1 Teaching the Lesson

▶ Math Message Follow-Up

WHOLE-CLASS DISCUSSION

Algebraic Thinking Children share their solution strategies and number models. The number models are $(2 \times 3) + (2 \times 2) = 10$ and its variations using the turn-around rules for multiplication and addition. Remind children that the operations in parentheses are done first. As you write the number models on the board, label them with words under each set of parentheses to support English language learners. For example, under the (2×3), write *2 three-point baskets.*

Variations:

$$(2 \times 2) + (2 \times 3) = 10$$

$$(3 \times 2) + (2 \times 2) = 10$$

$$(2 \times 2) + (3 \times 2) = 10$$

Adjusting the Activity

Break the problem into parts. Ask: How many points did Sheila score with 3-point baskets? 6 points; 2×3 How many points did Sheila score with 2-point baskets? 4 points; 2×2 That's how many points in all? 10 points; $(2 \times 3) + (2 \times 2) = 10$

AUDITORY ◆ KINESTHETIC ◆ TACTILE ◆ VISUAL

Student Page

Date Time

LESSON 7·5 **Scoring 10 Basketball Points** 

Find different ways to score 10 points in a basketball game.

Number of 3-point Baskets	Number of 2-point Baskets	Number of 1-point Baskets	Number Models
2	2	0	$(2 \times 3)+(2 \times 2)+(0 \times 1)=10$
2	1	2	$(2\times3)+(1\times2)+(2\times1)=10$
2	0	4	$(2\times3)+(0\times2)+(4\times1)=10$
1	3	1	$(1\times3)+(3\times2)+(1\times1)=10$
1	2	3	$(1\times3)+(2\times2)+(3\times1)=10$
1	1	5	$(1\times3)+(1\times2)+(5\times1)=10$
1	0	7	$(1\times3)+(0\times2)+(7\times1)=10$
0	5	0	$(0\times3)+(5\times2)+(0\times1)=10$
0	4	2	$(0\times3)+(4\times2)+(2\times1)=10$
0	3	4	$(0\times3)+(3\times2)+(4\times1)=10$
0	2	6	$(0\times3)+(2\times2)+(6\times1)=10$
0	1	8	$(0\times3)+(1\times2)+(8\times1)=10$
0	0	10	$(0\times3)+(0\times2)+(10\times1)=10$
3	0	1	$(3\times3)+(0\times2)+(1\times1)=10$

Math Journal 2, p. 166

▶ Finding Different Ways to Score 10 Points in Basketball

(*Math Journal 2,* p. 166)

Algebraic Thinking Review the scoring rules in basketball: A player scores 2 points or 3 points for a field goal, depending on where the shot is made, and 1 point for a free throw.

Ask children to find as many ways as they can of scoring 10 basketball points using parentheses in the number models. The Math Message describes one way. Find two or three other solutions together. Children record them in the table on journal page 166, as you do the same in the table on the board. (*See* Advance Preparation.)

To write each number model, use the information in each column. Show the number of baskets times the number of points per basket in parentheses. For example, two 3-point baskets would be recorded as: 2 (baskets) × 3 (points per basket).

Number of 3-pt baskets	Number of 2-pt baskets	Number of 1-pt baskets	Number models
2	2	0	$(2 \times 3) + (2 \times 2) + (0 \times 1) = 10$
1	3	1	$(1 \times 3) + (3 \times 2) + (1 \times 1) = 10$
0	4	2	$(0 \times 3) + (4 \times 2) + (2 \times 1) = 10$

Working in small groups, children try to find as many other solutions as possible. After about 15 minutes, bring the class together to share answers and solution strategies. List the different combinations on the board.

Ongoing Assessment: Informing Instruction

Watch for children who are having difficulty finding different combinations of points. Encourage them to find a systematic way of looking for solutions. (For example, start by finding all combinations for zero 3-point baskets, then all combinations for one 3-point basket, and so on.)

Ongoing Assessment: Recognizing Student Achievement

Exit Slip 

Use **journal page 166** and an **Exit Slip** (*Math Masters,* p. 398) to assess children's progress toward recognizing that the operation inside the parentheses is carried out first. Children are making adequate progress if they are able to record a number model with parentheses from the page and explain why the answer is 10. Some children may be able to use parentheses to regroup the numbers so the number model has a different value.

[Patterns, Functions, and Algebra Goal 3]

2 Ongoing Learning & Practice

▶ Solving Problems with Parentheses in Name-Collection Boxes

(*Math Journal 2,* p. 167)

Algebraic Thinking Children determine which names do not belong in the name-collection boxes. They write names that contain parentheses in name-collection boxes.

Student Page

Date ____________ Time ____________

LESSON 7·5 **Names with Parentheses**

Cross out the names that don't belong in each name-collection box.

1. **12**

(3 × 3) + 3	~~3 × (3 + 3)~~
~~2 + (4 × 2)~~	(2 + 4) × 2
~~4 × (4 – 4)~~	(4 × 4) – 4

2. **20**

2 × (9 + 1)	~~(2 × 9) + 1~~
30 – (5 × 2)	~~(30 – 5) × 2~~
(100 ÷ 10) + 10	~~100 ÷ (10 + 10)~~

Write names that contain parentheses in each name-collection box.

3. **16**

Sample answers:
1 × (32 – 16)
(86 – 80) + 10
(20 ÷ 4) + 11
9 + (7 × 1)

4. **24**

Sample answers:
(93 – 24) – 45
15 + (3 × 3)
48 – (12 × 2)
(31 – 20) + 13

5. Write a parentheses problem. Describe how you solved the problem.
Answers vary.

Math Journal 2, p. 167

▶ Math Boxes 7•5

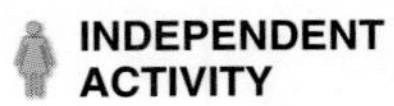

(*Math Journal 2,* p. 168)

Mixed Practice The Math Boxes in this lesson are linked with the Math Boxes in Lessons 7-7 and 7-9. The skill in Problem 6 previews Unit 8 content.

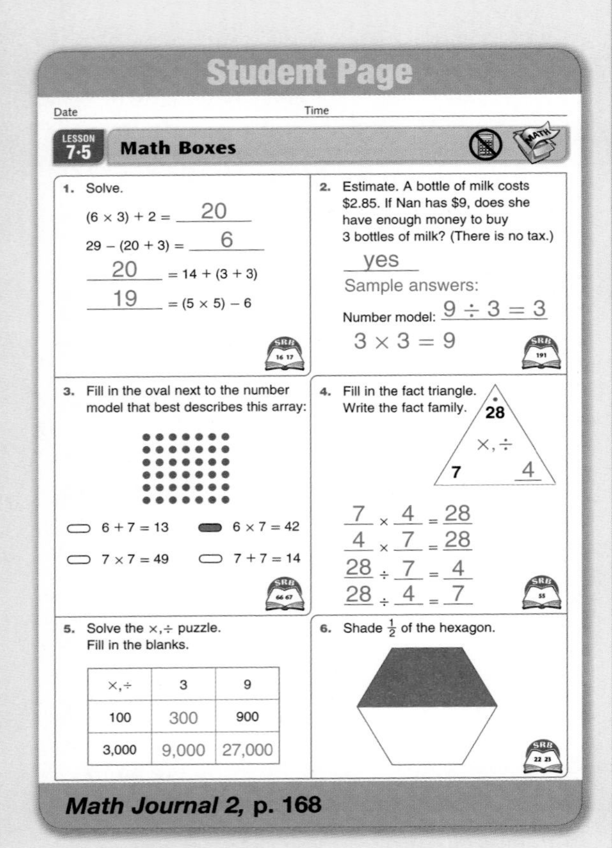

Student Page

Date Time

LESSON 7•5 **Math Boxes**

1. Solve.
   $(6 \times 3) + 2 =$ 20
   $29 - (20 + 3) =$ 6
   20 $= 14 + (3 + 3)$
   19 $= (5 \times 5) - 6$

2. Estimate. A bottle of milk costs \$2.85. If Nan has \$9, does she have enough money to buy 3 bottles of milk? (There is no tax.)
   yes
   Sample answers:
   Number model: $9 \div 3 = 3$
   $3 \times 3 = 9$

3. Fill in the oval next to the number model that best describes this array:
   ○ $6 + 7 = 13$ ● $6 \times 7 = 42$
   ○ $7 \times 7 = 49$ ○ $7 + 7 = 14$

4. Fill in the fact triangle. Write the fact family.
   28; ×, ÷; 7; 4
   $7 \times 4 = 28$
   $4 \times 7 = 28$
   $28 \div 7 = 4$
   $28 \div 4 = 7$

5. Solve the ×, ÷ puzzle. Fill in the blanks.

×, ÷	3	9
100	300	900
3,000	9,000	27,000

6. Shade $\frac{1}{2}$ of the hexagon.

Math Journal 2, p. 168

▶ Home Link 7•5

INDEPENDENT ACTIVITY

(*Math Masters,* p. 217)

Home Connection Children list various ways of scoring 15 points in a basketball game.

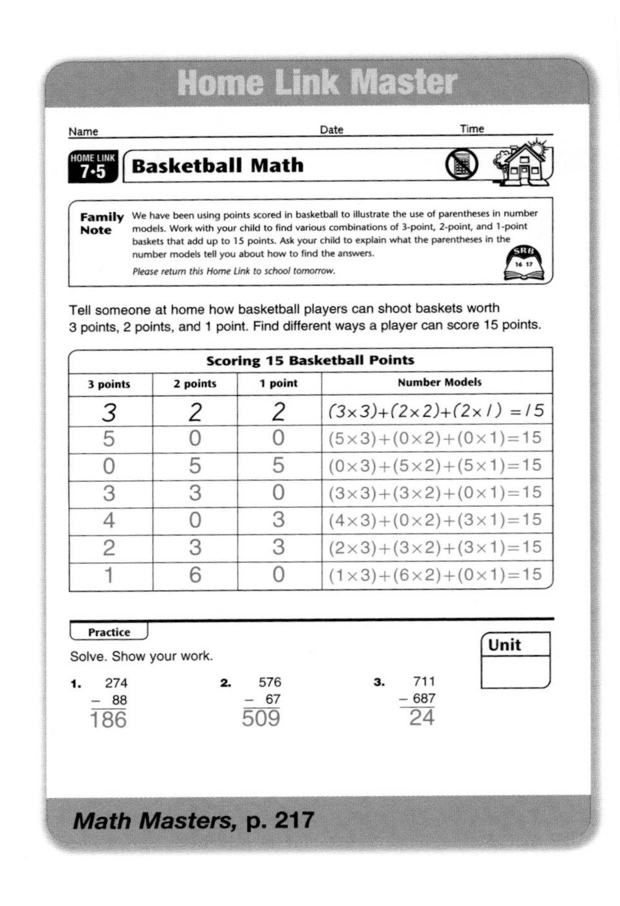

Home Link Master

Name Date Time

HOME LINK 7•5 **Basketball Math**

Family Note We have been using points scored in basketball to illustrate the use of parentheses in number models. Work with your child to find various combinations of 3-point, 2-point, and 1-point baskets that add up to 15 points. Ask your child to explain what the parentheses in the number models tell you about how to find the answers.

Please return this Home Link to school tomorrow.

Tell someone at home how basketball players can shoot baskets worth 3 points, 2 points, and 1 point. Find different ways a player can score 15 points.

Scoring 15 Basketball Points

3 points	2 points	1 point	Number Models
3	2	2	$(3\times3)+(2\times2)+(2\times1)=15$
5	0	0	$(5\times3)+(0\times2)+(0\times1)=15$
0	5	5	$(0\times3)+(5\times2)+(5\times1)=15$
3	3	0	$(3\times3)+(3\times2)+(0\times1)=15$
4	0	3	$(4\times3)+(0\times2)+(3\times1)=15$
2	3	3	$(2\times3)+(3\times2)+(3\times1)=15$
1	6	0	$(1\times3)+(6\times2)+(0\times1)=15$

Practice

Solve. Show your work.

Unit

1. $274 - 88 = 186$
2. $576 - 67 = 509$
3. $711 - 687 = 24$

Math Masters, p. 217

3 Differentiation Options

READINESS

 PARTNER ACTIVITY

▶ Finding Equivalent Names

 5–15 Min

(*Math Masters,* p. 218)

To provide experience with equivalent names for 10, have children use equal groupings to find combinations for 10 pennies. Children record their combinations on *Math Masters,* page 218.

ENRICHMENT

 PARTNER ACTIVITY

▶ Writing Names for Digits

 15–30 Min

(*Math Masters,* p. 219)

Portfolio Ideas

To apply children's understanding of using parentheses to write equivalent names, have them write names for the 10 digits on *Math Masters,* page 219. Encourage children to use parentheses or to show the steps. For example, to make 2, children may write: (3 ÷ 3) + (3 ÷ 3). Review that 3 ÷ 3 is an equivalent name for 1.

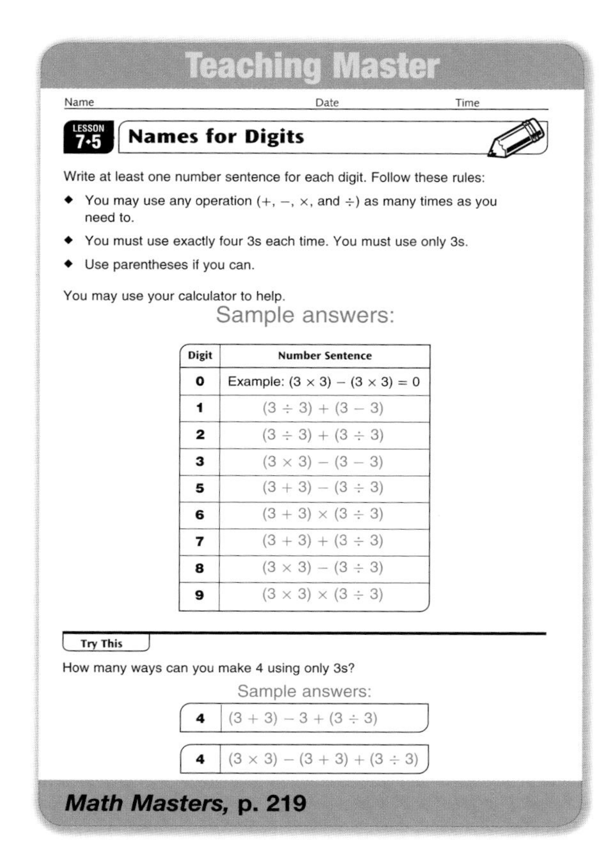

Teaching Master

Name Date Time

LESSON 7•5 **Names for Digits**

Write at least one number sentence for each digit. Follow these rules:

- You may use any operation (+, −, ×, and ÷) as many times as you need to.
- You must use exactly four 3s each time. You must use only 3s.
- Use parentheses if you can.

You may use your calculator to help.

Sample answers:

Digit	Number Sentence
0	Example: (3 × 3) − (3 × 3) = 0
1	(3 ÷ 3) + (3 − 3)
2	(3 ÷ 3) + (3 ÷ 3)
3	(3 × 3) − (3 − 3)
5	(3 + 3) − (3 ÷ 3)
6	(3 + 3) × (3 ÷ 3)
7	(3 + 3) + (3 ÷ 3)
8	(3 × 3) − (3 ÷ 3)
9	(3 × 3) × (3 ÷ 3)

Try This

How many ways can you make 4 using only 3s?

Sample answers:

4	(3 + 3) − 3 + (3 ÷ 3)
4	(3 × 3) − (3 + 3) + (3 ÷ 3)

Math Masters, p. 219

Teaching Master

Name Date Time

LESSON 7•5 **Equivalent Names** 

You need ten pennies.

1. Look at the first row on the table below. Using 10 pennies, you can make 3 groups of 3 pennies. A 3 is in the first column.
2. Because there is only 1 penny left, you cannot make any groups of 2 pennies. 0 is written in the Groups of 2 pennies column.
3. Because there is 1 penny left, you can make 1 group of 1 penny. 1 is written in the third column.
4. 10 pennies in all were used. 10 is written in the last column.
5. Complete the table. Find different ways to use 10 pennies in all for each row.

Sample answers:

Groups of 3 pennies	Groups of 2 pennies	Groups of 1 penny	Total pennies
3	0	1	10
2	2	0	10
1	2	3	10
0	3	4	10
0	2	6	10
2	1	2	10
0	4	2	10
1	3	1	10

Math Masters, p. 218

7•6 Extended Facts: Multiplication and Division

Objectives To guide children as they multiply 1-digit numbers by multiples of 10, 100, and 1,000 and divide such multiples by 1-digit numbers.

www.everydaymathonline.com

ePresentations

eToolkit

Algorithms Practice

EM Facts Workshop Game™

Family Letters

Assessment Management

Common Core State Standards

Curriculum Focal Points

Interactive Teacher's Lesson Guide

1 Teaching the Lesson

Key Concepts and Skills

- Recognize multiples of 10.
  [Number and Numeration Goal 3]
- Use multiplication facts to solve problems.
  [Operations and Computation Goal 3]
- Use multiplication facts to solve division problems.
  [Operations and Computation Goal 3]
- Share solution strategies for solving number stories.
  [Operations and Computation Goal 4]
- Use relationships between units of time to solve number stories.
  [Measurement and Reference Frames Goal 3]

Key Activities

Children develop strategies for multiplying and dividing using 1-digit numbers and multiples of 10, 100, and 1,000.

Ongoing Assessment: Informing Instruction
See pages 608 and 610.

Ongoing Assessment: Recognizing Student Achievement
Use journal page 169.
[Measurement and Reference Frames Goal 3]

Key Vocabulary

extended facts

Materials

Math Journal 2, p. 169
Home Link 7•5
slate

2 Ongoing Learning & Practice

Playing *Beat the Calculator* (Multiplication)
Student Reference Book, p. 279
per group: 4 each of number cards 1–10 (from the Everything Math Deck, if available), calculator
Children practice basic multiplication facts.

Math Boxes 7•6
Math Journal 2, p. 170
Children practice and maintain skills through Math Box problems.

Home Link 7•6
Math Masters, p. 220
Children practice and maintain skills through Home Link activities.

3 Differentiation Options

READINESS

Using Multiples of 10s
Math Masters, p. 221
per partnership: base-10 blocks, calculator
Children use calculators and base-10 blocks to find patterns in counting.

EXTRA PRACTICE

Minute Math+
Minute Math®+, pp. 5, 7, and 14
Children practice counting with 10s, 100s, and 1,000s.

Advance Preparation

***Teacher's Reference Manual,* Grades 1–3** pp. 227, 228

Getting Started

Mathematical Practices
SMP2, **SMP3,** SMP4, SMP6, **SMP7**
Content Standards
3.OA.6, 3.OA.7, 3.NBT.3

Mental Math and Reflexes

Pose the following problems.

Children record their answers on their slates. Have them share solution strategies after each problem.

●○○ One side of a square is 10 centimeters long. What is the perimeter of the square? 40 cm

●●○ The sides of an equilateral triangle are 5 meters long. What is the perimeter of the triangle? 15 m (You may want to review the meaning of *equilateral.*)

●●● The longer side of a rectangle measures 8 inches. The shorter side is half as long. What is the perimeter of the rectangle? 24 inches

Math Message

The distance around a racetrack is 500 meters. How far does a racer travel in 8 laps? Record the answer on your slate. 4,000 meters

Home Link 7·5 Follow-Up

Have children share a few ways to get 15 points in basketball.

1 Teaching the Lesson

▶ Math Message Follow-Up

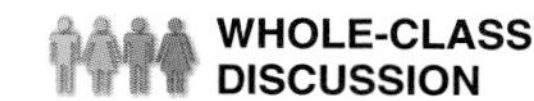

WHOLE-CLASS DISCUSSION

Children share solution strategies as you record them on the board. *Possible strategies:*

- Each lap is 500 meters. So I can add 500 eight times: $500 + 500 + 500 + 500 + 500 + 500 + 500 + 500 = 4{,}000$. If someone suggests this strategy, it can be used as a lead-in to the next strategy.
- Group the 500s in pairs to show that the sum of each pair is 1,000. Then the sum of each pair of 1,000s is 2,000; and the sum of each pair of 2,000s is 4,000.
- Repeated doubling: 2 laps = 1,000 meters, so 4 laps = 2,000 meters, and 8 laps = 4,000 meters.
- 500 = 5 hundreds, so 8 [500s] are 8 times as many hundreds, or 40 hundreds, or 4,000.
- 8 [5s] are 40, so 8 [50s] are 10 times as much as 40, or 400, and 8 [500s] are 10 times as much as 400, or 4,000.

There are a number of ways to solve problems like 8 [500s]. Children should use whatever method makes sense to them.

NOTE Devise a shorthand notation to record children's solution strategies. In *Everyday Mathematics,* brackets are used to separate pairs of quantities. For example, 8 [500s] represents 8 five hundreds. Children will quickly adapt to whatever notation you adopt, as long as it is used consistently.

$2 \times 3 = 6$ or 2×3 one time

$20 \times 3 = 60$ or 2×3 ten times

$200 \times 3 = 600$; 20×3 ten times; 2×3 one hundred times

▶ Multiplying by Multiples of 10, 100, and 1,000

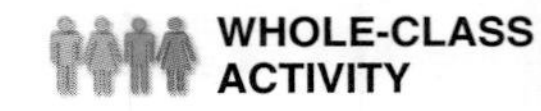

Pose the following problems. Ask children to identify and discuss the patterns within each triple.

$$2 \times 3 = 6$$
$$20 \times 3 = 60$$
$$200 \times 3 = 600$$

$$7 \times 5 = 35$$
$$70 \times 5 = 350$$
$$700 \times 5 = 3{,}500$$

For each triple, ask why the second product is always 10 times as much as the first product and the third product is always 100 times as much as the first product. For each triple the first factor in the second number sentence is 10 times as much as the first factor in the first number sentence. The first factor in the third number sentence is 100 times as much as the first factor in the first number sentence.

Ongoing Assessment: Informing Instruction

Watch for children who are having difficulty understanding the magnitude of a number that is 100 times as much as another number. Draw arrays on the board to show how the magnitude increases. (*See margin.*)

Pose problems like the following. Children record answers on slates and share solution strategies with the class. Record the children's solutions on the board. Summarize with a number model.

How much are

- 6 [80s]? $6 \times 80 = 480$
- 9 [500s]? $9 \times 500 = 4{,}500$
- 3 [8,000s]? $3 \times 8{,}000 = 24{,}000$

Include problems in which the multiple of 10, 100, or 1,000 names the number of sets. For example:

- How many dollars are in 50 5-dollar bills? $50 \times \$5 = \$250$
  Is it the same amount as 5 50-dollar bills? Yes; $5 \times \$50 = \$250$
- How much is $3{,}000 \times 6$? 18,000

Expressions like 5×30, 700×8, and $4 \times 2{,}000$ are called **extended facts** because they are derived from basic facts (5×3, 7×8, 4×2).

NOTE Some children may discover that one way to find products such as 9×500 is to multiply the nonzero digits ($9 \times 5 = 45$), count how many zeros are in the multiple (two), and attach the zeros to the product to get 4,500. If a child mentions this discovery to the class, support the other children by explaining and writing the strategy as $(9 \times 5) \times 100$, not as just counting zeros and attaching them to the end. The authors suggest that you not introduce this strategy to your children; using this shortcut prematurely may discourage children from thinking the problem through and often leads to errors when multiplying decimals. For example, 0.2×0.30 is not equal to 0.60.

Dividing Multiples of 10, 100, and 1,000 by 1-Digit Numbers

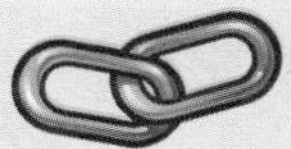
WHOLE-CLASS ACTIVITY

Pose related division problems like the ones below. Children write their answers on their slates. Discuss the patterns in the problems and the answers.

Examples:

- How many 3s are in 21? 7; $21 \div 3 = 7$
- How many 3s are in 210? 70; $210 \div 3 = 70$
- How many 3s are in 2,100? 700; $2{,}100 \div 3 = 700$
- How many 5s are in 50? 10; $50 \div 5 = 10$
- How many 5s are in 500? 100; $500 \div 5 = 100$
- How many 5s are in 5,000? 1,000; $5{,}000 \div 5 = 1{,}000$
- How many 7s are in 63? 9; $63 \div 7 = 9$
- How many 7s are in 630? 90; $630 \div 7 = 90$
- How many 7s are in 6,300? 900; $6{,}300 \div 7 = 900$

Ask children to share their solution strategies. Discuss the strategies and summarize with a number model. Children may solve these problems any way they can but make sure the following two strategies are discussed.

Example: How many 3s are in 210?

One possible strategy:

There are 7 [3s] in 21 and 10 [21s] in 210. Therefore, there are 10 times as many 3s in 210 as there are in 21.

$10 \times 7 = 70$, so there are 70 [3s] in 210.

Another strategy:

3 multiplied by what number equals 210? Because $3 \times 70 = 210$, there are 70 [3s] in 210.

Links to the Future

Multiplying by multiples of 10, 100, and 1,000 is an introduction to computing extended multiplication facts. Using basic facts to compute extended facts is a Grade 4 Goal.

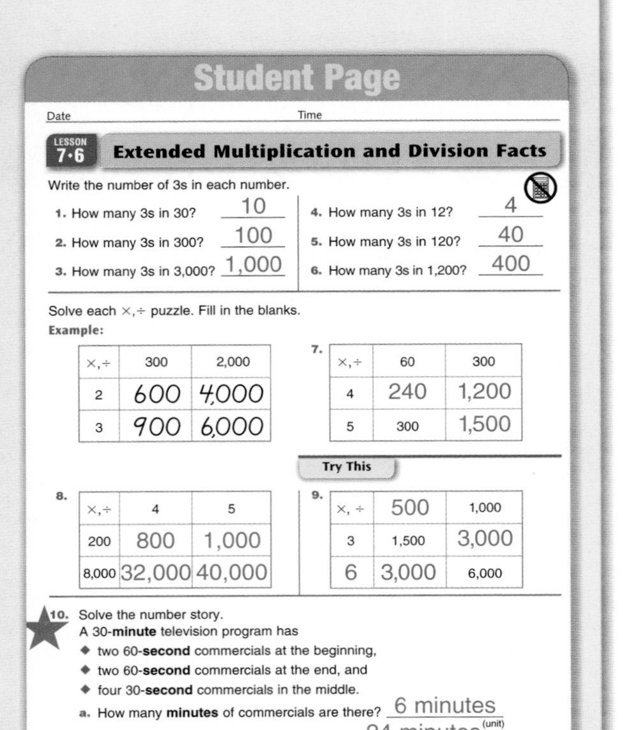

Student Page

Date Time

LESSON 7·6 **Extended Multiplication and Division Facts**

Write the number of 3s in each number.

1. How many 3s in 30? 10
2. How many 3s in 300? 100
3. How many 3s in 3,000? 1,000
4. How many 3s in 12? 4
5. How many 3s in 120? 40
6. How many 3s in 1,200? 400

Solve each ×, ÷ puzzle. Fill in the blanks.

Example:

×, ÷	300	2,000
2	600	4,000
3	900	6,000

7.

×, ÷	60	300
4	240	1,200
5	300	1,500

8.

×, ÷	4	5
200	800	1,000
8,000	32,000	40,000

Try This

9.

×, ÷	500	1,000
3	1,500	3,000
6	3,000	6,000

10. Solve the number story.
A 30-**minute** television program has
- two 60-**second** commercials at the beginning,
- two 60-**second** commercials at the end, and
- four 30-**second** commercials in the middle.

a. How many **minutes** of commercials are there? 6 minutes (unit)

b. How many **minutes** is the actual program? 24 minutes (unit)

c. Number model: Sample answer: 30 − 6 = 24

Math Journal 2, p. 169

Student Page

Date Time

LESSON 7·6 **Math Boxes**

1. Solve.
$6 \times 6 =$ 36
$7 \times 7 =$ 49
$8 \times 8 =$ 64
$81 =$ 9 × 9
$100 =$ 10 × 10

2. Fill in the missing whole number factors. Sample answers:
7 × 2 = 14
28 = 7 × 4
32 = 8 × 4
6 × 8 = 48
54 = 9 × 6

3. Add parentheses to complete the number models.
$30 = (10 \times 2) + 10$
$(46 - 23) - 13 = 10$
$(4 \div 2) + 6 = 8$

4. Complete.
in → Rule ÷2 → out

in	out
8	4
16	8
20	10
50	25
Answers vary.	

5. Solve.
$6 \times 10 =$ 60
$6 \times 30 =$ 180
$50 \times 6 =$ 300
420 $= 70 \times 6$
$6 \times 90 =$ 540

6. Color $\frac{1}{2}$ of the circle.
Sample answer:
How many fourths are shaded?
2 fourths

Math Journal 2, p. 170

Solving Extended Multiplication and Division Facts

(*Math Journal 2,* p. 169)

Children complete journal page 169 on their own or with a partner. Note that two of the factors are missing in Problem 9. Thus, multiplication and division are called for to complete the puzzle.

Ongoing Assessment: Informing Instruction

Watch for children who are having difficulty with Problems 7 through 9. Consider drawing the table for the example on the board. Instead of recording the products in the table, write the multiplication expression for each product (for example, 2 × 300, 2 × 2,000). Carry out each multiplication problem and write it in the table. Help children find the missing factors for Problem 9 and continue as above.

Ongoing Assessment: Recognizing Student Achievement

Journal Page 169 Problem 10

Use **journal page 169, Problem 10** to assess children's progress toward using relationships between units of time to solve number stories. Children are making adequate progress if they complete Problem 10a successfully. Some children may complete Problems 10b and 10c successfully.

[Measurement and Reference Frames Goal 3]

2 Ongoing Learning & Practice

Playing *Beat the Calculator* (Multiplication)

SMALL-GROUP ACTIVITY

(*Student Reference Book,* p. 279)

Children practice basic facts by playing *Beat the Calculator* (Multiplication). Detailed instructions are on *Student Reference Book,* page 279.

Adjusting the Activity

Play a variation to continue practice on a specific set of facts. Have children keep one of the two numbers the same for each round so it is always a factor (e.g., always keep 6 as a factor, and draw one other card each turn so the child is always multiplying $6 \times n$).

AUDITORY ◆ KINESTHETIC ◆ TACTILE ◆ VISUAL

▶ Math Boxes 7◆6

INDEPENDENT ACTIVITY

(*Math Journal 2*, p. 170)

Mixed Practice The Math Boxes in this lesson are paired with the Math Boxes in Lesson 7-8. The skill in Problem 6 previews Unit 8 content.

Writing/Reasoning Have children write an answer to the following: *Describe a pattern you see in Problem 1 and write three more facts that follow the same pattern.* Sample answers: The 2 factors in each number sentence are the same. $3 \times 3 = 9$; $4 \times 4 = 16$; $5 \times 5 = 25$. Each fact can be represented by a square array. The products increase by successive odd numbers: $36 + 13 = 49$; $49 + 15 = 64$; $64 + 17 = 81$; $81 + 19 = 100$.

▶ Home Link 7◆6

INDEPENDENT ACTIVITY

(*Math Masters*, p. 220)

Home Connection Children complete Fact Triangles with extended multiplication and division fact families involving multiples of 10, 100, and 1,000.

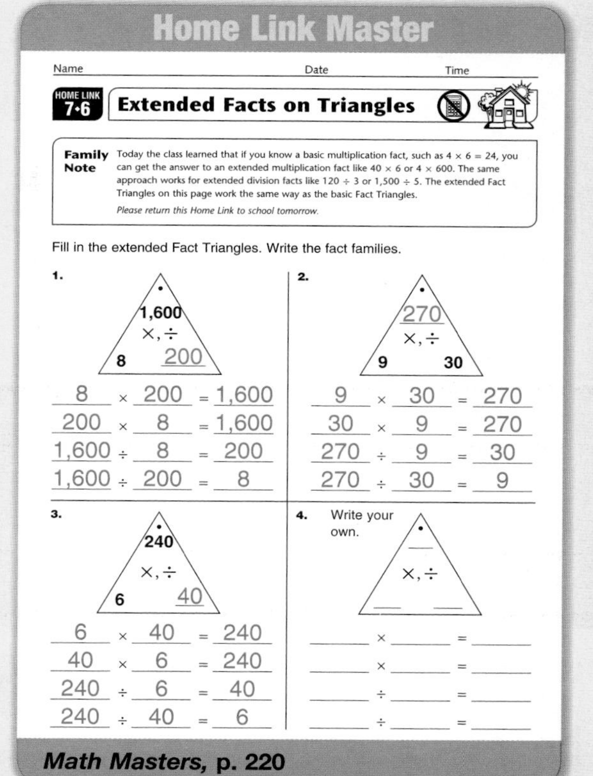

Home Link Master

Name _______ Date _______ Time _______

HOME LINK 7◆6 **Extended Facts on Triangles**

Family Note Today the class learned that if you know a basic multiplication fact, such as 4 × 6 = 24, you can get the answer to an extended multiplication fact like 40 × 6 or 4 × 600. The same approach works for extended division facts like 120 ÷ 3 or 1,500 ÷ 5. The extended Fact Triangles on this page work the same way as the basic Fact Triangles.

Please return this Home Link to school tomorrow.

Fill in the extended Fact Triangles. Write the fact families.

1. Triangle: 1,600; ×, ÷; 8, 200

8 × 200 = 1,600
200 × 8 = 1,600
1,600 ÷ 8 = 200
1,600 ÷ 200 = 8

2. Triangle: 270; ×, ÷; 9, 30

9 × 30 = 270
30 × 9 = 270
270 ÷ 9 = 30
270 ÷ 30 = 9

3. Triangle: 240; ×, ÷; 6, 40

6 × 40 = 240
40 × 6 = 240
240 ÷ 6 = 40
240 ÷ 40 = 6

4. Write your own. Triangle: ×, ÷

___ × ___ = ___
___ × ___ = ___
___ ÷ ___ = ___
___ ÷ ___ = ___

Math Masters, p. 220

NOTE For practice with multiplication facts through 12 × 12, go to www.everydaymathonline.com.

3 Differentiation Options

SMALL-GROUP ACTIVITY

▶ Using Multiples of 10s

5–15 Min

(*Math Masters*, p. 221)

To explore multiples of 10s, 100s, and 1,000s, have children use a calculator and base-10 blocks to find patterns in counts. Children skip count with their calculators and build numbers with base-10 blocks as they complete the chart on *Math Masters*, page 221.

Teaching Master

Name _______ Date _______ Time _______

LESSON 7◆6 **Multiples of 10s**

Work with a partner.

One partner uses a calculator to skip-count by 1, 10, 100, and 1,000. Record the numbers in the correct place in the chart as they are displayed in the calculator. The other partner models each count with base-10 blocks. Use cube ▪, long |, and flat □ to record the count in the chart.

The first two numbers are done for you.

Count by 1s.				
one 1	two 1s	three 1s	four 1s	five 1s
1 •	2 ••	3 •••	4 ••••	5 •••••

Count by 10s.				
one 10	two 10s	three 10s	four 10s	five 10s
10 |	20 ||	30 |||	40 ||||	50 |||||

Count by 100s.				
one 100	two 100s	three 100s	four 100s	five 100s
100 □	200 □□	300 □□□	400 □□□□	500 □□□□□

Try This

Using the patterns you see in the table above, complete the table below for 1,000s.

Count by 1000s.				
one 1,000	two 1,000s	three 1,000s	four 1,000s	five 1,000s
1,000	2,000	3,000	4,000	5,000

Math Masters, p. 221

SMALL-GROUP ACTIVITY

▶ *Minute Math+*

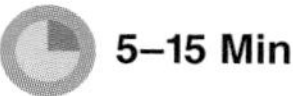
5–15 Min

To offer children more experience working with multiples of 10, see the following pages in *Minute Math+*:

Basic Routines: pp. 5, 7, and 14

7•7 Estimating Costs

Objectives To guide children as they determine when an estimate is appropriate and as they practice making estimates.

Technology Resources www.everydaymathonline.com

ePresentations

eToolkit

Algorithms Practice

EM Facts Workshop Game™

Family Letters

Assessment Management

Common Core State Standards

Curriculum Focal Points

Interactive Teacher's Lesson Guide

1 Teaching the Lesson

Key Concepts and Skills

- Calculate the cost of an item.
  [Operations and Computation Goal 2]
- Discuss situations where it is sensible to make an estimate and those where it is sensible to compute an exact answer.
  [Operations and Computation Goal 5]
- Use estimation strategies to solve number stories.
  [Operations and Computation Goal 5]

Key Activities

Children discuss situations in which it is not necessary to find an exact answer. Children estimate the cost of a number of the same item. They find and compare the exact cost to an estimated cost.

Ongoing Assessment: Informing Instruction See page 614.

Ongoing Assessment: Recognizing Student Achievement Use an Exit Slip (*Math Masters,* page 398).
[Operations and Computation Goal 5]

Key Vocabulary

estimate

Materials

Math Journal 2, p. 171
Student Reference Book, pp. 191, 216, and 217
Home Link 7•6
Math Masters, p. 398
per small group: 2 each of number cards 1–9 (from the Everything Math Deck, if available)
◆ calculator ◆ slate

2 Ongoing Learning & Practice

Examining Head-Size Data Displayed on a Line Graph
Student Reference Book, pp. 236 and 237
Children examine head-size data over time as displayed on a line graph.

Math Boxes 7•7
Math Journal 2, p. 172
Children practice and maintain skills through Math Box problems.

Home Link 7•7
Math Masters, p. 222
Children practice and maintain skills through Home Link activities.

3 Differentiation Options

READINESS
Rounding Numbers
Math Masters, pp. 21 and 223
Student Reference Book, p. 194
Children explore strategies for rounding whole numbers and decimals.

ENRICHMENT
Calculating Paper Consumption
Math Masters, p. 224
Children estimate paper consumption averages in the United States.

ELL SUPPORT
Making a Word Chart
paper ◆ markers or crayons
Children make a chart of words from this lesson.

Advance Preparation

***Teacher's Reference Manual,* Grades 1–3** pp. 190, 200

Getting Started

Mathematical Practices
SMP2, **SMP3,** SMP4, SMP5, **SMP6,** SMP7
Content Standards
3.OA.3, **3.OA.8, 3.NBT.1, 3.NBT.3**

Mental Math and Reflexes

Children record answers on slates. You may want to write each series of related problems on the board to highlight patterns.

●○○	4 × 10 40	8 × 3 24
	4 × 100 400	80 × 3 240
	4 × 1,000 4,000	800 × 3 2,400
●●○	20 ÷ 4 5	6 × 5 30
	200 ÷ 4 50	6 × 50 300
	2,000 ÷ 4 500	6 × 500 3,000
●●●	15 ÷ 3 5	7 × 3 21
	150 ÷ 3 50	700 × 3 2,100
	150 ÷ 30 5	7,000 × 3 21,000

Math Message

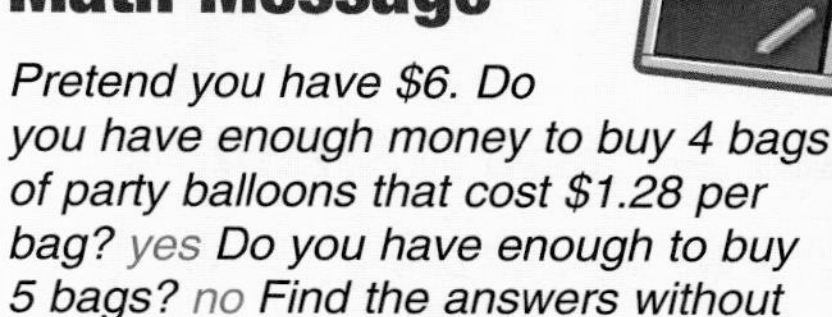

Pretend you have $6. Do you have enough money to buy 4 bags of party balloons that cost $1.28 per bag? yes *Do you have enough to buy 5 bags?* no *Find the answers without calculating the exact costs.*

Home Link 7·6 Follow-Up

Briefly go over the answers to Problems 1 through 3. Ask a few children to share the Fact Triangles they made up.

1 Teaching the Lesson

▶ Math Message Follow-Up

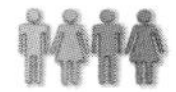
WHOLE-CLASS DISCUSSION

Children share their solution strategies. Some possible strategies for estimating the cost of 4 bags of balloons:

Possible strategies:

- 4 × $1.50 = $6.00 (double $1.50 twice)
  Because $1.28 is less than $1.50, the cost of 4 bags of balloons is less than $6.
- Round $1.28 to the nearest $0.10, which is $1.30.
  4 × $1.00 = $4.00, and 4 × $0.30 = $1.20. Therefore, 4 × $1.30 = $5.20, which is less than $6.
- 4 × $1.25 = $5.00 (double $1.25 twice). Therefore, 4 × $1.28 is just a little more than $5.
- A possible strategy for estimating the cost of 5 bags of balloons: 5 × $1.25 = $6.25, so $6 is not enough.

▶ Reviewing the Meaning of Estimation

WHOLE-CLASS DISCUSSION

(*Student Reference Book,* p. 191)

Remind children that there are times when it is not necessary to calculate exact answers. In the Math Message problem, for example, you only need to know whether the total cost is more than or less than $6—you don't need to find the exact cost. Ask whether they can think of other situations that call for an **estimate.**

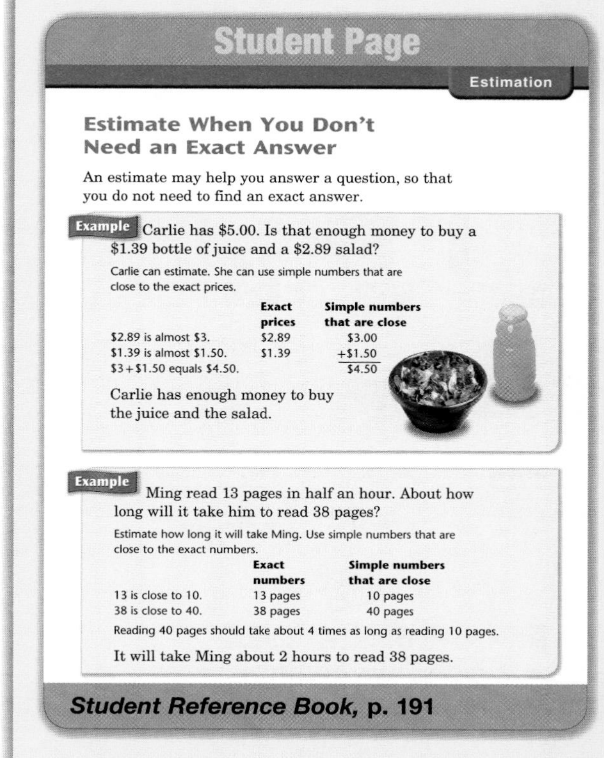
Student Page

Estimation

Estimate When You Don't Need an Exact Answer

An estimate may help you answer a question, so that you do not need to find an exact answer.

Example Carlie has $5.00. Is that enough money to buy a $1.39 bottle of juice and a $2.89 salad?

Carlie can estimate. She can use simple numbers that are close to the exact prices.

	Exact prices	Simple numbers that are close
$2.89 is almost $3.	$2.89	$3.00
$1.39 is almost $1.50.	$1.39	+$1.50
$3 + $1.50 equals $4.50.		$4.50

Carlie has enough money to buy the juice and the salad.

Example Ming read 13 pages in half an hour. About how long will it take him to read 38 pages?

Estimate how long it will take Ming. Use simple numbers that are close to the exact numbers.

	Exact numbers	Simple numbers that are close
13 is close to 10.	13 pages	10 pages
38 is close to 40.	38 pages	40 pages

Reading 40 pages should take about 4 times as long as reading 10 pages.

It will take Ming about 2 hours to read 38 pages.

***Student Reference Book,* p. 191**

Student Page

Data Bank

Stock-Up Sale Poster #1

Student Reference Book, p. 216

Examples:

- About how far can a car be driven on a full tank of gasoline?
- About how many pounds does a car weigh?
- About how long does it take you to get to school?
- How old are you?
- What is the distance from your home to school?
- How tall are you?
- What will be the high temperature tomorrow?

Generally, exact answers are not needed in these situations; an estimate is appropriate.

You might want to use the examples on page 191 in the *Student Reference Book* during the discussion.

Ongoing Assessment: Informing Instruction

Watch for children who find it difficult to accept that in some situations, an estimate is correct. Provide practice with estimation in contexts in which it clearly makes sense to estimate. Point out that it is usually easier and quicker to make an estimate in situations in which exact answers are not needed.

▶ Estimating Costs

(*Student Reference Book*, pp. 216 and 217)

Discuss the Stock-Up Sale posters on *Student Reference Book* pages 216 and 217. For each item, two prices are shown: The higher price is the price per item if fewer than 5 items are purchased, and the sale price (next to the sale logo) is the price per item for purchases of 5 or more items.

Discuss why a store lowers the price of an item when it is purchased in larger quantities. Lower prices encourage more customer purchases. Although the profit per item is less, the store makes up for its lower profits by selling more items.

Remind children of the Math Message problem, where estimation was used to determine whether there was enough money to buy certain items. For the following problem, have children write their answers on slates.

You want to buy 4 cans of tennis balls. Estimate the cost.

Share estimation strategies. *Possible strategies:*

- *Close:* Change \$2.59 to \$3. $4 \times \$3 = \$12$.
- *Closer:* Change \$2.59 to \$2.50. $4 \times \$2.50 = \$10$, so $4 \times \$2.59$ is more than \$10 but less than \$11.
- *Even closer:* Change \$2.59 to \$2.60. $4 \times \$2 = \$8$; $4 \times \$0.60 = \$2.40$; $\$8.00 + \$2.40 = \$10.40$.

Student Page

Data Bank

Stock-Up Sale Poster #2

Greeting Cards Box of 12 $3.29 — 5 or More Sale: You pay $2.63 per box	Bath Soap $0.88 — 5 or More Sale: You pay $0.65 per bar	Gift Wrapping Paper $2.35 per roll — 5 or More Sale: You pay $1.86 per roll
Toothbrush $1.38 — 5 or More Sale: You pay $1.13 per brush	Garbage Bags $3.75 — 5 or More Sale: You pay $3.18 per box	Night Light Bulbs 2-Pack $0.96 — 5 or More Sale: You pay $0.76 per pack
Glue $1.15 — 5 or More Sale: You pay $0.94 per bottle	Construction Paper $0.67 per pad — 5 or More Sale: You pay $0.54 per pad	Shoelaces $1.27 per pair — 5 or More Sale: You pay $1.08 per pair

Student Reference Book, p. 217

Adjusting the Activity

ELL

As children share their strategies, record them on the board and leave them there as a reference throughout the lesson.

AUDITORY ◆ KINESTHETIC ◆ TACTILE ◆ VISUAL

Repeat this routine using other items from the poster. Only one possible solution strategy is listed for each problem. Accept all reasonable responses.

Examples:

- 3 boxes of tissues $3 \times \$0.70 = \$2.10$; \$0.70 is a little less than \$0.73, so the cost is a little more than \$2.10.
- 4 packages of batteries $4 \times \$3.50 = \$14$; \$3.50 is less than \$3.59, so the cost is between \$14 and \$15.
- 8 ballpoint pens $8 \times \$0.25 = \$2.00$; $8 \times \$0.02 = \$0.16$, so the exact cost is $\$2.00 + \$0.16 = \$2.16$.
- 6 paperback books $6 \times \$2.00 = \$12.00$; and $6 \times \$.25 = \$1.50$; $\$12.00 + \$1.50 = \$13.50$. Note that \$2.25 is a nice number to work with. It is easy to calculate the exact answer mentally.

▶ Solving Problems by Estimation

(*Math Journal 2,* p. 171; *Student Reference Book,* pp. 216 and 217)

Each group of children needs a calculator and a set of number cards consisting of two each of cards 1 through 9.

The cards are shuffled and placed number-side down on the playing surface. In each round, the top two cards from the deck are turned over. The first card identifies the item on the poster to be purchased; the second card tells how many of those items will be purchased. For example, using Poster #1, if the first card shows a 3 and the second card shows a 4, a purchase of 4 boxes of tissues is indicated. If the second card shows a 1, another card is turned over in its place. Be sure that each group has chosen to work with only one poster from *Student Reference Book* pages 216 and 217. Children record the information about items purchased and their estimates of the cost on journal page 171.

One child then finds the exact cost using a calculator. Children compare their estimates to the exact cost to see how close they came. They share estimation strategies with other members of the group.

Student Page

Date ______ Time ______

LESSON 7·7 **Stock-up Sale Record**

Use the items on pages 216 and 217 in your *Student Reference Book.*

Answers vary.

Round 1:	Round 2:
Item to be purchased: ______	Item to be purchased: ______
How many? ______	How many? ______
Regular or sale price? ______	Regular or sale price? ______
Price per item: ______	Price per item: ______
Estimated cost: ______	Estimated cost: ______

Round 3:	Round 4:
Item to be purchased: ______	Item to be purchased: ______
How many? ______	How many? ______
Regular or sale price? ______	Regular or sale price? ______
Price per item: ______	Price per item: ______
Estimated cost: ______	Estimated cost: ______

Round 5:	Round 6:
Item to be purchased: ______	Item to be purchased: ______
How many? ______	How many? ______
Regular or sale price? ______	Regular or sale price? ______
Price per item: ______	Price per item: ______
Estimated cost: ______	Estimated cost: ______

Math Journal 2, p. 171

NOTE In addition to their usefulness in everyday life, estimation skills are powerful tools in developing number sense and paper-and-pencil computational skills.

Student Page

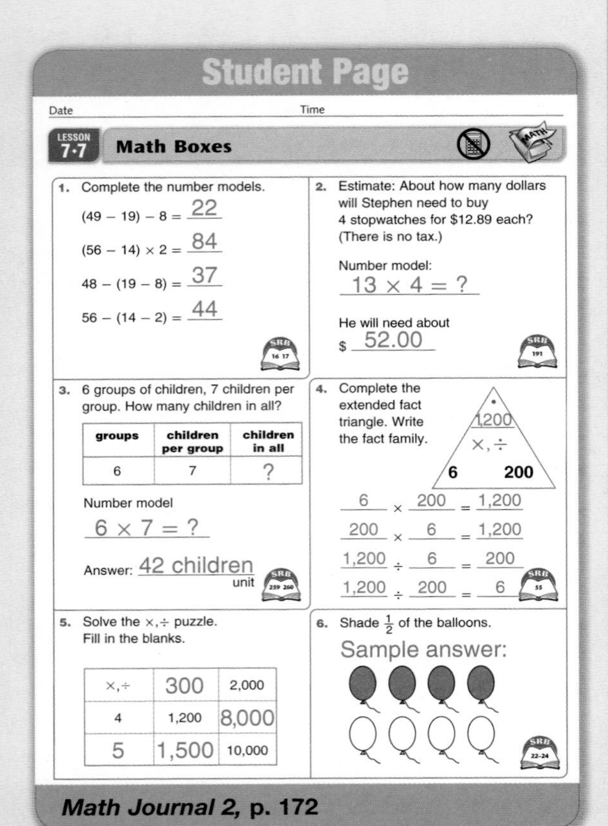
Date Time

LESSON 7·7 **Math Boxes**

1. Complete the number models.
   (49 – 19) – 8 = 22
   (56 – 14) × 2 = 84
   48 – (19 – 8) = 37
   56 – (14 – 2) = 44

2. Estimate: About how many dollars will Stephen need to buy 4 stopwatches for $12.89 each? (There is no tax.)
   Number model: 13 × 4 = ?
   He will need about $ 52.00

3. 6 groups of children, 7 children per group. How many children in all?

groups	children per group	children in all
6	7	?

   Number model: 6 × 7 = ?
   Answer: 42 children (unit)

4. Complete the extended fact triangle. Write the fact family.
   1,200; ×, ÷; 6; 200
   6 × 200 = 1,200
   200 × 6 = 1,200
   1,200 ÷ 6 = 200
   1,200 ÷ 200 = 6

5. Solve the ×, ÷ puzzle. Fill in the blanks.

×, ÷	300	2,000
4	1,200	8,000
5	1,500	10,000

6. Shade $\frac{1}{2}$ of the balloons.
   Sample answer:

Math Journal 2, p. 172

Home Link Master

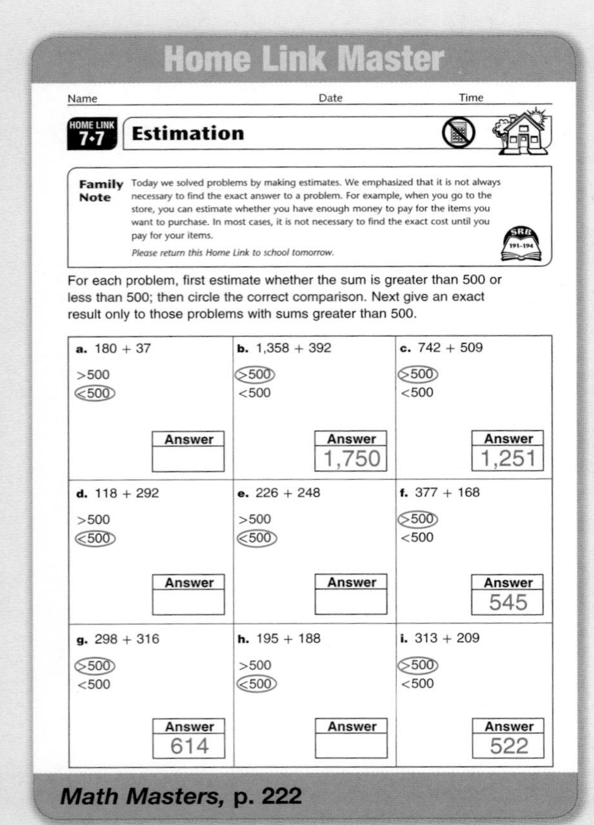
Name Date Time

HOME LINK 7·7 **Estimation**

Family Note Today we solved problems by making estimates. We emphasized that it is not always necessary to find the exact answer to a problem. For example, when you go to the store, you can estimate whether you have enough money to pay for the items you want to purchase. In most cases, it is not necessary to find the exact cost until you pay for your items.

Please return this Home Link to school tomorrow.

For each problem, first estimate whether the sum is greater than 500 or less than 500; then circle the correct comparison. Next give an exact result only to those problems with sums greater than 500.

a. 180 + 37 >500 (<500 circled) Answer:	b. 1,358 + 392 (>500 circled) <500 Answer: 1,750	c. 742 + 509 (>500 circled) <500 Answer: 1,251
d. 118 + 292 >500 (<500 circled) Answer:	e. 226 + 248 >500 (<500 circled) Answer:	f. 377 + 168 (>500 circled) <500 Answer: 545
g. 298 + 316 (>500 circled) <500 Answer: 614	h. 195 + 188 >500 (<500 circled) Answer:	i. 313 + 209 (>500 circled) <500 Answer: 522

Math Masters, p. 222

Ongoing Assessment: Recognizing Student Achievement

Portfolio Ideas Use an **Exit Slip** (*Math Masters,* p. 398) to assess children's knowledge of estimation. Have children answer the following: *When you are shopping, why might you make an estimate? Explain how you would make the estimate.* Children are making adequate progress if they include at least one appropriate reason why they might make an estimate and explain how they would make it. Some children may include additional reasons for making estimates.

[Operations and Computation Goal 5]

2 Ongoing Learning & Practice

Examining Head-Size Data Displayed on a Line Graph

(*Student Reference Book,* pp. 236 and 237)

The line graph on *Student Reference Book,* page 237 shows how head size increases as people get older. The graph shows the median head size for each age. After studying the line graph, have children answer the questions posed on *Student Reference Book,* page 236.

Math Boxes 7·7

(*Math Journal 2,* p. 172)

Mixed Practice The Math Boxes in this lesson are linked with the Math Boxes in Lessons 7-5 and 7-9. The skill in Problem 6 previews Unit 8 content.

Writing/Reasoning Have children write the answer to the following: *Write each number sentence in Problem 1. Find a different answer for each by moving the parentheses.* 49 – (19 – 8) = 38; 56 – (14 × 2) = 28; (48 – 19) – 8 = 21; (56 – 14) – 2 = 40

Home Link 7·7

(*Math Masters,* p. 222)

Home Connection Children estimate answers and solve only the problems for which the estimated sum is greater than 500. Explain that there are problems whose estimated sums are less than 500. These problems should not be completed.

3 Differentiation Options

READINESS

SMALL-GROUP ACTIVITY

▶ Rounding Numbers

15–30 Min

(*Math Masters,* pp. 21 and 223; *Student Reference Book,* p. 194)

To explore strategies for rounding whole numbers and decimals, have children solve the problems on *Math Masters*, page 223. Have children shade the multiples of 10 on the number grid (*Math Masters,* page 21) before completing this activity. For further exploration, have children read the essay on page 194 of the *Student Reference Book* and answer the Check Your Understanding problems.

ENRICHMENT

PARTNER ACTIVITY

▶ Calculating Paper Consumption

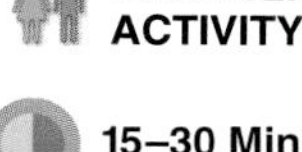

15–30 Min

(*Math Masters,* p. 224)

To apply their understanding of estimation, children complete *Math Masters,* page 224. They estimate the average weight of paper each person uses in one week and in one year in the United States. They also estimate the number of trees it takes to produce the amount of paper a person uses in one year.

ELL SUPPORT

SMALL-GROUP ACTIVITY

▶ Making a Word Chart

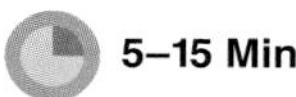

5–15 Min

To provide language support for estimation, have children make a chart of words from this lesson that can be used as naming words (nouns) or action words (verbs). Guide children to practice pronouncing the different forms of words: *estimate* the cost (emphasize the long a sound); get an estimate (emphasize the short i sound). Children include these words in their charts: *estimate* (n., v.), *estimation* (n.), *calculate* (v.), *calculator* (n.), *calculation* (n.), and *cost* (n., v.).

Teaching Master

Name Date Time

LESSON 7·7 **Rounding Numbers**

Sometimes an exact answer to a problem is not needed. An answer that is close to the exact answer might be helpful enough. When we round a number, we find a number that is close to it but easier to use. Numbers ending in 0 are often easier to use. Here are some strategies for rounding a number.

1. Shade in the multiples of 10 on the number grid on *Math Masters,* page 21.

Put your finger on 27. When we round 27, it will go up or down to the nearest multiple of ten.

Is it fewer steps from 27 to 30 or from 27 to 20? 27 to 30

Use your number grid to round these numbers. (Hint: When a number is exactly half-way between, we usually round to the higher number.) Sample answers:

2. 42 40 3. 79 80 4. 63 60 5. 55 60

Here is another way to think of rounding numbers.

Round 27. What would be multiples of 10 that are close to 27? 20, 30

What number would be at the top of the hill? 25

Would 27 be heading toward 20 or toward 30? 30

25 27 20 30

6. Draw a picture to show how you would round 82.

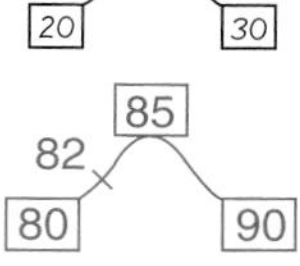

Try This

7. Draw a picture or explain how you would round 4.7 to the nearest whole number.

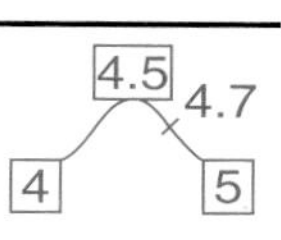

Math Masters, p. 223

Teaching Master

Name Date Time

LESSON 7·7 **Estimating Paper Consumption**

On average, the total weight of all the paper used in the United States each day is about $1\frac{1}{2}$ pounds per person.

1. About how many pounds of paper per person are used in 1 week? Explain what you did. About $10\frac{1}{2}$ pounds

Possible strategy: Double $1\frac{1}{2}$ pounds. $1\frac{1}{2}$ pounds per day is equivalent to 3 pounds per 2 days. Then multiply by 3: 3 pounds per 2 days is equivalent to 9 pounds per 6 days. Add $1\frac{1}{2}$ pounds for the seventh day. That's about $10\frac{1}{2}$ pounds per person per week.

2. About how many pounds of paper per person are used in one year? Explain what you did. About 520 pounds

There are 52 weeks in one year; the average yearly use is about 52 × 10, or about 520 pounds per person per year.

3. A 40-foot pine tree will produce about 12,000 sheets of paper. 100 sheets of paper weigh about 1 pound. About how many trees does it take to produce the amount of paper the average person uses in 1 year? Explain your thinking. About 4 trees

There are about 50,000 sheets of paper in 500 pounds. About 4 pinetrees will yield 50,000 sheets.

Math Masters, p. 224

7•8 Extended Facts: Products of Tens

Objective To guide children as they multiply multiples of 10 by multiples of 10.

www.everydaymathonline.com

ePresentations

eToolkit

Algorithms Practice

EM Facts Workshop Game™

Family Letters

Assessment Management

Common Core State Standards

Curriculum Focal Points

Interactive Teacher's Lesson Guide

1 Teaching the Lesson

Key Concepts and Skills

- Find multiples of 10.
  [Number and Numeration Goal 3]
- Find products of multiples of 10.
  [Operations and Computation Goal 3]
- Explore strategies to solve multiplication number stories.
  [Operations and Computation Goal 4]

Key Activities

Children develop strategies for multiplying multiples of 10 by multiples of 10.

Ongoing Assessment: Recognizing Student Achievement
Use journal page 173.
[Operations and Computation Goal 4]

Materials

Math Journal 2, p. 173
Home Link 7•7
slate ◆ play money (optional)

2 Ongoing Learning & Practice

Making a Line Graph of Temperature Differences

Math Journal 1, p. 43 or *Math Masters,* p. 48
Math Journal 2, pp. 175–177
ruler or straightedge
Children make a line graph of the range of high and low temperatures they have recorded thus far.

Math Boxes 7•8

Math Journal 2, p. 174
Children practice and maintain skills through Math Box problems.

Home Link 7•8

Math Masters, p. 225
Children practice and maintain skills through Home Link activities.

3 Differentiation Options

READINESS

Patterns in Extended Facts

Math Masters, p. 226
base-10 blocks ◆ calculator (optional)
Children use base-10 longs to find multiples of 10.

ENRICHMENT

Multidigit Multiplication

Math Masters, p. 227
Children explore strategies for solving a 2-digit multiplication problem.

EXTRA PRACTICE

Playing *Baseball Multiplication* with Tens

Math Masters, p. 445
Student Reference Book, pp. 274 and 275
per group: 2 six-sided dice, 4 pennies or counters
Children practice multiplication skills with factors that are multiples of 10.

Advance Preparation

For the line graph activity in Part 2, you may wish to make copies of the class record of the high/low temperatures for each child.

Getting Started

Mathematical Practices
SMP2, SMP3, SMP4, SMP6, **SMP7**
Content Standards
3.OA.3, **3.NBT.3**

Mental Math and Reflexes

Children record answers on slates.

●○○ 6 × 10; 6 × 100; 6 × 1,000 60; 600; 6,000
4 × 8; 4 × 80; 4 × 800; 4 × 8,000 32; 320; 3,200; 32,000

●●○ 9 × 7; 90 × 7; 900 × 7; 9,000 × 7 63; 630; 6,300; 63,000
24 ÷ 6; 240 ÷ 6; 2,400 ÷ 6 4; 40; 400

●●● 480 ÷ 6; 480 ÷ 60; 4,800 ÷ 600 80; 8; 8
560 ÷ 7; 560 ÷ 70; 5,600 ÷ 70 80; 8; 80

Math Message

Do Problems 1 through 6 on journal page 173.

Home Link 7·7 Follow-Up

Have children describe their estimation strategies.

1 Teaching the Lesson

▶ Math Message Follow-Up

WHOLE-CLASS DISCUSSION

(*Math Journal 2,* p. 173)

Have children share answers and solution strategies with the class. One solution strategy is: ten $10 bills equal $100, so 100 $10 bills are 10 times as much, or $1,000, and 1,000 $10 bills are 10 times as much again, or $10,000. Consider providing play money for children to count.

NOTE One way to find products such as 40 × 30 is to multiply the leading digits 4 × 3 = 12, count how many zeros are in the factors 2 zeros in all, and attach the zeros to the product of the leading digits 1,200. Teaching this approach may discourage children from thinking through problems to find products. If children do share this strategy, write the factors as *n* tens × *n* tens and explain that the product is *n* hundreds. For example, 40 × 30 is 4 tens × 3 tens or 12 (100s).

▶ Introducing Products of Multiples of 10

WHOLE-CLASS ACTIVITY

Pose the following problem:

The Evergreen Landscape Company bought 40 rosebushes for $30 each. How much did the company pay in all?

Children share solution strategies. Possible strategies include:

- 10 rosebushes cost $300. 10 [$30s] I can double $300 to find the cost of 20 bushes $600 and double $600 to find the cost of 40 bushes. $1,200
- 10 rosebushes cost $300. 10 [$30s] Therefore, 40 rosebushes cost 4 times as much. 4 × $300 = $1,200
- 4 rosebushes cost $120. 4 [$30s] Therefore, 40 rosebushes cost 10 times as much. 10 × $120 = $1,200
- 40 × 30 can be renamed as 4 tens × 3 tens. Because tens × tens = hundreds, 4 tens × 3 tens = (4 × 3) hundreds = 12 hundreds, or 1,200.

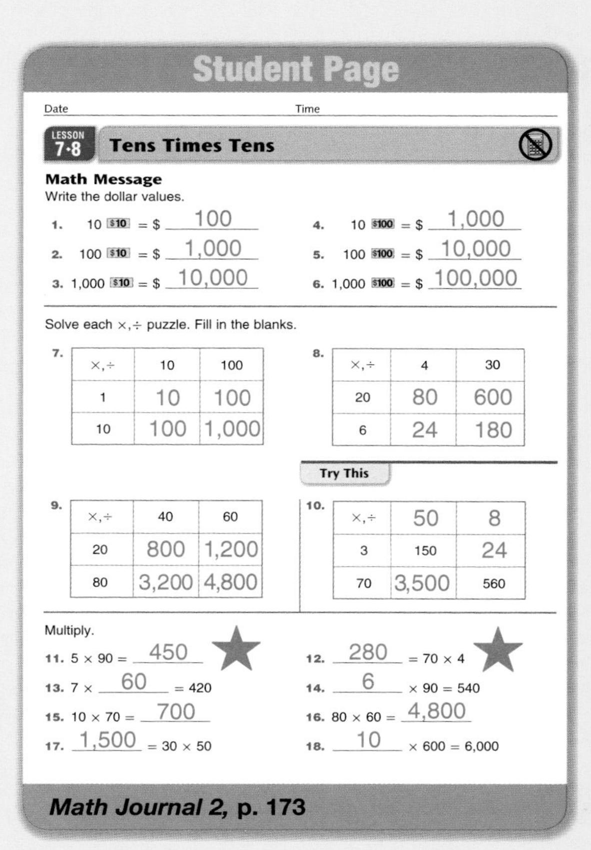

Student Page

Date Time

LESSON 7·8 **Tens Times Tens**

Math Message
Write the dollar values.

1. 10 [$10] = $ 100
2. 100 [$10] = $ 1,000
3. 1,000 [$10] = $ 10,000
4. 10 [$100] = $ 1,000
5. 100 [$100] = $ 10,000
6. 1,000 [$100] = $ 100,000

Solve each ×, ÷ puzzle. Fill in the blanks.

7.

×, ÷	10	100
1	10	100
10	100	1,000

8.

×, ÷	4	30
20	80	600
6	24	180

Try This

9.

×, ÷	40	60
20	800	1,200
80	3,200	4,800

10.

×, ÷	50	8
3	150	24
70	3,500	560

Multiply.

11. 5 × 90 = 450 ★
12. 280 = 70 × 4 ★
13. 7 × 60 = 420
14. 6 × 90 = 540
15. 10 × 70 = 700
16. 80 × 60 = 4,800
17. 1,500 = 30 × 50
18. 10 × 600 = 6,000

Math Journal 2, p. 173

Adjusting the Activity

ELL

As children share their strategies, record them on the board and leave them up as a reference throughout the lesson.

AUDITORY ◆ KINESTHETIC ◆ TACTILE ◆ VISUAL

Pose problems like the ones below. Children record their answers on slates and share solution strategies. Summarize with a number sentence.

Examples:

- 10 [40s]? $10 \times 40 = 400$
- 70 [10s]? $70 \times 10 = 700$
- 40 [20s]? $40 \times 20 = 800$
- 30 [70s]? $30 \times 70 = 2{,}100$

Discuss what these four problems and their answers have in common.

Adjusting the Activity

Pose problems like the following: How much are

10 [400s]? $10 \times 400 = 4{,}000$

500 [10s]? $500 \times 10 = 5{,}000$

200 [20s]? $200 \times 20 = 4{,}000$

30 [500s]? $30 \times 500 = 15{,}000$

You might also pose the following problems:

How many digits can the product of two 2-digit numbers have? 3 or 4; for example, $10 \times 10 = 100$ and $20 \times 70 = 1{,}400$ How many digits can the product of a 2-digit and a 3-digit number have? 4 or 5; for example, $10 \times 200 = 2{,}000$ and $20 \times 600 = 12{,}000$

AUDITORY ◆ KINESTHETIC ◆ TACTILE ◆ VISUAL

▶ Finding Products of Multiples of 10

INDEPENDENT ACTIVITY

FACTS PRACTICE

(*Math Journal 2,* p. 173)

Children complete the page on their own or with a partner.

Ongoing Assessment: Recognizing Student Achievement

Journal page 173 Problems 11 and 12 ★

Use **journal page 173, Problems 11 and 12** to assess children's ability to multiply 2-digit numbers by a 1-digit number. Children are making adequate progress if they are able to successfully complete problems 11 and 12. Some children may be able to complete the remaining problems.

[Operations and Computation Goal 4]

Student Page

Date Time

LESSON 2·6 **National High/Low Temperatures Project**

Date	Highest Temperature (maximum)		Lowest Temperature (minimum)		Difference (range)
	Place	Temperature	Place	Temperature	
		°F		°F	°F
		°F		°F	°F
		°F		°F	°F
		°F		°F	°F
		°F		°F	°F
		°F		°F	°F
		°F		°F	°F
		°F		°F	°F
		°F		°F	°F
		°F		°F	°F
		°F		°F	°F
		°F		°F	°F
		°F		°F	°F
		°F		°F	°F
		°F		°F	°F
		°F		°F	°F
		°F		°F	°F
		°F		°F	°F
		°F		°F	°F
		°F		°F	°F

Math Journal 1, **p. 43**

2 Ongoing Learning & Practice

▶ Making a Line Graph of Temperature Differences

WHOLE-CLASS ACTIVITY

ELL

PROBLEM SOLVING

(*Math Journal 1,* p. 43 or *Math Masters,* p. 48; *Math Journal 2,* pp. 175–177)

In Lesson 2-6, children began a weekly routine of recording the highest and lowest temperatures in cities in the United States on a given day. They marked the locations of these cities on a map and calculated the range, or the difference between the greatest number (maximum) and the least number (minimum) in a set of data.

Pass out copies of the class record of the high/low temperatures for each child. (Children should have the same information in their first journal.)

1. Ask children to copy the dates from the Class Record Page (or journal page 43) to the date boxes below the grid on journal page 176. The slash in each date box separates the month and day.
2. Next, discuss the scale on the vertical axis. The labels represent temperature differences in degrees Fahrenheit. Each interval between consecutive horizontal rules represents 2 degrees.
3. Have children find the difference between the highest and lowest temperatures for the first date. Demonstrate how to graph the difference in the correct place on the vertical line above the first date box.
4. Ask children to graph all the temperature differences they have recorded so far on page 43. After all the data have been graphed onto journal page 176, children use their rulers to connect each pair of consecutive dots.
5. Ask: *Are there patterns in the graph?* Answers vary. Unlike the Length of Day graph, this graph may have no consistent pattern.

From now on, whenever children record high/low temperatures for a certain day on journal page 175, they should also plot the range, or temperature difference, on their line graphs on journal pages 176 and 177.

To support English language learners, discuss the different pronunciations of the noun *record* and the verb *record.* Compare the phrase, "Record the temperature in the table" to the phrase, "The record shows that today's highest temperature was 50°."

Student Page

Date Time

LESSON 7·8 **National High/Low Temperatures Project**

Date	Highest Temperature (maximum)		Lowest Temperature (minimum)		Difference (range)
	Place	Temperature	Place	Temperature	
		°F		°F	°F
		°F		°F	°F
		°F		°F	°F
		°F		°F	°F
		°F		°F	°F
		°F		°F	°F
		°F		°F	°F
		°F		°F	°F
		°F		°F	°F
		°F		°F	°F
		°F		°F	°F
		°F		°F	°F
		°F		°F	°F
		°F		°F	°F
		°F		°F	°F
		°F		°F	°F
		°F		°F	°F
		°F		°F	°F
		°F		°F	°F
		°F		°F	°F
		°F		°F	°F

Math Journal 2, p. 175

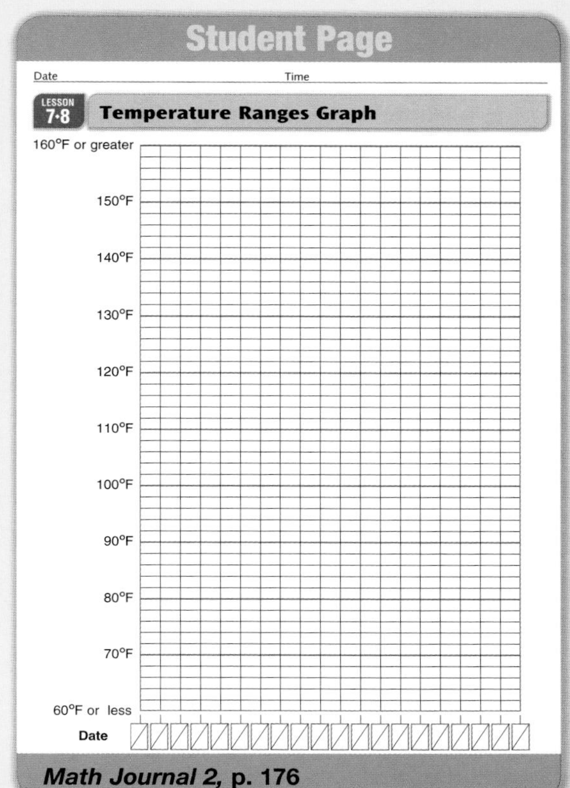

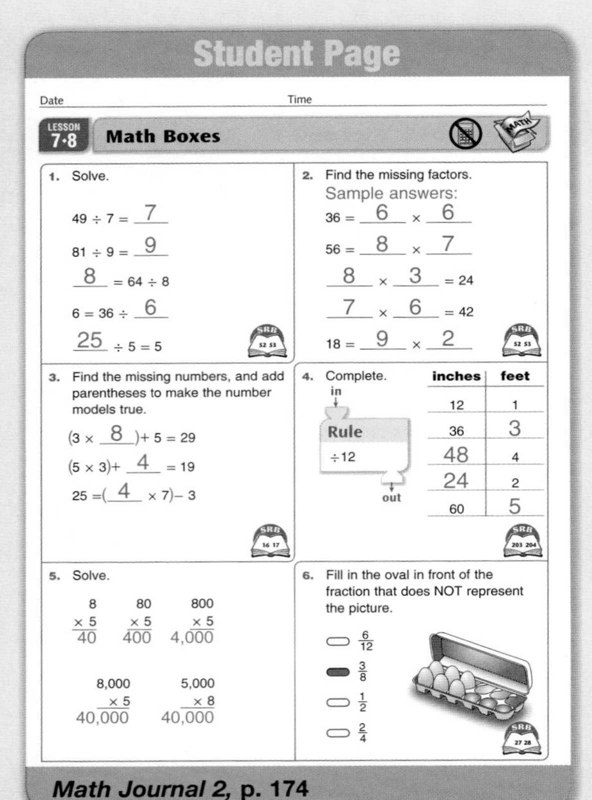
Student Page

Date　　　　Time

LESSON 7·8 **Math Boxes**

1. Solve.

$49 \div 7 =$ 7

$81 \div 9 =$ 9

8 $= 64 \div 8$

$6 = 36 \div$ 6

25 $\div 5 = 5$

2. Find the missing factors.
Sample answers:

$36 =$ 6 $\times$ 6

$56 =$ 8 $\times$ 7

8 $\times$ 3 $= 24$

7 $\times$ 6 $= 42$

$18 =$ 9 $\times$ 2

3. Find the missing numbers, and add parentheses to make the number models true.

$(3 \times 8) + 5 = 29$

$(5 \times 3) + 4 = 19$

$25 = (4 \times 7) - 3$

4. Complete.

in → Rule $\div 12$ → out

inches	feet
12	1
36	3
48	4
24	2
60	5

5. Solve.

$8 \times 5 = 40$　$80 \times 5 = 400$　$800 \times 5 = 4{,}000$

$8{,}000 \times 5 = 40{,}000$　$5{,}000 \times 8 = 40{,}000$

6. Fill in the oval in front of the fraction that does NOT represent the picture.

○ $\frac{6}{12}$

● $\frac{3}{8}$

○ $\frac{1}{2}$

○ $\frac{2}{4}$

Math Journal 2, p. 174

▶ Math Boxes 7·8

INDEPENDENT ACTIVITY

(*Math Journal 2,* p. 174)

Mixed Practice The Math Boxes in this lesson are paired with the Math Boxes in Lesson 7-6. The skill in Problem 6 previews Unit 8 content.

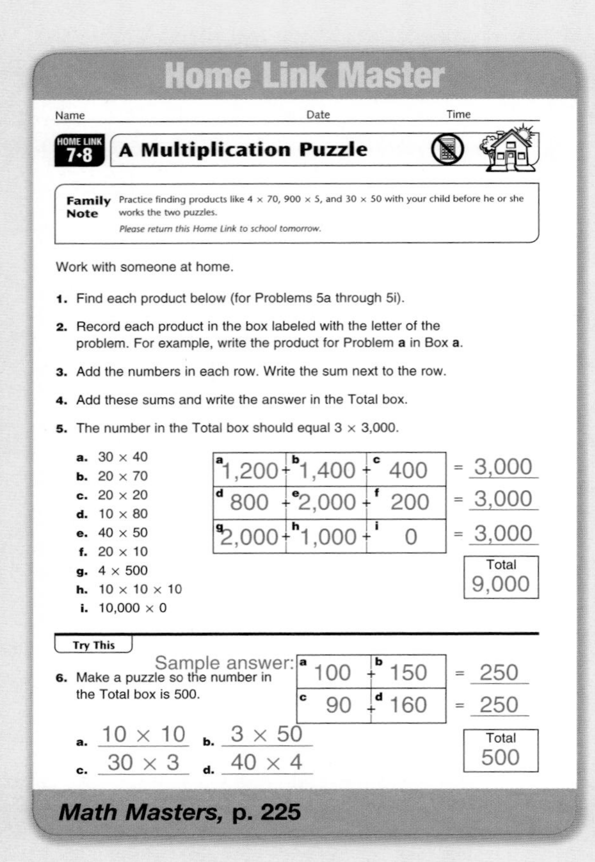
Home Link Master

Name　　　　Date　　　　Time

HOME LINK 7·8 **A Multiplication Puzzle**

Family Note Practice finding products like 4×70, 900×5, and 30×50 with your child before he or she works the two puzzles.

Please return this Home Link to school tomorrow.

Work with someone at home.

1. Find each product below (for Problems 5a through 5i).
2. Record each product in the box labeled with the letter of the problem. For example, write the product for Problem **a** in Box **a**.
3. Add the numbers in each row. Write the sum next to the row.
4. Add these sums and write the answer in the Total box.
5. The number in the Total box should equal $3 \times 3{,}000$.

a. 30×40
b. 20×70
c. 20×20
d. 10×80
e. 40×50
f. 20×10
g. 4×500
h. $10 \times 10 \times 10$
i. $10{,}000 \times 0$

a 1,200 +	b 1,400 +	c 400	= 3,000
d 800 +	e 2,000 +	f 200	= 3,000
g 2,000 +	h 1,000 +	i 0	= 3,000

Total 9,000

Try This

6. Make a puzzle so the number in the Total box is 500.

Sample answer:

a 100 +	b 150	= 250
c 90 +	d 160	= 250

Total 500

a. 10×10　**b.** 3×50

c. 30×3　**d.** 40×4

Math Masters, p. 225

▶ Home Link 7·8

INDEPENDENT ACTIVITY

(*Math Masters,* p. 225)

Home Connection Children practice finding products of multiples of 10 with someone at home.

3 Differentiation Options

READINESS

▶ Patterns in Extended Facts

(*Math Masters*, p. 226)

To explore patterns in extended facts, have children use base-10 blocks to model problems on *Math Masters,* page 226. Review what a row and column are. Children may use a calculator to check their work. When they have finished the problems, have them describe the patterns they see in Problem 1.

ENRICHMENT

▶ Multidigit Multiplication

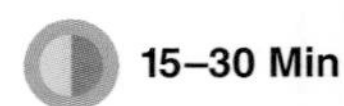

(*Math Masters*, p. 227)

To apply children's understanding of extended facts and multiplication, have them solve the problem on *Math Masters,* page 227. Explain that a mosaic is a piece of art made from small colorful clay tiles or stones. Encourage children to look for more than one way to solve the problem.

EXTRA PRACTICE

▶ Playing *Baseball Multiplication* with Tens

(*Math Masters*, p. 445; *Student Reference Book*, pp. 274 and 275)

Children practice multiplication skills by playing *Baseball Multiplication.* For detailed instructions, see Lesson 4-7 or pages 274 and 275 in the *Student Reference Book*. When played with 10s, attach a zero to the numbers that come up when rolling the dice. For example, if the numbers 3 and 5 come up, multiply 30×50. The score is 1,500.

Teaching Master

Name ______ Date ______ Time ______

LESSON 7•8 Patterns in Extended Facts

1. Use base-10 blocks to help you solve the problems in the first 2 columns. Use the patterns from the first row and column to help you solve the other problems in the table.

2 × 1 = 2	20 × 1 = 20	200 × 1 = 200
2 × 10 = 20	20 × 10 = 200	200 × 10 = 2,000
2 × 100 = 200	20 × 100 = 2,000	200 × 100 = 20,000

2. Use what you learned in Problem 1 to help you solve the problems in the table below.

2 × 2 = 4	20 × 2 = 40	200 × 2 = 400
2 × 20 = 40	20 × 20 = 400	200 × 20 = 4,000
2 × 200 = 400	20 × 200 = 4,000	200 × 200 = 40,000

3. Explain how knowing 2 × 2 can help you find the answer to 20 × 20.

I know that 2 × 2 = 4. 20 × 20 is 2[10s] × 2[10s]. Since 10 × 10 = 100, 20 × 20 is the same as 4[100s] or 400.

Math Masters, **p. 226**

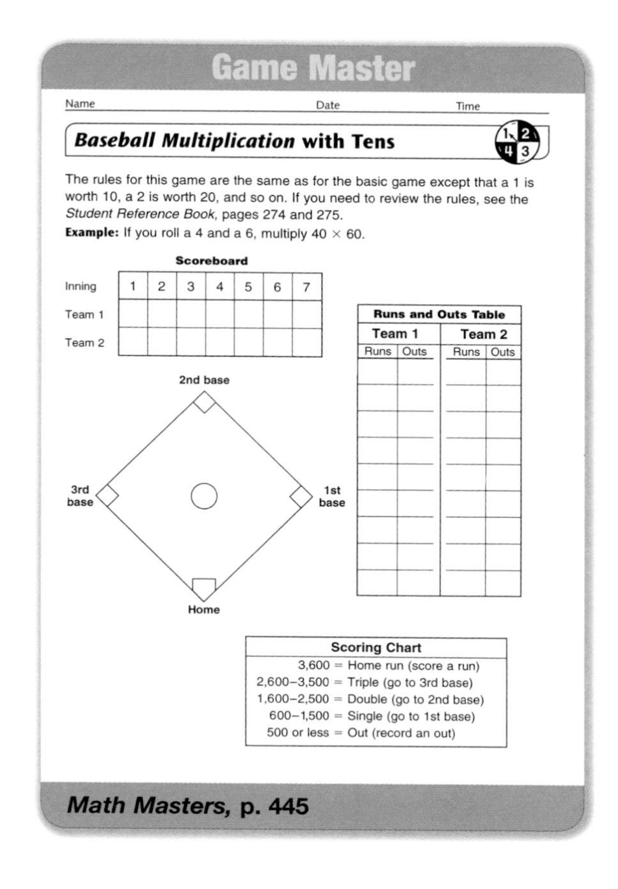

Game Master

Name ______ Date ______ Time ______

***Baseball Multiplication* with Tens**

The rules for this game are the same as for the basic game except that a 1 is worth 10, a 2 is worth 20, and so on. If you need to review the rules, see the *Student Reference Book*, pages 274 and 275.

Example: If you roll a 4 and a 6, multiply 40 × 60.

Scoreboard

Inning	1	2	3	4	5	6	7
Team 1							
Team 2							

Runs and Outs Table

Team 1		Team 2	
Runs	Outs	Runs	Outs

Scoring Chart

3,600 = Home run (score a run)
2,600–3,500 = Triple (go to 3rd base)
1,600–2,500 = Double (go to 2nd base)
600–1,500 = Single (go to 1st base)
500 or less = Out (record an out)

Math Masters, **p. 445**

Teaching Master

Name ______ Date ______ Time ______

LESSON 7•8 Multidigit Multiplication

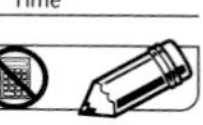

Solve the following problem:

An artist made a square mosaic with 99 rows of tiles and 99 tiles in each row. How many tiles were used?

Do not use your calculator. Show your work. Explain what you did.

9,801 tiles Sample answers:
(100 × 99) is (1 × 99) more than (99 × 99). I know that 100 × 99 = 9,900. If I subtract (1 × 99) from 9,900, I'll get 9,900 – 99 = 9,801; so 99 × 99 = 9,801.
100 × 100 is 100 rows with 100 tiles in each row or 10,000 tiles in all. I need to subtract 1 row of tiles because there are only 99 rows in the problem. 10,000 – 100= 9,900. Now there are 99 rows of 100 tiles left. I need to subtract 1 tile from each of the 99 rows so there will be 99 rows of 99 tiles. 9,900 – 99 = 9,801.

Math Masters, **p. 227**

7•9 Exploring Ratios and Geometric Figures

Explorations

Objectives To provide experiences with exploring similar polygons, solving ratio problems, and exploring geometric configurations.

 www.everydaymathonline.com

ePresentations

eToolkit

Algorithms Practice

EM Facts Workshop Game™

Family Letters

Assessment Management

Common Core State Standards

Curriculum Focal Points

Interactive Teacher's Lesson Guide

1 Teaching the Lesson

Key Concepts and Skills

- Use equal groups to solve problems. [Operations and Computation Goal 6]
- Construct 2- and 3-dimensional shapes from straws and twist-ties. [Geometry Goal 2]
- Use pattern blocks to explore similar polygons. [Geometry Goal 2]

Key Activities

Exploration A: Children use pattern blocks to construct figures of the same shape.

Exploration B: Groups solve number stories involving a ratio. They write number stories for others to solve.

Exploration C: Children follow directions to build triangles out of straws.

Ongoing Assessment: Recognizing Student Achievement Use Mental Math and Reflexes. [Geometry Goal 2]

Key Vocabulary

similar figures

Materials

Home Link 7•8

Exploration A: Per group:
Math Masters, p. 228
pattern blocks (square, triangle, large rhombus, small rhombus, trapezoid, and hexagon; at least 9 of each shape) ◆ Pattern-Block Template ◆ paper ◆ straightedge (optional)

Exploration B: Per group:
Math Masters, p. 229
calculator (optional) ◆ counters (optional) ◆ paper (optional)

Exploration C: Per child:
Math Masters, p. 230
9 short straws of equal length ◆ about 20 twist-ties

2 Ongoing Learning & Practice

Playing *Roll to 100*
Math Masters, p. 456
Student Reference Book, pp. 307 and 308
six-sided dice

Math Boxes 7•9
Math Journal 2, p. 178

Home Link 7•9
Math Masters, p. 231

3 Differentiation Options

ENRICHMENT

Finding the Next-Larger Shapes in a Series
Math Masters, pp. 228 and 232
per group: pattern blocks (square, triangle, large rhombus, small rhombus, and trapezoid; at least 16 of each shape)

EXTRA PRACTICE

Minute Math+
Minute Math®+, pp. 95, 98, and 132

Advance Preparation

For the Math Message, draw a three-leaf clover on the board.

***Teacher's Reference Manual,* Grades 1–3** pp. 62, 63

Getting Started

Mathematical Practices
SMP1, SMP2, SMP3, SMP4, SMP5, **SMP6,** SMP7, SMP8

Mental Math and Reflexes 

Have children find 3-D shapes around the room. Children name them; identify the shapes of their bases; and count the faces, vertices, and edges.
Sample answers:

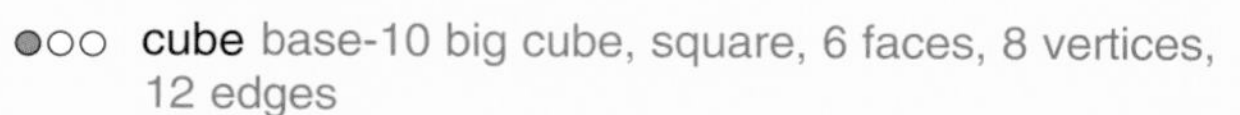

●○○ cube base-10 big cube, square, 6 faces, 8 vertices, 12 edges

●●○ cylinder paper towel roll, circle, 2 faces, 0 vertices, 2 edges, 1 curved surface

●●● cone sharpened part of a pencil or crayon, circle, 1 face, 1 vertex/apex, 1 edge, 1 curved surface

Math Message

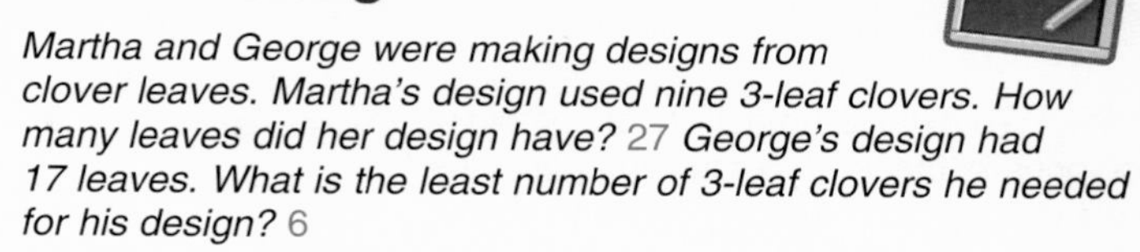

Martha and George were making designs from clover leaves. Martha's design used nine 3-leaf clovers. How many leaves did her design have? 27 *George's design had 17 leaves. What is the least number of 3-leaf clovers he needed for his design?* 6

Home Link 7·8 Follow-Up

Go over the answers. Ask children who did the Try This problem to share their puzzles for the class to solve.

Ongoing Assessment: Recognizing Student Achievement

Mental Math and Reflexes

Use **Mental Math and Reflexes** to assess children's progress toward identifying and describing solid figures. Children are making adequate progress if they are able to complete the ●○○ and ●●○ problems successfully. Some children may complete the ●●● problem successfully.

[Geometry Goal 2]

1 Teaching the Lesson

▶ Math Message Follow-Up

WHOLE-CLASS DISCUSSION

Children share solution strategies. Discuss that George needed at least 6 three-leaf clovers to make a design with 17 leaves. He used all but 1 leaf.

Possible strategy for solving Math Message.

▶ Exploration A: Exploring Similar Polygons

(*Math Masters,* p. 228)

Figures that have the same shape (but are not necessarily the same size) are called **similar figures.** To support English language learners, discuss the mathematical and everyday meanings of *similar* using examples. Children explore this concept by making a larger square out of 4 square pattern blocks. They repeat the exercise with 4 triangles, 4 large rhombuses, 4 small rhombuses, and 4 trapezoids, respectively, and build the next-larger shape.

Suggest that for Parts 1 through 3, children in the group divide up the work: One child works with each shape. Children work on Parts 4 and 5 together. They will discover that they cannot make a larger hexagon out of hexagon pattern blocks. They may find that they can do so by combining 3 hexagons with 3 large rhombuses.

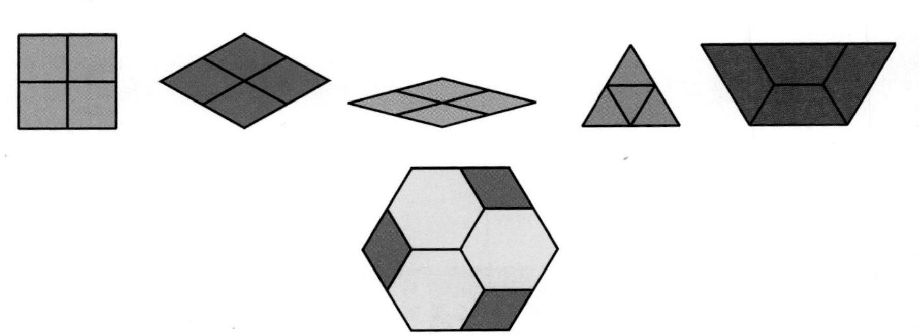

Pattern blocks make similar polygons.

NOTE To extend the activity of combining polygons to that of decomposing polygons, have children use a straightedge to divide the polygons shown in Problem 3, *Math Masters,* page 228 into smaller similar and/or non-similar polygons.

Links to the Future

The activities in Exploration A are an exposure to the concept of similar figures. Identifying, describing, and modeling similar figures are Grade 6 Goals.

Teaching Master

Name Date Time

LESSON 7·9 **Similar Pattern-Block Shapes**

Exploration A:

Share the work with other members of your group for Problems 1 through 3. Work together on Problems 4 and 5.

1. Try to make a square out of square pattern blocks. The square should be larger than a single pattern block. Use as few squares as you can. Record the result on a sheet of paper by tracing around the pattern blocks or by using a template. 4 squares
2. Make a larger triangle out of triangle pattern blocks. Again, use as few triangles as you can. Record the result by tracing around the blocks or by using a template. 4 triangles
3. Do the same thing with each of the following pattern blocks:

   4 large rhombuses — large rhombus; 4 small rhombuses — small rhombus; 4 trapezoids — trapezoid

   Hint: Use four trapezoid pattern blocks to make the larger trapezoid.
4. Can you make a larger hexagon out of hexagon pattern blocks? no
5. Make a larger hexagon by combining hexagon pattern blocks with pattern blocks of another shape. Record the result by tracing around the blocks or by using a template on the back of your paper.
   3 hexagons and 3 large rhombuses

Follow-Up

6. How many pattern blocks did you use to make larger squares, triangles, rhombuses, and trapezoids? 4 each
7. How many pattern blocks would you need to make the next larger square? The next larger triangle? The next larger rhombus? Try to make them. 9 each

Math Masters, p. 228

Exploration B: Exploring Ratio Problems

(*Math Masters,* p. 229)

Children are presented with the following situation: *A farmer is switching from raising cows to raising sheep. She estimates that 7 sheep eat about as much as 1 cow.*

Children answer questions based on the ratio of 1 cow to 7 sheep without using a calculator. Then they write a group report describing how they got their answers. Note that the third question (About how many cows for 67 sheep?) does not have an exact answer. According to the farmer's estimate, she can replace 9 cows with 63 sheep, or 10 cows with 70 sheep. Ask children whether she should replace 9 or 10 cows with 67 sheep and to justify their answers.

Adjusting the Activity

ELL

Encourage children to draw pictures or use counters to model the problem.

AUDITORY ◆ KINESTHETIC ◆ TACTILE ◆ VISUAL

As a follow-up, group members make up stories based on the ratio of cows to sheep. They may use calculators to solve these stories. They record two or three of their stories on the group report.

Exploration C: Solving a Geometry Problem

(*Math Masters,* p. 230)

Children try to make 5 triangles out of 9 straws using twist-ties to join the straws together. The solution is a large triangle divided into four smaller triangles. The larger triangle is counted as 1-triangle. Next, children try to make 7 triangles out of the 9-straws. The solution is a 3-dimensional figure consisting of two tetrahedrons.

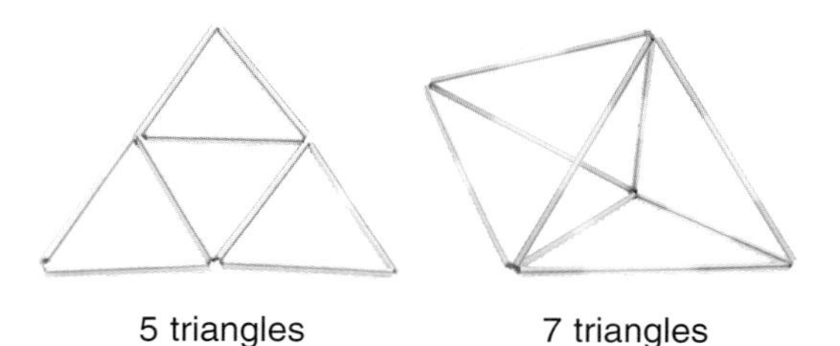

5 triangles 7 triangles

Name Date Time

LESSON 7•9 **Seven Sheep versus One Cow**

Exploration B:

A farmer is switching from raising cows to raising sheep. She estimates that 7 sheep eat about as much as 1 cow.

Work as a group to answer the three questions below. Find the answers without using a calculator.

1. If a farmer has 10 well-fed cows in the pasture, how many sheep can she replace them with? 70 sheep
2. How many sheep can she replace 50 cows with? 350 sheep
3. A neighbor wants to sell the farmer 67 sheep. About how many of her cows will these sheep replace? 9 or 10 cows

On the back of this page, or on a separate sheet of paper, write a group report telling what your group did to find the answers.

Try This

4. Make up a problem about 7 sheep eating as much as 1 cow.
Answers vary.

Use calculators, if you wish, to solve the problem.
Write it in your group report.

Math Masters, **p. 229**

Links to the Future

The activities in Exploration B are a beginning exposure to solving number stories involving a ratio. Solving problems involving ratios of parts of a set to the whole set is a Grade 5 Goal.

Teaching Master

Name Date Time

LESSON 7•9 **Straw Triangles**

Exploration C:

1. Try to build 5 triangles out of 9 straws, without bending the straws. Draw a picture of your solution below.

Try This

2. Take the 9 straws apart. Then try to build 7 triangles out of 9 straws. Show your solution to your teacher. Then do your best to draw a picture of it below.
Hint: The solution is a 3-dimensional figure.

Math Masters, **p. 230**

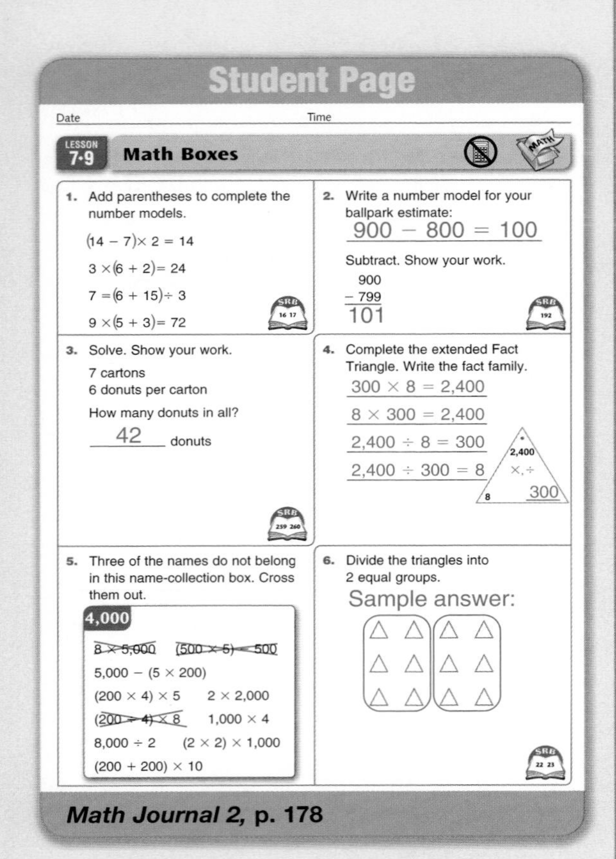
Student Page

Date Time

LESSON 7·9 **Math Boxes**

1. Add parentheses to complete the number models.
(14 − 7) × 2 = 14
3 × (6 + 2) = 24
7 = (6 + 15) ÷ 3
9 × (5 + 3) = 72

SRB 16 17

2. Write a number model for your ballpark estimate:
900 − 800 = 100
Subtract. Show your work.
900
− 799
101

SRB 192

3. Solve. Show your work.
7 cartons
6 donuts per carton
How many donuts in all?
42 donuts

SRB 259 260

4. Complete the extended Fact Triangle. Write the fact family.
300 × 8 = 2,400
8 × 300 = 2,400
2,400 ÷ 8 = 300
2,400 ÷ 300 = 8
(Fact Triangle: 2,400; ×, ÷; 8; 300)

5. Three of the names do not belong in this name-collection box. Cross them out.

4,000	
~~8 × 5,000~~	~~(500 × 5) − 500~~
5,000 − (5 × 200)	
(200 × 4) × 5	2 × 2,000
~~(200 + 4) × 8~~	1,000 × 4
8,000 ÷ 2	(2 × 2) × 1,000
(200 + 200) × 10	

6. Divide the triangles into 2 equal groups.
Sample answer:

SRB 22 23

Math Journal 2, p. 178

2 Ongoing Learning & Practice

▶ Playing *Roll to 100*

(*Math Masters,* p. 456; *Student Reference Book,* pp. 307 and 308)

Partners practice mental computation as they play *Roll to 100*. For detailed instructions, see Lesson 2.1 or pages 307 and 308 in the *Student Reference Book*.

▶ Math Boxes 7·9

INDEPENDENT ACTIVITY

(*Math Journal 2,* p. 178)

Mixed Practice The Math Boxes in this lesson are linked with the Math Boxes in Lessons 7-5 and 7-7. The skill in Problem 6 previews Unit 8 content.

▶ Home Link 7·9

(*Math Masters,* p. 231)

Home Connection Children identify mystery numbers from given clues. They make up mystery-number puzzles and ask someone to find the mystery numbers.

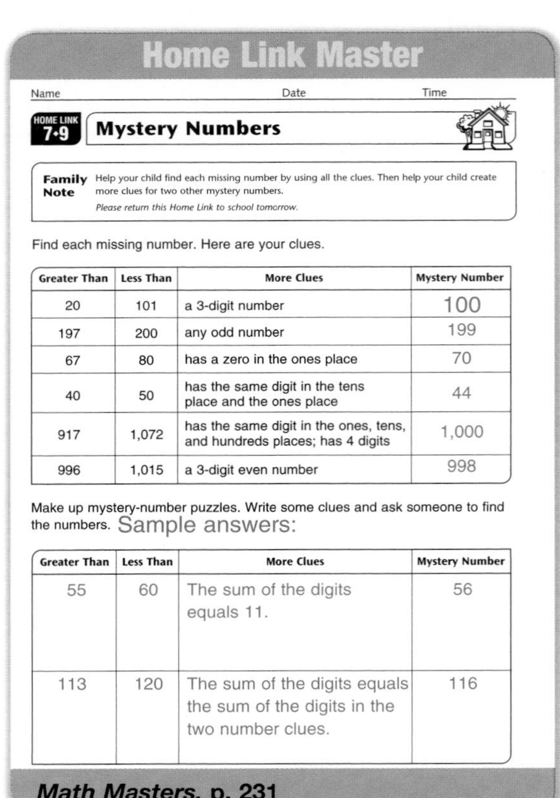
Home Link Master

Name Date Time

HOME LINK 7·9 **Mystery Numbers**

Family Note Help your child find each missing number by using all the clues. Then help your child create more clues for two other mystery numbers.
Please return this Home Link to school tomorrow.

Find each missing number. Here are your clues.

Greater Than	Less Than	More Clues	Mystery Number
20	101	a 3-digit number	100
197	200	any odd number	199
67	80	has a zero in the ones place	70
40	50	has the same digit in the tens place and the ones place	44
917	1,072	has the same digit in the ones, tens, and hundreds places; has 4 digits	1,000
996	1,015	a 3-digit even number	998

Make up mystery-number puzzles. Write some clues and ask someone to find the numbers. Sample answers:

Greater Than	Less Than	More Clues	Mystery Number
55	60	The sum of the digits equals 11.	56
113	120	The sum of the digits equals the sum of the digits in the two number clues.	116

Math Masters, p. 231

3 Differentiation Options

ENRICHMENT

PARTNER ACTIVITY

15–30 Min

▶ Finding the Next-Larger Shapes in a Series

(*Math Masters,* pp. 228 and 232)

To further explore similar polygons, have children fill in the chart on *Math Masters,* page 232 with the results of Exploration A (*Math Masters,* page 228). Children create the next-larger trapezoid out of 9 trapezoid pattern blocks. Then they build the next-larger size of each shape and record their results. Finally, children look for patterns in each series of shapes. Have children describe the patterns they see and their strategies for building the next-larger similar shape.

EXTRA PRACTICE

SMALL-GROUP ACTIVITY

5–15 Min

▶ *Minute Math+*

To offer children more experience working with ratios in number stories, see the following pages in *Minute Math+*:

Number Stories: pages 95, 98, and 132

Planning Ahead

For Lesson 8-2, you will need a paper bag about the size of a lunch bag and a number of colored blocks that are the same size and shape. One possibility is to use small rhombus pattern blocks and to attach different-colored dots to them to represent various colors; another is to color an edge of each rhombus block with a crayon. (The color can be washed off.) The activity in Part 1 uses 5 blocks: 2 of one color, 2 of a second color, and 1 of a third color. The game in Part 3 requires a paper bag and 7 blocks, in 2 or 3 different colors, for each group of 3 or more children.

Teaching Master

Name Date Time

LESSON 7•9 Next-Larger Shapes

You will need *Math Masters,* page 228 and the shapes you made during Exploration A.

Follow these steps:

1. In the chart below, write the number of pattern blocks you used to make each of the different-size shapes in Exploration A.
2. Build the two next-larger squares, triangles, rhombuses, and trapezoids.
3. Record the number of pattern blocks you used for each shape in the chart.

Number of Pattern Blocks in Shapes

	smallest	next larger	next larger	next larger
square	1	4	9	16
triangle	1	4	9	16
large rhombus	1	4	9	16
small rhombus	1	4	9	16
trapezoid	1	4	9	16

What patterns do you see in each series of shapes? Sample answer: The number of pattern blocks needed is always a square number; the number of pattern blocks needed to make each size shape is the same no matter which shape is made.

Math Masters, p. 232

7•10 Progress Check 7

Objective To assess children's progress on mathematical content through the end of Unit 7.

1 Looking Back: Cumulative Assessment

Input children's data from Progress Check 7 into the **Assessment Management System**.

Materials
- Home Link 7•9
- *Assessment Handbook,* pp. 102–109, 177–181, 208, and 252–255
- straightedge; slate; counters (optional)

CONTENT ASSESSED	LESSON(S)	ASSESSMENT ITEMS				
		SELF	ORAL/SLATE	WRITTEN PART A	WRITTEN PART B	OPEN RESPONSE
Find multiples of 2, 5, and 10. [Number and Numeration Goal 3]	7•6, 7•8					✔
Solve problems involving + and −. [Operations and Computation Goal 2]	7•1–7•5, 7•7, 7•9	5		16b, 17b		
Demonstrate automaticity with multiplication facts through 10 × 10. [Operations and Computation Goal 3]	7•1–7•6, 7•8, 7•9	2	1, 2	1–10		
Solve problems involving the multiplication of 2- and 3-digit whole numbers by 1-digit whole numbers. [Operations and Computation Goal 4]					22	
Make reasonable estimates for whole number addition and subtraction problems. [Operations and Computation Goal 5]	7•2, 7•3, 7•7, 7•9	6		16a, 17a	23	
Use repeated addition, arrays, and skip counting to model multiplication. Use equal sharing and equal grouping to model division. [Operations and Computation Goal 6]	7•4–7•9	1, 3	3, 4	11, 12		✔
Identify and draw parallel and intersecting lines and rays. [Geometry Goal 1]	7•1–7•5	4		13, 14		
Describe plane and solid figures. [Geometry Goal 2]	7•1–7•5			15		
Use numeric patterns to solve problems. [Patterns, Functions, and Algebra Goal 1]	7•3					✔
Recognize that parentheses affect the order in which operations are carried out. [Patterns, Functions, and Algebra Goal 3]	7•4–7•9				18–21	

2 Looking Ahead: Preparing for Unit 8

Math Boxes 7•10

Home Link 7•10: Unit 8 Family Letter

Materials
- *Math Journal 2,* p. 179
- *Math Masters,* pp. 233–236

Getting Started

Math Message • Self Assessment

Complete the Self Assessment (Assessment Handbook, *p. 177).*

Home Link 7·9 Follow-Up

Have partners share their own mystery-number puzzles for each other to solve.

1 Looking Back: Cumulative Assessment

▶ Math Message Follow-Up

(Self Assessment, *Assessment Handbook,* p. 177)

The Self Assessment offers children the opportunity to reflect upon their progress.

▶ Oral and Slate Assessment

Problems 1 and 3 provide summative information for grading purposes. Problems 2 and 4 provide formative information that can be useful in planning future instruction.

Oral Assessment

1. Do choral fact practice with the first set of Fact Triangles.
2. Do choral fact practice with the second set of Fact Triangles.

Slate Assessment

3. Tell multiplication number stories. Encourage children to use counters, draw arrays, use diagrams, and so on to help them solve the problems. Children record answers on slates.
   - 4 puppies. 4 legs on each puppy. How many legs in all? 16 legs
   - 8 sets of books. 5 books in each set. How many books in all? 40 books
4. Tell division number stories. Encourage children to use counters, draw arrays, use diagrams, and so on to help them solve the problems. Children record answers on slates.
   - 30 jelly beans for 7 children. How many jelly beans per child? 4 jelly beans with 2 left over
   - 57 pennies for 6 children. How many pennies per child? 9 pennies per child with 3 pennies left over

Assessment Master

Name Date Time

LESSON 7·10 **Self Assessment** Progress Check 7

Check one box for each skill.

Skills	I can do this on my own and explain how to do it.	I can do this on my own.	I can do this if I get help or look at an example.
1. Use arrays to help find answers.			
2. Know multiplication facts.			
3. Share things equally.			
4. Draw parallel and intersecting lines.			
5. Solve 3-digit addition problems.			
6. Make estimates to check problems.			

***Assessment Handbook,* p. 177**

Assessment Master

Name Date Time

LESSON 7·10 **Written Assessment** Progress Check 7

Part A

Fill in the missing factors and products.

1. 8 × 5 = 40
2. 10 × 3 = 30
3. 9 × 2 = 18
4. 7 × 10 = 70
5. 4 × 5 = 20
6. 2 × 8 = 16
7. 4 × 7 = 28
8. 3 × 6 = 18
9. 7 × 3 = 21
10. 4 × 6 = 24

Solve. Use diagrams, counters, arrays, pictures, or whatever you need to find the answer. Record your answer with a unit. Write a number model.

11. Linda has 32 crayons to put into boxes. 8 crayons fit into each box. How many boxes does she need?

boxes	crayons per box	crayons in all
?	8	32

Number model: $32 \div 8 = ?$ or $? \times 8 = 32$

Answer: 4 boxes (unit)

12. 7 children picked 42 apples. If they share the apples equally, how many will each child get?

children	apples per child	apples in all
7	?	42

Number model: $42 \div 7 = ?$ or $7 \times ? = 42$

Answer: 6 apples (unit)

***Assessment Handbook,* p. 178**

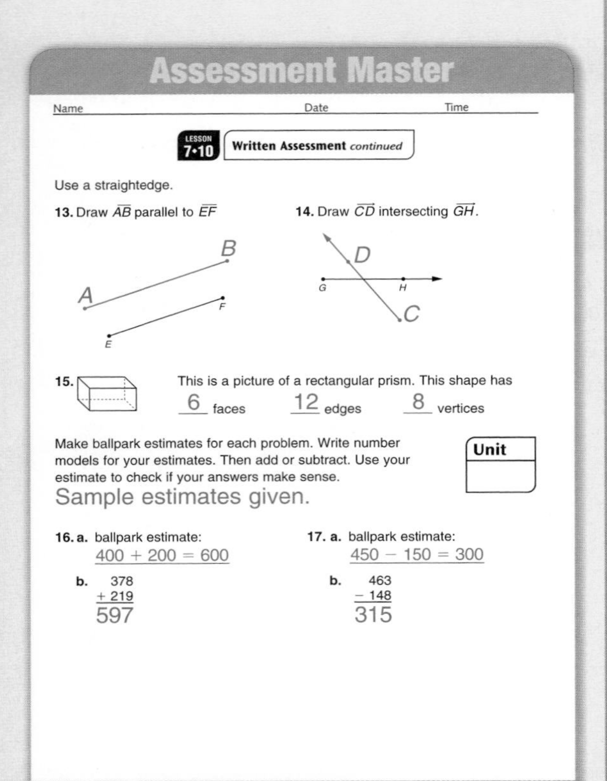
Assessment Master

Name ____ Date ____ Time ____

LESSON 7•10 Written Assessment *continued*

Use a straightedge.

13. Draw $\overline{AB}$ parallel to $\overline{EF}$

14. Draw $\overline{CD}$ intersecting $\overleftrightarrow{GH}$.

15. This is a picture of a rectangular prism. This shape has 6 faces 12 edges 8 vertices

Make ballpark estimates for each problem. Write number models for your estimates. Then add or subtract. Use your estimate to check if your answers make sense.
Sample estimates given.

Unit

16. a. ballpark estimate: 400 + 200 = 600

b. 378 + 219 = 597

17. a. ballpark estimate: 450 − 150 = 300

b. 463 − 148 = 315

Assessment Handbook, p. 179

Assessment Master

Name ____ Date ____ Time ____

LESSON 7•10 Written Assessment *continued*

Part B

18. 11 = (30 ÷ 5) + 5

19. 9 + (3 × 5) = 24

20. 7 + (8 × 8) = 71

21. 6 = 12 − (12 ÷ 2)

Solve the multiplication/division puzzle. Fill in the blanks.

22.

×, ÷	40	600
8	320	4,800
7	280	4,200

Estimate to answer the question below. Assume that there is no tax on the items.

23. Allen wants to buy a notebook for \$3.89 and a pen for \$1.99. He has \$5.00. Does he have enough money? no

Explain your thinking: Sample answer: \$1.99 is almost \$2.00, and \$3.89 is almost \$4.00. That is almost \$6.00.

Number model you used: \$2.00 + \$4.00 = \$6.00

Assessment Handbook, p. 180

▶ Written Assessment

INDEPENDENT ACTIVITY

(*Assessment Handbook,* pp. 178–180)

Part A Recognizing Student Achievement

Problems 1 through 17 provide summative information and can be used for grading purposes.

Problem(s)	Description
1–10	Fill in missing factors and products.
11, 12	Solve equal-groups and equal-shares number stories.
13, 14	Draw parallel and intersecting line segments and rays.
15	Identify faces, vertices, and edges.
16a, 17a	Make ballpark estimates.
16b, 17b	Solve multidigit addition and subtraction problems.

Part B Informing Instruction

Problems 18 through 23 provide formative information that can be useful in planning future instruction.

Problem(s)	Description
18–21	Use parentheses in number sentences.
22	Solve an extended facts multiplication puzzle.
23	Estimate the answer to a number story involving money.

Use the checklists on pages 253 and 255 of the *Assessment Handbook* to record results. Then input the data into the **Assessment Management System** to keep an ongoing record of children's progress toward Grade-Level Goals.

▶ Open Response

INDEPENDENT ACTIVITY

(*Assessment Handbook,* p. 181)

Button Dolls

The open-response item requires children to apply skills and concepts from Unit 7 to solve a multistep problem. See *Assessment Handbook,* pages 105–109 for rubrics and children's work samples for this problem.

2 Looking Ahead: Preparing for Unit 8

Math Boxes 7•10

INDEPENDENT ACTIVITY

(*Math Journal 2*, p. 179)

Mixed Practice This Math Boxes page previews Unit 8 content.

Home Link 7•10: Unit 8 Family Letter

(*Math Masters*, pp. 233–236)

Home Connection The Unit 8 Family Letter provides parents and guardians with information and activities related to Unit 8 topics.

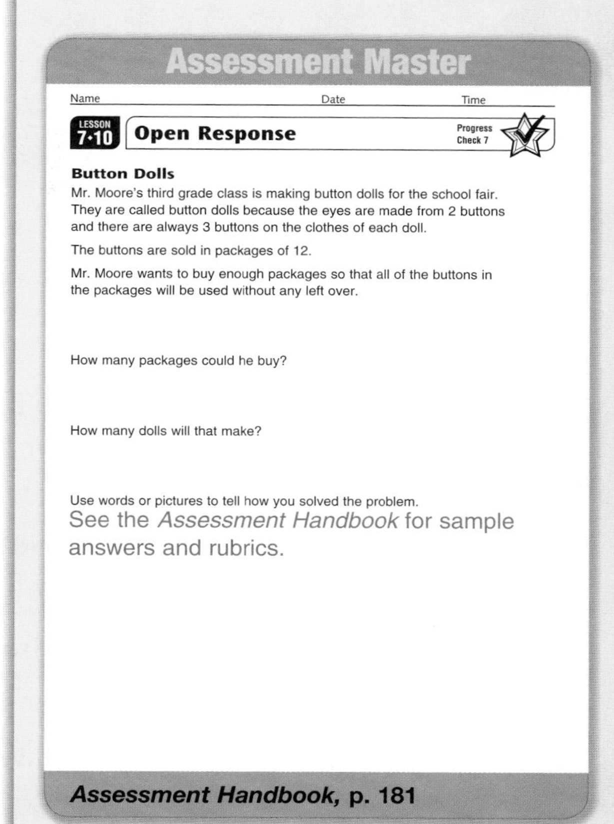

Assessment Master

Name Date Time

LESSON 7•10 **Open Response** Progress Check 7

Button Dolls

Mr. Moore's third grade class is making button dolls for the school fair. They are called button dolls because the eyes are made from 2 buttons and there are always 3 buttons on the clothes of each doll.

The buttons are sold in packages of 12.

Mr. Moore wants to buy enough packages so that all of the buttons in the packages will be used without any left over.

How many packages could he buy?

How many dolls will that make?

Use words or pictures to tell how you solved the problem.

See the *Assessment Handbook* for sample answers and rubrics.

Assessment Handbook, p. 181

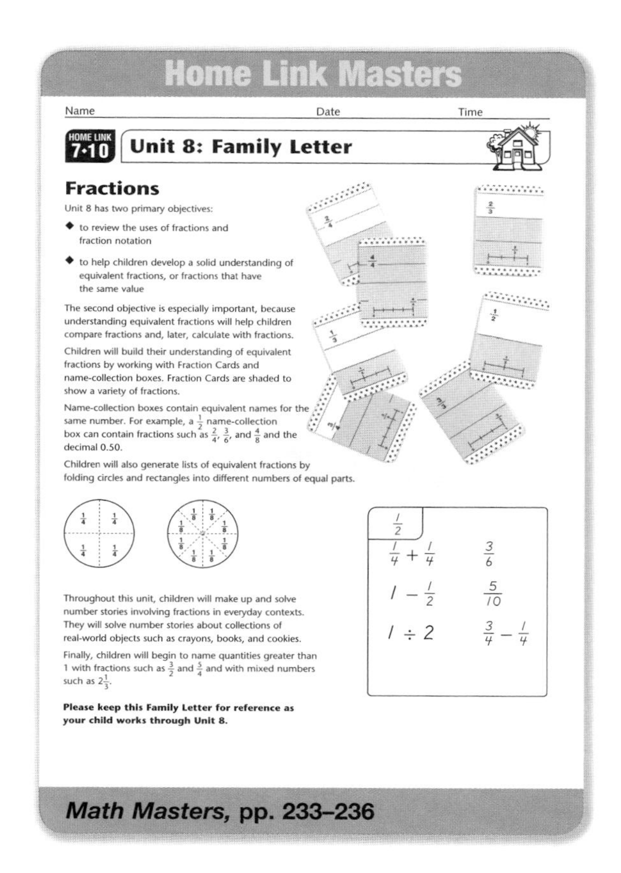

Home Link Masters

Name Date Time

HOME LINK 7•10 **Unit 8: Family Letter**

Fractions

Unit 8 has two primary objectives:

- to review the uses of fractions and fraction notation
- to help children develop a solid understanding of equivalent fractions, or fractions that have the same value

The second objective is especially important, because understanding equivalent fractions will help children compare fractions and, later, calculate with fractions.

Children will build their understanding of equivalent fractions by working with Fraction Cards and name-collection boxes. Fraction Cards are shaded to show a variety of fractions.

Name-collection boxes contain equivalent names for the same number. For example, a $\frac{1}{2}$ name-collection box can contain fractions such as $\frac{2}{4}$, $\frac{3}{6}$, and $\frac{4}{8}$ and the decimal 0.50.

Children will also generate lists of equivalent fractions by folding circles and rectangles into different numbers of equal parts.

Throughout this unit, children will make up and solve number stories involving fractions in everyday contexts. They will solve number stories about collections of real-world objects such as crayons, books, and cookies.

Finally, children will begin to name quantities greater than 1 with fractions such as $\frac{3}{2}$ and $\frac{5}{4}$ and with mixed numbers such as $2\frac{1}{3}$.

Please keep this Family Letter for reference as your child works through Unit 8.

Math Masters, pp. 233–236

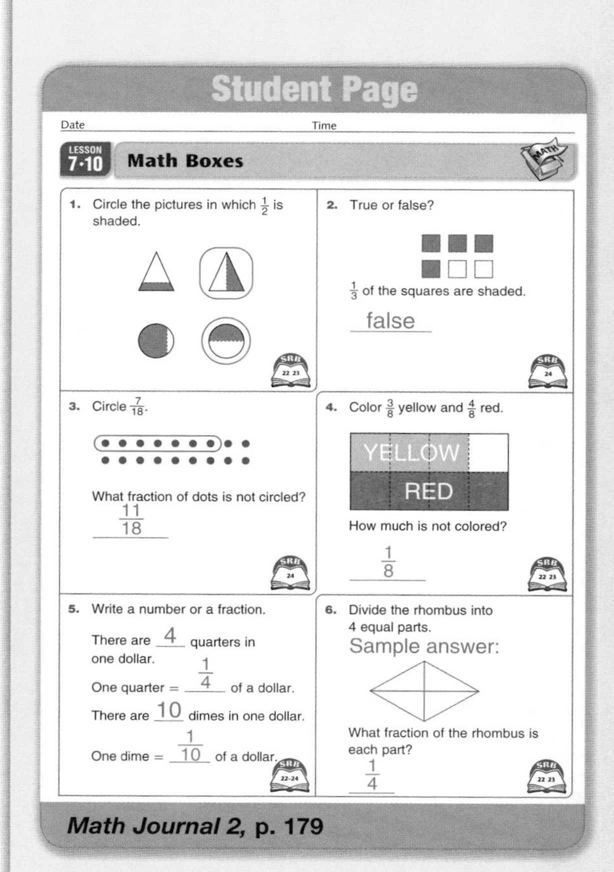

Student Page

Date Time

LESSON 7•10 **Math Boxes**

1. Circle the pictures in which $\frac{1}{2}$ is shaded.

2. True or false?
   $\frac{1}{3}$ of the squares are shaded. false

3. Circle $\frac{7}{18}$.
   What fraction of dots is not circled? $\frac{11}{18}$

4. Color $\frac{3}{8}$ yellow and $\frac{4}{8}$ red.

   How much is not colored? $\frac{1}{8}$

5. Write a number or a fraction.
   There are 4 quarters in one dollar.
   One quarter = $\frac{1}{4}$ of a dollar.
   There are 10 dimes in one dollar.
   One dime = $\frac{1}{10}$ of a dollar.

6. Divide the rhombus into 4 equal parts.
   Sample answer:
   What fraction of the rhombus is each part? $\frac{1}{4}$

Math Journal 2, p. 179

Unit 8 Organizer

Fractions

Overview

Unit 8 has two primary objectives: to review the uses of fractions and fraction notation and to help children develop a solid understanding of equivalent fractions—a key element in comparing fractions and, later, in calculating with fractions. The approach to equivalent fractions in third grade is informal and includes many hands-on activities. Unit 8 has six main areas of focus:

- To explore fractional and spatial relationships,
- To introduce the number line for fractions,
- To find equivalent fractions,
- To compare fractions using region models,
- To name quantities greater than 1 with fractions and mixed numbers, and
- To solve number stories involving fractions.

Linking to the Common Core State Standards

The content of Unit 8 addresses the Common Core State Standards for Mathematics in *Number and Operations–Fractions* and *Geometry.* The correlation of the Common Core State Standards to the *Everyday Mathematics* Grade 3 lessons begins on page CS1.

Contents

*Visit www.everydaymathonline.com for Guiding Questions that support Standards for Mathematical Practice (SMPs).

Learning In Perspective

	Lesson Objectives	Links to the Past	Links to the Future
8•1	To guide children as they use fractions to name *a* of *b* equal parts.	In Grades 1 and 2, children use sets of pennies to investigate fractional parts of a collection.	Children continue to identify fractional parts of sets in the context of application problems in Grades 4–6.
8•2	To guide children as they make predictions based on outcomes and construct situations that meet given conditions.	In earlier grades, children do the Dice-Roll and Tally activity and graph outcomes of rolling two dice.	Authentic problem situations challenge children to use real-life data to predict outcomes in Grades 4 and 5.
8•3	To provide opportunities to explore fractional relationships, spatial relationships, and combinations.	Children in Grade 1 use geoboards and fold paper to investigate fractional parts of a region. In Grade 2, children also investigate fractional parts of regions with pattern blocks.	Children continue to identify fractional parts of regions in the context of application problems in Grades 4–6.
8•4	To introduce the number line as a model for fractions.	Children use number lines to investigate whole numbers beginning in Kindergarten.	In later grades, children put fractions into the context of real numbers on a number line.
8•5	To guide children as they find equivalent fractions.	In Grade 1, children fold strips of paper to illustrate equivalent fractions. In Grade 2, children match fractional parts of paper circles and use Fraction Cards.	Children continue to work with equivalent fractions in Grade 4 and extend the concept to include decimals and percents.
8•6	To guide children as they compare fractions using region models.	Children in Grade 1 use geoboards and fold paper to investigate fractional parts of a region. In Grade 2, children also investigate fractional parts of regions with pattern blocks. They use Fraction Cards and compare fractions.	Children continue to identify fractional parts of regions in the context of application problems in Grades 4–6.
8•7	To demonstrate naming quantities greater than 1 with fractions and mixed numbers.	Children work with the idea of equivalent names for numbers beginning in Grade 1.	Children continue to convert between mixed numbers and fractions in the context of application problems in Grades 4–6.
8•8	To provide experiences with solving number stories involving fractions.	Children begin to make up and solve fraction number stories in Grade 2.	Throughout the grades, children continue to create and solve number stories.

Lesson	Key Concepts and Skills	Grade 3 Goals*
8·1	Use manipulatives to solve problems involving fractional parts of collections.	Number and Numeration Goal 2
	Identify equivalent halves and fourths of a shaded region.	Number and Numeration Goal 5
	Use shaded regions to compare fractions.	Number and Numeration Goal 6
	Use equal sharing to solve fractional part-of-a-collection problems.	Operations and Computation Goal 6
8·2	Describe results of a random-draw experiment using basic probability terms.	Data and Chance Goal 3
	Make predictions from the results of a random-draw experiment.	Data and Chance Goal 4
	Test predictions using manipulatives.	Data and Chance Goal 4
8·3	Solve problems involving fractional parts of a collection.	Number and Numeration Goal 2
	Identify the fractional part one shape is of another.	Number and Numeration Goal 2
	Explore polygon relationships by constructing figures from polygons.	Geometry Goal 2
	Use patterning rules to find all possible combinations of pants and socks.	Patterns, Functions, and Algebra Goal 1
8·4	Identify fractions on a number line.	Number and Numeration Goal 2
	Compare fractions using a number-line model.	Number and Numeration Goal 6
8·5	Read and write fractions.	Number and Numeration Goal 2
	Represent, identify, and generate equivalent fractions using manipulatives and drawings.	Number and Numeration Goal 5
8·6	Read fractions.	Number and Numeration Goal 2
	Compare fractions to $\frac{1}{2}$.	Number and Numeration Goal 6
	Use an area model to compare fractions.	Number and Numeration Goal 6
	Identify patterns and relationships between numerators and denominators of fractions.	Patterns, Functions, and Algebra Goal 1
8·7	Shade fractional parts of regions to represent fractions greater than 1.	Number and Numeration Goal 2
	Model and name mixed numbers and fractions.	Number and Numeration Goal 2
	Identify equivalent fractions.	Number and Numeration Goal 5
	Use lines of symmetry to divide figures into equal parts.	Geometry Goal 3
8·8	Use pennies, counters, or pictures to solve fraction number stories.	Number and Numeration Goal 2
	Describe solution strategies for solving fraction number stories.	Number and Numeration Goal 2
	Use Fraction Cards to compare fractions.	Number and Numeration Goal 6
	Measure and draw a line segment to the nearest $\frac{1}{4}$ inch.	Measurement and Reference Frames Goal 1

*See the Appendix for a complete list of Grade 3 Goals.

A Balanced Curriculum

Ongoing Practice

Everyday Mathematics provides numerous opportunities for ongoing practice. These activities are embedded throughout the lessons:

Mental Math and Reflexes activities promote speed and accuracy in mental computation.

Math Boxes offer mixed practice and are paired across lessons as shown in the brackets below. This makes them useful as assessment tools. The last one or two boxes on each page preview the next unit's content.

Mixed practice	[8•1, 8•3], [8•2, 8•4], [8•5, 8•7], [8•6, 8•8]
Mixed practice with multiple choice	8•1, 8•2, 8•5, 8•6
Mixed practice with writing/reasoning opportunity	8•2, 8•3, 8•4, 8•7, 8•8

Home Links are daily homework assignments that review the content of the lesson and often contain ongoing facts practice or computation practice.

Minute Math+ problems are offered for additional practice in Lessons 8•3 and 8•8.

EM Facts Workshop Game provides online practice of basic facts and computation.

EXTRA PRACTICE **Extra Practice** activities are included in Lessons 8•2, 8•3, 8•7, and 8•8.

Practice through Games

Games are an essential component of practice in the *Everyday Mathematics* program. Games offer skills practice and promote strategic thinking. See the *Differentiation Handbook* for ways to adapt games to meet children's needs.

Lesson	Game	Skill Practiced
8•2, 8•5	*The Block-Drawing Game*	**Practicing making predictions** [DC Goal 4]
8•3	*Multiplication Bingo*	**Practicing multiplication facts** [OC Goal 3]
8•5, 8•7	*Equivalent Fractions Game*	**Finding equivalent fractions** [NN Goals 2 and 5]
8•6, 8•7	*Fraction Top-It*	**Comparing fractions** [NN Goals 2 and 6]

[NN] Number and Numeration
[MRF] Measurement and Reference Frames
[OC] Operations and Computation
[GEO] Geometry
[DC] Data and Chance
[PFA] Patterns, Functions, and Algebra

Problem Solving

PROBLEM SOLVING

Good problem solvers use a variety of strategies, including the following:

- Draw a picture.
- Act out the problem.
- Make a table, chart, or list.
- Look for a pattern.
- Try a simpler version of the problem.
- Make a guess and try it out.

The table below lists some of the opportunities in this unit for children to practice these strategies.

Lessons that teach *through* problem solving, not just *about* problem solving

Lesson	Activity
8•1	Use fractions to name parts of regions and sets.
8•2	Solve problems involving chance outcomes.
8•3	Find fractional parts with pattern blocks.
8•3	Make one large square from smaller squares.
8•3	Find different combinations of pants and socks.
8•4	Solve Frames-and-Arrows problems.
8•5	Investigate equivalent fractions.
8•8	Solve number stories involving fractions.

See Chapter 18: Problem Solving in the *Teacher's Reference Manual* for more information.

The Language of Mathematics

Everyday Mathematics provides lesson-specific suggestions to help all children acquire, process, and express mathematical ideas. Throughout Unit 8, there are lesson-specific language development notes that address the needs of English language learners, indicated by ELL.

ELL SUPPORT Activities to support English language learners are in Part 3 of Lessons 8•1, 8•2, 8•5, and 8•7.

The *English Learners Handbook* and the *Differentiation Handbook* have suggestions for promoting language development and acquisition of mathematics vocabulary. See Unit 8 in each handbook.

Unit 8 Vocabulary

denominator
equal
equivalent fractions
mixed number
numerator
random draw
unit fraction
whole (the ONE)

Literacy Connection

Apple Fractions, by Jerry Pallotta, Cartwheel, 2003

Lesson 8•3 *Grandfather Tang's Story,* by Ann Tompert, Dragonfly Books, 1997

Ed Emberley's Picture Pie: A Cut and Paste Drawing Book, by Ed Emberley, Little, Brown, 2006

Pizza Counting, by Christina Dobson, Charlesbridge, 2003

Fraction Fun, by David Adler, Holiday House Inc., 1997

Lesson 8•8 *Math Curse,* by Jon Scieszka and Lane Smith, Viking, 1995

Give Me Half!, by Stuart J. Murphy, Steck-Vaughn, 1999

Do You Wanna Bet?, by Jean Cushman, Houghton Mifflin, 2007

For more literacy connections, see the *Home Connection Handbook,* Grades 1–3.

Balanced Assessment

Daily Assessments

- **Recognizing Student Achievement** – A daily assessment that is included in every lesson to evaluate children's progress toward the Grade 3 Grade-Level Goals.
- **Informing Instruction** – Notes that appear throughout the unit to help anticipate children's common errors and suggest appropriate problem-solving strategies.

Lesson	Recognizing Student Achievement	Informing Instruction
8•1	Identify and write fractions that name regions. [NN Goal 2]	Distinguish between numerator and denominator. Act out fraction number stories.
8•2	Apply basic probability terms to describe single events. [DC Goal 3]	
8•3	Understand that parentheses affect the order of operations. [PFA Goal 3]	
8•4	Identify the value of digits in numbers through hundred thousands. [NN Goal 1]	Use the number line to determine fractions.
8•5	Make and test predictions for simple experiments. [DC Goal 4]	
8•6	Describe relationships between equivalent units of time. [MRF Goal 3]	
8•7	Use Fraction Cards to find equivalent fractions. [NN Goal 5]	Write mixed numbers.
8•8	Solve problems involving fractional parts of a collection. [NN Goal 2]	Solve problems with fractions of sets.

[NN] Number and Numeration
[MRF] Measurement and Reference Frames
[OC] Operations and Computation
[GEO] Geometry
[DC] Data and Chance
[PFA] Patterns, Functions, and Algebra

Portfolio Opportunities

Portfolio Ideas

The following lessons provide opportunities to gather samples of children's mathematical writings, drawings, and creations to add balance to the assessment process: Lessons 8•2, 8•3, 8•4, 8•5, 8•7, 8•8, and 8•9.

See pages 16 and 17 in the *Assessment Handbook* for more information about portfolios and how to use them.

Unit Assessment

Progress Check 8 – A cumulative assessment of concepts and skills taught in Unit 8 and in previous units, providing information for evaluating children's progress and planning for future instruction. These assessments include oral/slate, written, and open-response activities, as shown below in the sample Progress Check lesson opener.

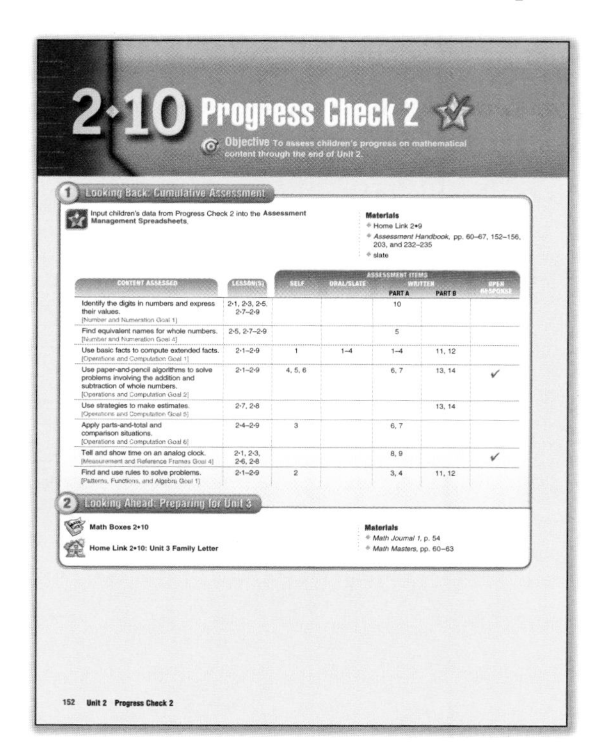

2·10 Progress Check 2

Objective To assess children's progress on mathematical content through the end of Unit 2.

1 Looking Back: Cumulative Assessment

Input children's data from Progress Check 2 into the **Assessment Management Spreadsheets.**

Materials
- Home Link 2•9
- *Assessment Handbook,* pp. 60–67, 152–156, 203, and 232–235
- slate

Content Assessed	Lesson(s)	Assessment Items: Self	Oral/Slate	Written: Part A	Written: Part B	Open Response
Identify the digits in numbers and express their values. [Number and Numeration Goal 1]	2·1, 2·3, 2·5, 2·7–2·9			10		
Find equivalent names for whole numbers. [Number and Numeration Goal 4]	2·5, 2·7–2·9			5		
Use basic facts to compute extended facts. [Operations and Computation Goal 1]	2·1–2·9	1	1–4	1–4	11, 12	
Use paper-and-pencil algorithms to solve problems involving the addition and subtraction of whole numbers. [Operations and Computation Goal 2]	2·1–2·9	4, 5, 6		6, 7	13, 14	✓
Use strategies to make estimates. [Operations and Computation Goal 5]	2·7, 2·8				13, 14	
Apply parts-and-total and comparison situations. [Operations and Computation Goal 6]	2·4–2·9	3		6, 7		
Tell and show time on an analog clock. [Measurement and Reference Frames Goal 4]	2·1, 2·3, 2·6, 2·8			8, 9		✓
Find and use rules to solve problems. [Patterns, Functions, and Algebra Goal 1]	2·1–2·9	2		3, 4	11, 12	

2 Looking Ahead: Preparing for Unit 3

Math Boxes 2•10

Home Link 2•10: Unit 3 Family Letter

Materials
- *Math Journal 1,* p. 54
- *Math Masters,* pp. 60–63

152 Unit 2 Progress Check 2

Core Assessment Resources

Assessment Handbook

- **Unit 8 Assessment Overview,** pages 110–117
- **Unit 8 Assessment Masters,** pages 182–186
- **Unit 8 Individual Profiles of Progress,** pages 256, 257, and 280
- **Unit 8 Class Checklists,** pages 258, 259, and 281
- **Math Logs,** pages 286–288
- **Exit Slip,** page 283
- **Other Student Assessment Forms,** pages 284, 285, 289, and 290

Assessment Management Spreadsheets

The Assessment Management Spreadsheets consist of the Digital Class Checklists and Individual Profile of Progress Checklists. Use them to monitor, record, and report children's progress.

Addressing All Needs

Differentiated Instruction

Adjusting the Activity – suggests adaptations that target advanced learners, English language learners, or learners who need additional instructional support.

ELL SUPPORT / ELL – provides lesson-specific suggestions to help English language learners understand and process the mathematical content.

READINESS – accesses children's prior knowledge or previews content that prepares children to engage in the lesson's Part 1 activities.

EXTRA PRACTICE – provides additional opportunities to apply the mathematical content of the lesson.

ENRICHMENT – enables children to apply or further explore the mathematical content of the lesson.

Lesson	Adjusting the Activity	ELL Support/ ELL	Readiness	Extra Practice	Enrichment
8•1	•	•	•		•
8•2	•	•	•	•	
8•3		•	•	•	•
8•4	•		•		•
8•5	•	•	•		•
8•6	•		•		•
8•7	•	•	•	•	•
8•8	•			•	•

Additional Resources

Differentiation Handbook
Provides ideas and strategies for differentiating instruction.
Pages 97–103

English Learners Handbook
Contains lesson-specific comprehension strategies.
Pages 75–82

Multilingual Handbook
Previews concepts and vocabulary. It is written in six languages.
Pages 149–164

Planning Tips

Multiage Classroom

Companion Lessons from Grades 2 and 4 can help you meet instructional needs of a multiage classroom. The full Scope and Sequence can be found in the Appendix.

Grade 2	8•1–8•3, 9•3		8•2, 10•7	9•3	8•4, 8•5	8•6, 10•7	10•7	8•7
Grade 3	**8•1**	**8•2**	**8•3**	**8•4**	**8•5**	**8•6**	**8•7**	**8•8**
Grade 4	7•1, 7•2	7•1			7•6	7•9		

Pacing for Success

Pacing depends on a number of factors, such as children's individual needs and how long your school has been using *Everyday Mathematics*. At the beginning of Unit 8, you may want to use tools available at www.everydaymathonline.com to help you set your pace.

Home Support

Unit 8 Family Letter (English/Spanish) provides families with an overview, Do-Anytime Activities, Building Skills through Games, a list of vocabulary, and answers to the daily homework (Home Links). Family Letters in English, Spanish, and seven other languages are also available online.

Home Links are the daily homework assignments. They consist of active projects and ongoing review problems.

▶ Home Support Resources

Home Connection Handbook
Offers ideas and reproducible masters for communicating with families. See Table of Contents for unit information.

Student Reference Book
Provides a resource for children and parents.
Pages 79–81, 280, 281, 283, 284, 287, 288, 295

Technology Resources

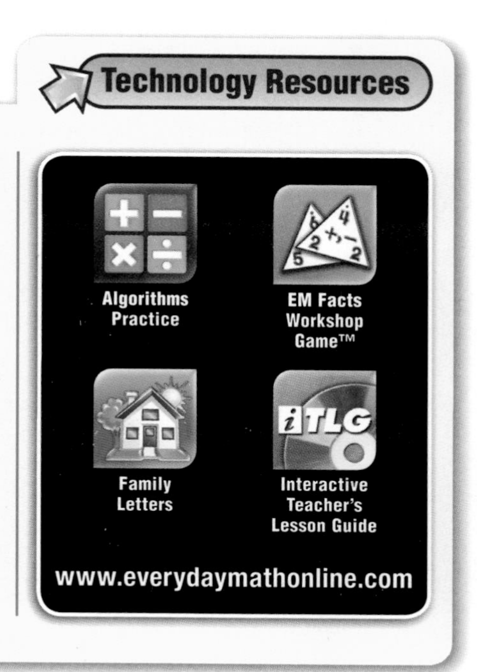

Materials

Technology Resources www.everydaymathonline.com

ePresentations

eToolkit

Algorithms Practice

EM Facts Workshop Game™

Family Letters

Assessment Management

Common Core State Standards

Curriculum Focal Points

Interactive Teacher's Lesson Guide

Lesson	Masters	Manipulative Kit	Other Items
8•1	Home Link Master, p. 237 Teaching Masters, pp. 238 and 239 *Differentiation Handbook,* p. 132	slate; ruler	25 pennies or counters; ×, ÷ Fact Triangles; centimeter cubes; straightedge*
8•2	Home Link Master, p. 240 Teaching Master, p. 241 *Differentiation Handbook,* p. 133	slate; dice	small paper bag with 5 blocks of the same size and shape in 3 different colors (2 + 2 + 1); blue crayon or colored pencil; red and blue blocks*; Class Data Pad*; paper bag with 7 blocks of the same size and shape in 2 or 3 different colors; paper
8•3	Teaching Masters, pp. 242–244 and 246 Home Link Master, p. 245 Game Master, p. 449 Teaching Aid Master, p. 435	4 each of number cards 2–9; pattern blocks; slate	scissors; tape; paper; blue, red, green, and black crayons; pennies or counters; half-sheets of paper; *Grandfather Tang's Story*; Pattern-Block Template
8•4	Teaching Masters, pp. 247 and 249–251 Home Link Master, p. 248	ruler; Class Number Line	scissors; crayons; pennies or other counters*; half-sheets of paper; tape or glue
8•5	Home Link Masters, pp. 252 and 253 Teaching Aid Master, p. 398 Teaching Masters, pp. 254 and 255 *Differentiation Handbook,* p. 132	Fraction Cards or Everything Math Deck; slate	scissors; envelopes; straightedge; paper bag with 7 blocks of the same size and shape in 2 or 3 different colors; counters; paper*; posterboard; markers
8•6	Home Link Master, p. 256 Teaching Master, p. 257	dice	Fraction Cards; 3" by 5" index cards, 3 sheets of $8\frac{1}{2}$" by 11" paper; straightedge
8•7	Teaching Aid Master, p. 436 Home Link Masters, pp. 258 and 259 Teaching Masters, pp. 260 and 261 *Differentiation Handbook,* p. 132	slate; pattern blocks	scissors; glue; crayons; Fraction Cards; half-sheets of paper; Pattern-Block Template
8•8	Home Link Master, p. 262	inch ruler; tool-kit clock*; slate	pennies or counters*; Fraction Cards*; stick-on notes; *Math Curse;* paper
8•9	Assessment Masters, pp. 182–186 Home Link Masters, pp. 263–266	slate; tool-kit clock	straightedge; Fraction Cards; counters; coins

*Denotes optional materials

Mathematical Background

The discussion below highlights the major content ideas presented in Unit 8 and helps establish instructional priorities.

Review of Fraction Concepts

(Lessons 8◆1–8◆4)

It is important to emphasize that a fraction is meaningless unless it is considered with reference to a whole—called the ONE in this program. Most of this unit focuses on fractions in real-world contexts. Children make up fraction number stories; they solve problems about collections of objects (such as books, crayons, eggs, and fruit) and about partially filled containers, elapsed time, and so on.

Fractions (and decimals) also play an important role in measurement. Measures are continuous; for example, the length of a line segment might be between 4 and 5 inches, or between $4\frac{1}{2}$ and $4\frac{3}{4}$ inches, or between $4\frac{1}{2}$ and $4\frac{5}{8}$ inches, and so on. No matter how precise a measurement is, it can always be refined—at least in theory.

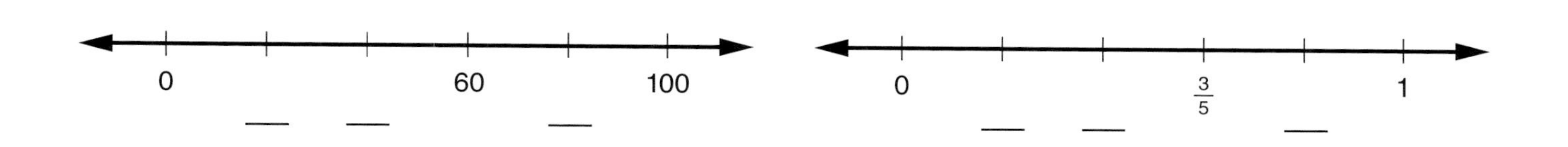

In previous units, children often worked on problems that called for them to fill in the missing whole numbers for points on a number line. (See above.) However, working with fractions is different: when the missing numbers are fractions, the denominators of the fractions must be found first. To find the denominator, children must count the intervals, not the marks, between two consecutive whole numbers on the number line. While most children realize this quickly, be alert to errors in counting intervals as you observe children at work.

For additional information about fraction concepts, see Section 9.3 of the *Teacher's Reference Manual.*

Blocks-in-a-Bag Experiment

(Lesson 8◆2)

Everyday Mathematics wants children to become aware that the more often they repeat an experiment, the more reliable their predictions will be. This important idea is illustrated by the experiment in Lesson 8-2, in which children are asked to figure out how many blocks of different colors are hidden in a bag by examining the results of repeatedly drawing a block from the bag. The more times they draw a block, the more likely it is that they will make a correct guess.

For additional information about making predictions, see Section 12.1.3 of the *Teacher's Reference Manual.*

Explorations: Fractions, Re-Forming Squares, and Combinations

(Lesson 8◆3)

Children explore fractional relationships between pattern blocks of different shapes. They also explore spatial relationships by cutting up two squares and forming one square from the pieces. They explore combinations by finding the total number of outfits that can be put together with pants of four different colors and pairs of socks of four different colors.

Equivalent Fractions (Lessons 8◆3 and 8◆5)

The emphasis in both lessons is on pictorial representations of equivalent fractions. In Lesson 8-4, children assemble number lines that are divided into various numbers of parts. By cutting and pasting, they observe that the same point can be named by more than one fraction.

In Lesson 8-4, children enlarge their lists of equivalent fractions with the help of Fraction Cards, which are shaded to represent a variety of fractions. Children match cards that have equal amounts of shading.

After children have found several equivalent fractions, they may discover that they can rename a fraction by multiplying or dividing its numerator and denominator by the same number. (Try not to bring up the rule yourself.) To ensure that children internalize the concept of equivalent fractions, it is best that they have as many experiences as possible with concrete models before they adopt more abstract, symbolic techniques.

$$\frac{1}{2} = \frac{1 \times 3}{2 \times 3} = \frac{3}{6} \qquad \frac{6}{8} = \frac{6 \div 2}{8 \div 2} = \frac{3}{4}$$

You may encounter a child who discovers that two fractions $\frac{a}{b}$ and $\frac{c}{d}$ are equivalent if the product of a and d is equal to the product of b and c. This is mentioned only for your information. It would be premature to teach the cross-multiplication rule at this time.

For additional information about equivalent fractions, see Section 9.3.1 of the *Teacher's Reference Manual.*

$\frac{3}{4}$ of a cake is equivalent to $\frac{6}{8}$ of a cake

Fractions Greater Than ONE

(Lesson 8•7)

This lesson conveys the important message that fractions can represent numbers greater than 1 (the whole, or ONE, the fraction refers to), as well as whole numbers. In addition, mixed numbers are introduced as another way to name numbers greater than 1. Children model fractions greater than 1 and equivalent mixed numbers by pasting fractional parts onto unit circles. They practice naming numbers of fractional parts with fractions and mixed numbers, and they convert between fractions and mixed numbers.

Fraction Number Stories

(Lesson 8•8 and examples throughout)

Abundant fraction number stories are provided, and children make up and solve additional stories. Children solve the problems by using counters, pictures, and so on.

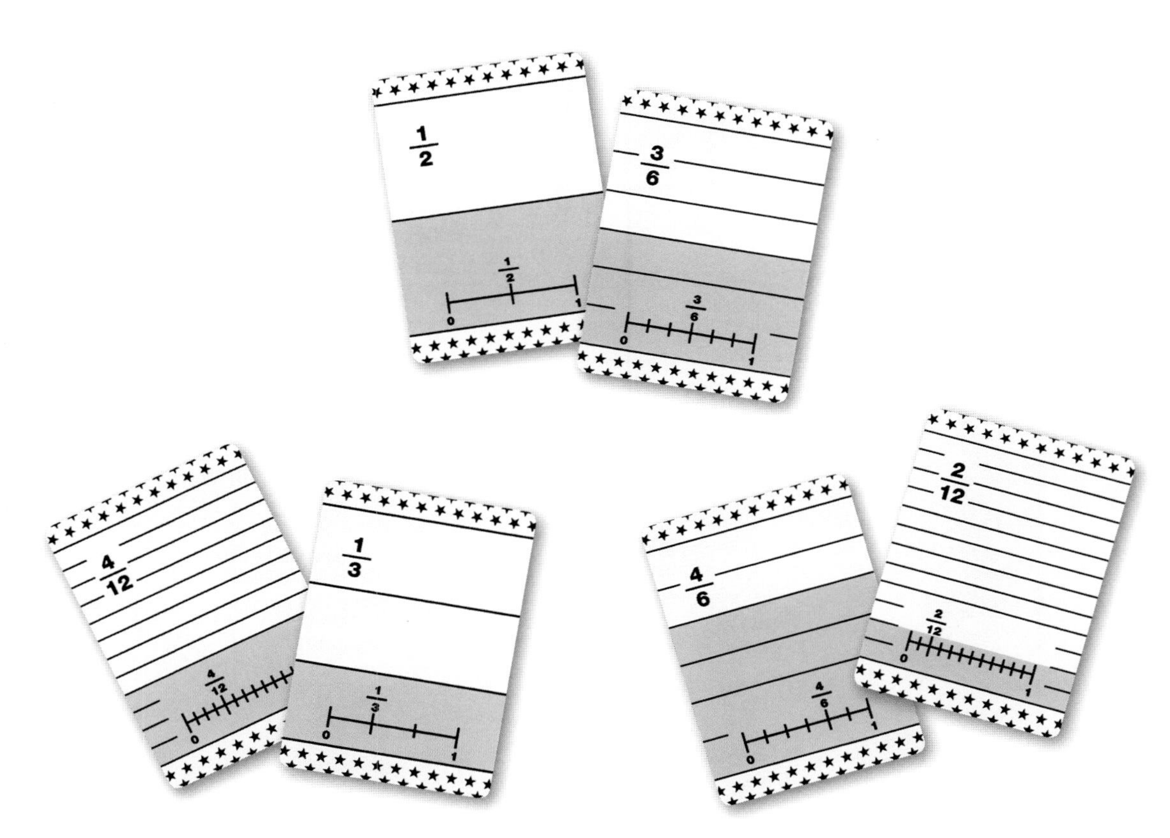

Fraction cards found in the Everything Math Deck are useful in comparing fractions and finding equivalencies.

8·1 Naming Parts with Fractions

Objective To guide children as they use fractions to name *a* of *b* equal parts.

Technology Resources www.everydaymathonline.com

ePresentations

eToolkit

Algorithms Practice

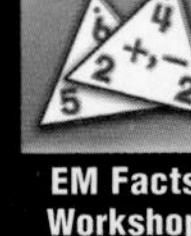
EM Facts Workshop Game™

Family Letters

Assessment Management

Common Core State Standards

Curriculum Focal Points

Interactive Teacher's Lesson Guide

1 Teaching the Lesson

Key Concepts and Skills

- Use manipulatives to solve problems involving fractional parts of collections. [Number and Numeration Goal 2]
- Identify equivalent halves and fourths of a shaded region. [Number and Numeration Goal 5]
- Use shaded regions to compare fractions. [Number and Numeration Goal 6]
- Use equal sharing to solve fractional part-of-a-collection problems. [Operations and Computation Goal 6]

Key Activities

Children review basic fraction concepts and notation. They name fractional parts of regions and sets of objects.

Ongoing Assessment: Informing Instruction See pages 650 and 651.

Ongoing Assessment: Recognizing Student Achievement Use journal page 180. [Number and Numeration Goal 2]

Key Vocabulary

equal ◆ whole (the ONE) ◆ denominator ◆ numerator ◆ unit fraction

Materials

Math Journal 2, pp. 180 and 181
slate ◆ 25 pennies or counters

2 Ongoing Learning & Practice

Practicing with Fact Triangles
×, ÷ Fact Triangles
Children practice multiplication and division facts with Fact Triangles.

Math Boxes 8·1
Math Journal 2, p. 182
Children practice and maintain skills through Math Box problems.

Home Link 8·1
Math Masters, p. 237
Children practice and maintain skills through Home Link activities.

3 Differentiation Options

READINESS
Exploring Fractions
Math Masters, p. 238
counters ◆ ruler or straightedge
Children explore the concept of a fraction of a set.

ENRICHMENT
Solving Fraction Puzzles
Math Masters, p. 239
centimeter cubes
Children solve Fraction Puzzles to create the whole when a part is given.

ELL SUPPORT
Building a Math Word Bank
Differentiation Handbook, p. 132
Children add the terms *numerator* and *denominator* to their Math Word Banks.

Advance Preparation

***Teacher's Reference Manual,* Grades 1–3** pp. 59–62

Mathematical Practices
SMP2, SMP3, **SMP4,** SMP5, SMP6
Content Standards
3.NF.1, 3.NF.3c, 3.G.2

Getting Started

Mental Math and Reflexes

Pose problems like the following. Children write their answers on slates and share their strategies. Encourage children to write number models to show their strategies.

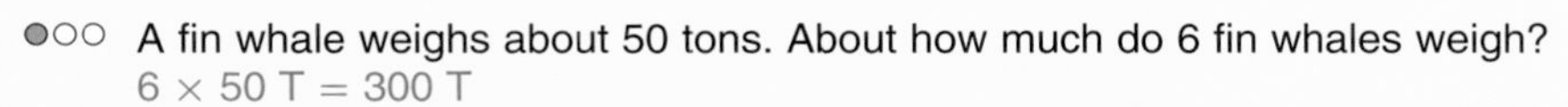

●○○ A fin whale weighs about 50 tons. About how much do 6 fin whales weigh? 6×50 T = 300 T

●●○ 1 ton = 2,000 pounds. About how much does 1 fin whale weigh in pounds? $50 \times 2{,}000$ lb = 100,000 lb

●●● A 9-year-old's heart beats about 90 times per minute. About how many times does it beat per hour? 60×90 beats = 5,400 beats About how many times does it beat in 10 hours? 54,000 beats

Math Message

Turn to page 180 in your journal. Do Problems 1–5 only.

1 Teaching the Lesson

Math Message Follow-Up

WHOLE-CLASS DISCUSSION

(*Math Journal 2,* p. 180)

Go over the answers to the Math Message problems while reviewing the use of fractions to express parts of wholes. Be sure to include the following points in the discussion:

▷ Fraction notation is one way to express **equal** parts of any whole. (Decimal notation is another way.)

▷ Fractions are not meaningful unless they refer to a part of a particular **whole (the ONE).** Throughout this unit, consistently ask children to identify the ONE in problem situations. For example, $\frac{1}{4}$ of a *large* pizza is not the same as $\frac{1}{4}$ of a *small* pizza.

▷ A fraction has two parts. The **denominator** names the number of equal parts into which the whole (the ONE) has been divided. The **numerator** names the number of those equal parts being used or considered.

$$\frac{3}{7} \begin{array}{l} \longleftarrow \text{numerator} \\ \longleftarrow \text{denominator} \end{array}$$

▷ A fraction with the same numerator and denominator names all the parts of the whole (the ONE). For example, $\frac{3}{3}$, $\frac{4}{4}$, and $\frac{5}{5}$ are all equivalent names for 1.

▷ A fraction with 1 in the numerator is called a **unit fraction.** $\frac{1}{4}$, $\frac{1}{8}$, and $\frac{1}{25}$ are examples of unit fractions.

Interactive whiteboard-ready ePresentations are available at www.everydaymathonline.com to help you teach the lesson.

NOTE To extend fraction review, have children compare the fractions in Problems 2–5, Math Journal 2, page 180.

Student Page

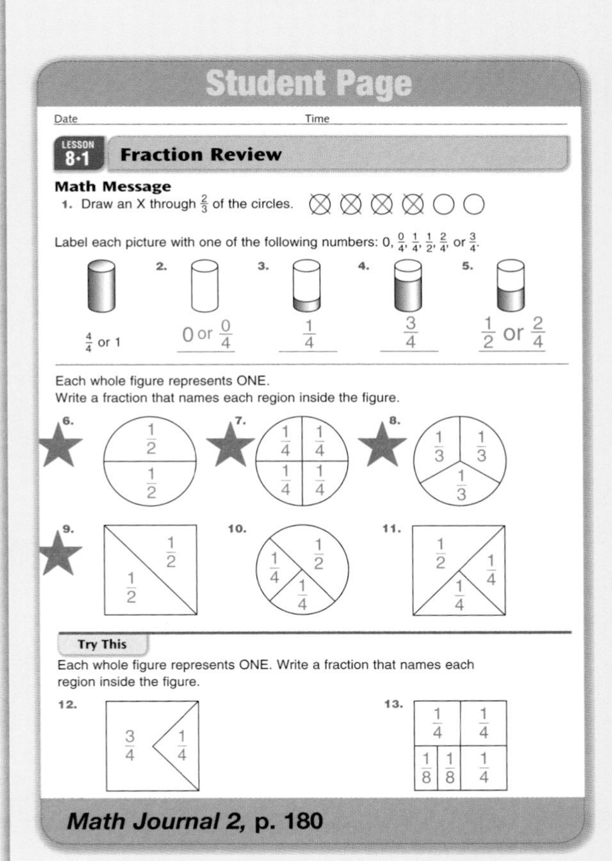

Date Time

LESSON 8•1 **Fraction Review**

Math Message

1. Draw an X through $\frac{2}{3}$ of the circles.

Label each picture with one of the following numbers: 0, $\frac{0}{4}$, $\frac{1}{4}$, $\frac{1}{2}$, $\frac{2}{4}$, or $\frac{3}{4}$.

2. 3. 4. 5.

$\frac{4}{4}$ or 1 — 0 or $\frac{0}{4}$ — $\frac{1}{4}$ — $\frac{3}{4}$ — $\frac{1}{2}$ or $\frac{2}{4}$

Each whole figure represents ONE.
Write a fraction that names each region inside the figure.

6. 7. 8. 9. 10. 11.

Try This

Each whole figure represents ONE. Write a fraction that names each region inside the figure.

12. 13.

Math Journal 2, p. 180

NOTE The numerator of a fraction can be 0; for example, $\frac{0}{1}$, $\frac{0}{2}$, and $\frac{0}{3}$ are names for no parts of the whole, or 0. The denominator of a fraction cannot be 0. Because the reason for this is beyond the grasp of most third graders, do not mention this unless someone makes up a fraction with 0 in the denominator. You might also enter a fraction such as $\frac{3}{0}$ into a calculator to see what the display shows. Some calculators will display an error message when the = key is pressed. Others will not allow 0 to be entered.

▷ Any whole number can be named as a fraction with 1 in the denominator. For example, a fraction name for 6 is $\frac{6}{1}$. The numerator 6 tells how many copies you have of the unit fraction with the denominator 1:

$$\begin{aligned}\frac{6}{1} &= 6 \times \frac{1}{1}\\ &= \frac{1}{1} + \frac{1}{1} + \frac{1}{1} + \frac{1}{1} + \frac{1}{1} + \frac{1}{1}\\ &= 1 + 1 + 1 + 1 + 1 + 1\\ &= 6\end{aligned}$$

Ongoing Assessment: Informing Instruction

Watch for children who have difficulty remembering which part of a fraction is the numerator and which part is the denominator. Explain that they might remember the *numerator* by thinking that the word has a *u* for *up* and *denominator* has a *d* for *down.*

As you continue to discuss fractions with children, emphasize the importance of equal parts and consistently ask them to identify the ONE in problem situations.

▶ Reviewing Fractions as Names for Parts of Regions

WHOLE-CLASS ACTIVITY

When a slate is divided into equal parts, each part can be expressed as a fraction. The slate's drawing surface is the ONE. Lead the class in activities such as the following:

- Divide the slate into 2 equal parts. First shade one part, and then the other. What is equal to the two halves? The whole slate, or the ONE How would you write this as a fraction? $\frac{2}{2}$
- Divide the slate into 3 equal parts. What fraction of the slate is each part? $\frac{1}{3}$ of the slate Divide it into 6 equal parts. What is each part called? $\frac{1}{6}$ of the slate Share your strategies for dividing the slate to show 6 equal parts. Use one line to divide the thirds in half. Or add three more parts by dividing each third with a line.
- Divide the slate into 4 equal parts. Shade 3 of the 4 parts. What fractional part of the slate have you shaded? $\frac{3}{4}$ of the slate What fractional part is not shaded? $\frac{1}{4}$ of the slate
- Which is larger, $\frac{1}{2}$ or $\frac{1}{4}$ of the slate? $\frac{1}{2}$ Why? With the fraction $\frac{1}{2}$, the slate is divided into fewer equal parts so each of those parts is larger. Which is smaller, $\frac{1}{2}$ or $\frac{2}{4}$? Neither; they're equal. Why? The same amount is shaded.
- Divide the slate into 6 equal parts. Shade 0 sixths. How much of the slate is shaded? Nothing is shaded. How would you write that as a fraction? $\frac{0}{6}$

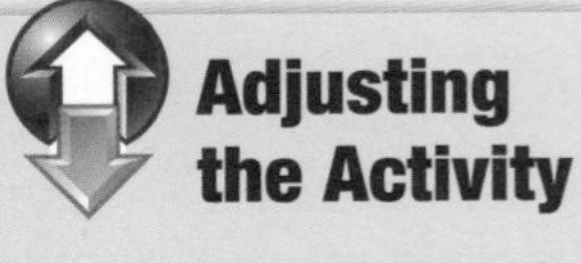

Adjusting the Activity

ELL

Have one child divide a slate in half and shade one half, and another child divide another slate into 4 equal parts and shade 2 fourths. Then compare the shaded parts. Explain that $\frac{1}{2}$ and $\frac{2}{4}$ are equivalent fractions.

AUDITORY ◆ KINESTHETIC ◆ TACTILE ◆ VISUAL

▶ Reviewing Fractions as Names for Parts of Sets

Ask 5 children to lend their journals to make a set of books. Show the pile of 5 books. The 5 books are the whole set, or the ONE. To support English language learners, discuss the meaning of the word *set* in this context. Hold up several books, and ask children to name the fractional part of the set.

Ask: *What fractional part of the set is 1 book?* $\frac{1}{5}$ *3 books?* $\frac{3}{5}$ *No books?* $\frac{0}{5}$ *5 books?* $\frac{5}{5}$, the whole set, or the ONE

Name a fractional part, and ask children to tell you how many books to hold up.

Ask: *How many books are* $\frac{2}{5}$ *of the set?* 2 books $\frac{4}{5}$ *of the set?* 4 books

Repeat with a set of 9 books.

Ask: *How many books are in* $\frac{8}{9}$ *of the set?* 8 books *How many books are* $\frac{1}{3}$ *of the books?* 3 books *What fractional part are 6 of the books?* $\frac{6}{9}$ or $\frac{2}{3}$

Continue with similar questions.

Adjusting the Activity

ELL

Ask children how many books each child would get if 3 children were to share the 9 books equally. 3 books Each share is $\frac{1}{3}$ of the set. Ask: *How many total books would 2 of the children get?* 6 books *What fraction of books do the 2 children get?* $\frac{2}{3}$ of the set Have children model this and other situations using counters.

AUDITORY ◆ KINESTHETIC ◆ TACTILE ◆ VISUAL

Say that you have a case of juice boxes. Five juice boxes are $\frac{1}{2}$ of the case. Ask: *How many juice boxes are in the whole case?* 10 juice boxes

Say that 4 apples are $\frac{1}{4}$ of a bag. *How many apples are in the whole bag?* 16 apples

Say that 8 girls are $\frac{2}{3}$ of a group. *How many children are in the group?* 12 children

Say that the set is $1.00 or 100 cents. *What fraction of $1.00 is 50 cents?* $\frac{50}{100}$ of a dollar *What is another way to write* $\frac{50}{100}$ *of a dollar?* $\frac{1}{2}$ of a dollar *What fraction of $1.00 is 25 cents?* $\frac{25}{100}$ of a dollar *What is another way to write* $\frac{25}{100}$ *of a dollar?* $\frac{1}{4}$ of a dollar *What fraction of $1.00 is 75 cents?* $\frac{75}{100}$ of a dollar *What is another way to write* $\frac{75}{100}$ *of a dollar?* $\frac{3}{4}$ of a dollar

Continue with similar questions.

Student Page

Date Time

LESSON 8·1 Fraction Review *continued*

You need at least 25 pennies or other counters to help you solve these problems. Share solution strategies with others in your group.

Unit: counters

14. a. Show $\frac{1}{4}$ of a set of 8 counters. How many counters is that? 2
    b. Show $\frac{2}{4}$ of the set. How many counters? 4
    c. Show $\frac{3}{4}$ of the set. How many counters? 6
15. a. Show $\frac{1}{3}$ of a set of 12 counters. How many counters is that? 4
    b. Show $\frac{2}{3}$ of the set. How many counters? 8
    c. Show $\frac{3}{3}$ of the set. How many counters? 12
16. a. Show $\frac{1}{5}$ of a set of 15 counters. How many counters is that? 3
    b. Show $\frac{4}{5}$ of the set. How many counters? 12
17. Show $\frac{3}{4}$ of a set of 20 counters. How many counters? 15
18. Show $\frac{2}{3}$ of a set of 18 counters. How many counters? 12
19. Five counters is $\frac{1}{5}$ of a set. How many counters are in the whole set? 25
20. Six counters is $\frac{1}{3}$ of a set. How many counters are in the whole set? 18

Try This

21. Twelve counters is $\frac{3}{4}$ of a set. How many counters are in the complete set? 16 counters
22. Pretend that you have a set of 15 cheese cubes. What is $\frac{1}{2}$ of that set? Use a fraction or decimal in your answer. $7\frac{1}{2}$ or 7.5 cheese cubes

Math Journal 2, p. 181

Ongoing Assessment: Informing Instruction

Watch for children who are having difficulty solving the fractional part-of-a-set number stories. Have them divide their slates and act out the problems. For example, to show $\frac{3}{4}$ of a set of 20 counters, have children divide their slates into 4 sections. They distribute the 20 counters equally among the sections and then count to find the total in 3 of the 4 sections.

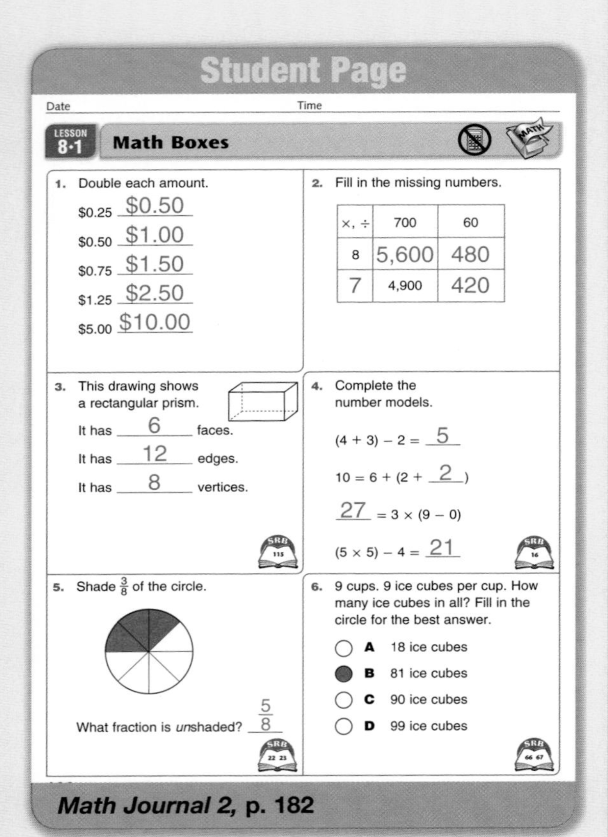
Student Page

Date Time

LESSON 8•1 **Math Boxes**

1. Double each amount.
$0.25 $0.50
$0.50 $1.00
$0.75 $1.50
$1.25 $2.50
$5.00 $10.00

2. Fill in the missing numbers.

×, ÷	700	60
8	5,600	480
7	4,900	420

3. This drawing shows a rectangular prism.
It has 6 faces.
It has 12 edges.
It has 8 vertices.

4. Complete the number models.
(4 + 3) – 2 = 5
10 = 6 + (2 + 2)
27 = 3 × (9 – 0)
(5 × 5) – 4 = 21

5. Shade $\frac{3}{8}$ of the circle.
What fraction is *un*shaded? $\frac{5}{8}$

6. 9 cups. 9 ice cubes per cup. How many ice cubes in all? Fill in the circle for the best answer.
A 18 ice cubes
B 81 ice cubes
C 90 ice cubes
D 99 ice cubes

Math Journal 2, p. 182

▶ Using Fractions to Name Parts of Regions and Sets

INDEPENDENT ACTIVITY

PROBLEM SOLVING

(*Math Journal 2,* pp. 180 and 181)

Children work alone or with a partner to complete the journal pages. They can use counters to help solve problems involving fractional parts of sets. Bring the class together to discuss children's solutions.

Ongoing Assessment: Recognizing Student Achievement

Journal Page 180 Problems 6–9

Use **journal page 180, Problems 6–9** to assess children's ability to identify and write fractions that name regions. Children are making adequate progress if they are able to successfully complete Problems 6–9. Some children may be able to complete problems 10 and 11.

[Number and Numeration Goal 2]

2 Ongoing Learning & Practice

▶ Practicing with Fact Triangles

PARTNER ACTIVITY

Partners practice basic facts by flashing ×, ÷ Fact Triangles. Children can keep track of the facts they miss so they can focus on those facts during a second round.

▶ Math Boxes 8•1

(*Math Journal 2,* p. 182)

Mixed Practice Math Boxes in this lesson are paired with Math Boxes in Lesson 8-3. The skill in Problem 6 previews Unit 9 content.

▶ Home Link 8•1

(*Math Masters,* p. 237)

Home Connection Children use fractions to name parts of objects and sets. They are asked to bring in items with fractions or decimals printed on them for the Fractions Museum.

Home Link Master

Name Date Time

HOME LINK 8•1 **Fractions All Around**

Family Note Help your child understand the idea of the ONE as well as fractions of objects and sets. Help your child look for objects and pictures that have fractions or decimals printed on them.
Please return this Home Link to school tomorrow.

Each square flag below represents the ONE. Write the fractions that name each region inside each flag.

1. $\frac{1}{2}$ $\frac{1}{2}$
2. $\frac{1}{4}$ $\frac{1}{4}$ $\frac{1}{4}$ $\frac{1}{4}$
3. $\frac{1}{4}$ $\frac{3}{4}$

Write the fractions.

4. $\frac{5}{7}$ of the buttons have 4 holes.
5. $\frac{2}{7}$ of the buttons have 2 holes.

Look for items around your home that have fractions or decimals on them, such as recipes, measuring cups, wrenches, package labels, or pictures in newspapers. Ask permission to bring them to school to display in our Fractions Museum.

Practice

Unit

Solve. Show your work.

6. 275 – 88 = 187
7. 684 – 97 = 587
8. 429 – 237 = 192

Math Masters, p. 237

3 Differentiation Options

READINESS

PARTNER ACTIVITY

▶ Exploring Fractions

5–15 Min

(*Math Masters,* p. 238)

To explore the concept of a fraction of a collection, have children solve the fraction problems on *Math Masters,* page 238. When children have finished the page, have them discuss how they can find $\frac{1}{4}$ of any number. Sample answer: I can divide the number into four equal piles or the area into 4 equal parts. Each pile or part is $\frac{1}{4}$.

ENRICHMENT

PARTNER ACTIVITY

▶ Solving Fraction Puzzles

5–15 Min

(*Math Masters,* p. 239)

To apply children's understanding of fractions as parts of wholes, have them solve Fraction Puzzles on *Math Masters,* page 239.

ELL SUPPORT

PARTNER ACTIVITY

▶ Building a Math Word Bank

5–15 Min

(*Differentiation Handbook,* p. 132)

To provide language support for fractions, have children use the Word Bank template found on *Differentiation Handbook,* page 132. Ask children to write the terms *numerator* and *denominator,* draw a picture representing each term, and write other related words. See the *Differentiation Handbook* for more information.

Teaching Master

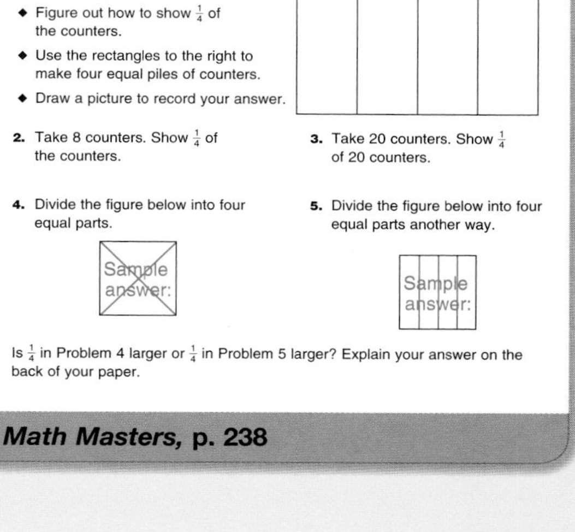

Name Date Time

LESSON 8•1 **Exploring Fractions**

These show $\frac{1}{4}$.	These do **NOT** show $\frac{1}{4}$.

1. Explain how you can tell whether something shows $\frac{1}{4}$.
Sample answer: If something has four equal parts and one part is represented, then that shows $\frac{1}{4}$.

For Problems 2 and 3—
- Take the number of counters.
- Figure out how to show $\frac{1}{4}$ of the counters.
- Use the rectangles to the right to make four equal piles of counters.
- Draw a picture to record your answer.

2. Take 8 counters. Show $\frac{1}{4}$ of the counters.
3. Take 20 counters. Show $\frac{1}{4}$ of 20 counters.
4. Divide the figure below into four equal parts.
Sample answer:
5. Divide the figure below into four equal parts another way.
Sample answer:

Is $\frac{1}{4}$ in Problem 4 larger or $\frac{1}{4}$ in Problem 5 larger? Explain your answer on the back of your paper.

***Math Masters,* p. 238**

NOTE Remind children to continue to record the sunrise, sunset, and length of day in their journals on pages 279–281. They will also continue to record the national high and low temperatures on journal page 175 and then graph the temperature ranges on journal pages 176 and 177.

Teaching Master

Name Date Time

LESSON 8•1 **Fraction Puzzles**

Use centimeter cubes to help you solve the puzzles.

1. The 1st graders are building a little house with centimeter cubes. The drawing shows $\frac{2}{3}$ of the floor of their house. Use centimeter cubes to build the whole floor of the house. Then finish the picture.
Sample answer:

2. This drawing shows $\frac{7}{10}$ of a line segment. Use centimeter cubes to figure out how long the line segment is. Figure out how much longer the line segment should be to make it whole. Use a ruler to draw the rest of the whole line segment.

3. Make up a puzzle. Ask a partner to solve it. Answers vary.
This drawing shows $\frac{\square}{\square}$ of a __________.

Draw the whole __________.

***Math Masters,* p. 239**

8·2 Blocks-in-a-Bag Experiment

Objectives To guide children as they make predictions based on outcomes and construct situations that meet given conditions.

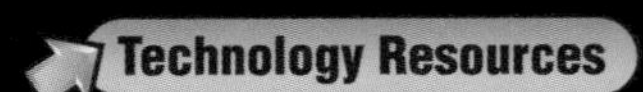

www.everydaymathonline.com

ePresentations

eToolkit

Algorithms Practice

EM Facts Workshop Game™

Family Letters

Assessment Management

Common Core State Standards

Curriculum Focal Points

Interactive Teacher's Lesson Guide

1 Teaching the Lesson

Key Concepts and Skills

- Describe results of a random-draw experiment using basic probability terms. [Data and Chance Goal 3]
- Make predictions from the results of a random-draw experiment. [Data and Chance Goal 4]
- Test predictions using manipulatives. [Data and Chance Goal 4]

Key Activities

Children predict how many blocks of each color are in a bag based on repeated drawings from the bag. They decide how many colored blocks to place in a bag to meet given probability conditions.

Ongoing Assessment: Recognizing Student Achievement
Use journal page 183.
[Data and Chance Goal 3]

Key Vocabulary

random draw

Materials

Math Journal 2, p. 183
Home Link 8•1
small paper bag with 5 blocks of the same size and shape in 3 different colors (2 of one color, 2 of a second color, and 1 of a third color) ◆ slate ◆ blue crayon or colored pencil ◆ red and blue blocks (optional) ◆ Class Data Pad (optional)

2 Ongoing Learning & Practice

Playing *The Block-Drawing Game*
Student Reference Book, pp. 280 and 281
per group: paper bag with 7 blocks of the same size and shape in 2 or 3 different colors, slate or paper
Children collect data to make predictions.

Math Boxes 8·2
Math Journal 2, p. 184
Children practice and maintain skills through Math Box problems.

Home Link 8·2
Math Masters, p. 240
Children practice and maintain skills through Home Link activities.

3 Differentiation Options

READINESS

Exploring Dice Data
Math Masters, p. 241
2 six-sided dice
Children make and test predictions.

EXTRA PRACTICE

Finding Even Combinations
per partnership: paper, 2 dice
Children list all the possible combinations of rolling an even sum with 2 dice.

ELL SUPPORT

Building a Math Word Bank
Differentiation Handbook, p. 133
Children add the terms *possible outcomes, equally likely outcomes,* and *random* to their Math Word Banks.

Advance Preparation

Set up a Fractions Museum display. Draw a chart (such as the one on page 656) on the board or Class Data Pad to record the results from each random-draw experiment.

***Teacher's Reference Manual,* Grades 1–3** pp. 116–119

Getting Started

Mathematical Practices
SMP1, SMP2, SMP3, **SMP4,** SMP5, SMP6, **SMP8**

Mental Math and Reflexes

Children solve multiplication and division number stories. Allow time for children to discuss their strategies.

Suggestions:

●○○ There are 9 bags of candy with 3 pieces in each bag. How many pieces in all? 27 pieces

●●○ Liz and her 3 friends go to the game arcade. Game tokens are sold in sets of 10. How many sets must they buy in order to share the tokens equally with none left over? If they buy 2 sets, they will get 5 tokens each; 4 sets, 10 tokens each; and so on.

●●● 68 pennies are shared equally by 8 children. How many pennies per child? 8 pennies per child with 4 left over

Math Message

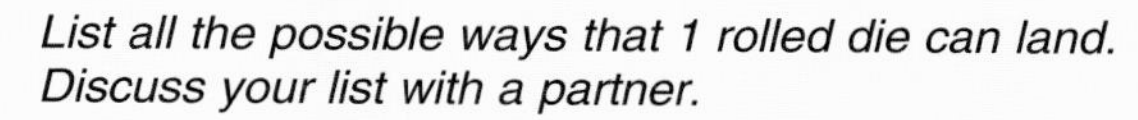

List all the possible ways that 1 rolled die can land. Discuss your list with a partner.

Home Link 8•1 Follow-Up

Discuss the use of fractions for the figures. For Problem 3, imagine the square separated into equal parts that are the *same size* as the smaller part shown.

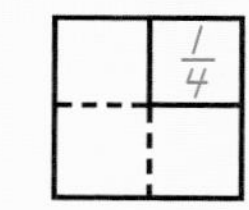

The fraction names equal-size parts.

Add items brought in by children to the Fractions Museum. Encourage children to keep adding to the Fractions Museum.

1 Teaching the Lesson

▶ Math Message Follow-Up

A rolled die has 6 equally likely outcomes: 1, 2, 3, 4, 5, or 6. There is a 1-out-of-6 chance that the die will land with any given face on top.

▶ Making Predictions in a Random-Draw Experiment

Secretly put 5 blocks in a paper bag: 2 of one color, 2 of a second color, and 1 of a third color. The blocks must be the same size and shape. (Do not use pattern blocks.)

Show the bag to the class and tell children that there are 5 colored blocks in the bag. Explain that they will collect data to make predictions. Ask the class to form a single line. One at a time, the first 10 children in line take part in the following routine:

1. Mix the blocks by shaking the bag. (You may want to assign this task to one of the children.)
2. The first child in line draws a block from the bag. Explain that each draw is a **random draw** because all the blocks in the bag have the same chance of being selected. To support English language learners, clarify the meaning of the word *draw* in this case.
3. Record the color of the block in the chart you have drawn on the board or the Class Data Pad. (*See* Advance Preparation.)
4. The child puts the block back into the bag and goes to the back of the line.

Student Page

Date Time

LESSON 8·2 **Drawing Blocks**

Color the blocks in the bags blue. Then fill in the blanks by answering this question: How many red blocks would you put into each bag?

1. If I wanted to be sure of taking out a blue block, I would put in 0 red block(s).
2. If I wanted to have an equal chance of taking out red or blue, I would put in 1 red block(s).
3. If I wanted to be more likely to take out blue than red, I would put in 1 red block(s).
4. If I wanted to take out a red block about 3 times as often as a blue one, I would put in 3 red block(s).
5. If I wanted to take out a red block about half as often as a blue one, I would put in 1 red block(s).
6. If I wanted to take out a red block about $\frac{1}{3}$ of the time, I would put in 1 red block(s).

Try This

7. If I wanted to take out a red block about $\frac{2}{3}$ of the time, I would put in 4 red block(s).

Math Journal 2, **p. 183**

NOTE Children should become aware that the more they repeat an experiment, the more reliable their predictions will be. This important idea is illustrated by the block-drawing experiment. The more times children draw a block, the more likely it is that they will make the correct guess.

Student Page

Games

The Block-Drawing Game

Materials □ 1 paper bag
□ 7 blocks (all the same size and shape) in 2 or 3 different colors

Players 3 or more

Skill Using chance data to estimate

Object of the game To correctly guess how many blocks of each color are in a bag.

Directions

1. Choose one player to be the "Director."
2. The Director secretly puts 3, 4, or 5 blocks (not all the same color) into a paper bag. The Director tells the other players *how many blocks* are in the bag, *but not their colors.*
3. Players take turns taking 1 block out of the bag, showing it, and replacing it.
4. After each draw, the Director records the color and keeps a tally on a slate or piece of paper.
5. A player may try to guess the colors of the blocks and the number of blocks of each color at any time.
6. If a player guesses incorrectly, that player is out of the game.
7. The first player to guess correctly wins the game.

SRB 280 two hundred eighty

Student Reference Book, **p. 280**

After following Steps 1–4, ask children to identify the colors of the 5 blocks. Then ask them to guess how many blocks of each color are in the bag, and record their guesses on their slates. Write some of the children's guesses on the board. Ask each child to vote for one of the guesses. Record the results of the vote.

Draws	Round Totals	Cumulative Totals
1st 10 draws: BRRBGBBRBB	6B, 3R, 1G	6B, 3R, 1G
2nd 10 draws: RGBRBBRRRR	3B, 6R, 1G	9B, 9R, 2G
3rd 10 draws: RRRBGGRGRB	2B, 5R, 3G	11B, 14R, 5G

Sample results for a bag with 2 blue blocks, 2 red blocks, and 1 green block

Repeat this routine with the next 10 children in line. Record the outcome of each draw, adding to the record of the first 10 draws. Again, ask children for their guesses and hold a vote for the best guess.

Repeat this routine until each child has had one or two turns. Discuss the predictions. Ask children how they decided how many blocks of each color were in the bag and whether they changed their mind as more blocks were drawn. Then show the blocks one at a time to check the predictions.

Adjusting the Activity

Repeat this activity with a different number of blocks and a different combination of colors.

AUDITORY ♦ KINESTHETIC ♦ TACTILE ♦ VISUAL

▶ Solving Problems Involving Chance Outcomes

INDEPENDENT ACTIVITY

(*Math Journal 2,* p. 183)

Children color the blocks blue on journal page 183, and then decide how many red blocks are necessary to meet given probability conditions. Children can model the problems with actual blocks. Encourage them to think of the problems as *fractions of sets.* For example, for a red block to be taken out about $\frac{1}{3}$ of the time, $\frac{1}{3}$ of the blocks would be red.

Ongoing Assessment: Recognizing Student Achievement

Journal Page 183 Problems 1–3

Use **journal page 183, Problems 1–3** to assess children's ability to apply basic probability terms to describe single events. Children are making adequate progress if they are able to complete Problems 1–3 correctly. Some children may complete the remaining problems correctly.

[Data and Chance Goal 3]

2 Ongoing Learning & Practice

▶ Playing *The Block-Drawing Game*

(*Student Reference Book,* pp. 280 and 281)

This game is an extension of the block-drawing activity described in Part 1. Read the directions with the children in their *Student Reference Books* on pages 280 and 281.

▶ Math Boxes 8·2

(*Math Journal 2,* p. 184)

Mixed Practice Math Boxes in this lesson are paired with Math Boxes in Lesson 8-4. The skill in Problem 6 previews Unit 9 content.

Writing/Reasoning Have children write an answer to the following: *For Problem 1, write a subtraction number model to show the fraction of the books that are not shaded.* $\frac{7}{7} - \frac{3}{7} = \frac{4}{7}$ *Explain your answer.* Sample answer: The 7 books are the whole set or the ONE. 3 out of 7 or $\frac{3}{7}$ of the books are shaded and 4 out of 7 or $\frac{4}{7}$ of the books are not shaded. *Write a subtraction number model to show the fraction of the books that are shaded.* $\frac{7}{7} - \frac{4}{7} = \frac{3}{7}$ *Explain your answer.* Sample answer: The 7 books are the ONE. If $\frac{4}{7}$ of the books are not shaded and the rest are shaded, then $\frac{3}{7}$ of the books are shaded.

▶ Home Link 8·2

(*Math Masters,* p. 240)

Home Connection Children decide how many red blocks should be put into bags to meet given probability conditions.

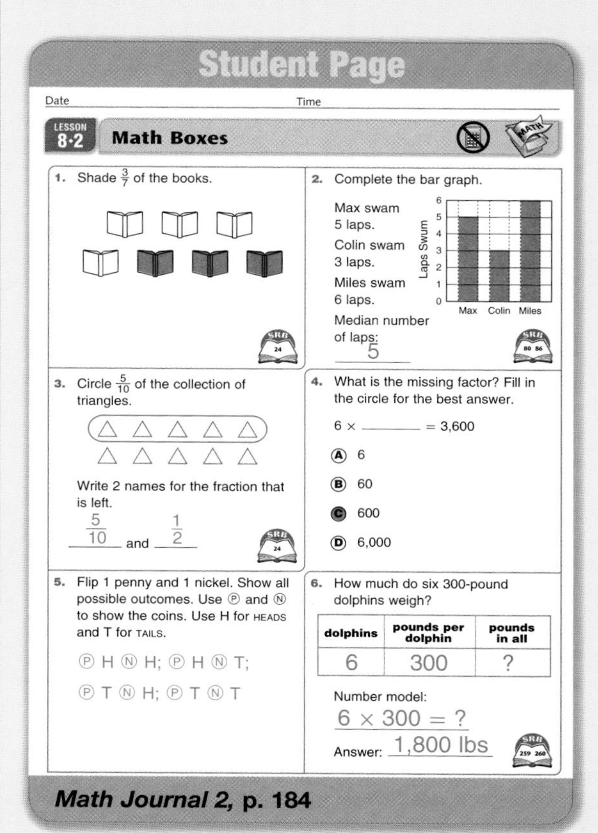

Student Page

Date Time

LESSON 8·2 **Math Boxes**

1. Shade $\frac{3}{7}$ of the books.

2. Complete the bar graph.
Max swam 5 laps.
Colin swam 3 laps.
Miles swam 6 laps.
Median number of laps: 5

3. Circle $\frac{5}{10}$ of the collection of triangles.
Write 2 names for the fraction that is left.
$\frac{5}{10}$ and $\frac{1}{2}$

4. What is the missing factor? Fill in the circle for the best answer.
6 × ______ = 3,600
(A) 6
(B) 60
(C) 600
(D) 6,000

5. Flip 1 penny and 1 nickel. Show all possible outcomes. Use Ⓟ and Ⓝ to show the coins. Use H for HEADS and T for TAILS.
Ⓟ H Ⓝ H; Ⓟ H Ⓝ T;
Ⓟ T Ⓝ H; Ⓟ T Ⓝ T

6. How much do six 300-pound dolphins weigh?

dolphins	pounds per dolphin	pounds in all
6	300	?

Number model: 6 × 300 = ?
Answer: 1,800 lbs

Math Journal 2, p. 184

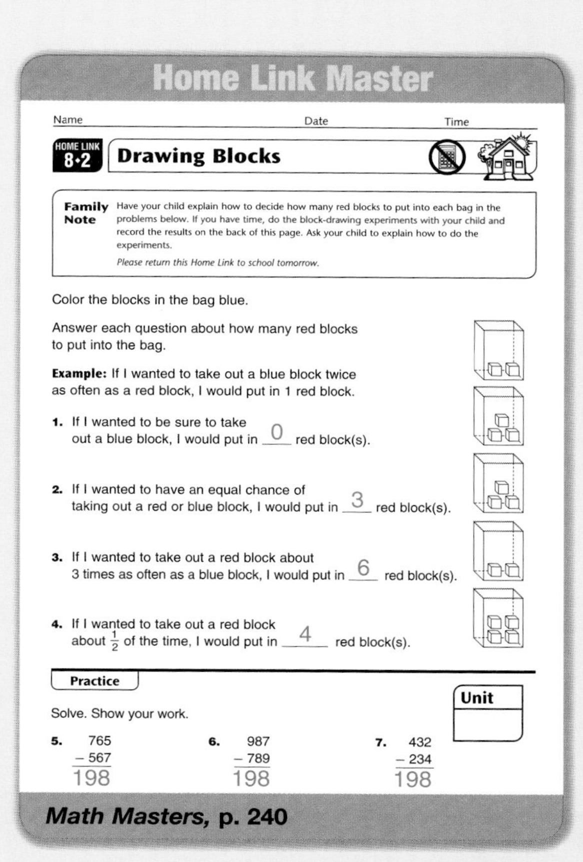

Home Link Master

Name Date Time

HOME LINK 8·2 **Drawing Blocks**

Family Note Have your child explain how to decide how many red blocks to put into each bag in the problems below. If you have time, do the block-drawing experiments with your child and record the results on the back of this page. Ask your child to explain how to do the experiments.

Please return this Home Link to school tomorrow.

Color the blocks in the bag blue.

Answer each question about how many red blocks to put into the bag.

Example: If I wanted to take out a blue block twice as often as a red block, I would put in 1 red block.

1. If I wanted to be sure to take out a blue block, I would put in 0 red block(s).
2. If I wanted to have an equal chance of taking out a red or blue block, I would put in 3 red block(s).
3. If I wanted to take out a red block about 3 times as often as a blue block, I would put in 6 red block(s).
4. If I wanted to take out a red block about $\frac{1}{2}$ of the time, I would put in 4 red block(s).

Practice

Solve. Show your work.

Unit

5. 765 − 567 = 198
6. 987 − 789 = 198
7. 432 − 234 = 198

Math Masters, p. 240

Teaching Master

Name ______ Date ______ Time ______

LESSON 8·2 **Dice Data**

Is it more likely that you will roll a 4 if you roll 1 die or that you will roll a sum of 4 if you roll 2 dice? Answers vary.

Check your prediction.

ONE DIE Roll 1 die 20 times and keep a tally of the results.

1	2	3	4	5	6

(You should have 20 tally marks in the chart when you are done.)

- What fraction of the time did you roll a 4? $\frac{\square}{20}$
- What fraction of the time did you roll an even number? $\frac{\square}{20}$

If you roll 2 dice, do you think the sum is less likely, more likely, or equally likely to be even? ______
Check your prediction.

TWO DICE Roll 2 dice 20 times and keep a tally of the results.

2	3	4	5	6	7	8	9	10	11	12

(You should have 20 tally marks in the chart when you are done.)

- What fraction of the time did you roll a sum of 4? $\frac{\square}{20}$
- What fraction of the time did you roll a sum of an even number? $\frac{\square}{20}$

Describe how rolling 1 die is the same as and different from rolling 2 dice. Think about which results are the same and which results are different. Write your answers on the back of this page.

***Math Masters,* p. 241**

3 Differentiation Options

READINESS

▶ Exploring Dice Data

5–15 Min

(*Math Masters,* p. 241)

To explore probability and probability terms, have children complete *Math Masters,* page 241. When children have finished the page, have them discuss the various outcomes, and compare the probability for the different events. Have children share some of their predictions using probability terms. Sample answers: I have an equal chance of rolling an even number with both 1 die or 2 dice. I am more likely to roll the sum of 4 with 2 dice than to roll a 4 with 1 die.

EXTRA PRACTICE

▶ Finding Even Combinations

To provide additional practice with finding possible outcomes of an event, have children generate a list of all the possible combinations of rolling an even sum with 2 dice. Children record the combinations on a sheet of paper. Sample answers: 12 combinations or 18 combinations (with turn-arounds) Ask children to explain how they know they have found all the possible combinations.

ELL SUPPORT

▶ Building a Math Word Bank

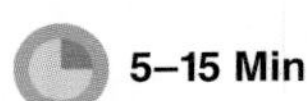

(*Differentiation Handbook,* p. 133)

To provide support for probability, have children use the Word Bank template found on *Differentiation Handbook,* page 133. Ask children to write the terms *possible outcomes, equally likely outcomes,* and *random,* draw a picture representing each term, and write other related words. See the *Differentiation Handbook* for more information.

8•3 Exploring Fractions, Re-Forming Squares, and Combinations

Explorations

Objective To provide opportunities to explore fractional relationships, spatial relationships, and combinations.

Technology Resources www.everydaymathonline.com

ePresentations

eToolkit

Algorithms Practice

EM Facts Workshop Game™

Family Letters

Assessment Management

Common Core State Standards

Curriculum Focal Points

Interactive Teacher's Lesson Guide

1 Teaching the Lesson

Key Concepts and Skills

- Solve problems involving fractional parts of a collection. [Number and Numeration Goal 2]
- Identify the fractional part one shape is of another. [Number and Numeration Goal 2]
- Explore polygon relationships by constructing figures from polygons. [Geometry Goal 2]
- Use patterning rules to find all possible combinations of pants and socks. [Patterns, Functions, and Algebra Goal 1]

Key Activities

Exploration A: Children use pattern blocks to find fractional relationships.

Exploration B: Children cut two same-size squares into pieces and reassemble them into a single square.

Exploration C: Children find all possible combinations of pants and socks in four colors.

Materials

Home Link 8•2
slate

Exploration A: Per partnership:
Math Journal 2, pp. 185–187
pattern blocks: green triangle and blue rhombus ◆ Pattern-Block Template

Exploration B: Per partnership:
Math Masters, pp. 242 and 243
scissors ◆ tape ◆ paper

Exploration C: Per group:
Math Journal 2, pp. 188 and 189
Math Masters, p. 244
blue, red, green, and black crayons ◆ scissors ◆ tape

2 Ongoing Learning & Practice

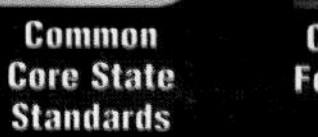

Playing *Multiplication Bingo*
Math Masters, p. 449
Student Reference Book, p. 295
per group: 4 each of number cards 2–9 (from the Everything Math Deck, if available), 8 counters or pennies per player

Math Boxes 8•3
Math Journal 2, p. 190

Ongoing Assessment: Recognizing Student Achievement
Use Math Boxes, Problem 4.
[Patterns, Functions, and Algebra Goal 3]

Home Link 8•3
Math Masters, p. 245

3 Differentiation Options

READINESS

Solving Pattern-Block Puzzles
Math Masters, p. 246
Pattern-Block Template ◆ pattern blocks

ENRICHMENT

Exploring with Tangrams
Math Masters, p. 435
Grandfather Tang's Story
half-sheets of paper

EXTRA PRACTICE

Minute Math+
Minute Math®+, pp. 12, 35, and 40

Advance Preparation

For the optional Enrichment activity in Part 3, obtain a copy of the book ***Grandfather Tang's Story*** by Ann Tompert (Dragonfly Books, 1997). Copy *Math Masters,* page 435 onto cardstock—one for every 2–4 children.

Mathematical Practices
SMP1, SMP2, **SMP3,** SMP4, SMP5, SMP7
Content Standards
3.G.2

Getting Started

Mental Math and Reflexes

Have children write numbers on slates as dictated. Then they identify digits in given places.

●○○ Write thirty-two hundredths. Underline the digit in the tenths place. 0.3̲2

●●○ Write five hundredths. Circle the digit in the tenths place. 0.⓪5
Write two and nine-tenths. Write an X through the digit in the tenths place. 2.9̸

●●● Write four hundred six thousandths. Circle the digit in the thousandths place. Write an X through the digit in the tenths place. 0.4̸0⑥

Math Message

Hank said, "I shared 24 pieces of candy with my friends.

I gave $\frac{1}{2}$ of the candy to Kim, $\frac{1}{3}$ to Juan, and $\frac{1}{4}$ to Moira."

Explain how you know Hank made a mistake.

Home Link 8·2 Follow-Up

Briefly review answers. Have children share their strategies.

1 Teaching the Lesson

▶ Math Message Follow-Up

Children share their answers. Hank could not possibly have done what he said. He would have had to give 12 pieces of candy to Kim ($\frac{1}{2}$ of the candy), 8 pieces to Juan ($\frac{1}{3}$ of the candy), and 6 pieces to Moira ($\frac{1}{4}$ of the candy). This adds up to 26 pieces, which is more than he had to give.

▶ Exploration A: Finding Relationships among Shapes

PARTNER ACTIVITY

(*Math Journal 2,* pp. 185–187)

Children use green pattern-block triangles and blue pattern-block rhombuses. Various shapes are displayed on journal pages 185–187. Children find what fractional part of each shape is covered by one or two triangles and one or two rhombuses. Some shapes on journal pages 186 and 187 cannot be tiled entirely by rhombuses, but children can solve these problems by rediscovering that a pattern-block rhombus has the same area as two triangles.

Children are reminded on journal page 187 that the number under the fraction bar (the denominator) names the number of equal parts into which the whole shape is divided. Children record their fractions and use their Pattern-Block Templates to draw how the blocks were used to divide the shapes.

For a follow-up activity, partners in each group can compare their fractions and use the blocks to check their answers. In some cases, more than one fraction is correct.

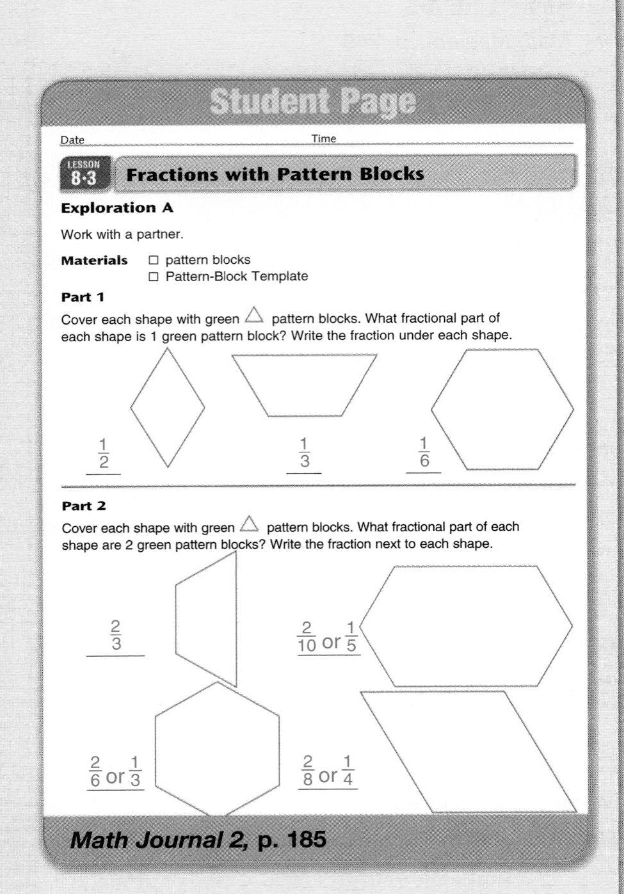

Student Page

Date Time

LESSON 8·3 **Fractions with Pattern Blocks**

Exploration A

Work with a partner.

Materials □ pattern blocks
□ Pattern-Block Template

Part 1

Cover each shape with green △ pattern blocks. What fractional part of each shape is 1 green pattern block? Write the fraction under each shape.

$\frac{1}{2}$ $\frac{1}{3}$ $\frac{1}{6}$

Part 2

Cover each shape with green △ pattern blocks. What fractional part of each shape are 2 green pattern blocks? Write the fraction next to each shape.

$\frac{2}{3}$ $\frac{2}{10}$ or $\frac{1}{5}$

$\frac{2}{6}$ or $\frac{1}{3}$ $\frac{2}{8}$ or $\frac{1}{4}$

Math Journal 2, p. 185

▶ Exploration B: Taking Apart and Putting Together Squares

INDEPENDENT ACTIVITY

(*Math Masters,* pp. 242 and 243)

Children work independently or with a partner to find ways to cut two same-size squares into pieces and reassemble the pieces into a single square.

The solution involves cutting each square into same-size triangles. The most efficient way is to cut each square along one of the diagonals. The pieces can then be reassembled as shown below.

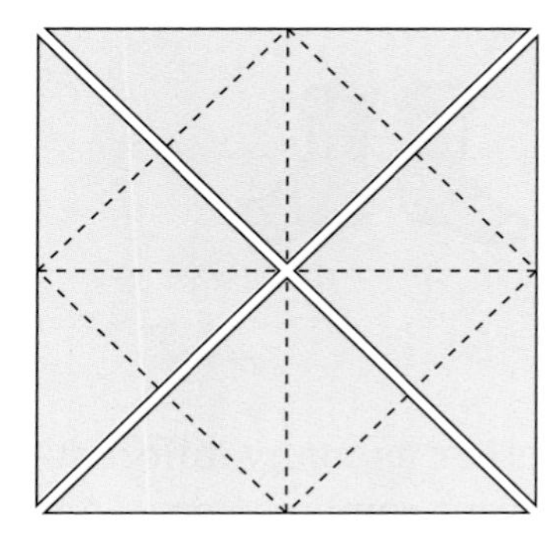

One solution for Exploration B

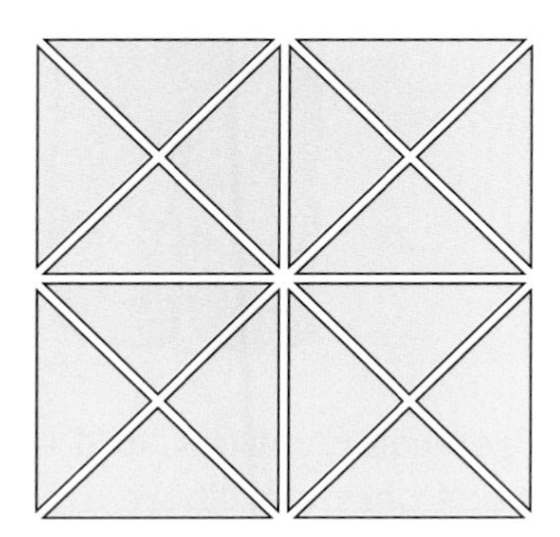

Another solution for Exploration B

The squares can also be cut into 8 or 16 same-size triangles, but this makes it more difficult to reassemble them into a square. It is not possible to solve the problem by cutting the squares into smaller squares. Have children share strategies as time allows.

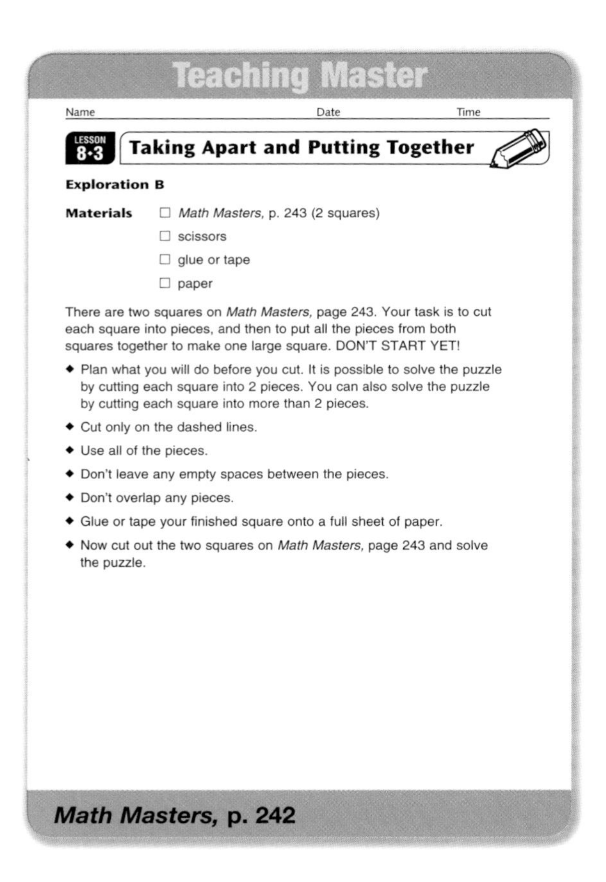

Teaching Master

Name Date Time

LESSON 8·3 **Taking Apart and Putting Together**

Exploration B

Materials
- ☐ *Math Masters,* p. 243 (2 squares)
- ☐ scissors
- ☐ glue or tape
- ☐ paper

There are two squares on *Math Masters,* page 243. Your task is to cut each square into pieces, and then to put all the pieces from both squares together to make one large square. DON'T START YET!

- ◆ Plan what you will do before you cut. It is possible to solve the puzzle by cutting each square into 2 pieces. You can also solve the puzzle by cutting each square into more than 2 pieces.
- ◆ Cut only on the dashed lines.
- ◆ Use all of the pieces.
- ◆ Don't leave any empty spaces between the pieces.
- ◆ Don't overlap any pieces.
- ◆ Glue or tape your finished square onto a full sheet of paper.
- ◆ Now cut out the two squares on *Math Masters,* page 243 and solve the puzzle.

Math Masters, p. 242

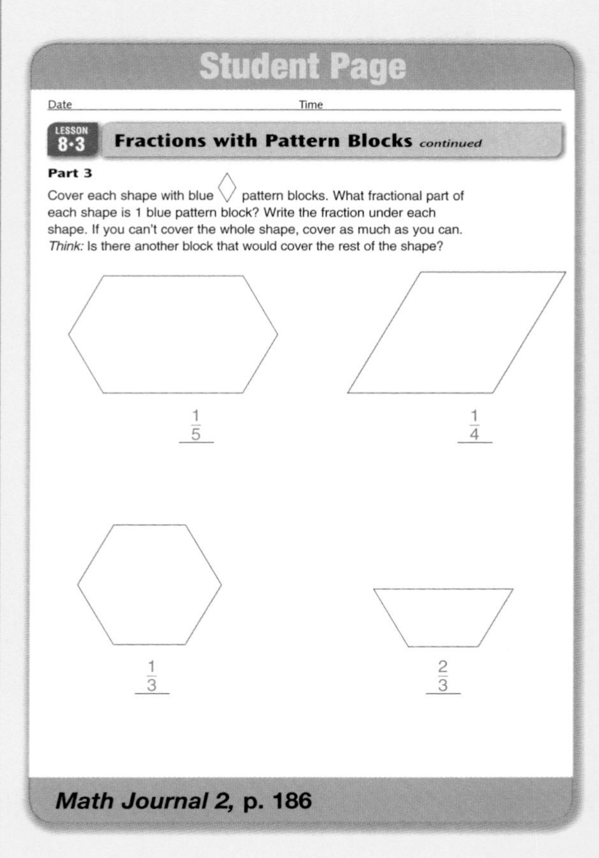

Student Page

Date Time

LESSON 8·3 **Fractions with Pattern Blocks** *continued*

Part 3

Cover each shape with blue ◇ pattern blocks. What fractional part of each shape is 1 blue pattern block? Write the fraction under each shape. If you can't cover the whole shape, cover as much as you can. *Think:* Is there another block that would cover the rest of the shape?

$\frac{1}{5}$ $\frac{1}{4}$

$\frac{1}{3}$ $\frac{2}{3}$

Math Journal 2, p. 186

NOTE For additional practice combining shapes, have children use pattern blocks to create quadrangles, pentagons, hexagons, and octagons. Children share their shapes and identify the pattern blocks they used.

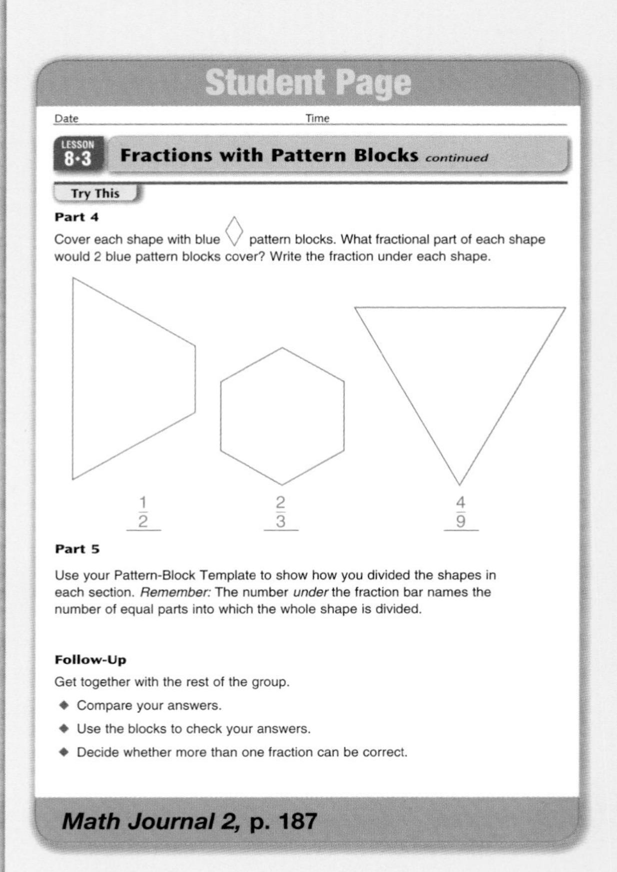

Student Page

Date Time

LESSON 8·3 **Fractions with Pattern Blocks** *continued*

Try This

Part 4

Cover each shape with blue ◇ pattern blocks. What fractional part of each shape would 2 blue pattern blocks cover? Write the fraction under each shape.

$\frac{1}{2}$ $\frac{2}{3}$ $\frac{4}{9}$

Part 5

Use your Pattern-Block Template to show how you divided the shapes in each section. *Remember:* The number *under* the fraction bar names the number of equal parts into which the whole shape is divided.

Follow-Up

Get together with the rest of the group.
- ◆ Compare your answers.
- ◆ Use the blocks to check your answers.
- ◆ Decide whether more than one fraction can be correct.

Math Journal 2, p. 187

Student Page

Date ______ Time ______

LESSON 8·3 **Dressing for the Party**

Exploration C

Work in a group of four.

Materials
- ☐ *Math Masters,* p. 244 (Pants and Socks Cutouts)
- ☐ scissors
- ☐ tape
- ☐ blue, red, green, and black crayons or coloring pencils

Problem

Pretend that you have 4 pairs of pants: blue, red, green, and black. You also have 4 pairs of socks: blue, red, green, and black. You have been invited to a party. You need to choose a pair of pants and a pair of socks to wear. (Of course, both socks must be the same color.) For example, the pants could be blue and both socks black.

How many different combinations of pants and socks are possible?

Strategy

Use the cutouts on *Math Masters,* page 244, and crayons to help you answer the question.

Before you answer the question, decide on a way for your group to share the following work.

- Color the pants in the first row blue.
- Color the pants in the second row red.
- Color the pants in the third row green and those in the fourth row black.
- Color the socks in the same way.
- Cut out each pair of pants and each pair of socks.
- Tape together pairs of pants and pairs of socks to show different outfits. Check that you have only one of each outfit.

Math Journal 2, p. 188

Student Page

Date ______ Time ______

LESSON 8·3 **Dressing for the Party** *continued*

1. How many different combinations of pants and socks did your group find? 16 combinations
2. Is this all of the possible combinations? yes
3. How do you know?
   Sample answer: Each color of pants is paired with each color of socks.
4. How did your group divide up the work?
   Answers vary.
5. How did your group solve the problem?
   Answers vary.

Math Journal 2, p. 189

▶ Exploration C: Dressing for the Party

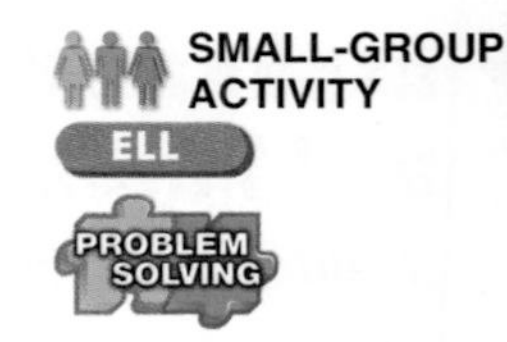

(*Math Journal 2,* pp. 188 and 189; *Math Masters,* p. 244)

Children work in groups of four to find all possible color combinations of pants and socks when 4 pairs of pants and 4 pairs of socks come in 4 different colors. To support English language learners, discuss the different uses of the word *pair*.

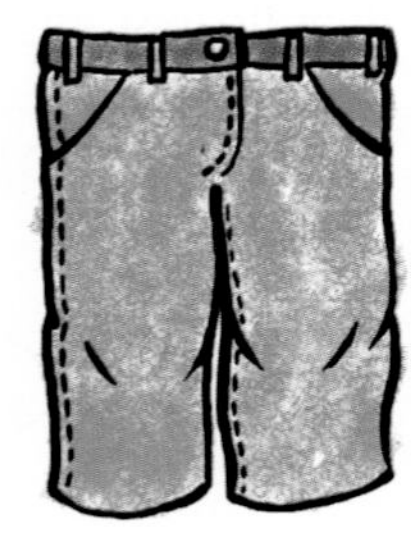

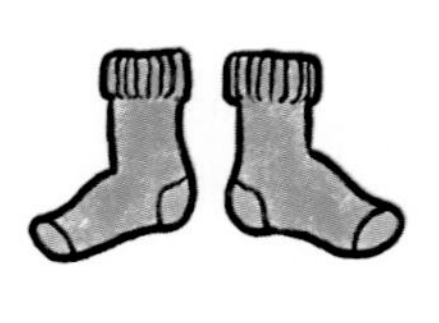

Children color, cut out, and tape together as many different-color outfits as possible. There are 16 different combinations. (Additional pants and socks are included on *Math Masters,* page 244 in case of mistakes.)

Have children within each group share the work equally. When they have made all possible combinations, each group writes a report on journal page 189 describing how they found the answer.

2 Ongoing Learning & Practice

▶ Playing *Multiplication Bingo*

(*Math Masters,* p. 449; *Student Reference Book,* p. 295)

Children play *Multiplication Bingo* introduced in Lesson 7-3 to practice multiplication facts. See the rules for *Multiplication Bingo* (All Facts) on page 295 in the *Student Reference Book.*

Math Boxes 8·3

INDEPENDENT ACTIVITY

(*Math Journal 2,* p. 190)

Mixed Practice Math Boxes in this lesson are paired with Math Boxes in Lesson 8-1. The skill in Problem 6 previews Unit 9 content.

Ongoing Assessment: Recognizing Student Achievement

Math Boxes Problem 4 

Use **Math Boxes, Problem 4** to assess children's progress toward understanding that parentheses affect the order in which operations are carried out. Children are making adequate progress if they successfully complete 2 of the number sentences. Some children may be able to successfully complete all of the number sentences.

[Patterns, Functions, and Algebra Goal 3]

Writing/Reasoning Have children write an answer to the following: *In Problem 2, how does knowing that 5 × 9 = 45 help you know that 5 × 900 = 4,500?* Sample answer: 5 × 900 is 100 times as much as 5 × 9, or 4,500.

Home Link 8·3

INDEPENDENT ACTIVITY

(*Math Masters,* p. 245)

Home Connection Children solve problems involving fractions. Explain that they may use pennies or counters to model the problems.

3 Differentiation Options

READINESS

Solving Pattern-Block Puzzles

INDEPENDENT ACTIVITY

5–15 Min

(*Math Masters,* p. 246)

To provide experience with fractions of regions, have children cover pattern-block shapes with smaller pattern blocks. They record their work on *Math Masters,* page 246.

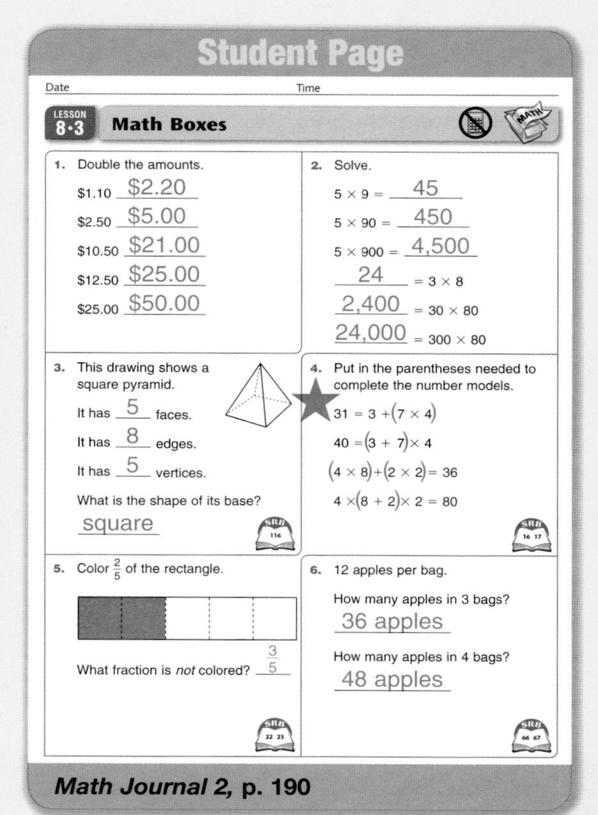

Student Page

Date Time

LESSON 8·3 **Math Boxes**

1. Double the amounts.
$1.10 $2.20
$2.50 $5.00
$10.50 $21.00
$12.50 $25.00
$25.00 $50.00

2. Solve.
5 × 9 = 45
5 × 90 = 450
5 × 900 = 4,500
24 = 3 × 8
2,400 = 30 × 80
24,000 = 300 × 80

3. This drawing shows a square pyramid.
It has 5 faces.
It has 8 edges.
It has 5 vertices.
What is the shape of its base? square

4. Put in the parentheses needed to complete the number models.
31 = 3 + (7 × 4)
40 = (3 + 7) × 4
(4 × 8) + (2 × 2) = 36
4 × (8 + 2) × 2 = 80

5. Color $\frac{2}{5}$ of the rectangle.
What fraction is *not* colored? $\frac{3}{5}$

6. 12 apples per bag.
How many apples in 3 bags? 36 apples
How many apples in 4 bags? 48 apples

Math Journal 2, p. 190

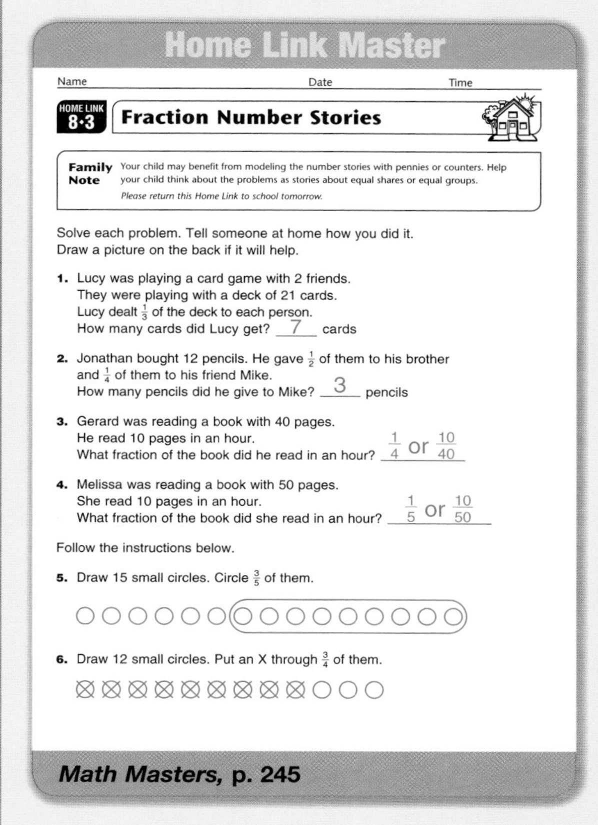

Home Link Master

Name Date Time

HOME LINK 8·3 **Fraction Number Stories**

Family Note Your child may benefit from modeling the number stories with pennies or counters. Help your child think about the problems as stories about equal shares or equal groups.
Please return this Home Link to school tomorrow.

Solve each problem. Tell someone at home how you did it.
Draw a picture on the back if it will help.

1. Lucy was playing a card game with 2 friends.
They were playing with a deck of 21 cards.
Lucy dealt $\frac{1}{3}$ of the deck to each person.
How many cards did Lucy get? 7 cards

2. Jonathan bought 12 pencils. He gave $\frac{1}{2}$ of them to his brother and $\frac{1}{4}$ of them to his friend Mike.
How many pencils did he give to Mike? 3 pencils

3. Gerard was reading a book with 40 pages.
He read 10 pages in an hour.
What fraction of the book did he read in an hour? $\frac{1}{4}$ or $\frac{10}{40}$

4. Melissa was reading a book with 50 pages.
She read 10 pages in an hour.
What fraction of the book did she read in an hour? $\frac{1}{5}$ or $\frac{10}{50}$

Follow the instructions below.

5. Draw 15 small circles. Circle $\frac{3}{5}$ of them.

6. Draw 12 small circles. Put an X through $\frac{3}{4}$ of them.

Math Masters, p. 245

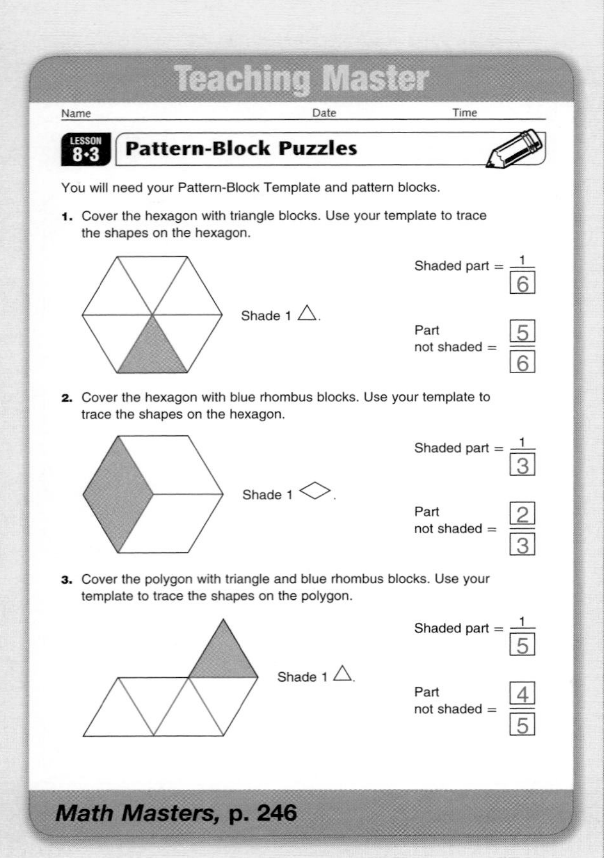
Teaching Master

Name Date Time

LESSON 8·3 **Pattern-Block Puzzles**

You will need your Pattern-Block Template and pattern blocks.

1. Cover the hexagon with triangle blocks. Use your template to trace the shapes on the hexagon.

Shade 1 △.

Shaded part = $\frac{1}{6}$

Part not shaded = $\frac{5}{6}$

2. Cover the hexagon with blue rhombus blocks. Use your template to trace the shapes on the hexagon.

Shade 1 ◇.

Shaded part = $\frac{1}{3}$

Part not shaded = $\frac{2}{3}$

3. Cover the polygon with triangle and blue rhombus blocks. Use your template to trace the shapes on the polygon.

Shade 1 △.

Shaded part = $\frac{1}{5}$

Part not shaded = $\frac{4}{5}$

Math Masters, p. 246

ENRICHMENT

▶ Exploring with Tangrams

15–30 Min

(*Math Masters*, p. 435)

To further explore relationships among polygons, have children use tangrams to make a variety of shapes. Read the book ***Grandfather Tang's Story*** with the children. When you have finished the story, have children choose one of the tangram puzzles in the book to solve. They should record their solutions on a half-sheet of paper.

EXTRA PRACTICE

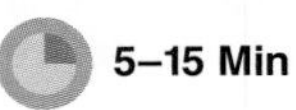

▶ *Minute Math+*

5–15 Min

To offer children more experience with fractions, see the following pages in *Minute Math+*:

Basic Routines: p. 12–Levels 2 and 3

Counting: p. 35–Level 3

Operations: p. 40

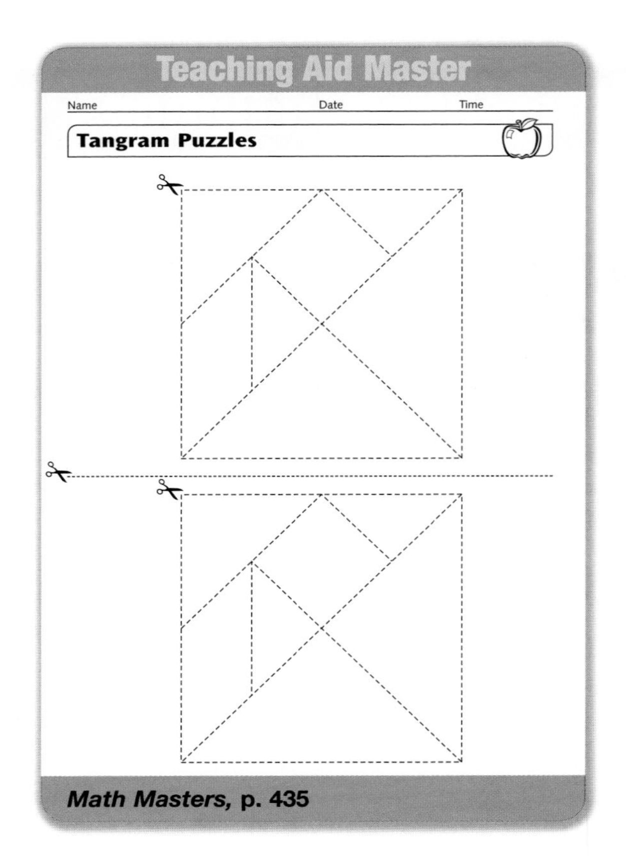
Teaching Aid Master

Name Date Time

Tangram Puzzles

Math Masters, p. 435

8•4 Number-Line Posters for Fractions

Objective To introduce the number line as a model for fractions.

www.everydaymathonline.com

ePresentations

eToolkit

Algorithms Practice
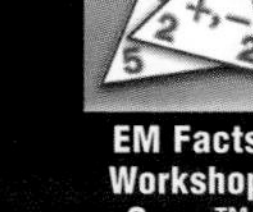
EM Facts Workshop Game™

Family Letters

Assessment Management

Common Core State Standards

Curriculum Focal Points

Interactive Teacher's Lesson Guide

1 Teaching the Lesson

Key Concepts and Skills

- Identify fractions on a number line. [Number and Numeration Goal 2]
- Compare fractions using a number-line model. [Number and Numeration Goal 6]

Key Activities

Children make a number-line poster for fractions. They use the poster to review and extend fraction concepts.

Ongoing Assessment: Recognizing Student Achievement Use Mental Math and Reflexes. [Number and Numeration Goal 1]

Ongoing Assessment: Informing Instruction See page 667.

Materials

Math Journal 2, p. 191
Home Link 8•3
Math Masters, p. 247
scissors ◆ pennies or other counters (optional) ◆ half-sheets of paper ◆ tape or glue

2 Ongoing Learning & Practice

Solving Frames-and-Arrows Problems

Math Journal 2, pp. 191 and 192
Children use the Fraction Number-Line Poster as well as addition, subtraction, and multiplication to solve Frames-and-Arrows problems.

Math Boxes 8•4

Math Journal 2, p. 193
Children practice and maintain skills through Math Box problems.

Home Link 8•4

Math Masters, p. 248
Children practice and maintain skills through Home Link activities.

3 Differentiation Options

READINESS

Comparing Rulers and Number Lines

Math Masters, pp. 249 and 250
ruler ◆ Class Number Line
Children compare the markings on a ruler to the fractions on a number line.

ENRICHMENT

Solving Fraction-Strip Problems

Math Masters, pp. 247 and 251
crayons
Children use a set of fraction strips to solve problems.

Advance Preparation

Make one copy of *Math Masters,* page 247 for each child (or two copies, if children do the optional Enrichment activity in Part 3). Place copies near the Math Message.

***Teacher's Reference Manual,* Grades 1–3** pp. 74–76

Getting Started

Mathematical Practices
SMP1, SMP2, SMP3, SMP4, **SMP5,** SMP6, SMP7, SMP8
Content Standards
3.NF.1, 3.NF.2, 3.NF.2a, 3.NF.2b, 3.NF.3, 3.NF.3a, 3.NF.3b, 3.NF.3c, 3.NF.3d, 3.G.2

Mental Math and Reflexes 

Pass out half-sheets of paper. Children write numbers from dictation and then identify digits in given places.

For example:

●○○ Write 78,403. Circle the ten-thousands digit. Put an X through the ones digit. Underline the thousands digit.
⑦8,40X

●●○ Write 906,152. Circle the hundred-thousands digit. Put an X through the hundreds digit. Underline the tens digit.
⑨06,X52

●●● Write 1,862,305. Circle the ten-thousands digit. Put an X through the millions digit. Underline the hundreds digit.
X,8⑥2,305

Continue as time allows.

Math Message

Take one copy (or two copies, if children will do the Enrichment activity in Part 3) *of* Math Masters, *page 247. Cut apart on the dashed lines.*

Solve this problem: Jonah sorted 20 marbles by color. He found that $\frac{1}{4}$ of them were blue and $\frac{1}{5}$ were yellow. Does he have more blue marbles or more yellow marbles? Be ready to explain how you know. Use pennies or counters to model the problem if you want.

Home Link 8·3 Follow-Up

Have partners share their solution strategies for Problems 5 and 6 with each other.

Ongoing Assessment: Recognizing Student Achievement

Mental Math and Reflexes 

Use **Mental Math and Reflexes** to assess children's progress toward identifying the value of digits in numbers through hundred thousands. Children are making adequate progress if they are able to correctly identify the value of the digits in 5- and 6-digit numbers. Some children may be able to identify the value of the digits in 7-digit or more numbers.

[Number and Numeration Goal 1]

NOTE If you had children cut out 2 sets of fraction strips, have them put aside one set for the Enrichment activity in Part 3.

Teaching Master

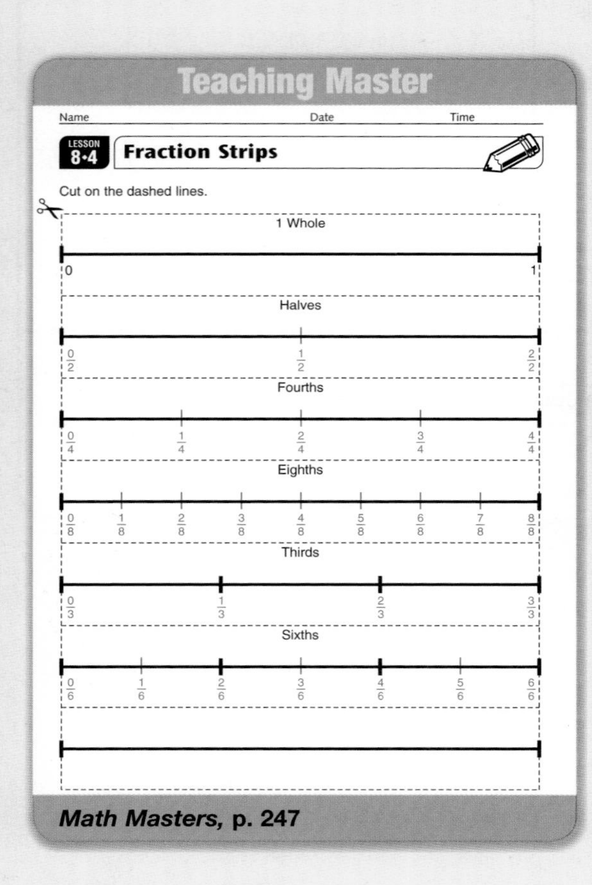

Name Date Time

LESSON 8·4 **Fraction Strips**

Cut on the dashed lines.

1 Whole: 0, 1

Halves: $\frac{0}{2}$, $\frac{1}{2}$, $\frac{2}{2}$

Fourths: $\frac{0}{4}$, $\frac{1}{4}$, $\frac{2}{4}$, $\frac{3}{4}$, $\frac{4}{4}$

Eighths: $\frac{0}{8}$, $\frac{1}{8}$, $\frac{2}{8}$, $\frac{3}{8}$, $\frac{4}{8}$, $\frac{5}{8}$, $\frac{6}{8}$, $\frac{7}{8}$, $\frac{8}{8}$

Thirds: $\frac{0}{3}$, $\frac{1}{3}$, $\frac{2}{3}$, $\frac{3}{3}$

Sixths: $\frac{0}{6}$, $\frac{1}{6}$, $\frac{2}{6}$, $\frac{3}{6}$, $\frac{4}{6}$, $\frac{5}{6}$, $\frac{6}{6}$

Math Masters, **p. 247**

1 Teaching the Lesson

▶ Math Message Follow-Up

WHOLE-CLASS DISCUSSION

(*Math Masters,* p. 247)

Check that children have a set of 7 fraction strips.

Go over the answer to the problem. Jonah has more blue marbles. Have children share their strategies. For example, one of 4 equal parts of a whole is larger than one of 5 equal parts of the same whole. So $\frac{1}{4}$ is larger than $\frac{1}{5}$. If no one suggests it, have a volunteer demonstrate how to model the problem with counters or pictures.

▶ Making a Number-Line Poster for Fractions

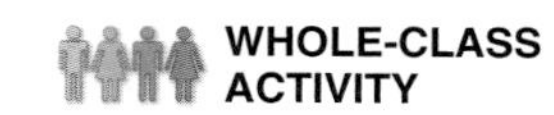

WHOLE-CLASS ACTIVITY

(*Math Journal 2,* p. 191; *Math Masters,* p. 247)

Children are familiar with two kinds of fraction models: region (area) models such as circles and polygons, and set models (collections of things). This lesson introduces a third model—the fraction number line. Region models (rectangular strips) are used to locate points on the number line.

Children use the strips they cut out from *Math Masters,* page 247 to make the Fraction Number-Line Poster on journal page 191. Each strip includes a number line.

The top strip from the master shows a number line from 0 to 1. It represents the whole, or ONE. Have children carefully glue or tape it over the strip on the journal page for 1 whole.

Ask children to fold the Halves strip in half. Check that they fold it into 2 equal parts. Show them how to make a mark where the crease meets the number line, and how to label the number line. (*See margin.*) Children then carefully glue or tape the labeled number line strip exactly over the strip on the journal page for halves.

Ongoing Assessment: Informing Instruction

Watch for children who count the small dividing marks on the number line, rather than the intervals, to determine fractions. Have them begin with their finger on the 0 and count each fractional part as they reach one of the small marks, until they count to 1. This way, they are counting the number of intervals, not the number of marks.

Adjusting the Activity

Use the language of multiplication to describe what children do to find sixths, eighths, twelfths, and so on. For example, to divide the number line into sixths, children first find the thirds, then they fold the thirds in half. One half of one third is one sixth.

AUDITORY ◆ KINESTHETIC ◆ TACTILE ◆ VISUAL

Children continue gluing and labeling number-line strips for fourths, eighths, thirds, and sixths. The strips for thirds and sixths have small marks to indicate where folds for three equal parts should be made. To fold a strip into sixths, first fold it into thirds and then in half. Children might choose to fold the last strip into twelfths, sixteenths, or perhaps even ninths. Someone might try to fold it into fifths by measuring with a ruler.

When children finish the journal page, ask them to discuss how the number-line model is different from the region and set models. Also ask if they can think of places in the everyday world where fraction number lines are found. Sample answer: Rulers and measuring cups

Student Page

Date Time

LESSON 8·4 **Fraction Number-Line Poster**

1 Whole
Halves
Fourths
Eighths
Thirds
Sixths

Math Journal 2, p. 191

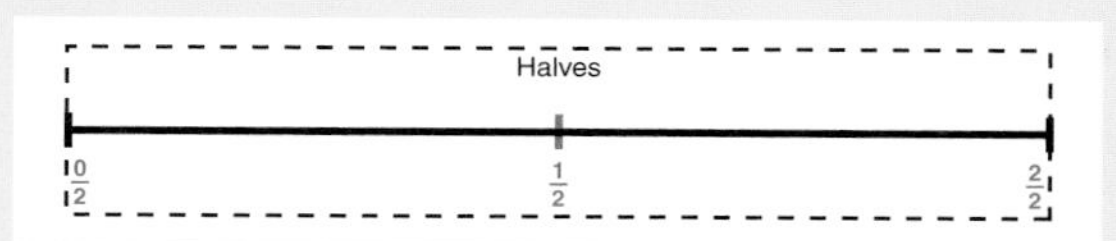

Number-line model for halves

NOTE Expect that some children may still confuse the region model with the number-line model, because they are folding to find the indicated fraction on the number line. Measurement and other practice problems will provide opportunities to practice using the number-line model.

▶ Reviewing Fraction Concepts

WHOLE-CLASS DISCUSSION

(*Math Journal 2,* p. 191)

While children look at their Fraction Number-Line Poster, review concepts such as the following:

- Except for *half,* fraction words such as *third, fourth, sixth,* and *eighth* suggest the number of equal parts. What are the fraction words for five equal parts and ten equal parts? Fifths and tenths
- What do the denominators (the numbers under the fraction bar) tell? The number of equal parts into which the whole has been divided
- What do the numerators (the numbers over the fraction bar) tell? The number of equal parts represented by the fraction
- What does the fraction $\frac{3}{4}$ represent? The whole is divided into 4 equal parts. The fraction represents 3 of these parts.
- What does the fraction $\frac{0}{3}$ represent? The whole is divided into 3 equal parts. The fraction represents 0, or none, of these parts.
- What does the fraction $\frac{8}{8}$ represent? The whole is divided into 8 equal parts. The fraction represents 8, or all, of these parts.

Have children use their Fraction Number-Line Posters to answer the following questions:

- Is $\frac{1}{3}$ larger or smaller than 1? smaller
- Is $\frac{1}{2}$ larger or smaller than 0? larger
- Look at the eighths strip. Between which fractions is $\frac{5}{8}$? $\frac{4}{8}$ and $\frac{6}{8}$
- Which fractions have numerators and denominators that are the same? $\frac{2}{2}, \frac{4}{4}, \frac{8}{8}, \frac{3}{3}, \frac{6}{6}$
- What do you notice about the fractions that have numerators and denominators that are the same? Sample answers: Each is at the end of the number line strip; each is in the same place as 1 on the 1-Whole strip.
- Look at $\frac{2}{8}$ and $\frac{5}{8}$. Which is larger? $\frac{5}{8}$ How do you know? Sample answer: On the number line, I see that $\frac{2}{8}$ is closer to 0 and $\frac{5}{8}$ is closer to 1, so I know that $\frac{5}{8}$ is larger than $\frac{2}{8}$.
- Look at $\frac{1}{8}$ and $\frac{1}{4}$. Which is larger? $\frac{1}{4}$ How do you know? Sample answer: On the number lines, I see that $\frac{1}{8}$ is closer to 0 than $\frac{1}{4}$, so $\frac{1}{4}$ is larger than $\frac{1}{8}$.
- Look at $\frac{3}{8}$ and $\frac{3}{4}$. Which is larger? $\frac{3}{4}$ How do you know? Sample answer: I see that $\frac{3}{4}$ is to the right of $\frac{1}{2}$ and that means $\frac{3}{4}$ is larger than $\frac{1}{2}$. I see that $\frac{3}{8}$ is to the left of $\frac{1}{2}$ and that means that $\frac{3}{8}$ is smaller than $\frac{1}{2}$. So $\frac{3}{4}$ is larger than $\frac{3}{8}$.

Student Page

Date Time

LESSON 8·4 **Frames-and-Arrows Problems**

Solve each Frames-and-Arrows problem. Use your Fraction Number-Line Poster on *Math Journal 2,* page 191 for Problems 1 and 2.

1. Rule: $\frac{1}{8}$ more — $\frac{3}{8}$, $\frac{4}{8}$, $\frac{5}{8}$, $\frac{6}{8}$, $\frac{7}{8}$, $\frac{8}{8}$
2. Rule: $-\frac{1}{6}$ — $\frac{5}{6}$, $\frac{4}{6}$, $\frac{3}{6}$, $\frac{2}{6}$, $\frac{1}{6}$, $\frac{0}{6}$
3. Rule: ×2 — 3, 6, 12, 24, 48, 96
4. +25¢ / −10¢ — 10¢, 35¢, 25¢, 50¢, 40¢, 65¢

Try This

5. ×5 / −50 — 12, 60, 10, 50, 0

Math Journal 2, p. 192

2 Ongoing Learning & Practice

▶ Solving Frames-and-Arrows Problems

(*Math Journal 2,* pp. 191 and 192)

Children use the Fraction Number-Line Poster on journal page 191 to help solve Problems 1 and 2 on *Math Journal 2,* page 192. They use multiplication, addition, and subtraction to solve the remaining problems on the page.

▶ Math Boxes 8•4

(*Math Journal 2,* p. 193)

Mixed Practice Math Boxes in this lesson are paired with Math Boxes in Lesson 8-2. The skill in Problem 6 previews Unit 9 content.

Writing/Reasoning Have children write an answer to the following: *Explain your answer to Problem 5.* Sample answer: True. There are the same number of blue and red blocks. There is an equal chance of pulling either a red block or a blue block from the bag.

▶ Home Link 8•4

(*Math Masters,* p. 248)

Home Connection Children label fractions of sets and number lines. They are encouraged to continue looking for objects that are labeled with fractions or decimals to donate (or loan) to the Fractions Museum.

Student Page

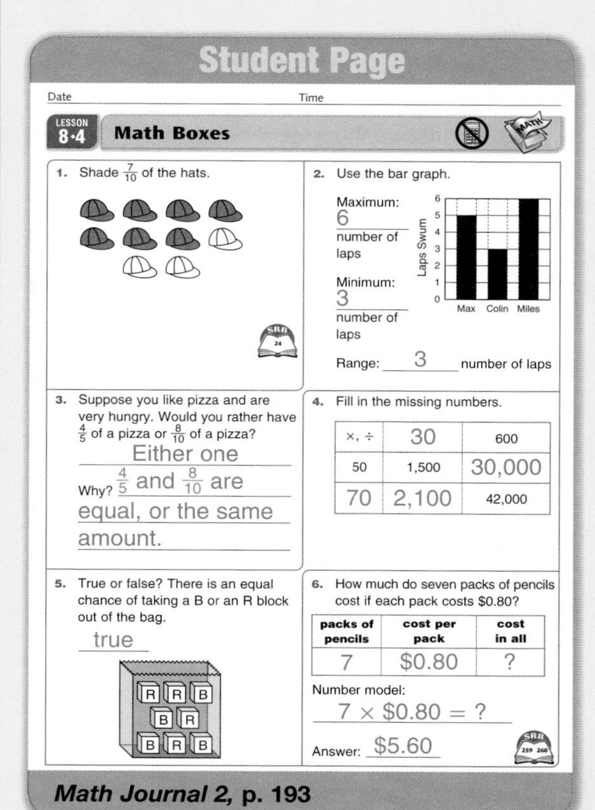

Date Time

LESSON 8•4 **Math Boxes**

1. Shade $\frac{7}{10}$ of the hats.

2. Use the bar graph.
Maximum: 6 number of laps
Minimum: 3 number of laps
Range: 3 number of laps

3. Suppose you like pizza and are very hungry. Would you rather have $\frac{4}{5}$ of a pizza or $\frac{8}{10}$ of a pizza?
Either one
Why? $\frac{4}{5}$ and $\frac{8}{10}$ are equal, or the same amount.

4. Fill in the missing numbers.

×, ÷	30	600
50	1,500	30,000
70	2,100	42,000

5. True or false? There is an equal chance of taking a B or an R block out of the bag.
true

6. How much do seven packs of pencils cost if each pack costs \$0.80?

packs of pencils	cost per pack	cost in all
7	\$0.80	?

Number model: 7 × \$0.80 = ?
Answer: \$5.60

Math Journal 2, p. 193

Home Link Master

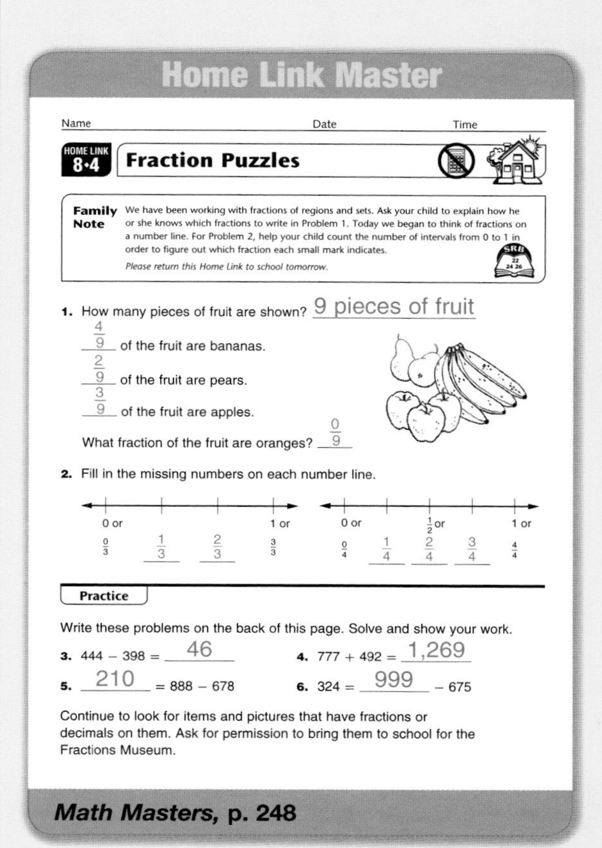

Name Date Time

HOME LINK 8•4 **Fraction Puzzles**

Family Note We have been working with fractions of regions and sets. Ask your child to explain how he or she knows which fractions to write in Problem 1. Today we began to think of fractions on a number line. For Problem 2, help your child count the number of intervals from 0 to 1 in order to figure out which fraction each small mark indicates.
Please return this Home Link to school tomorrow.

1. How many pieces of fruit are shown? 9 pieces of fruit
$\frac{4}{9}$ of the fruit are bananas.
$\frac{2}{9}$ of the fruit are pears.
$\frac{3}{9}$ of the fruit are apples.
What fraction of the fruit are oranges? $\frac{0}{9}$

2. Fill in the missing numbers on each number line.

Practice

Write these problems on the back of this page. Solve and show your work.

3. 444 − 398 = 46
4. 777 + 492 = 1,269
5. 210 = 888 − 678
6. 324 = 999 − 675

Continue to look for items and pictures that have fractions or decimals on them. Ask for permission to bring them to school for the Fractions Museum.

Math Masters, p. 248

Name ______ Date ______ Time ______

LESSON 8•4 **Comparing Rulers & Number Lines**

1. Look at your ruler and the Class Number Line. Sample answers:
   How is a ruler like a number line?
   A ruler has equally spaced marks like a number line, and the numbers are in order.
2. Look at the small lines between 0 and 1 on the inch ruler. What do these small lines mean?
   They show parts of an inch.
3. Give examples of numbers that come between 0 and 1.
   $\frac{1}{4}$, $\frac{1}{2}$, $\frac{3}{4}$, and so on
4. Look at the magnified inches on *Math Masters,* page 250.
   Fill in the blanks under each ruler with the correct fractions.
   How did you know which fractions to write?
   For the denominator, I counted the total number of equal spaces on each ruler. For each numerator, I counted the number of spaces up to the small lines that marked each equal part of the ruler.

***Math Masters,* p. 249**

Teaching Master

Name ______ Date ______ Time ______

LESSON 8•4 **Comparing Rulers & Number Lines** *cont.*

inches 0 1 2 3 4 5 6

0 $\frac{1}{4}$ $\frac{2}{4}$ or $\frac{1}{2}$ $\frac{3}{4}$ 1

inches 0 1 2 3 4 5 6

0 $\frac{1}{8}$ $\frac{2}{8}$ or $\frac{1}{4}$ $\frac{3}{8}$ $\frac{4}{8}$ or $\frac{1}{2}$ $\frac{5}{8}$ $\frac{6}{8}$ or $\frac{3}{4}$ $\frac{7}{8}$ 1

***Math Masters,* p. 250**

3 Differentiation Options

READINESS

SMALL-GROUP ACTIVITY

▶ Comparing Rulers and Number Lines

5–15 Min

(*Math Masters,* pp. 249 and 250)

To build a connection between fractions on a ruler and fractions on a number line, have children compare the two and label the fraction marks on a ruler. Have children describe the ways rulers and number lines are the same and the ways they are different. Emphasize the use of fraction vocabulary.

ENRICHMENT

INDEPENDENT ACTIVITY

▶ Solving Fraction-Strip Problems

5–15 Min

(*Math Masters,* pp. 247 and 251)

To apply children's understanding of a number-line model for fractions, have them solve the problems on *Math Masters,* page 251 using a set of fraction strips from *Math Masters,* page 247. When they have finished the page, have children describe how they used their fraction strips to solve the problems.

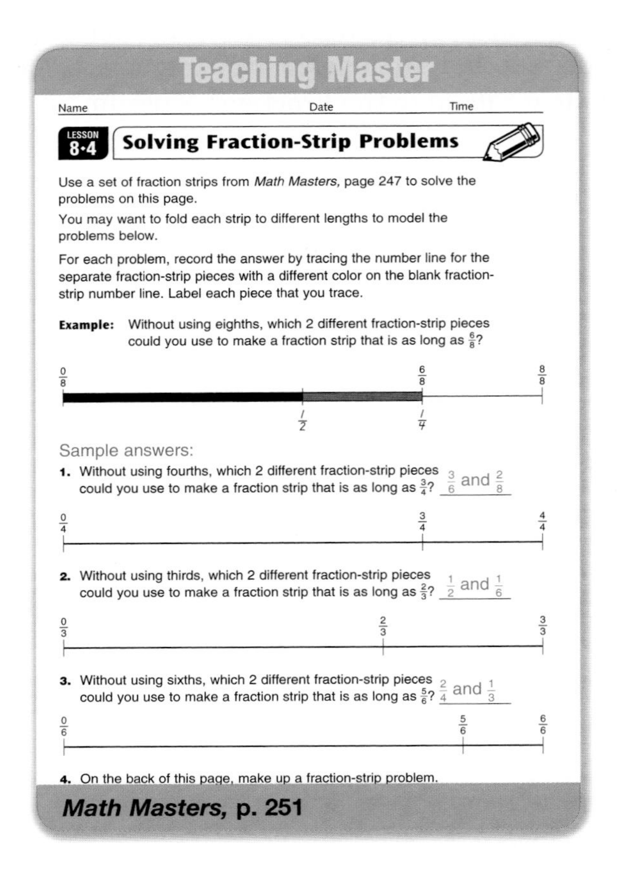

Teaching Master

Name ______ Date ______ Time ______

LESSON 8•4 **Solving Fraction-Strip Problems**

Use a set of fraction strips from *Math Masters,* page 247 to solve the problems on this page.

You may want to fold each strip to different lengths to model the problems below.

For each problem, record the answer by tracing the number line for the separate fraction-strip pieces with a different color on the blank fraction-strip number line. Label each piece that you trace.

Example: Without using eighths, which 2 different fraction-strip pieces could you use to make a fraction strip that is as long as $\frac{6}{8}$?

$\frac{0}{8}$ $\frac{6}{8}$ $\frac{8}{8}$ — $\frac{1}{2}$ $\frac{1}{4}$

Sample answers:

1. Without using fourths, which 2 different fraction-strip pieces could you use to make a fraction strip that is as long as $\frac{3}{4}$? $\frac{3}{6}$ and $\frac{2}{8}$
   $\frac{0}{4}$ $\frac{3}{4}$ $\frac{4}{4}$
2. Without using thirds, which 2 different fraction-strip pieces could you use to make a fraction strip that is as long as $\frac{2}{3}$? $\frac{1}{2}$ and $\frac{1}{6}$
   $\frac{0}{3}$ $\frac{2}{3}$ $\frac{3}{3}$
3. Without using sixths, which 2 different fraction-strip pieces could you use to make a fraction strip that is as long as $\frac{5}{6}$? $\frac{2}{4}$ and $\frac{1}{3}$
   $\frac{0}{6}$ $\frac{5}{6}$ $\frac{6}{6}$
4. On the back of this page, make up a fraction-strip problem.

***Math Masters,* p. 251**

8·5 Equivalent Fractions

Objective To guide children as they find equivalent fractions.

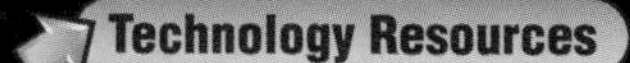

www.everydaymathonline.com

ePresentations | eToolkit | Algorithms Practice | EM Facts Workshop Game™ | Family Letters | Assessment Management | Common Core State Standards | Curriculum Focal Points | Interactive Teacher's Lesson Guide

1 Teaching the Lesson

Key Concepts and Skills

- Read and write fractions. [Number and Numeration Goal 2]
- Represent, identify, and generate equivalent fractions using manipulatives and drawings. [Number and Numeration Goal 5]

Key Activities

Children discuss the features of the Fraction Cards and use them to find equivalent fractions. They identify equivalent fractions on the Fraction Number-Line Poster. They play the *Equivalent Fractions Game.*

Key Vocabulary

equivalent fractions

Materials

Math Journal 2, pp. 191, 194, and Activity Sheets 5–8
Student Reference Book, pp. 283 and 284
Home Link 8•4
scissors ◆ envelopes ◆ straightedge ◆ slate ◆ counters

2 Ongoing Learning & Practice

Playing *The Block-Drawing Game*
Math Masters, p. 398
Student Reference Book, pp. 280 and 281
per group: paper bag with 7 blocks of the same size and shape in 2 or 3 different colors, slate or paper
Children practice making and testing predictions.

Ongoing Assessment: Recognizing Student Achievement
Use an Exit Slip (*Math Masters,* page 398). [Data and Chance Goal 4]

Math Boxes 8•5
Math Journal 2, p. 195
Children practice and maintain skills through Math Box problems.

Home Link 8•5
Math Masters, pp. 252 and 253
Children practice and maintain skills through Home Link activities.

3 Differentiation Options

READINESS

Shading Equivalent Fractions of Regions
Math Masters, p. 254
markers
Children shade regions to show equivalent fractions.

ENRICHMENT

Looking for a Rule
Math Journal 2, p. 194
Math Masters, p. 255
per partnership: Fraction Cards or Everything Math Deck, counters (optional)
Children explore equivalent fractions.

ENRICHMENT

Making Name-Collection Boxes for Fractions
per group: posterboard, markers, straightedges
Children create name-collection boxes for fractions.

ELL SUPPORT

Building a Math Word Bank
Differentiation Handbook, p. 132
Children add the term *equivalent fraction* to their Math Word Banks.

Advance Preparation

You may pre-cut Fraction Cards for children who have difficulty cutting. Place envelopes near the Math Message.

***Teacher's Reference Manual,* Grades 1–3** pp. 60, 61, 69

Getting Started

CCSS

Mathematical Practices
SMP1, **SMP2,** SMP3, SMP4, SMP5, SMP6, **SMP7,** SMP8
Content Standards
3.OA.3, 3.OA.5, **3.NF.1, 3.NF.2, 3.NF.2a, 3.NF.2b, 3.NF.3, 3.NF.3a, 3.NF.3b, 3.NF.3c, 3.NF.3d,** 3.G.2

Mental Math and Reflexes

Children solve division number stories. They write answers on slates and explain their strategies to the class. Provide counters.

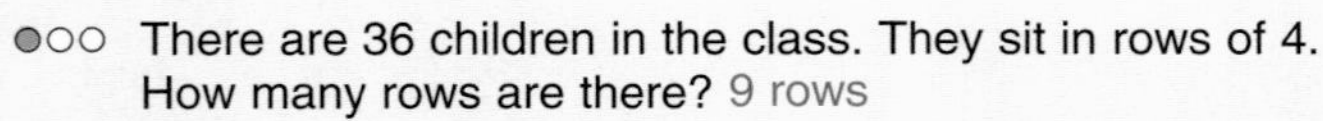

- ●○○ There are 36 children in the class. They sit in rows of 4. How many rows are there? 9 rows
- ●●○ 8 children share 72 pennies. How many pennies per child? 9 pennies
- ●●● 5 children share 56 strawberries. How many strawberries per child? 11 strawberries, with 1 left over

Math Message

Take an envelope. Carefully cut apart the 32 Fraction Cards on Activity Sheets 5–8 at the back of your journal. Put them in the envelope.

Home Link 8·4 Follow-Up

Briefly review answers. Place new items in the Fractions Museum.

Extend the activity by posing fraction addition problems about the picture of the fruit and asking children to write a number model to show what they did. *For example: What fraction of the fruit are the bananas and pears?* $\frac{6}{9}$ or $\frac{2}{3}$; $\frac{4}{9} + \frac{2}{9} = \frac{6}{9}$

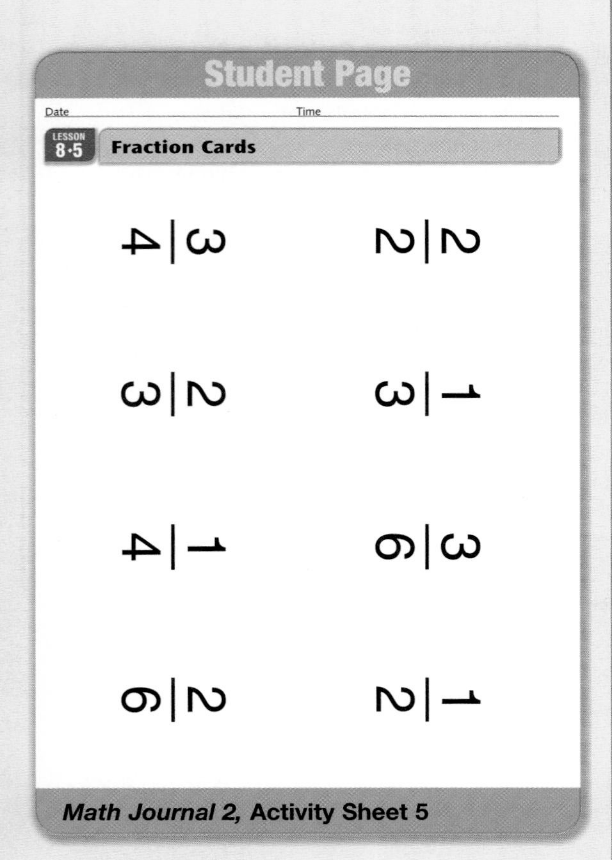
Student Page

Date Time

LESSON 8·5 **Fraction Cards**

$\frac{3}{4}$	$\frac{2}{2}$
$\frac{2}{3}$	$\frac{1}{3}$
$\frac{1}{4}$	$\frac{3}{6}$
$\frac{2}{6}$	$\frac{1}{2}$

Math Journal 2, Activity Sheet 5

1 Teaching the Lesson

▶ Math Message Follow-Up

WHOLE-CLASS ACTIVITY

(*Math Journal 2,* Activity Sheets 5–8)

Check that children have cut out all 32 Fraction Cards.

▶ Using Fraction Cards to Extend Fraction Concepts

WHOLE-CLASS DISCUSSION
ELL

(*Math Journal 2,* Activity Sheets 5–8)

Ask children to turn their cards to the picture side. Share observations. (Keep this part of the lesson brief.)

- ▷ Each card represents a whole, or ONE. All cards are the same size.
- ▷ The number of strips (or bars) varies from card to card. Some strips are shaded; others are unshaded.
- ▷ The fraction shown on the back of the card represents the shaded fractional part of the ONE.
- ▷ Some fractions have the same numerator and different denominators. That means the ONE is divided into different numbers of equal parts.
- ▷ The larger the denominator, the more parts the ONE is divided into, and the smaller each part.

Remind children that any fraction with 1 in the numerator is called a unit fraction. For example, $\frac{1}{2}$ is a unit fraction.

Ask children to name other unit fractions. Sample answers: $\frac{1}{3}$, $\frac{1}{4}$, $\frac{1}{10}$, $\frac{1}{98}$ To support English language learners, write *unit fraction* on the board along with a list of examples.

Investigating Equivalent Fractions

WHOLE-CLASS ACTIVITY

PROBLEM SOLVING

(*Math Journal 2,* p. 194)

Each partnership uses one set of 32 Fraction Cards. Guide the class through the following activities.

Adjusting the Activity

At first, use the 16 cards on Activity Sheets 5 and 6. Then use the full deck of 32 cards.

AUDITORY • KINESTHETIC • TACTILE • VISUAL

Have children find the $\frac{1}{2}$ card. Their task is to find as many other cards in the deck as they can that have exactly the same amount shaded. Demonstrate side-by-side comparisons for exact matches. As children name fractions equivalent to $\frac{1}{2}$, they record them in the Table of Equivalent Fractions on journal page 194. Remind them that these fractions are called **equivalent fractions.** Equivalent fractions name the same fractional part of the ONE. Have children find cards with fractions equivalent to the $\frac{1}{3}$ card and record them in the table.

Repeat with the $\frac{2}{3}$ card, checking for patterns and predictions before matching equivalent Fraction Cards.

Partners then sort the rest of the cards into as many sets of equivalent fractions as they can and record them in the table.

Bring the class together to share the equivalent fractions found in the deck and the patterns they observed among the equivalent fractions.

Student Page

Date Time

LESSON 8·5 **Table of Equivalent Fractions**

Use your deck of Fraction Cards to find equivalent fractions. Record them in the table.

Fraction	Equivalent Fractions
$\frac{0}{2}$	$\frac{0}{4}$
$\frac{1}{2}$	$\frac{2}{4}$, $\frac{3}{6}$, $\frac{4}{8}$, $\frac{5}{10}$, $\frac{6}{12}$
$\frac{2}{2}$	$\frac{4}{4}$, $\frac{5}{5}$, $\frac{9}{9}$
$\frac{1}{3}$	$\frac{2}{6}$, $\frac{3}{9}$, $\frac{4}{12}$
$\frac{2}{3}$	$\frac{4}{6}$, $\frac{6}{9}$, $\frac{8}{12}$
$\frac{1}{4}$	$\frac{2}{8}$
$\frac{3}{4}$	$\frac{6}{8}$
$\frac{1}{5}$	$\frac{2}{10}$
$\frac{4}{5}$	$\frac{8}{10}$
$\frac{1}{6}$	$\frac{2}{12}$
$\frac{5}{6}$	$\frac{10}{12}$

Describe any patterns you see.

Sample answers: Each of the fractions equivalent to $\frac{2}{2}$ has the same numerator and denominator. Except for the row of fractions equivalent to $\frac{2}{2}$, all the numerators and denominators in each row are multiples of the numerators and denominators of the given fraction for that row.

Math Journal 2, p. 194

Identifying Equivalent Fractions

WHOLE-CLASS ACTIVITY

(*Math Journal 2,* p. 191)

Discuss how to use the Fraction Number-Line Poster to identify equivalent fractions.

Ask: *What part of the fourths strip is the same size as $\frac{1}{2}$ of the ONE strip?* $\frac{2}{4}$ *Is $\frac{2}{4}$ another name for $\frac{1}{2}$?* Yes *What are some other names on the Fraction Number-Line Poster for $\frac{1}{2}$?* $\frac{3}{6}$, $\frac{4}{8}$

Show how to place a straightedge vertically on the page next to the fraction $\frac{1}{2}$ to find fractions equivalent to $\frac{1}{2}$. Have children use a straightedge to find other names for $\frac{1}{4}$, for $\frac{3}{4}$, for $\frac{1}{3}$, for $\frac{2}{3}$, and for 1. (You may need to point out that equivalent fractions may not line up exactly if they are off slightly in the gluing or cutting. Because the intervals are so large, the error should not prevent children from finding the equivalencies.)

Ask: *If the ONE strip were divided into 10 equal parts, how many of these parts would be the same size as $\frac{1}{2}$ of the ONE strip?* 5 parts *What fraction of the ONE strip is this?* $\frac{5}{10}$

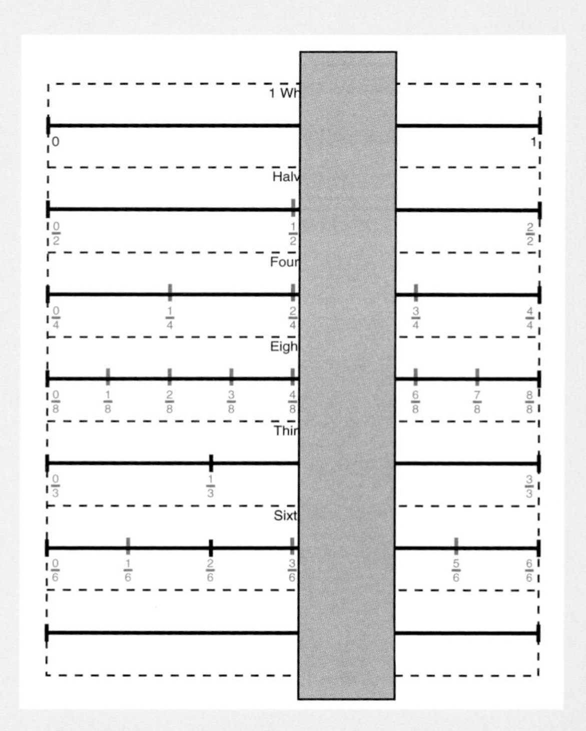

A straightedge highlights equal fractions.

Student Page

Games

Equivalent Fractions Game

Materials □ 1 deck of Fraction Cards (*Math Journal* 2, Activity Sheets 5–8)

Players 2

Skill Recognizing fractions that are equivalent

Object of the game To collect more Fraction Cards.

Directions

1. Shuffle the Fraction Cards and place the deck picture-side down on the table.
2. Turn the top card over near the deck of cards.
3. Players take turns. When it is your turn, turn over the top card from the deck. Try to match this card with a picture-side up card on the table.
   - If you find a match, take the 2 matching cards. Then, if there are no cards left picture-side up, turn the top card over near the deck.
   - If you cannot find a match, place your card picture-side up next to the other cards. Your turn is over.
4. The game ends when all cards have been matched. The player with more cards wins.

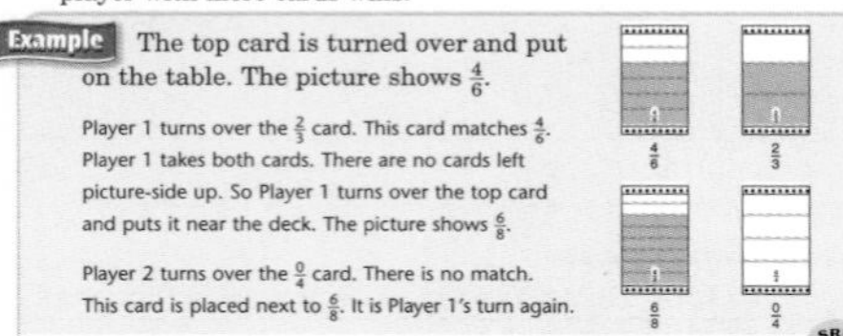

Example The top card is turned over and put on the table. The picture shows $\frac{4}{6}$.

Player 1 turns over the $\frac{2}{3}$ card. This card matches $\frac{4}{6}$. Player 1 takes both cards. There are no cards left picture-side up. So Player 1 turns over the top card and puts it near the deck. The picture shows $\frac{6}{8}$.

Player 2 turns over the $\frac{0}{4}$ card. There is no match. This card is placed next to $\frac{6}{8}$. It is Player 1's turn again.

two hundred eighty-three SRB 283

Student Reference Book, p. 283

Student Page

Games

Equivalent Fractions Game

(Advanced Version)

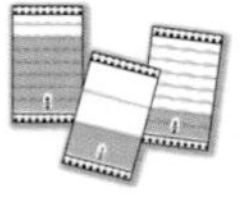

Materials □ 1 deck of Fraction Cards (*Math Journal 2,* Activity Sheets 5–8)

Players 2

Skill Recognizing fractions that are equivalent

Object of the game To collect more Fraction Cards.

Directions

1. Shuffle the Fraction Cards and place the deck picture-side down on the table.
2. Turn the top card over near the deck of cards.
3. Players take turns. When it is your turn, take the top card from the deck, **but do not turn it over** (keep the picture side down). Try to match the fraction with one of the picture-side up cards on the table.
   - If you find a match, turn the card over to see if you matched the cards correctly. If you did, take both cards. Then, if there are no cards left picture-side up, turn the top card over.
   - If there is no match, place your card next to the other cards, picture-side up. Your turn is over.
   - If there is a match but you did not find it, the other player can take the matching cards.
4. The game ends when all cards have been matched. The player with more cards wins.

SRB 284 two hundred eighty-four

Student Reference Book, p. 284

▶ Playing the *Equivalent Fractions Game*

WHOLE-CLASS ACTIVITY

(*Student Reference Book,* pp. 283 and 284)

Have children read the rules for the *Equivalent Fractions Game* on page 283 in the *Student Reference Book*. Demonstrate how to play the game.

Before children put their cards in their tool kits, they should store them in an envelope. The Fraction Cards will be used again in Lesson 8-6.

Adjusting the Activity

Another version of *Equivalent Fractions Game* has players match the fraction sides of cards with the picture sides of the cards. The rules for this version are on page 284 in the *Student Reference Book.*

AUDITORY ◆ KINESTHETIC ◆ TACTILE ◆ VISUAL

2 Ongoing Learning & Practice

▶ Playing *The Block-Drawing Game*

SMALL-GROUP ACTIVITY

(*Math Masters,* p. 398; *Student Reference Book,* pp. 280 and 281)

Children practice making and testing predictions by playing *The Block-Drawing Game,* introduced in Lesson 8-2. Detailed directions are on pages 280 and 281 in the *Student Reference Book*. Have children record their predictions on an Exit Slip (*Math Masters,* page 398).

Ongoing Assessment: Recognizing Student Achievement

Exit Slip

Use an **Exit Slip** (*Math Masters,* page 398) to assess children's progress toward making and testing predictions for simple experiments. Children are making adequate progress if they make reasonable predictions based on the data collected from the draws. Some children may be able to make the connection between the number of draws made and the reliability of their predictions.

[Data and Chance Goal 4]

▶ Math Boxes 8•5

INDEPENDENT ACTIVITY

(*Math Journal 2,* p. 195)

Mixed Practice Math Boxes in this lesson are paired with Math Boxes in Lesson 8-7. The skill in Problem 6 previews Unit 9 content.

▶ Home Link 8•5

INDEPENDENT ACTIVITY

(*Math Masters,* pp. 252 and 253)

Home Connection Children shade fractions of regions, identify fractions of sets, and identify equivalent fractions.

3 Differentiation Options

READINESS

SMALL-GROUP ACTIVITY

▶ Shading Equivalent Fractions of Regions

5–15 Min

(*Math Masters,* p. 254)

To provide experience with equivalent fractions, have children shade regions of similar shapes on *Math Masters,* page 254.

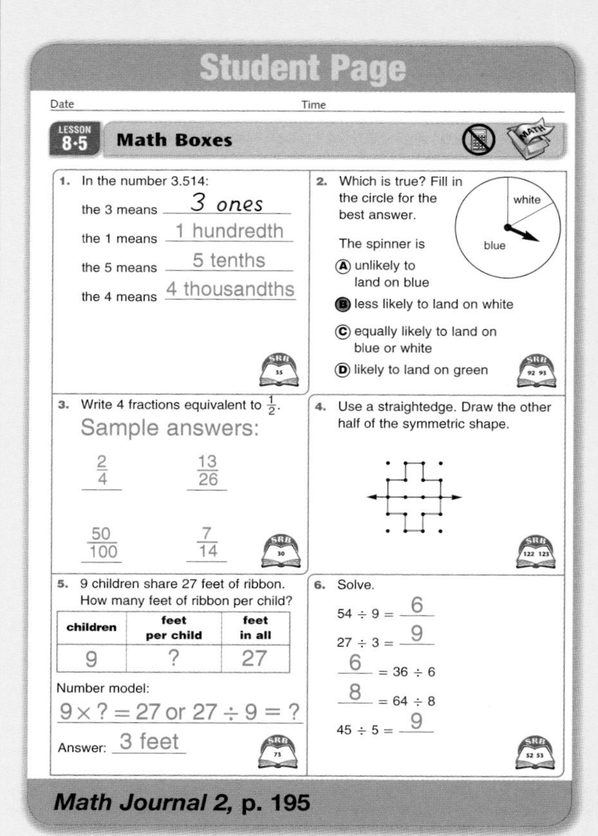

Student Page

Date Time

LESSON 8•5 **Math Boxes**

1. In the number 3.514:
   the 3 means 3 ones
   the 1 means 1 hundredth
   the 5 means 5 tenths
   the 4 means 4 thousandths

2. Which is true? Fill in the circle for the best answer.
   The spinner is
   (A) unlikely to land on blue
   (B) less likely to land on white
   (C) equally likely to land on blue or white
   (D) likely to land on green

3. Write 4 fractions equivalent to $\frac{1}{2}$.
   Sample answers:
   $\frac{2}{4}$ $\frac{13}{26}$ $\frac{50}{100}$ $\frac{7}{14}$

4. Use a straightedge. Draw the other half of the symmetric shape.

5. 9 children share 27 feet of ribbon. How many feet of ribbon per child?

children	feet per child	feet in all
9	?	27

Number model: $9 \times ? = 27$ or $27 \div 9 = ?$

Answer: 3 feet

6. Solve.
   $54 \div 9 = 6$
   $27 \div 3 = 9$
   $6 = 36 \div 6$
   $8 = 64 \div 8$
   $45 \div 5 = 9$

Math Journal 2, p. 195

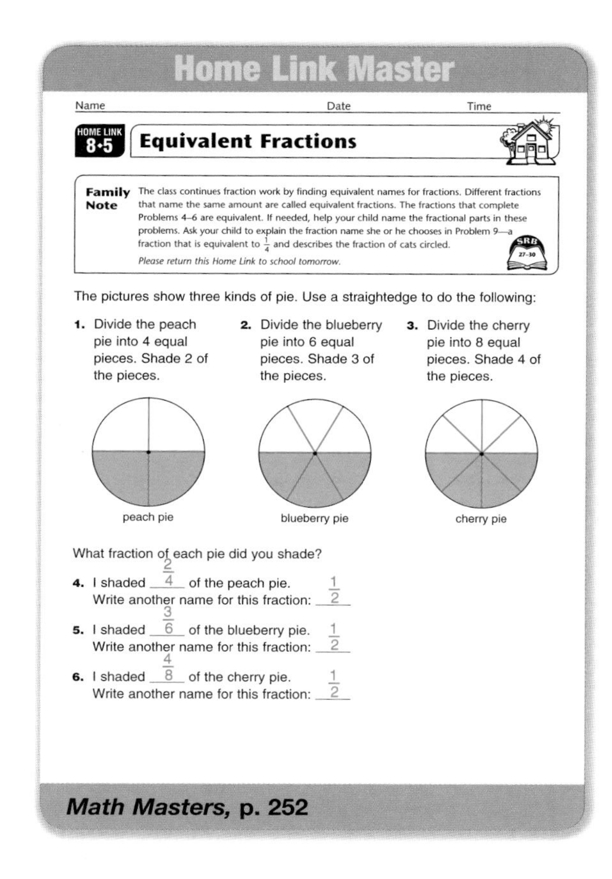

Home Link Master

Name Date Time

HOME LINK 8•5 **Equivalent Fractions**

Family Note The class continues fraction work by finding equivalent names for fractions. Different fractions that name the same amount are called equivalent fractions. The fractions that complete Problems 4–6 are equivalent. If needed, help your child name the fractional parts in these problems. Ask your child to explain the fraction name she or he chooses in Problem 9—a fraction that is equivalent to $\frac{1}{4}$ and describes the fraction of cats circled.

Please return this Home Link to school tomorrow.

The pictures show three kinds of pie. Use a straightedge to do the following:

1. Divide the peach pie into 4 equal pieces. Shade 2 of the pieces.
2. Divide the blueberry pie into 6 equal pieces. Shade 3 of the pieces.
3. Divide the cherry pie into 8 equal pieces. Shade 4 of the pieces.

What fraction of each pie did you shade?

4. I shaded $\frac{2}{4}$ of the peach pie. Write another name for this fraction: $\frac{1}{2}$
5. I shaded $\frac{3}{6}$ of the blueberry pie. Write another name for this fraction: $\frac{1}{2}$
6. I shaded $\frac{4}{8}$ of the cherry pie. Write another name for this fraction: $\frac{1}{2}$

Math Masters, p. 252

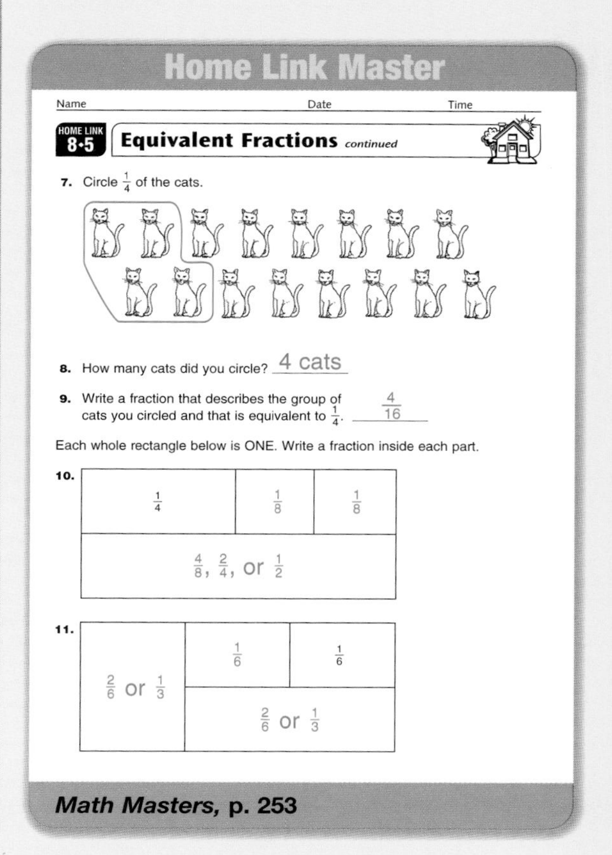

Home Link Master

Name Date Time

HOME LINK 8•5 **Equivalent Fractions** *continued*

7. Circle $\frac{1}{4}$ of the cats.
8. How many cats did you circle? 4 cats
9. Write a fraction that describes the group of cats you circled and that is equivalent to $\frac{1}{4}$. $\frac{4}{16}$

Each whole rectangle below is ONE. Write a fraction inside each part.

10. $\frac{1}{4}$, $\frac{1}{8}$, $\frac{1}{8}$; $\frac{4}{8}$, $\frac{2}{4}$, or $\frac{1}{2}$

11. $\frac{2}{6}$ or $\frac{1}{3}$; $\frac{1}{6}$, $\frac{1}{6}$; $\frac{2}{6}$ or $\frac{1}{3}$

Math Masters, p. 253

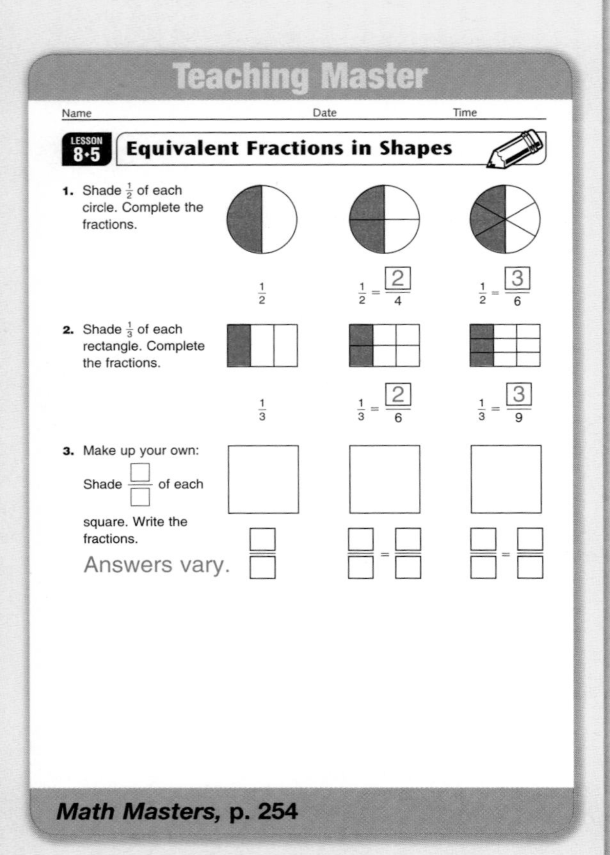
Teaching Master

Name Date Time

LESSON 8·5 **Equivalent Fractions in Shapes**

1. Shade $\frac{1}{2}$ of each circle. Complete the fractions.

$\frac{1}{2}$ $\frac{1}{2} = \frac{2}{4}$ $\frac{1}{2} = \frac{3}{6}$

2. Shade $\frac{1}{3}$ of each rectangle. Complete the fractions.

$\frac{1}{3}$ $\frac{1}{3} = \frac{2}{6}$ $\frac{1}{3} = \frac{3}{9}$

3. Make up your own: Shade $\frac{\square}{\square}$ of each square. Write the fractions.

Answers vary.

Math Masters, p. 254

ENRICHMENT

▶ Looking for a Rule

5–15 Min

(*Math Journal 2,* p. 194; *Math Masters,* p. 255)

To apply children's understanding of equivalent fractions, have them look for a rule about how fractions equivalent to $\frac{1}{2}$ are related to one another. (For example, equivalent fractions can be generated by multiplying the numerator and the denominator by the same whole number.) They use their rule to complete the remaining problems on *Math Masters,* page 255.

NOTE Not every pair of equivalent fractions can be found easily with this rule, for example, $\frac{3}{6}$ and $\frac{4}{8}$. However, applying the rule when one of the fractions is a unit fraction is usually easy. For example, if the numerator and denominator of $\frac{1}{3}$ are multiplied by 2, the result is the equivalent fraction $\frac{2}{6}$; if the multiplier is 3, the result is $\frac{3}{9}$, and so on.

ENRICHMENT

SMALL-GROUP ACTIVITY

▶ Making Name-Collection Boxes for Fractions

To apply children's understanding of fraction concepts, have them work in small groups to make poster-size name-collection boxes for familiar fractions. Encourage them to include region, collection, and number-line representations as well as equivalent fractions, expressions with numbers, and expressions with words. Assign each small group a fraction for their name-collection box—for example, $\frac{1}{3}$ or $\frac{1}{4}$.

ELL SUPPORT

▶ Building a Math Word Bank

(*Differentiation Handbook,* p. 132)

To provide language support for fractions, have children use the Word Bank template found on *Differentiation Handbook,* page 132. Ask children to write the term *equivalent fraction,* draw a picture representing the term, and write other related words. See the *Differentiation Handbook* for more information.

Teaching Master

Name Date Time

LESSON 8·5 **Rules for Equivalent Fractions**

1. Look at *Math Journal 2,* page 194. Record the fractions equivalent to $\frac{1}{2}$ below. As you record them, put them in an order that will help you find a pattern.

$\frac{1}{2}$	$\frac{2}{4}$	$\frac{3}{6}$	$\frac{4}{8}$	$\frac{5}{10}$	$\frac{6}{12}$

2. Use your pattern to write a rule for finding equivalent fractions. Write your rule on the lines below. Sample answer: Multiply the numerator and denominator by the same whole number to find equivalent fractions.

Try your rule to see whether it works. List 3 other fractions equivalent to $\frac{1}{2}$ using your rule. (Use pictures or counters to check your fractions.) $\frac{7}{14}$ $\frac{8}{16}$ $\frac{9}{18}$

3. Use your rule to find 2 fractions equivalent to $\frac{1}{3}$. $\frac{2}{6}$ $\frac{3}{9}$ Check your answers with the Fraction Cards.

Try This

4. Use your rule to find equivalent fractions for the fractions in the table below. Show any work that you do on the back of this page.

Sample answers:

Fraction	Equivalent Fractions
$\frac{1}{8}$	$\frac{2}{16}, \frac{3}{24}, \frac{4}{32}, \frac{5}{40}$
$\frac{5}{8}$	$\frac{10}{16}, \frac{15}{24}, \frac{20}{32}$
$\frac{2}{9}$	$\frac{4}{18}, \frac{6}{27}, \frac{8}{36}$

Math Masters, p. 255

8•6 Comparing Fractions

Objective To guide children as they compare fractions using region models.

Technology Resources www.everydaymathonline.com

ePresentations

eToolkit

Algorithms Practice

EM Facts Workshop Game™

Family Letters

Assessment Management

Common Core State Standards

Curriculum Focal Points

Interactive Teacher's Lesson Guide

1 Teaching the Lesson

Key Concepts and Skills

- Read fractions.
  [Number and Numeration Goal 2]
- Compare fractions to $\frac{1}{2}$.
  [Number and Numeration Goal 6]
- Use an area model to compare fractions.
  [Number and Numeration Goal 6]
- Identify patterns and relationships between numerators and denominators of fractions.
  [Patterns, Functions, and Algebra Goal 1]

Key Activities

Children use Fraction Cards to identify fractions that are greater than $\frac{1}{2}$, less than $\frac{1}{2}$, equal to $\frac{1}{2}$, close to 0, and close to 1.
Children play *Fraction Top-It.*

Materials

Student Reference Book, pp. 287 and 288
Home Link 8•5
Fraction Cards

2 Ongoing Learning & Practice

Playing *Fraction Top-It*
Student Reference Book, pp. 287 and 288
per partnership: 1 deck of Fraction Cards
Children practice comparing fractions.

Math Boxes 8•6
Math Journal 2, p. 196
Children practice and maintain skills through Math Box problems.

Ongoing Assessment: Recognizing Student Achievement
Use Math Boxes, Problem 2.
[Measurement and Reference Frames Goal 3]

Home Link 8•6
Math Masters, p. 256
Children practice and maintain skills through Home Link activities.

3 Differentiation Options

READINESS

Exploring Fraction Patterns
Math Masters, p. 257
straightedge
Children construct fractions on a grid.

ENRICHMENT

Comparing and Ordering Fractions
per group: 2 six-sided dice, 3" by 5" index cards, 3 sheets of $8\frac{1}{2}$" by 11" paper
Children compare and order fractions.

Advance Preparation

For the optional Enrichment activity in Part 3, label three sheets of blank $8\frac{1}{2}$" by 11" paper with one of the following measures: 0, $\frac{1}{2}$, and 1.

Mathematical Practices
SMP2, SMP5, **SMP6,** SMP7, **SMP8**
Content Standards
3.NF.2, 3.NF.3a, 3.NF.3b, 3.NF.3d

Getting Started

Mental Math and Reflexes

Pose problems like the following:

●○○ 3 [30s] 90
30 [30s] 900
300 [30s] 9,000

●●○ 70 [60s] 4,200
700 [60s] 42,000
7,000 [60s] 420,000

●●● 50 [400s] 20,000
500 [400s] 200,000
5,000 [400s] 2,000,000

Math Message

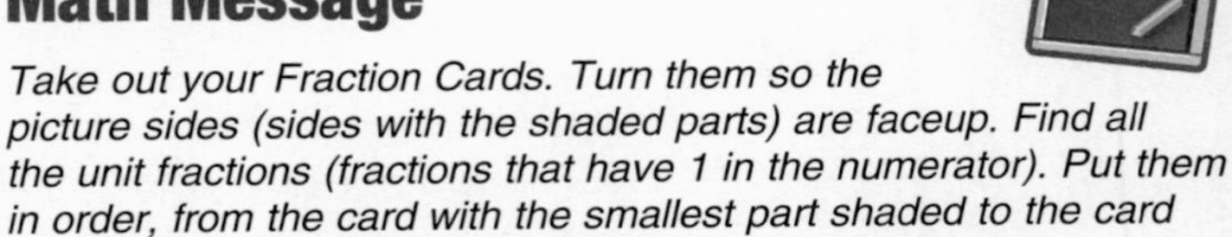

Take out your Fraction Cards. Turn them so the picture sides (sides with the shaded parts) are faceup. Find all the unit fractions (fractions that have 1 in the numerator). Put them in order, from the card with the smallest part shaded to the card with the largest part shaded. What pattern do you notice?

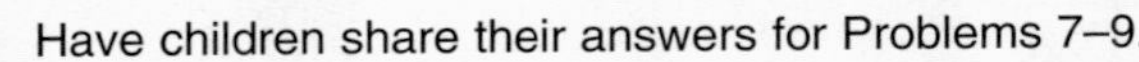

Home Link 8·5 Follow-Up

Have children share their answers for Problems 7–9.

1 Teaching the Lesson

▶ Math Message Follow-Up

WHOLE-CLASS DISCUSSION

Check to make sure that children have their unit fraction cards in order from smallest to largest ($\frac{1}{6}$, $\frac{1}{5}$, $\frac{1}{4}$, $\frac{1}{3}$, and $\frac{1}{2}$). Have them share their observations about the cards. Expect children to point out that all of the fractions have 1 in the numerator and that the denominators get smaller from left to right. Guide children to conclude that when the numerators are the same, the larger the denominator, the smaller the shaded part, and, therefore, the smaller the fraction. Ask children to use different fraction cards to show that this holds true for other fractions with the same numerator.

Next, have children find and order the following fraction cards from smallest to largest: $\frac{2}{10}$, $\frac{5}{10}$, and $\frac{8}{10}$. Ask: *What do you notice about the cards?* They each have 10 in the denominator. *Describe which fraction is smallest and which is largest.* Sample answer: The smallest fraction has the smallest numerator and the largest fraction has the largest numerator. Guide them to conclude that when the denominators are the same, the larger the numerator, the larger the shaded part, and, therefore, the larger the fraction. Ask children to use different fraction cards to show that this holds true for other fractions with the same denominator.

▶ Comparing Fractions to $\frac{1}{2}$, 0, and 1

Ask children to take out the following Fraction Cards: $\frac{1}{2}$, $\frac{1}{4}$, $\frac{2}{10}$, $\frac{10}{12}$, $\frac{4}{8}$, $\frac{4}{5}$, $\frac{3}{9}$, $\frac{0}{4}$, $\frac{2}{2}$, and $\frac{2}{3}$. Guide them in the following activities:

- Use the $\frac{1}{2}$ card to help you find all the cards that are less than half-shaded. $\frac{1}{4}$, $\frac{2}{10}$, $\frac{3}{9}$, and $\frac{0}{4}$ Compare the numerators and denominators of these fractions. What do you observe? The numerator is less than half of the denominator. Ask children to name a fraction that is less than half and has a denominator of 8. Sample answers: $\frac{3}{8}$, $\frac{2}{8}$, $\frac{1}{8}$, $\frac{0}{8}$
- Find all the cards that are more than half-shaded. $\frac{4}{5}$, $\frac{2}{2}$, $\frac{10}{12}$, and $\frac{2}{3}$ Compare the numerators and denominators of these fractions. What do you observe? The numerator is more than half of the denominator. Ask children to name a fraction that is more than half and has a denominator of 8. Sample answers: $\frac{5}{8}$, $\frac{6}{8}$, $\frac{7}{8}$, $\frac{8}{8}$, $\frac{9}{8}$, and so on
- Find all the cards that are exactly half-shaded. $\frac{1}{2}$ and $\frac{4}{8}$ Compare the numerators and denominators of these fractions. What do you observe? The numerator is exactly half of the denominator. Ask children to name a fraction that is equal to half and that has a denominator of 12. $\frac{6}{12}$
- Put all the cards back in the deck and take out the following cards: $\frac{1}{4}$, $\frac{3}{4}$, $\frac{1}{5}$, $\frac{4}{5}$, $\frac{1}{6}$, $\frac{5}{6}$, $\frac{2}{10}$, $\frac{8}{10}$, $\frac{2}{12}$, and $\frac{10}{12}$ Find all the cards that show more than $\frac{3}{4}$ of the card shaded. $\frac{5}{6}$, $\frac{10}{12}$, $\frac{4}{5}$, and $\frac{8}{10}$ Ask children which card they used to guide their comparisons. $\frac{3}{4}$ What do you observe about the numerators and denominators of these fractions? When most of a card is shaded, the numerator of the fraction is close to the denominator. The difference between the numerator and denominator is small.
- Find all the cards that show less than $\frac{1}{4}$ of the card shaded. $\frac{1}{5}$, $\frac{2}{10}$, $\frac{1}{6}$, and $\frac{2}{12}$ Ask children which card they used to guide their comparisons. $\frac{1}{4}$ What do you observe about the numerators and denominators of these fractions? When a very small part of a card is shaded, the numerator of the fraction is very small compared to the denominator. The difference between the numerator and denominator is large.

▶ Playing *Fraction Top-It*

(*Student Reference Book*, pp. 287 and 288)

Have children read the rules for *Fraction Top-It* in the *Student Reference Book* on page 287. Demonstrate a few rounds and then have partners play the game.

Student Page

Games

Fraction Top-It

Materials □ 1 deck of Fraction Cards (*Math Journal 2*, Activity Sheets 5–8)

Players 2

Skill Comparing fractions

Object of the game To collect more cards.

Directions

1. Shuffle the Fraction Cards and place the deck picture-side down on the table.
2. Each player turns over a card from the top of the deck. Players compare the shaded parts of the cards. The player with the larger fraction shaded takes both cards.
3. If the shaded parts are equal, the fractions are equivalent. Each player then turns over another card. The player with the larger fraction shaded takes all the cards from both plays.
4. The game is over when all cards have been taken from the deck. The player with more cards wins.

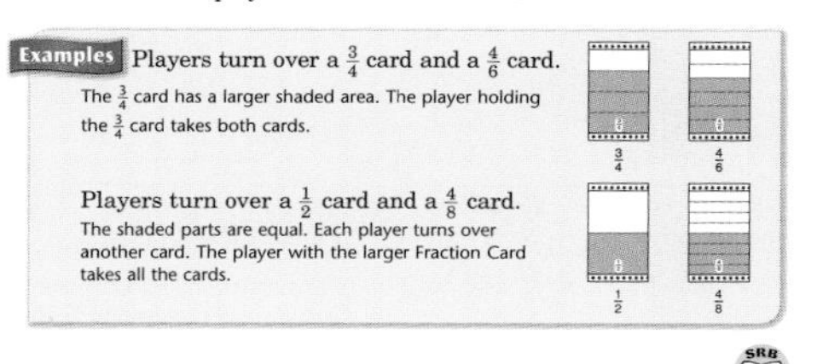
Examples Players turn over a $\frac{3}{4}$ card and a $\frac{4}{6}$ card.
The $\frac{3}{4}$ card has a larger shaded area. The player holding the $\frac{3}{4}$ card takes both cards.

Players turn over a $\frac{1}{2}$ card and a $\frac{4}{8}$ card.
The shaded parts are equal. Each player turns over another card. The player with the larger Fraction Card takes all the cards.

two hundred eighty-seven SRB 287

Student Reference Book, p. 287

Adjusting the Activity

Play the advanced version of *Fraction Top-It*. Directions are on page 288 in the *Student Reference Book.*

AUDITORY ◆ KINESTHETIC ◆ TACTILE ◆ VISUAL

Student Page

Games

Fraction Top-It (Advanced Version)

Materials □ 1 deck of Fraction Cards (*Math Journal 2*, Activity Sheets 5–8)

Players 2

Skill Comparing fractions

Object of the game To collect more cards.

Directions

1. Shuffle the Fraction Cards and place the deck picture-side down on the table.
2. Each player takes a card from the top of the deck **but does not turn it over.** The cards remain picture-side down.
3. Players take turns. When it is your turn:
   - Say whether you think your fraction is greater than, less than, or equivalent to the other player's fraction.
   - Turn the cards over and compare the shaded parts. If you were correct, take both cards. If you were wrong, the other player takes both cards.
4. The game is over when all cards have been taken from the deck. The player with more cards wins.

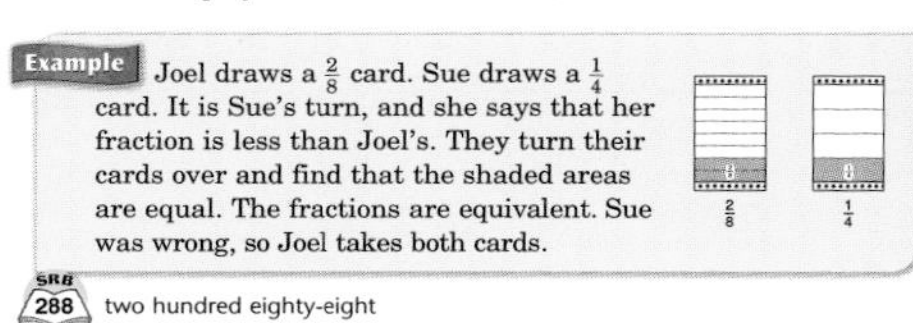
Example Joel draws a $\frac{2}{8}$ card. Sue draws a $\frac{1}{4}$ card. It is Sue's turn, and she says that her fraction is less than Joel's. They turn their cards over and find that the shaded areas are equal. The fractions are equivalent. Sue was wrong, so Joel takes both cards.

SRB 288 two hundred eighty-eight

Student Reference Book, p. 288

Student Page

Date Time

LESSON 8·6 **Math Boxes**

1. Write 4 fractions equivalent to $\frac{1}{4}$.
Sample answers:
$\frac{2}{8}$ $\frac{10}{40}$
$\frac{4}{16}$ $\frac{25}{100}$

2. Complete.
24 hours = 1 day
12 hours = $\frac{1}{2}$ day
3 weeks = 21 days
30 minutes = $\frac{1}{2}$ hour
15 minutes = $\frac{1}{4}$ hour

3. If I wanted to have an equal chance of taking out a circle or a square, I would put in 4 circle(s).

4. Draw a set of 12 Xs. Circle 9 of them. What fraction of the whole set are the 9 Xs?
$\frac{9}{12}$ or $\frac{3}{4}$

5. Solve. Fill in the circle that shows the best answer.
(2 × 90) + 7 = ______
Ⓐ 98
Ⓑ 99
Ⓒ 187
Ⓓ 194

6. Solve. Use your calculator. Pretend the division key is broken.
Christopher and Rochelle are packing 212 cookies in boxes. Each box holds 20 cookies. How many **full** boxes can they pack?
Answer: 10 boxes (unit)

Math Journal 2, p. 196

Home Link Master

Name Date Time

HOME LINK 8·6 **Comparing Fractions to $\frac{1}{2}$**

Family Note Your child's class is comparing fractions to determine whether they are larger, smaller, or equal to $\frac{1}{2}$. Ask your child to explain how to tell which category a fraction fits into. For more on this topic, see *Student Reference Book* pages 13, 31, and 32.
Please return this Home Link to school tomorrow.

Shade each rectangle to match the fraction below it. **Example:** $\frac{2}{4}$

1. $\frac{2}{3}$ 2. $\frac{3}{8}$ 3. $\frac{2}{5}$ 4. $\frac{3}{6}$

5. $\frac{1}{4}$ 6. $\frac{5}{10}$ 7. $\frac{7}{8}$ 8. $\frac{5}{9}$

9. List the fractions above that are greater than $\frac{1}{2}$. $\frac{2}{3}$, $\frac{7}{8}$, $\frac{5}{9}$

10. List the fractions above that are equal to $\frac{1}{2}$. $\frac{3}{6}$, $\frac{5}{10}$

Insert <, >, or = in each problem below. Draw pictures to help you.

11. $\frac{6}{8} > \frac{1}{2}$ 12. $\frac{2}{9} < \frac{1}{2}$

13. $\frac{10}{12} > \frac{1}{2}$ 14. $\frac{6}{12} = \frac{1}{2}$

< means *is less than*
> means *is greater than*
= means *is equal to*

Practice

Solve.

15. 7 × 8 = 56 16. 54 = 6 × 9

17. 8 × 3 = 24 18. 9 × 8 = 72

Math Masters, p. 256

2 Ongoing Learning & Practice

▶ Playing *Fraction Top-It*

PARTNER ACTIVITY

(*Student Reference Book,* pp. 287 and 288)

Children continue to practice comparing fractions by playing *Fraction Top-It.* Have children use half-sheets of paper to record each round using <, >, or = to compare the fraction pairs.

▶ Math Boxes 8·6

INDEPENDENT ACTIVITY

(*Math Journal 2,* p. 196)

Mixed Practice Math Boxes in this lesson are paired with Math Boxes in Lesson 8-8. The skill in Problem 6 previews Unit 9 content.

Ongoing Assessment: Recognizing Student Achievement

Math Boxes Problem 2

Use **Math Boxes, Problem 2** to assess children's ability to describe relationships between equivalent units of time. Children are making adequate progress if they successfully complete Problem 2. Some children may be able to describe the relationship between the number of hours in 1 day and the number of hours in 21 days.

[Measurement and Reference Frames Goal 3]

▶ Home Link 8·6

INDEPENDENT ACTIVITY

(*Math Masters,* p. 256)

Home Connection Children shade rectangles to represent given fractions. They use the shaded rectangles to determine which fractions are greater than or equal to $\frac{1}{2}$. Then they compare fractions without using shaded rectangles.

3 Differentiation Options

READINESS

PARTNER ACTIVITY

5–15 Min

▶ Exploring Fraction Patterns

(*Math Masters,* p. 257)

To explore the patterns between the numerators and denominators of fractions, have children use a straightedge to construct fractions on a grid. When children have finished with *Math Masters,* page 257, have them discuss the patterns they see. Sample answer: Every time the unit fractions are divided in half, the numerators stay the same and the denominators double. The numerators and denominators of the equivalent fractions are multiples. Multiply $\frac{1}{16} \times \frac{1}{2}$ to find the fraction that names the next smallest section, $\frac{1}{32}$. Continue with the pattern to find the next smallest section. $\frac{1}{32} \times \frac{1}{2} = \frac{1}{64}$, and so on.

ENRICHMENT

SMALL-GROUP ACTIVITY

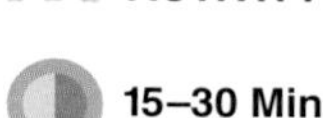
15–30 Min

▶ Comparing and Ordering Fractions

To apply children's understanding of comparing and ordering fractions based on relationships between numerators and denominators, have them make a set of 10 Fraction Cards to compare. Lay out the three labeled $8\frac{1}{2}$" by 11" papers in line from 0 to 1 with space between them. (*See* Advance Preparation.)

Children roll two dice, and make and record a 2-digit number from the digits. They repeat this. They use one of the numbers as the numerator of a fraction and the other as the denominator. (They should begin by making all their fractions less than or equal to one.) They write each fraction on a 3" by 5" index card.

When they have written 10 fractions, have them decide whether to place each fraction between or on the 0, $\frac{1}{2}$, and 1 labels. Some children may be able to put some of the fractions in order.

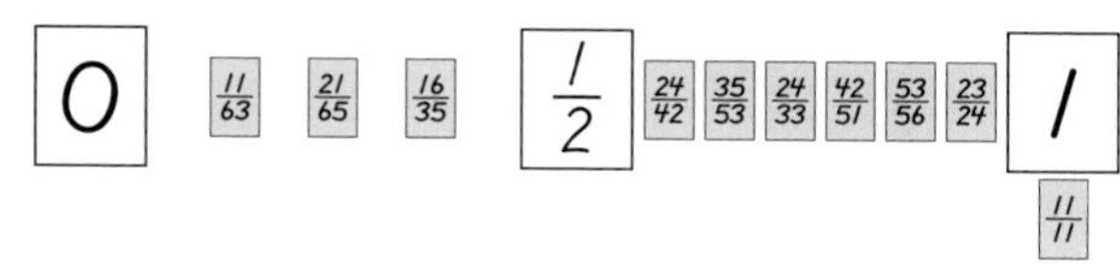

Variation: Roll only 1 die each time instead of 2 to generate 1-digit numbers.

Teaching Master

Name Date Time

LESSON 8•6 **Exploring Fraction Patterns**

For each problem, record your work on the grid below.

1. Use a straightedge to divide the square into halves. Label each $\frac{1}{2}$ on your drawing.

This is the WHOLE or ONE.

2. Use a straightedge to divide one of your halves into 2 equal parts.
   What fraction of the WHOLE is each new section worth? $\frac{1}{4}$
   Write the fraction equivalent to $\frac{1}{2}$. $\frac{2}{4}$
3. Use a straightedge to divide one of your smallest sections into 2 equal parts.
   What fraction of the WHOLE is each new section worth? $\frac{1}{8}$
   Write the fraction equivalent to $\frac{1}{2}$. $\frac{4}{8}$
4. If you were to divide your smallest section into 2 equal parts, what fraction of the WHOLE would each new section be worth? $\frac{1}{16}$ Write the fraction equivalent to $\frac{1}{2}$. $\frac{8}{16}$
5. On the back of your paper, list at least three patterns you notice in the fractions you have made on the grid and the fractions you have written on this paper.

Math Masters, p. 257

8·7 Fractions Greater Than ONE

Objective To demonstrate naming quantities greater than 1 with fractions and mixed numbers.

Technology Resources www.everydaymathonline.com

ePresentations

eToolkit

Algorithms Practice

EM Facts Workshop Game™

Family Letters

Assessment Management

Common Core State Standards

Curriculum Focal Points

Interactive Teacher's Lesson Guide

1 Teaching the Lesson

Key Concepts and Skills

- Shade fractional parts of regions to represent fractions greater than 1.
  [Number and Numeration Goal 2]
- Model and name mixed numbers and fractions.
  [Number and Numeration Goal 2]
- Identify equivalent fractions.
  [Number and Numeration Goal 5]
- Use lines of symmetry to divide figures into equal parts.
  [Geometry Goal 3]

Key Activities

Children model fractions greater than 1 and equivalent mixed numbers by gluing fractional parts of a unit circle onto unit circles. They practice naming numbers of fractional parts as fractions and mixed numbers.

Ongoing Assessment: Informing Instruction See page 685.

Key Vocabulary

mixed number

Materials

Math Journal 2, pp. 197 and 198
Home Link 8•6
Math Masters, p. 436 (one copy per 3 children)
scissors ◆ glue ◆ slates ◆ crayons

2 Ongoing Learning & Practice

Playing the *Equivalent Fractions Game*
Student Reference Book, pp. 283 and 284
per partnership: 1 deck of Fraction Cards, half-sheet of paper
Children practice recognizing equivalent fractions.

Ongoing Assessment: Recognizing Student Achievement
Use the record sheet for the *Equivalent Fractions Game.*
[Number and Numeration Goal 5]

Math Boxes 8·7
Math Journal 2, p. 199
Children practice and maintain skills through Math Box problems.

Home Link 8·7
Math Masters, pp. 258 and 259
Children practice and maintain skills through Home Link activities.

3 Differentiation Options

READINESS
Modeling Fractions of Regions Larger Than One Whole
Math Masters, p. 260
pattern blocks ◆ Pattern-Block Template
Children use pattern blocks to compare fractions of regions to one whole.

ENRICHMENT
Placing Fractions on a Number Line
Math Masters, p. 261
half-sheet of paper
Children write fractions on a number line.

EXTRA PRACTICE
Playing *Fraction Top-It*
Student Reference Book, pp. 287 and 288
per partnership: 1 deck of Fraction Cards (*Math Journal 2,* Activity Sheets 5–8)
Children play *Fraction Top-It.*

ELL SUPPORT
Building a Math Word Bank
Differentiation Handbook, p. 132
Children add the term *mixed number* to their Math Word Banks.

Advance Preparation

Make enough copies of *Math Masters,* page 436 so each child can have one strip of 4 circles. Cut the strips apart and place them next to the Math Message.

Getting Started

Mathematical Practices
SMP1, **SMP2,** SMP3, SMP4, SMP5, **SMP6,** SMP7
Content Standards
3.NF.1, 3.NF.2, 3.NF.2b, 3.NF.3a, 3.NF.3b, 3.NF.3c, 3.G.2

Mental Math and Reflexes

Dictate pairs of decimals. Children write them on their slates and circle the larger number. *Suggestions:*

●○○ twenty-seven hundredths; sixty-seven hundredths 0.27; (0.67)

●●○ five-tenths; five-hundredths (0.5); 0.05
three and six-tenths; three and sixteen-hundredths (3.6); 3.16

●●● seventy-two hundredths; nine-tenths 0.72; (0.9) forty and eighty-three hundredths; forty-eight and three tenths 40.83; (48.3)

Math Message

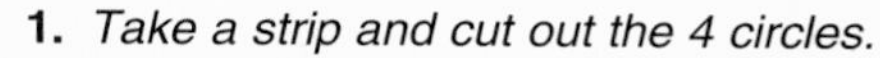

1. *Take a strip and cut out the 4 circles.*

2. *How would you answer the following problems?*

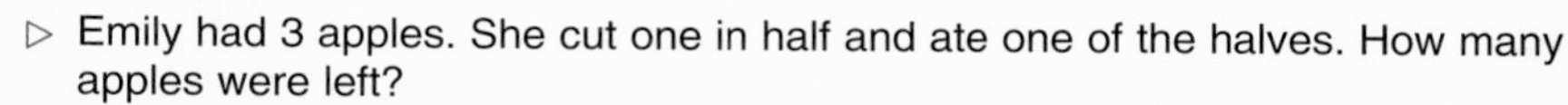

▷ Emily had 3 apples. She cut one in half and ate one of the halves. How many apples were left?

▷ Then she cut each of the other whole apples in half. She gave all the half-apples to her friends. How many half-apples did she give away?

Home Link 8·6 Follow-Up

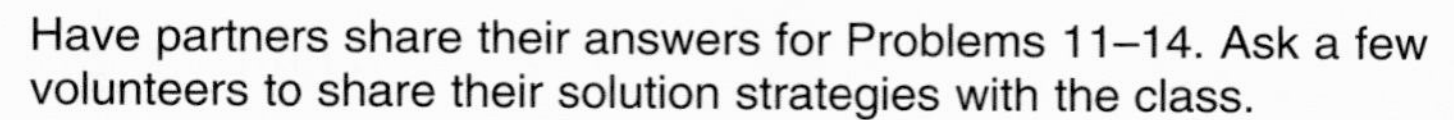

Have partners share their answers for Problems 11–14. Ask a few volunteers to share their solution strategies with the class.

1 Teaching the Lesson

▶ Math Message Follow-Up

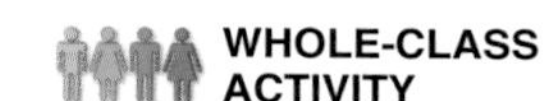

WHOLE-CLASS ACTIVITY

(*Math Masters,* p. 436)

Illustrate the number story in the Math Message on the board.

- Emily had 3 apples. She cut one in half and ate one of the halves. How many apples were left?

$2\frac{1}{2}$ apples

- Then she cut each of the other whole apples in half. She gave all of the half-apples to her friends. How many half-apples did she give away?

Five halves of apples

Write $2\frac{1}{2}$ and $\frac{5}{2}$ on the board. Ask: *Do these numbers—$2\frac{1}{2}$ and $\frac{5}{2}$—name equivalent amounts of apples?* Yes

Teaching Aid Master

Name Date Time

Fractions Greater than One

Math Masters, **p. 436**

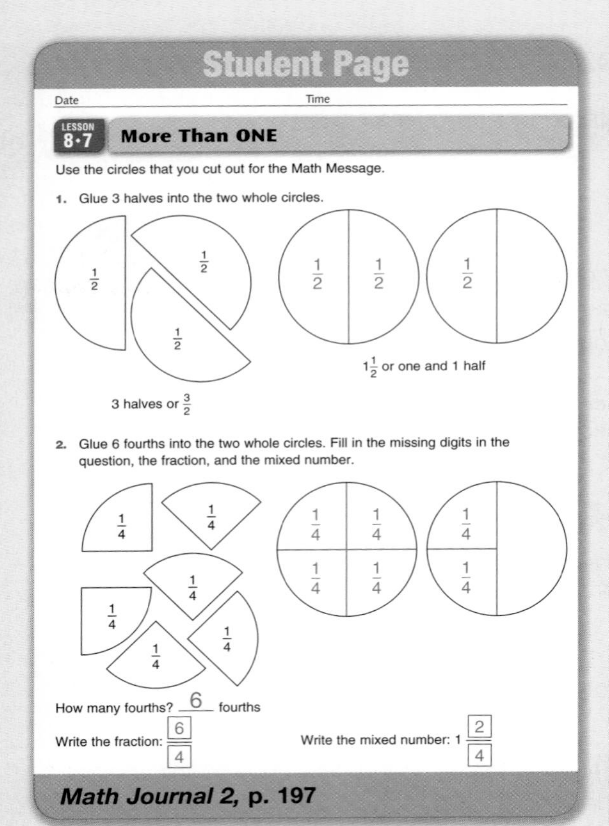
Student Page

Date Time

LESSON 8·7 **More Than ONE**

Use the circles that you cut out for the Math Message.

1. Glue 3 halves into the two whole circles.

$\frac{1}{2}$ $\frac{1}{2}$ $\frac{1}{2}$ $\frac{1}{2}$ $\frac{1}{2}$ $\frac{1}{2}$

3 halves or $\frac{3}{2}$

$1\frac{1}{2}$ or one and 1 half

2. Glue 6 fourths into the two whole circles. Fill in the missing digits in the question, the fraction, and the mixed number.

How many fourths? 6 fourths

Write the fraction: $\frac{6}{4}$

Write the mixed number: $1\frac{2}{4}$

Math Journal 2, p. 197

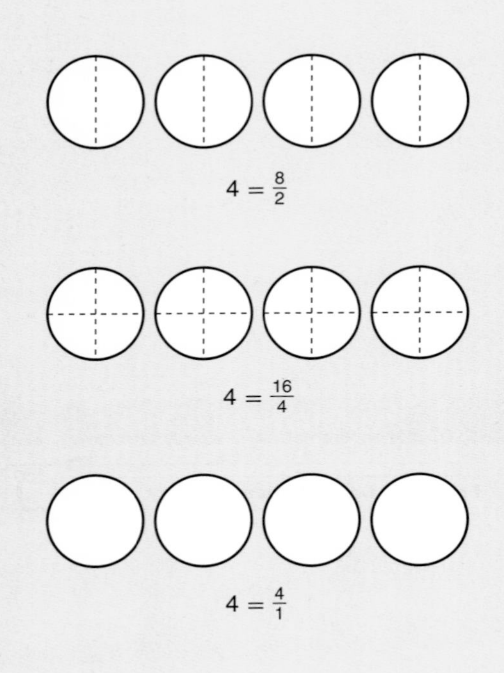

Adjusting the Activity

Ask children whether they can think of ways to name all four circles with an equivalent mixed number, such as $3\frac{4}{4}$ or $2\frac{4}{2}$.

AUDITORY ◆ KINESTHETIC ◆ TACTILE ◆ VISUAL

▶ Naming Fractional Parts Greater Than ONE

(*Math Journal 2,* p. 197; *Math Masters,* p. 436)

First, ask children to take two of the circles they cut out and fold them in half. Write $\frac{1}{2}$ on each half, and then cut each circle along the fold line. Have the class count halves while you write the fractions on the board: *one half* $\frac{1}{2}$ *two halves* $\frac{2}{2}$ *three halves,* STOP.

Ask: *How would you write a fraction that names three halves?* $\frac{3}{2}$ *How is this fraction different from the fractions you have used so far?* The numerator is greater than the denominator.

Draw two pairs of circles on the board. In one pair, divide both circles in half and shade three of the halves. Label the picture $\frac{3}{2}$. In the second pair, divide only one circle in half. Shade one of the halves and the complete circle. Label the picture $1\frac{1}{2}$. Ask children to compare the two pictures. The same amount of space is shaded.

Continue counting: *four halves.* Ask: *What fraction names four halves?* $\frac{4}{2}$

Next, have children glue three of the halves inside the two circles in Problem 1 on journal page 197. Point out that because each circle is ONE, or 1 *whole,* $\frac{3}{2}$ is $\frac{1}{2}$ more than 1, and can be written as $1\frac{1}{2}$. Emphasize that $\frac{3}{2}$ and $1\frac{1}{2}$ are equivalent names and represent the same amount. Write $1\frac{1}{2}$ on the board and explain that the number $1\frac{1}{2}$ is called a **mixed number** because it is made up of a whole number and a fraction.

Ask children to fold the other two circles into four equal parts: Write $\frac{1}{4}$ in each part and cut each circle along the fold lines. Have children glue six of the fourth pieces inside the two remaining circles (in Problem 2) on the journal page. Then they write a fraction that names the six pieces $\frac{6}{4}$ or $\frac{3}{2}$ and a mixed number that names the six pieces $1\frac{2}{4}$ or $1\frac{1}{2}$.

If no one wrote $\frac{3}{2}$ or $1\frac{1}{2}$, ask the class to compare the two pairs of circles for 3 halves and 6 fourths. Ask: *Why is* $\frac{6}{4}$ *equivalent to* $\frac{3}{2}$*? Why is* $1\frac{2}{4}$ *equivalent to* $1\frac{1}{2}$*?* Both name the same amount of circles.

Draw 4 equal-sized circles on the board. Ask children to think of ways to name all four circles with a fraction. From their journal work, children can probably come up with equivalent halves ($\frac{8}{2}$) and fourths ($\frac{16}{4}$). Encourage them to try other denominators. If no one suggests it, ask about $\frac{4}{1}$. Remind them that the denominator of the fraction names the number of parts into which the whole has been divided. If the circles are not divided into parts, then the denominator is 1. Since there are 4 circles, 4 is the number in the numerator.

Ongoing Assessment: Informing Instruction

Watch for children who have difficulty writing mixed numbers. Write them on the board as you say them to provide a visual reference for children.

Links to the Future

The activities in this lesson expose children to the concept of naming fractional parts greater than one as fractions and mixed numbers. Converting between fractions and mixed numbers is a Grade 5 Goal.

Naming Parts with Fractions and Mixed Numbers

PARTNER ACTIVITY

(*Math Journal 2,* p. 198)

You may want to do Problem 3 with the class to make sure children know what is expected. They color a given number of fractional parts of circles and use the resulting diagrams to name them with a fraction and a mixed number. Note that the answer to Problem 6 is a mixed number greater than 2.

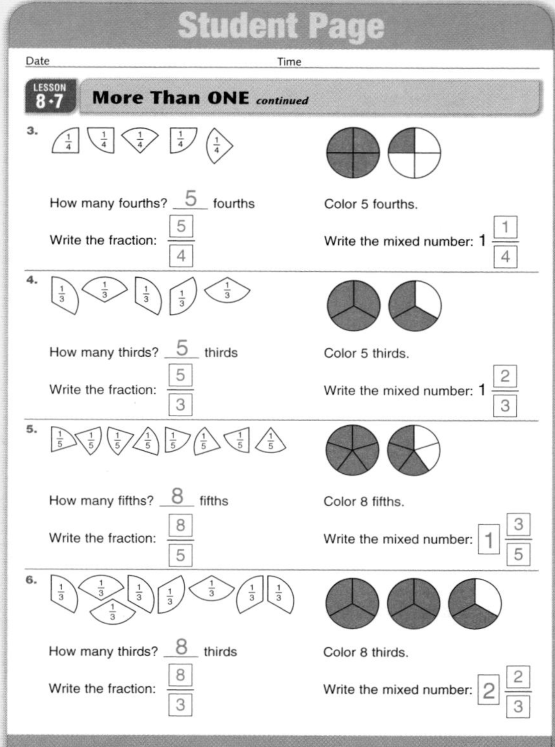

Student Page

Date Time

LESSON 8·7 **More Than ONE** *continued*

3. How many fourths? 5 fourths. Color 5 fourths.
Write the fraction: $\frac{5}{4}$ Write the mixed number: $1\frac{1}{4}$

4. How many thirds? 5 thirds. Color 5 thirds.
Write the fraction: $\frac{5}{3}$ Write the mixed number: $1\frac{2}{3}$

5. How many fifths? 8 fifths. Color 8 fifths.
Write the fraction: $\frac{8}{5}$ Write the mixed number: $1\frac{3}{5}$

6. How many thirds? 8 thirds. Color 8 thirds.
Write the fraction: $\frac{8}{3}$ Write the mixed number: $2\frac{2}{3}$

Math Journal 2, **p. 198**

2 Ongoing Learning & Practice

Playing the *Equivalent Fractions Game*

PARTNER ACTIVITY

(*Student Reference Book,* pp. 283 and 284)

The game was introduced in Lesson 8-5. If necessary, children can read the rules for the *Equivalent Fractions Game* in the *Student Reference Book* on pages 283 and 284. Have children record equivalent fraction pairs they make on a record sheet made from a half-sheet of paper. Remind them to write an = symbol between equivalent fractions.

Ongoing Assessment: Recognizing Student Achievement

Record Sheet

Use the **Record Sheet** for the *Equivalent Fractions Game* to assess children's progress toward using Fraction Cards to find equivalent fractions. Children are making adequate progress if they record at least 2 pairs. Some children may be able to identify equivalent fractions without using the shaded sides of the cards.

[Number and Numeration Goal 5]

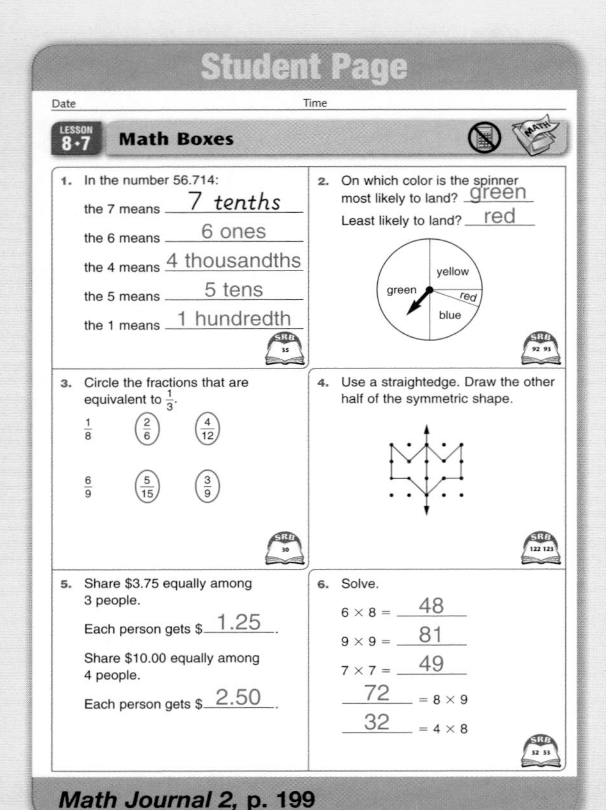
Student Page

Date Time

LESSON 8·7 **Math Boxes**

1. In the number 56.714:
the 7 means 7 tenths
the 6 means 6 ones
the 4 means 4 thousandths
the 5 means 5 tens
the 1 means 1 hundredth

2. On which color is the spinner most likely to land? green
Least likely to land? red

3. Circle the fractions that are equivalent to $\frac{1}{3}$.
$\frac{1}{8}$ $\frac{2}{6}$ $\frac{4}{12}$
$\frac{6}{9}$ $\frac{5}{15}$ $\frac{3}{9}$

4. Use a straightedge. Draw the other half of the symmetric shape.

5. Share $3.75 equally among 3 people.
Each person gets $ 1.25.
Share $10.00 equally among 4 people.
Each person gets $ 2.50.

6. Solve.
6 × 8 = 48
9 × 9 = 81
7 × 7 = 49
72 = 8 × 9
32 = 4 × 8

Math Journal 2, p. 199

▶ Math Boxes 8·7

INDEPENDENT ACTIVITY

(*Math Journal 2,* p. 199)

Mixed Practice Math Boxes in this lesson are paired with Math Boxes in Lesson 8-5. The skill in Problem 6 previews Unit 9 content.

Writing/Reasoning Have children write an answer to the following: *In Problem 5, what does* share equally *mean?* Sample answer: *Share equally* means to divide an amount or a group of things into equal parts. In Problem 5, each person gets an equal amount.

▶ Home Link 8·7

INDEPENDENT ACTIVITY

(*Math Masters,* pp. 258 and 259)

Home Connection Children color figures according to directions and then write fractions and mixed numbers to describe those pictures.

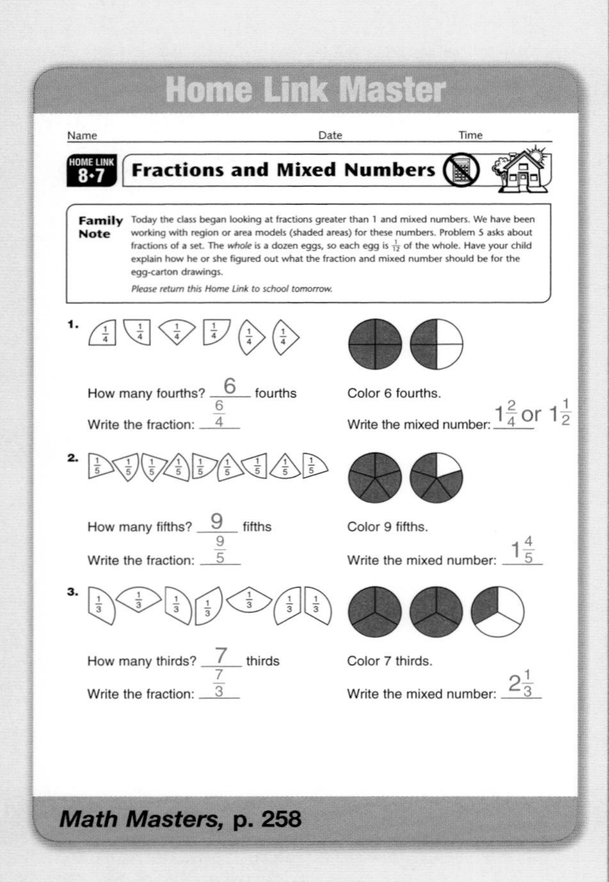
Home Link Master

Name Date Time

HOME LINK 8·7 **Fractions and Mixed Numbers**

Family Note Today the class began looking at fractions greater than 1 and mixed numbers. We have been working with region or area models (shaded areas) for these numbers. Problem 5 asks about fractions of a set. The whole is a dozen eggs, so each egg is $\frac{1}{12}$ of the whole. Have your child explain how he or she figured out what the fraction and mixed number should be for the egg-carton drawings.
Please return this Home Link to school tomorrow.

1. How many fourths? 6 fourths
Write the fraction: $\frac{6}{4}$
Color 6 fourths.
Write the mixed number: $1\frac{2}{4}$ or $1\frac{1}{2}$

2. How many fifths? 9 fifths
Write the fraction: $\frac{9}{5}$
Color 9 fifths.
Write the mixed number: $1\frac{4}{5}$

3. How many thirds? 7 thirds
Write the fraction: $\frac{7}{3}$
Color 7 thirds.
Write the mixed number: $2\frac{1}{3}$

Math Masters, p. 258

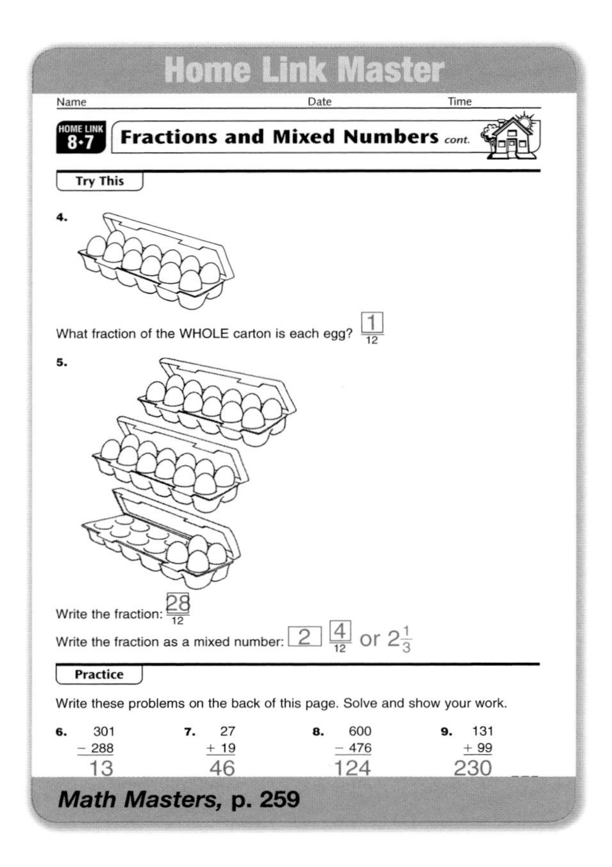
Home Link Master

Name Date Time

HOME LINK 8·7 **Fractions and Mixed Numbers** *cont.*

Try This

4. What fraction of the WHOLE carton is each egg? $\frac{1}{12}$

5. Write the fraction: $\frac{28}{12}$
Write the fraction as a mixed number: 2 $\frac{4}{12}$ or $2\frac{1}{3}$

Practice

Write these problems on the back of this page. Solve and show your work.

6. 301 − 288 = 13
7. 27 + 19 = 46
8. 600 − 476 = 124
9. 131 + 99 = 230

Math Masters, p. 259

3 Differentiation Options

READINESS

INDEPENDENT ACTIVITY

Modeling Fractions of Regions Larger Than One Whole

5–15 Min

(*Math Masters,* p. 260)

To provide experience with comparing fractions of regions to the WHOLE, have children build the shapes on *Math Masters,* page 260 with pattern blocks.

ENRICHMENT

INDEPENDENT ACTIVITY

Placing Fractions on a Number Line

5–15 Min

(*Math Masters,* p. 261)

To apply children's understanding of mixed numbers, have them identify and locate numbers between consecutive whole numbers on a number line. Have children discuss how they decided where to place their fractions on the number lines.

EXTRA PRACTICE

PARTNER ACTIVITY

Playing *Fraction Top-It*

5–15 Min

(*Student Reference Book,* pp. 287 and 288)

To provide practice with comparing fractions, have children play *Fraction Top-It,* which was introduced in Lesson 8-6. Children may play the advanced version of the game. If necessary, they can read the rules for both versions of *Fraction Top-It* in the *Student Reference Book* on pages 287 and 288.

ELL SUPPORT

SMALL-GROUP ACTIVITY

Building a Math Word Bank

5–15 Min

(*Differentiation Handbook,* p. 132)

To provide language support for fractions, have children use the Word Bank template found on *Differentiation Handbook,* page 132. Ask children to write the term *mixed number,* draw a picture representing the term, and write other related words. See the *Differentiation Handbook* for more information.

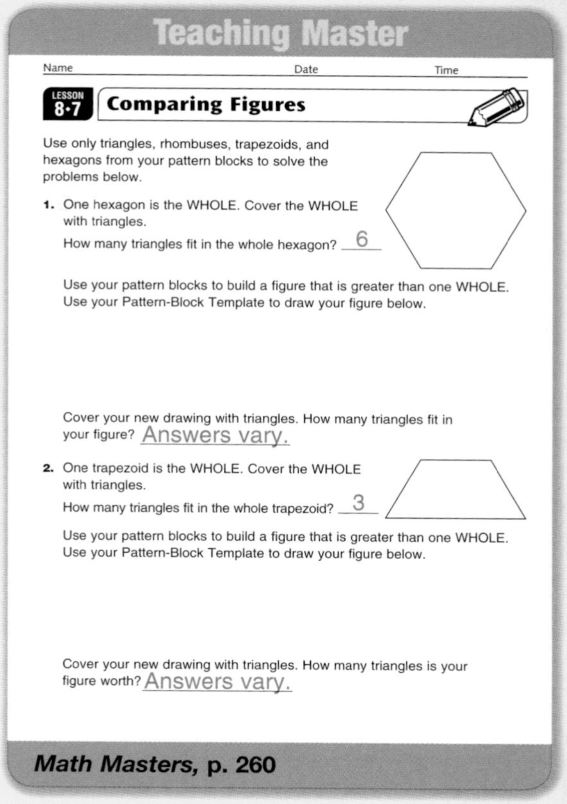

Teaching Master

Name Date Time

LESSON 8·7 **Comparing Figures**

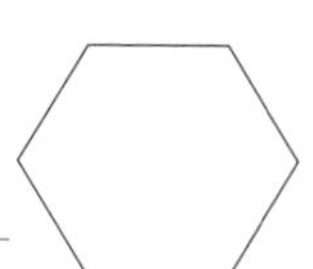

Use only triangles, rhombuses, trapezoids, and hexagons from your pattern blocks to solve the problems below.

1. One hexagon is the WHOLE. Cover the WHOLE with triangles.
   How many triangles fit in the whole hexagon? 6

   Use your pattern blocks to build a figure that is greater than one WHOLE. Use your Pattern-Block Template to draw your figure below.

   Cover your new drawing with triangles. How many triangles fit in your figure? Answers vary.

2. One trapezoid is the WHOLE. Cover the WHOLE with triangles.
   How many triangles fit in the whole trapezoid? 3

   Use your pattern blocks to build a figure that is greater than one WHOLE. Use your Pattern-Block Template to draw your figure below.

   Cover your new drawing with triangles. How many triangles is your figure worth? Answers vary.

Math Masters, p. 260

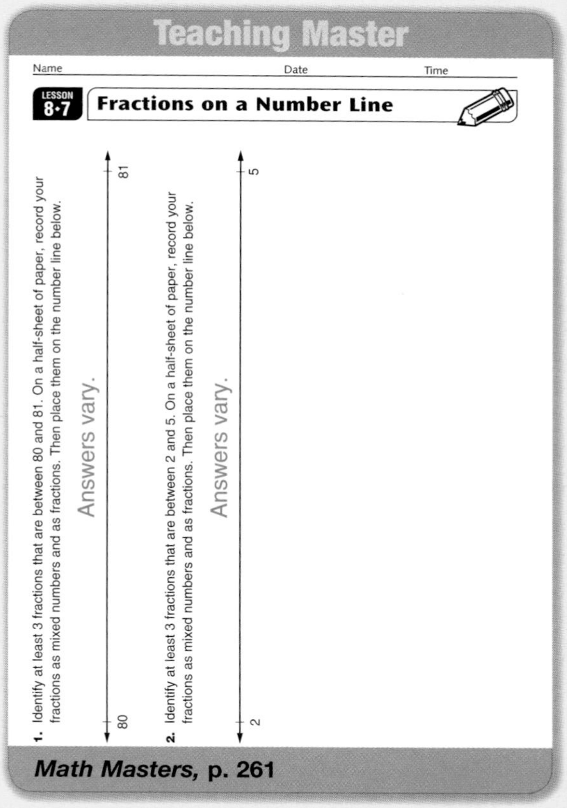

Teaching Master

Name Date Time

LESSON 8·7 **Fractions on a Number Line**

1. Identify at least 3 fractions that are between 80 and 81. On a half-sheet of paper, record your fractions as mixed numbers and as fractions. Then place them on the number line below.
   Answers vary.
   80 — 81

2. Identify at least 3 fractions that are between 2 and 5. On a half-sheet of paper, record your fractions as mixed numbers and as fractions. Then place them on the number line below.
   Answers vary.
   2 — 5

Math Masters, p. 261

8•8 Fractions in Number Stories

Objective To provide experiences with solving number stories involving fractions.

www.everydaymathonline.com

ePresentations

eToolkit

Algorithms Practice

EM Facts Workshop Game™

Family Letters

Assessment Management

Common Core State Standards

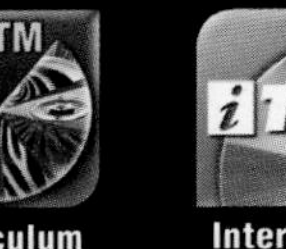

Curriculum Focal Points

Interactive Teacher's Lesson Guide

1 Teaching the Lesson

Key Concepts and Skills

- Use pennies, counters, or pictures to solve fraction number stories.
  [Number and Numeration Goal 2]
- Describe solution strategies for solving fraction number stories.
  [Number and Numeration Goal 2]
- Use Fraction Cards to compare fractions.
  [Number and Numeration Goal 6]
- Measure and draw a line segment to the nearest $\frac{1}{4}$ inch.
  [Measurement and Reference Frames Goal 1]

Key Activities

The teacher and children make up and solve number stories involving fractions. Children practice solving fraction number stories independently.

Ongoing Assessment: Informing Instruction See page 689.

Ongoing Assessment: Recognizing Student Achievement
Use journal page 201.
[Number and Numeration Goal 2]

Materials

Math Journal 2, pp. 200 and 201
Home Link 8•7
inch ruler ◆ pennies or counters (optional) ◆ Fraction Cards (optional) ◆ tool-kit clock (optional) ◆ slate

2 Ongoing Learning & Practice

Reviewing the Line Plot Routine
Student Reference Book, pp. 79–81
stick-on notes
Children describe landmarks on a line plot and compare chances for two different events.

Math Boxes 8•8
Math Journal 2, p. 202
Children practice and maintain skills through Math Box problems.

Home Link 8•8
Math Masters, p. 262
Children practice and maintain skills through Home Link activities.

3 Differentiation Options

ENRICHMENT

Solving *Math Curse* Number Stories
Math Curse ◆ paper
Children solve and write fraction number stories based on those found in the book *Math Curse.*

EXTRA PRACTICE

Minute Math+
Minute Math®+, pp. 86, 90, 92, and 155
Children solve number stories with fractions.

Advance Preparation

Prepare the line plot (pictured on page 692) for Part 2. For the optional Enrichment activity in Part 3, obtain a copy of the book ***Math Curse*** by Jon Scieszka and Lane Smith (Viking, 1995).

***Teacher's Reference Manual,* Grades 1–3** pp. 225–227

Getting Started

Mathematical Practices
SMP1, SMP2, **SMP3,** SMP4, **SMP5,** SMP6
Content Standards
3.NF.2, 3.NF.2a, 3.NF.2b, 3.NF.3, 3.NF.3a, 3.NF.3c, 3.NF.3d, 3.MD.4

Mental Math and Reflexes

Pose problems like the following as children write the answers on slates. They may use tool-kit clocks as needed.

●○○ 1 minute = _____ seconds 60
1 hour = _____ minutes 60
$\frac{1}{2}$ hour = _____ minutes 30

●●○ $\frac{1}{4}$ hour = _____ minutes 15
$\frac{2}{4}$ hour = _____ minutes 30
$\frac{3}{4}$ hour = _____ minutes 45

●●● $\frac{1}{3}$ hour = _____ minutes 20
$\frac{1}{12}$ hour = _____ minutes 5
$\frac{1}{6}$ hour = _____ minutes 10

Math Message

Using your ruler, draw a line segment that is $1\frac{3}{4}$ inches long on your slate. Divide the line segment into $\frac{1}{4}$-inch segments. How many $\frac{1}{4}$-inch segments are there?

PROBLEM SOLVING

Home Link 8·7 Follow-Up

Go over the answer to Problem 5. The diagram shows 2 wholes and $\frac{4}{12}$ (or $\frac{1}{3}$) of a whole. The corresponding mixed number, then, is $2\frac{4}{12}$ (or $2\frac{1}{3}$). You may want to have children write number models for Problems 1–3. *For example:*

Problem 1: $\frac{1}{4} + \frac{1}{4} + \frac{1}{4} + \frac{1}{4} + \frac{1}{4} + \frac{1}{4} = \frac{6}{4}$, or $1\frac{2}{4}$, or $1\frac{1}{2}$

1 Teaching the Lesson

▶ Math Message Follow-Up

WHOLE-CLASS DISCUSSION

If an overhead projector is available, use it to go over the solution. Lead children to the conclusion that since there are seven $\frac{1}{4}$-inch segments, the line segment is $\frac{7}{4}$ inches long. $\frac{7}{4}$ inches is another name for $1\frac{3}{4}$ inches.

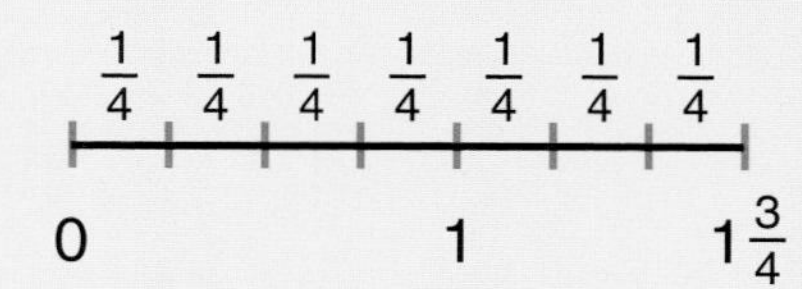

Math Message solution

▶ Writing and Solving Fraction Number Stories

WHOLE-CLASS ACTIVITY

PROBLEM SOLVING

You and the children make up stories involving fractions of sets. Children solve the problems in any way they can—using pennies or counters, drawing pictures or doodles, and so on. You might want to begin with stories such as the following:

- Andy bought 24 stamps for his stamp collection. $\frac{3}{4}$ of the stamps were from the United States. How many stamps were from the United States? 18 stamps

Possible solution strategy: Take 24 coins or counters and divide them into 4 equal sets. Each set consists of 6 counters and is $\frac{1}{4}$ of the total, so $\frac{1}{4}$ of 24 = 6. Three sets consist of 18 counters and are $\frac{3}{4}$ of the total, so $\frac{3}{4}$ of 24 = 18.

Adjusting the Activity

Extend the line segment $\frac{1}{4}$ inch. Think of the line segment as part of a number line from 0 to 2. With children, label the points that are $\frac{1}{4}$ inch apart.

AUDITORY ◆ KINESTHETIC ◆ TACTILE ◆ VISUAL

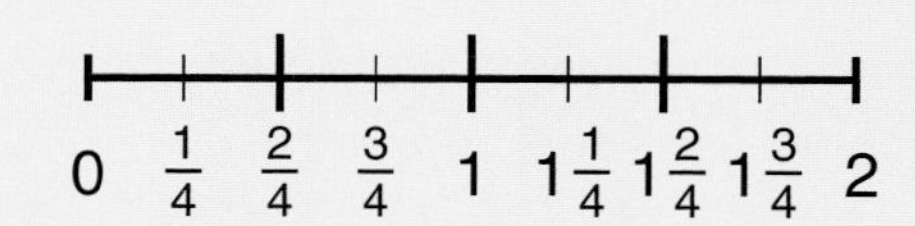

Extending the line segment

Ongoing Assessment: Informing Instruction

Watch for children who are having difficulty solving problems with fractions of sets. Remind them that the denominator (the bottom number in a fraction) tells the total number of equal groups, and the numerator (the top number in a fraction) tells the number of equal groups being considered. Children count the objects in the number of groups given by the numerator to solve the problem. Have children use manipulatives to act out each problem.

- Ruthann read 12 books in the last 4 months. Three were nonfiction. What fraction of the books were nonfiction? $\frac{3}{12}$ or $\frac{1}{4}$ of the books On average, how many books did she read per month? 3 books

  Possible solution strategy: Three out of 12 books is equivalent to $\frac{3}{12}$ of the total. Take 12 counters and divide them into 4 sets of 3. Each set is $\frac{1}{4}$ of the total. To find the average number read per month, divide 12 by 4.

- Kiko has done $\frac{3}{5}$ of the math problems. What fraction of the math problems does she still have to do? $\frac{2}{5}$ of the problems

  Possible solution strategy: Suppose Kiko has 5 problems to solve. She solved $\frac{3}{5}$ of the problems—3 problems. This leaves 2 problems still to be solved. Two out of 5 problems is $\frac{2}{5}$ of the problems.

- Which would you rather have— $\frac{2}{3}$ of a can of lemonade or $\frac{5}{6}$ of a can of lemonade? Assuming you like lemonade, $\frac{5}{6}$ of a can

  Possible solution strategy: Use Fraction Cards to compare the fractions, or reason as follows: $\frac{2}{3}$ is equivalent to $\frac{4}{6}$, which is less than $\frac{5}{6}$. Therefore, $\frac{5}{6}$ is more than $\frac{2}{3}$.

- Jim has $8. If he shares his money equally with 8 people, each person gets $\$8 \div 8 = \$\frac{8}{8} = \$1$; if he shares it equally with 4 people, each person gets $\$8 \div 4 = \$\frac{8}{4} = \$2$. If Jim doesn't share his money, how much money does he have? $8 Write a fraction to show how much money Jim has. $\$\frac{8}{1}$

  Possible solution strategy: The denominator names the number of people among whom Jim's $8 is divided. Since the money was not divided or shared with anyone but Jim, the denominator is 1. Since there are $8, 8 is the number in the numerator. $\$\frac{8}{1} = \$8 \div 1 = \$8$

- Which is the larger fraction, $\frac{1}{3}$ or $\frac{3}{1}$? $\frac{3}{1}$

  Possible solution strategy: The denominator tells how many parts the whole is divided into. For $\frac{1}{3}$, the whole is divided into 3 parts and $\frac{1}{3}$ is one of those parts. For $\frac{3}{1}$, the whole is divided into 1 part and there are 3 wholes. $\frac{3}{1} = 3 \times \frac{1}{1} = 3$ So, $\frac{3}{1}$ is more than $\frac{1}{3}$.

- It took Nathan $1\frac{1}{4}$ hours to do his homework. How many minutes did he spend on homework? 75 minutes

  Possible solution strategy: 1 hour = 60 minutes, $\frac{1}{4}$ hour = $\frac{1}{4}$ of 60 minutes, or 15 minutes. Therefore, $1\frac{1}{4}$ hours = 60 minutes + 15 minutes = 75 minutes.

Adjusting the Activity

Make up additional fraction number stories as appropriate before children solve problems independently. Use similar number stories in future *Minute Math+* sessions.

AUDITORY ◆ KINESTHETIC ◆ TACTILE ◆ VISUAL

- Tamekka had 20 books to put into her bookcase. She put $\frac{1}{2}$ of the books on the top shelf and $\frac{1}{2}$ of the remaining books on the second shelf. How many books did she still need to put into the bookcase? 5 books What fraction of the total number of books is that? $\frac{1}{4}$ of the total

  Possible solution strategy: $\frac{1}{2}$ of 20 = 10, so she put 10 books on the top shelf, which left 10 books to be shelved. She put $\frac{1}{2}$ of the remaining 10 books on the second shelf—that's 5 books. She put a total of 10 books + 5 books, or 15 books, into the bookcase which left 5 books to be shelved.

After working through a few examples, ask volunteers to make up stories for the class to solve.

Solving Fraction Stories

(*Math Journal 2,* pp. 200 and 201)

Children work with a partner or independently to complete journal pages 200 and 201.

Ongoing Assessment: Recognizing Student Achievement

Journal page 201 Problems 10–13 ★

Use **journal page 201, Problems 10–13** to assess children's progress toward solving problems involving fractional parts of a collection. Children are making adequate progress if they are able to successfully complete Problems 10–13. Some children may successfully complete Problems 14–16.

[Number and Numeration Goal 2]

NOTE For practice with adding and subtracting fractions, go to www.everydaymathonline.com.

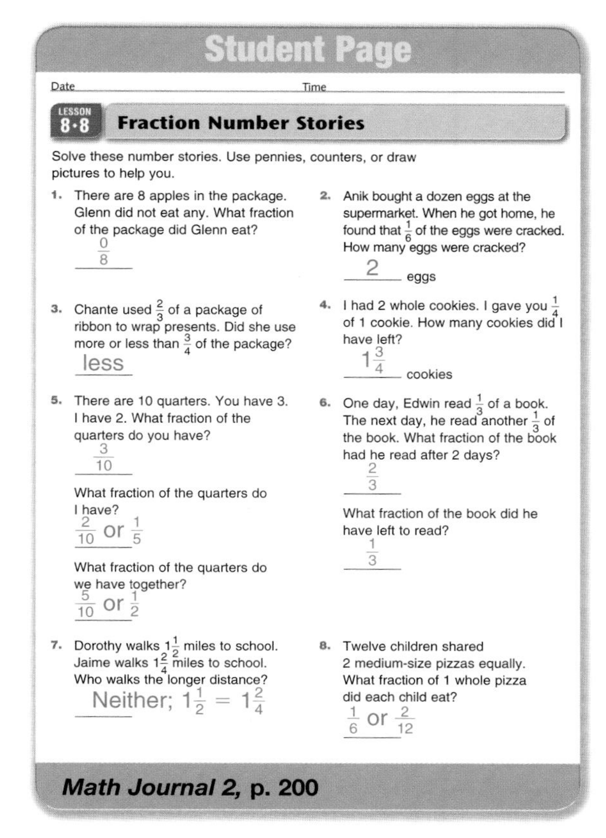

Student Page

Date Time

LESSON 8·8 **Fraction Number Stories**

Solve these number stories. Use pennies, counters, or draw pictures to help you.

1. There are 8 apples in the package. Glenn did not eat any. What fraction of the package did Glenn eat? $\frac{0}{8}$

2. Anik bought a dozen eggs at the supermarket. When he got home, he found that $\frac{1}{6}$ of the eggs were cracked. How many eggs were cracked? 2 eggs

3. Chante used $\frac{2}{3}$ of a package of ribbon to wrap presents. Did she use more or less than $\frac{3}{4}$ of the package? less

4. I had 2 whole cookies. I gave you $\frac{1}{4}$ of 1 cookie. How many cookies did I have left? $1\frac{3}{4}$ cookies

5. There are 10 quarters. You have 3. I have 2. What fraction of the quarters do you have? $\frac{3}{10}$
   What fraction of the quarters do I have? $\frac{2}{10}$ or $\frac{1}{5}$
   What fraction of the quarters do we have together? $\frac{5}{10}$ or $\frac{1}{2}$

6. One day, Edwin read $\frac{1}{3}$ of a book. The next day, he read another $\frac{1}{3}$ of the book. What fraction of the book had he read after 2 days? $\frac{2}{3}$
   What fraction of the book did he have left to read? $\frac{1}{3}$

7. Dorothy walks $1\frac{1}{2}$ miles to school. Jaime walks $1\frac{2}{4}$ miles to school. Who walks the longer distance? Neither; $1\frac{1}{2} = 1\frac{2}{4}$

8. Twelve children shared 2 medium-size pizzas equally. What fraction of 1 whole pizza did each child eat? $\frac{1}{6}$ or $\frac{2}{12}$

Math Journal 2, p. 200

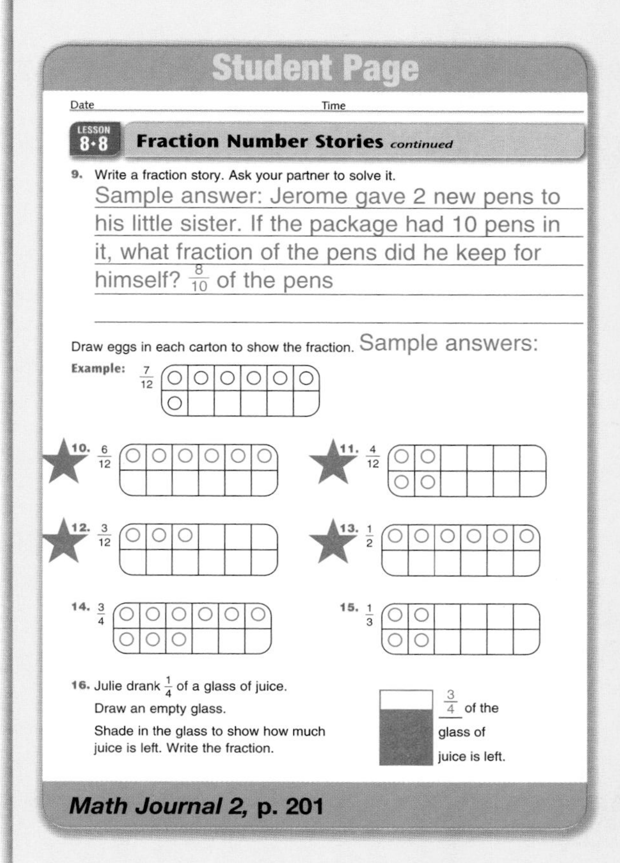

Student Page

Date Time

LESSON 8·8 **Fraction Number Stories** *continued*

9. Write a fraction story. Ask your partner to solve it.
   Sample answer: Jerome gave 2 new pens to his little sister. If the package had 10 pens in it, what fraction of the pens did he keep for himself? $\frac{8}{10}$ of the pens

Draw eggs in each carton to show the fraction. Sample answers:

Example: $\frac{7}{12}$

★ 10. $\frac{6}{12}$

★ 11. $\frac{4}{12}$

★ 12. $\frac{3}{12}$

★ 13. $\frac{1}{2}$

14. $\frac{3}{4}$

15. $\frac{1}{3}$

16. Julie drank $\frac{1}{4}$ of a glass of juice.
   Draw an empty glass.
   Shade in the glass to show how much juice is left. Write the fraction.
   $\frac{3}{4}$ of the glass of juice is left.

Math Journal 2, p. 201

2 Ongoing Learning & Practice

▶ Reviewing the Line Plot Routine

WHOLE-CLASS ACTIVITY

(*Student Reference Book,* pp. 79–81)

Use pages 79–81 in the *Student Reference Book* to review data landmarks. On the board, prepare a line plot with stick-on notes using this data: 42, 42, 43, 45, 45, 46, 46, 46, 46, 47, 47, 48, 48, 48, 48, 48, 50, 51, 53. To provide a context for children, suggest that the line plot shows the arm span measures in inches of a class of third graders.

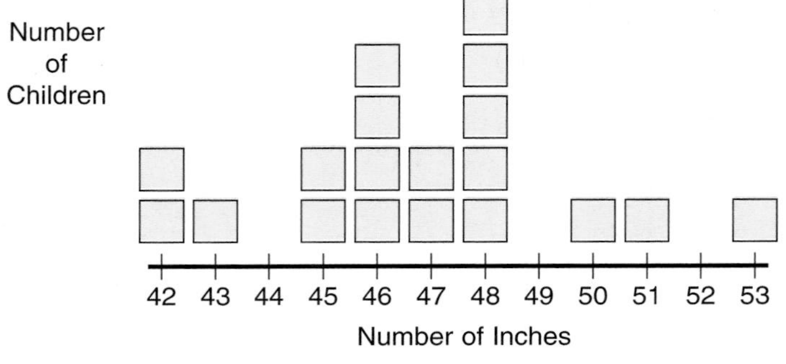

Line plot of 3rd grade arm spans

Ask children to identify the maximum arm span 53 inches, the minimum arm span 42 inches, the mode 48 inches, and the range 11 inches from the line-plot data. Next, ask children to think of another way to find the median without removing the stick-on notes from the line plot. If no one suggests it, have volunteers cross out the first and last stick-on note from each end of the line plot over and over until one remains—this is the median arm span. 47 inches

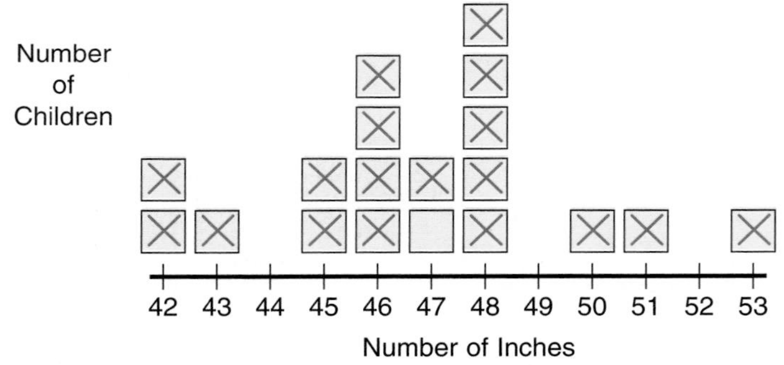

The median arm span is 47 inches.

Have children imagine that you will put all the stick-on notes in a container and draw one out at random without looking. To practice comparing chances for two different events, pose the following:

- Compare the chance of drawing a note that says 42 with the chance of getting a note that says 50. There is a greater chance of drawing 42 than 50. *Explain how you figured it out.* There are two 42s and only one 50.

- Compare the chances of drawing 42 and 47. The chances are equal because there are two 42s and two 47s.
- Compare the chances of drawing 46 and 48. There is a greater chance of drawing 48 because there are five 48s and four 46s.
- Compare the chances of drawing 48 or a number larger than 48. There is a greater chance of drawing 48 because there are five 48s and only three numbers larger than 48.

▶ Math Boxes 8•8

INDEPENDENT ACTIVITY

(*Math Journal 2,* p. 202)

Mixed Practice Math Boxes in this lesson are paired with Math Boxes in Lesson 8-6. The skill in Problem 6 previews Unit 9 content.

Writing/Reasoning Have children draw or write an answer to the following: *In Problem 4, is $\frac{1}{5}$ more or less than $\frac{1}{2}$? Use >, <, or = to compare the two fractions.* $\frac{1}{2} > \frac{1}{5}$ or $\frac{1}{5} < \frac{1}{2}$ *How do you know?* Sample answer: $\frac{1}{5}$ is less than $\frac{1}{2}$ because 1 of 5 equal parts is less than 1 of 2 equal parts.

▶ Home Link 8•8

INDEPENDENT ACTIVITY

(*Math Masters,* p. 262)

Home Connection Children solve fraction number stories like those in the lesson. They solve multidigit addition and subtraction problems.

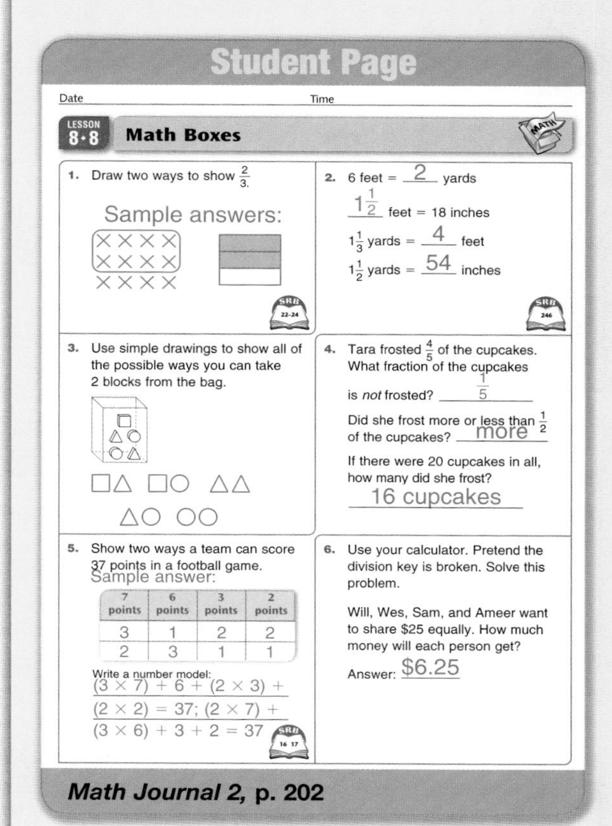

Student Page

Date Time

LESSON 8•8 **Math Boxes**

1. Draw two ways to show $\frac{2}{3}$.
Sample answers:

2. 6 feet = 2 yards
$1\frac{1}{2}$ feet = 18 inches
$1\frac{1}{3}$ yards = 4 feet
$1\frac{1}{2}$ yards = 54 inches

3. Use simple drawings to show all of the possible ways you can take 2 blocks from the bag.

4. Tara frosted $\frac{4}{5}$ of the cupcakes. What fraction of the cupcakes is *not* frosted? $\frac{1}{5}$
Did she frost more or less than $\frac{1}{2}$ of the cupcakes? more
If there were 20 cupcakes in all, how many did she frost? 16 cupcakes

5. Show two ways a team can score 37 points in a football game.
Sample answer:

7 points	6 points	3 points	2 points
3	1	2	2
2	3	1	1

Write a number model:
$(3 \times 7) + 6 + (2 \times 3) + (2 \times 2) = 37$; $(2 \times 7) + (3 \times 6) + 3 + 2 = 37$

6. Use your calculator. Pretend the division key is broken. Solve this problem.
Will, Wes, Sam, and Ameer want to share $25 equally. How much money will each person get?
Answer: $6.25

Math Journal 2, p. 202

3 Differentiation Options

ENRICHMENT

SMALL-GROUP ACTIVITY

▶ Solving *Math Curse* Number Stories

15–30 Min

To apply children's understanding of fraction concepts, read ***Math Curse*** and identify and solve the fraction problems in the story. Have children write their own fraction number stories based on daily activities, like those in *Math Curse*. The class can then discuss and solve these stories. Consider assembling the stories into a class book.

EXTRA PRACTICE

SMALL-GROUP ACTIVITY

▶ *Minute Math+*

5–15 Min

To offer children more experience with fractions, see the following pages in *Minute Math+*: pp. 86, 90, 92, and 155.

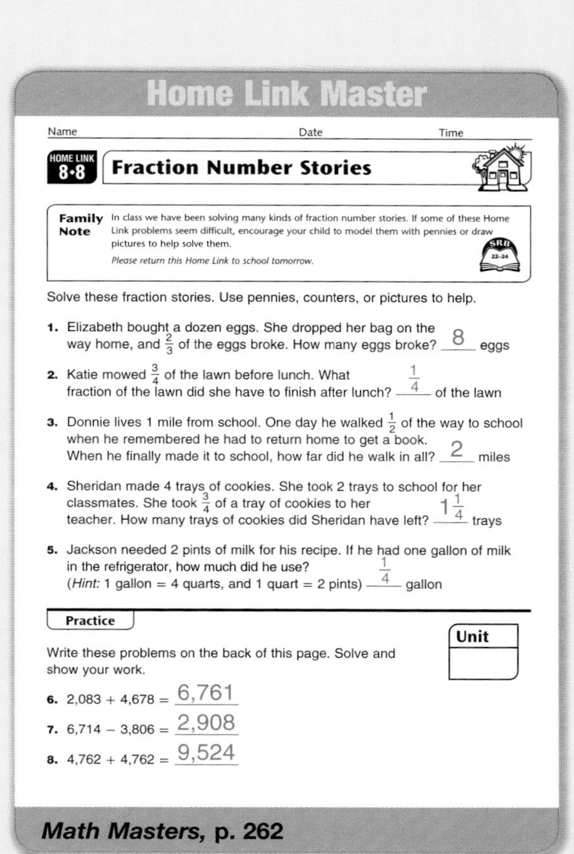

Home Link Master

Name Date Time

HOME LINK 8•8 **Fraction Number Stories**

Family Note In class we have been solving many kinds of fraction number stories. If some of these Home Link problems seem difficult, encourage your child to model them with pennies or draw pictures to help solve them.

Please return this Home Link to school tomorrow.

Solve these fraction stories. Use pennies, counters, or pictures to help.

1. Elizabeth bought a dozen eggs. She dropped her bag on the way home, and $\frac{2}{3}$ of the eggs broke. How many eggs broke? 8 eggs
2. Katie mowed $\frac{3}{4}$ of the lawn before lunch. What fraction of the lawn did she have to finish after lunch? $\frac{1}{4}$ of the lawn
3. Donnie lives 1 mile from school. One day he walked $\frac{1}{2}$ of the way to school when he remembered he had to return home to get a book. When he finally made it to school, how far did he walk in all? 2 miles
4. Sheridan made 4 trays of cookies. She took 2 trays to school for her classmates. She took $\frac{3}{4}$ of a tray of cookies to her teacher. How many trays of cookies did Sheridan have left? $1\frac{1}{4}$ trays
5. Jackson needed 2 pints of milk for his recipe. If he had one gallon of milk in the refrigerator, how much did he use? (*Hint:* 1 gallon = 4 quarts, and 1 quart = 2 pints) $\frac{1}{4}$ gallon

Practice

Unit

Write these problems on the back of this page. Solve and show your work.

6. 2,083 + 4,678 = 6,761
7. 6,714 − 3,806 = 2,908
8. 4,762 + 4,762 = 9,524

Math Masters, p. 262

8•9 Progress Check 8

Objective To assess children's progress on mathematical content through the end of Unit 8.

1 Looking Back: Cumulative Assessment

Input children's data from Progress Check 8 into the **Assessment Management System**.

Materials
- Home Link 8•8
- *Assessment Handbook,* pp. 110–117, 182–186, 209, and 256–259
- straightedge; slate; Fraction Cards; counters; tool-kit clock; coins

CONTENT ASSESSED	LESSON(S)	ASSESSMENT ITEMS				
		SELF	ORAL/SLATE	WRITTEN		OPEN RESPONSE
				PART A	PART B	
Identify the value of digits in decimals. [Number and Numeration Goal 1]	8•5, 8•7	6	2	6		
Read, write, and model fractions. [Number and Numeration Goal 2]	8•1–8•8	1	3		11, 12	✔
Solve problems involving fractional parts of a region or collection. Describe strategies used. [Number and Numeration Goal 2]	8•1–8•8	3	3, 4	1, 2, 8b	11, 12, 15	✔
Find equivalent names for fractions. [Number and Numeration Goal 5]	8•1, 8•2, 8•4–8•8			3	11–13	
Compare and order fractions. [Number and Numeration Goal 6]	8•1, 8•4, 8•6–8•8	2, 4	1	4, 5		
Use manipulatives, mental arithmetic, and paper-and-pencil algorithms to solve problems involving the addition of decimals in a money context. [Operations and Computation Goal 2]						✔
Use models to demonstrate division. [Operations and Computation Goal 6]	8•5–8•8			8a		
Predict the outcomes of simple experiments. [Data and Chance Goal 4]	8•2, 8•4–8•8			7	16	
Complete symmetric shapes. [Geometry Goal 3]	8•5, 8•7	5		10		
Describe relationships among units of time. [Measurement and Reference Frames Goal 3]	8•6, 8•8			9	14	

2 Looking Ahead: Preparing for Unit 9

Math Boxes 8•9

Home Link 8•9: Unit 9 Family Letter

Materials
- *Math Journal 2,* p. 203
- *Math Masters,* pp. 263–266

Key Concepts and Skills		Grade 3 Goals*
9•1	Find multiples of 10, 100, and 1,000.	Number and Numeration Goal 3
	Compare and order numbers.	Number and Numeration Goal 6
	Use multiplication facts to solve problems.	Operations and Computation Goal 3
	Solve number sentences involving the symbols ×, ÷, and =.	Patterns, Functions, and Algebra Goal 2
9•2	Use place-value concepts to calculate products.	Number and Numeration Goal 1
	Use strategies to solve 1-digit by multidigit multiplication problems.	Operations and Computation Goal 4
	Make reasonable estimates for problems involving multiplication and repeated addition.	Operations and Computation Goal 5
	Use a multiplication/division diagram to show multiples of equal groups.	Operations and Computation Goal 6
	Describe and apply the Associative Property of Multiplication; apply the Distributive Property of Multiplication over Addition.	Patterns, Functions, and Algebra Goal 4
9•3	Explore fraction multiplication using paper folding.	Number and Numeration Goal 2
	Use arrays to model multiplication.	Operations and Computation Goal 6
	Count unit squares to find the total area covered in an array model of a multidigit multiplication problem.	Measurement and Reference Frames Goal 2
	Draw rectangles and squares with given areas.	Measurement and Reference Frames Goal 2
9•4	Apply place-value concepts to find partial products.	Number and Numeration Goal 1
	Use the partial-products algorithm to solve problems.	Operations and Computation Goal 4
	Use arrays to model multiplication.	Operations and Computation Goal 6
	Apply the Distributive Property of Multiplication over Addition to find partial products.	Patterns, Functions, and Algebra Goal 4
9•5	Apply place-value concepts to find partial products.	Number and Numeration Goal 1
	Use multiplication facts to make estimates and calculate partial products.	Operations and Computation Goal 3
	Use the partial-products algorithm to multiply 1-digit by multidigit numbers.	Operations and Computation Goal 4
	Make reasonable estimates.	Operations and Computation Goal 5
9•6	Use multiplication facts to solve problems.	Operations and Computation Goal 3
	Use multiplication facts to find whole-number factors of a whole number.	Operations and Computation Goal 3
	Use arrays to model whole-number factors of a whole number.	Operations and Computation Goal 6
9•7	Model money exchanges with manipulatives.	Number and Numeration Goal 1
	Solve equal-sharing division stories involving money amounts.	Operations and Computation Goal 6
9•8	Interpret calculator displays for remainders in equal-sharing and equal-grouping problems.	Operations and Computation Goal 6
	Use equal sharing to solve division number stories.	Operations and Computation Goal 6
9•9	Use addition facts to solve lattice multiplication problems.	Operations and Computation Goal 1
	Use multiplication facts to solve lattice multiplication problems.	Operations and Computation Goal 3
	Explore a strategy for solving problems involving multiplication of 1-digit by multidigit numbers.	Operations and Computation Goal 4
9•10	Use arrays to model multiplication.	Number and Numeration Goal 6
	Collect and organize data in a table.	Data and Chance Goal 1
	Model and compare polygons.	Geometry Goal 2
	Describe number patterns.	Patterns, Functions, and Algebra Goal 1
9•11	Apply place-value concepts to find partial products.	Number and Numeration Goal 1
	Use addition to add partial products.	Operations and Computation Goal 2
	Use multiplication facts to calculate partial products.	Operations and Computation Goal 3
	Use base-10 blocks and array models to find products of 2-digit by 2-digit multiples of 10.	Operations and Computation Goal 6
9•12	Apply place-value concepts to find partial products.	Number and Numeration Goal 1
	Use addition to add partial products.	Operations and Computation Goal 2
	Use multiplication facts to calculate partial products.	Operations and Computation Goal 3
	Use base-10 blocks and arrays to model multiplication.	Operations and Computation Goal 6
9•13	Compare and order positive and negative numbers.	Number and Numeration Goal 6
	Solve number stories involving the addition and subtraction of positive and negative numbers.	Operations and Computation Goal 2

*See the Appendix for a complete list of Grade 3 Goals.

A Balanced Curriculum

Ongoing Practice

Everyday Mathematics provides numerous opportunities for ongoing practice. These activities are embedded throughout the lessons:

Mental Math and Reflexes activities promote speed and accuracy in mental computation.

Math Boxes offer mixed practice and are paired across lessons as shown in the brackets below. This makes them useful as assessment tools. The last one or two boxes on each page preview the next unit's content.

Mixed practice	[9•1, 9•3], [9•2, 9•4], [9•5, 9•7], [9•6, 9•8], [9•9, 9•11, 9•13], [9•10, 9•12]
Mixed practice with multiple choice	9•3, 9•4, 9•5, 9•8, 9•10, 9•11, 9•12, 9•13
Mixed practice with writing/reasoning opportunity	9•1, 9•2, 9•6, 9•7, 9•9, 9•12

Home Links are daily homework assignments that review the content of the lesson and often contain ongoing facts practice or computation practice.

Minute Math+ problems are offered for additional practice in Lessons 9•1 and 9•3.

EM Facts Workshop Game provides online practice of basic facts and computation.

EXTRA PRACTICE **Extra Practice** activities are included in Lessons 9•1, 9•3, 9•9, 9•10, and 9•12.

Practice through Games

Games are an essential component of practice in the *Everyday Mathematics* program. Games offer skills practice and promote strategic thinking. See the *Differentiation Handbook* for ways to adapt games to meet children's needs.

Lesson	Game	Skill Practiced
9•1	*Name That Number*	**Use two or more operations to find equivalent names for numbers** [NN Goal 4 and OC Goals 1–4]
9•5	*Fraction Top-It*	**Compare fractions** [NN Goals 2 and 6]
9•6, 9•8, 9•9	*Factor Bingo*	**Identify the factors of whole numbers** [OC Goal 3]
9•6	*Array Bingo*	**Practice multiplication for arrays and equal groups** [OC Goals 3 and 6]
9•6	*Finding Factors*	**Identify factors** [OC Goal 3]
9•7	*Money Trading Game*	**Practice making money exchanges** [NN Goal 1]
9•11	*Angle Race*	**Practice angle measurements** [MRF Goal 1]
9•12	*Beat the Calculator* (Multiplication)	**Practice multiplication facts** [OC Goal 3]

[NN] Number and Numeration
[MRF] Measurement and Reference Frames
[OC] Operations and Computation
[GEO] Geometry
[DC] Data and Chance
[PFA] Patterns, Functions, and Algebra

Problem Solving 

Good problem solvers use a variety of strategies, including the following:

- Draw a picture.
- Act out the problem.
- Make a table, chart, or list.
- Look for a pattern.
- Try a simpler version of the problem.
- Make a guess and try it out.

The table below lists some of the opportunities in this unit for children to practice these strategies.

Lessons that teach *through* problem solving, not just *about* problem solving

Lesson	Activity
9•1	Write and solve number stories involving animal weights.
9•2	Solve an allowance problem.
9•3	Determine the sides of a rectangle or square with a given area.
9•5	Find the cost of multiple items.
9•7	Share play money equally.
9•8	Use a calculator with a broken division key.
9•8	Solve number stories using division and interpreting the remainders.
9•13	Solve number stories with positive and negative temperatures.

See Chapter 18: Problem Solving in the *Teacher's Reference Manual* for more information.

The Language of Mathematics

Everyday Mathematics provides lesson-specific suggestions to help all children acquire, process, and express mathematical ideas. Throughout Unit 9, there are lesson-specific language development notes that address the needs of English language learners, indicated by ELL.

ELL SUPPORT Activities to support English language learners are in Part 3 of Lessons 9•1, 9•6, 9•8, and 9•12.

The *English Learners Handbook* and the *Differentiation Handbook* have suggestions for promoting language development and acquisition of mathematics vocabulary. See Unit 9 in each handbook.

Unit 9 Vocabulary

algorithm
Celsius scale
degrees Celsius
degrees Fahrenheit
equilateral triangle
factors
Fahrenheit scale
lattice multiplication
partial-products algorithm

Literacy Connection

Anno's Magic Seeds, by Mitsumasa Anno, Philomel, 1995

Less Than Zero, by Stuart J. Murphy, HarperTrophy, 2003

Ranger Rick (magazine), National Wildlife Federation, Zoobooks Wildlife Education

DK Encyclopedia of Nature, edited by Jenny Finch, DK Publishing, 2007

For more literacy connections, see the *Home Connection Handbook,* Grades 1–3.

Cross-Curricular Links 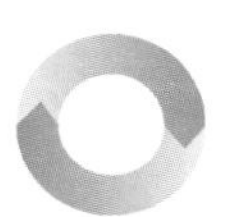

Science
Lesson 9•10 Children build triangular-shaped bridges.

Balanced Assessment

Daily Assessments

- **Recognizing Student Achievement** – A daily assessment that is included in every lesson to evaluate children's progress toward the Grade 3 Grade-Level Goals.
- **Informing Instruction** – Notes that appear throughout the unit to help anticipate children's common errors and suggest appropriate problem-solving strategies.

Lesson	Recognizing Student Achievement	Informing Instruction
9•1	Solve problems involving multiples of 10, 100, and 1,000. [NN Goal 3]	Emphasize that multiplication is a way to solve number stories about equal groups.
9•2	Use strategies to solve 1-digit by 2-digit multiplication problems. [OC Goal 4]	Give target weight in pounds.
9•3	Predict the outcome of an experiment. [DC Goal 4]	Find lengths of sides of geoboard shapes.
9•4	Use strategies to solve multiplication problems. [OC Goal 4]	
9•5	Compare fractions. [NN Goal 6]	
9•6	Use concrete materials to model common fractions. [NN Goal 2]	Use the partial-products algorithm.
9•7	Solve problems involving fractional parts of a region. [NN Goal 2]	Share dollars and cents.
9•8	Understand that parentheses affect the order of operations. [PFA Goal 3]	Interpret a calculator display. Illustrate division problems.
9•9	Identify and describe polygons. [GEO Goal 2]	Use strategies for lattice multiplication. Check fact recall.
9•10	Describe angle rotations. [MRF Goal 1]	
9•11	Describe angle rotations. [MRF Goal 1]	Write multidigit number in expanded notation before multiplying.
9•12	Demonstrate automaticity with multiplication facts. [OC Goal 3]	Write number in expanded notation before multiplying. Model partial product problems with base-10 blocks.
9•13	Find the areas of rectangular shapes. [MRF Goal 2]	

[NN] Number and Numeration
[OC] Operations and Computation
[DC] Data and Chance
[MRF] Measurement and Reference Frames
[GEO] Geometry
[PFA] Patterns, Functions, and Algebra

Portfolio Opportunities

The following lessons provide opportunities to gather samples of children's mathematical writings, drawings, and creations to add balance to the assessment process: Lessons 9•1, 9•2, 9•4, 9•6, 9•7, 9•8, 9•9, 9•10, 9•12, and 9•14. See pages 16 and 17 in the *Assessment Handbook* for more information about portfolios and how to use them.

Unit Assessment

Progress Check 9 – A cumulative assessment of concepts and skills taught in Unit 9 and in previous units, providing information for evaluating children's progress and planning for future instruction. These assessments include oral/slate, written, and open-response activities, as shown below in the sample Progress Check lesson opener.

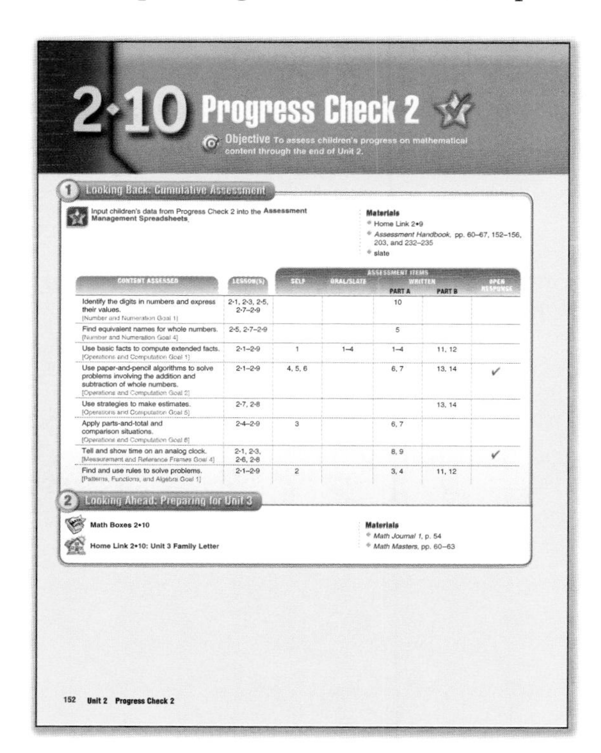

2·10 Progress Check 2

Objective To assess children's progress on mathematical content through the end of Unit 2.

1 Looking Back: Cumulative Assessment

Input children's data from Progress Check 2 into the **Assessment Management Spreadsheets**.

Materials
- Home Link 2•9
- *Assessment Handbook*, pp. 60–67, 152–156, 203, and 232–235
- slate

CONTENT ASSESSED	LESSON(S)	ASSESSMENT ITEMS				
		SELF	ORAL/SLATE	WRITTEN		OPEN RESPONSE
				PART A	PART B	
Identify the digits in numbers and express their values. [Number and Numeration Goal 1]	2·1, 2·3, 2·5, 2·7–2·9			10		
Find equivalent names for whole numbers. [Number and Numeration Goal 4]	2·5, 2·7–2·9			5		
Use basic facts to compute extended facts. [Operations and Computation Goal 1]	2·1–2·9	1	1–4	1–4	11, 12	
Use paper-and-pencil algorithms to solve problems involving the addition and subtraction of whole numbers. [Operations and Computation Goal 2]	2·1–2·9	4, 5, 6		6, 7	13, 14	✓
Use strategies to make estimates. [Operations and Computation Goal 5]	2·7, 2·8				13, 14	
Apply parts-and-total and comparison situations. [Operations and Computation Goal 6]	2·4–2·9	3		6, 7		
Tell and show time on an analog clock. [Measurement and Reference Frames Goal 4]	2·1, 2·3, 2·6, 2·8			8, 9		✓
Find and use rules to solve problems. [Patterns, Functions, and Algebra Goal 1]	2·1–2·9	2		3, 4	11, 12	

2 Looking Ahead: Preparing for Unit 3

Math Boxes 2•10

Home Link 2•10: Unit 3 Family Letter

Materials
- *Math Journal 1*, p. 54
- *Math Masters*, pp. 60–63

152 **Unit 2 Progress Check 2**

Core Assessment Resources

Assessment Handbook

- **Unit 9 Assessment Overview,** pages 118–125
- **Unit 9 Assessment Masters,** pages 187–191
- **Unit 9 Individual Profiles of Progress,** pages 260, 261, and 280
- **Unit 9 Class Checklists,** pages 262, 263, and 281
- **Quarterly Checklist: Quarter 3,** pages 276 and 277
- **Math Logs,** pages 286–288
- **Exit Slip,** page 283
- **Other Student Assessment Forms,** pages 284, 285, 289, and 290

Assessment Management Spreadsheets

The Assessment Management Spreadsheets consist of the Digital Class Checklists and Individual Profile of Progress Checklists. Use them to monitor, record, and report children's progress.

Addressing All Needs

Differentiated Instruction

Adjusting the Activity – suggests adaptations that target advanced learners, English language learners, or learners who need additional instructional support.

ELL SUPPORT / **ELL** – provides lesson-specific suggestions to help English language learners understand and process the mathematical content.

READINESS – accesses children's prior knowledge or previews content that prepares children to engage in the lesson's Part 1 activities.

EXTRA PRACTICE – provides additional opportunities to apply the mathematical content of the lesson.

ENRICHMENT – enables children to apply or further explore the mathematical content of the lesson.

Lesson	Adjusting the Activity	ELL Support/ ELL	Readiness	Extra Practice	Enrichment
9•1	•	•	•	•	
9•2			•		•
9•3			•	•	
9•4	•	•	•		•
9•5	•		•		•
9•6	•	•	•		•
9•7	•	•	•		•
9•8	•	•	•		•
9•9		•		•	•
9•10	•			•	•
9•11	•		•		•
9•12	•	•		•	•
9•13	•	•	•		•

Additional Resources

Differentiation Handbook
Provides ideas and strategies for differentiating instruction.
Pages 104–110

English Learners Handbook
Contains lesson-specific comprehension strategies.
Pages 83–95

Multilingual Handbook
Previews concepts and vocabulary. It is written in six languages.
Pages 165–190

Planning Tips

Multiage Classroom

Companion Lessons from Grades 2 and 4 can help you meet instructional needs of a multiage classroom. The full Scope and Sequence can be found in the Appendix.

Grade 2	7•2, 10•8, 11•6	7•3, 12•4	8•1, 8•2, 9•7	5•4, 6•9, 11•6	4•6, 7•3, 11•4	6•6, 11•8, 12•5	6•7, 6•10, 7•5	6•10, 11•5	5•4, 11•6	5•1, 6•8, 6•9	5•4, 6•9, 11•6	5•4, 6•9, 11•6	1•8, 4•3, 4•4
Grade 3	**9•1**	**9•2**	**9•3**	**9•4**	**9•5**	**9•6**	**9•7**	**9•8**	**9•9**	**9•10**	**9•11**	**9•12**	**9•13**
Grade 4	3•5, 5•9	3•2	5•1	5•5, 5•6	5•5, 5•6		5•1	3•5	5•7	1•3, 5•1	5•6	5•6	

Pacing for Success

Pacing depends on a number of factors, such as children's individual needs and how long your school has been using *Everyday Mathematics*. At the beginning of Unit 9, you may want to use tools available at www.everydaymathonline.com to help you set your pace.

Home Support

Unit 9 Family Letter (English/Spanish) provides families with an overview, Do-Anytime Activities, Building Skills through Games, a list of vocabulary, and answers to the daily homework (Home Links). Family Letters in English, Spanish, and seven other languages are also available online.

Home Links are the daily homework assignments. They consist of active projects and ongoing review problems.

Home Support Resources

Home Connection Handbook
Offers ideas and reproducible masters for communicating with families. See Table of Contents for unit information.

Student Reference Book
Provides a resource for children and parents.
Pages 68–72, 79–81, 89A, 89B, 170, 171, 216, 217, 271–273, 279, 285–287, 293, 294, 299, 300, 307, 308

Technology Resources

Materials

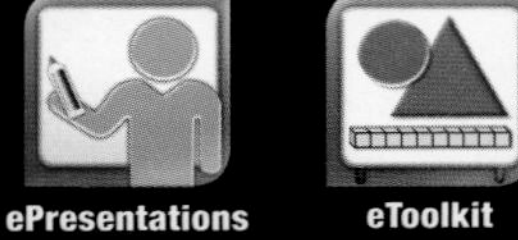
Technology Resources www.everydaymathonline.com

ePresentations

eToolkit

Algorithms Practice

EM Facts Workshop Game™

Family Letters

Assessment Management

Common Core State Standards

Curriculum Focal Points

Interactive Teacher's Lesson Guide

Lesson	Masters	Manipulative Kit	Other Items
9•1	Teaching Masters, pp. 268 and 406 Home Link Master, p. 267	4 each of number cards 0–10 and 1 each of number cards 11–20; base-10 blocks; slate	blank transparency*
9•2	Home Link Master, p. 269 Teaching Masters, pp. 270 and 271	slate	
9•3	Transparency of *Math Masters,* p. 273 Teaching Masters, pp. 272–277, 415*, and 418 Home Link Master, p. 278	base-10 blocks; geoboards; rubberbands; 5 square pattern blocks; slate	pennies*; quarter-sheet of paper; red and blue crayons; scissors; paper; tape (or glue); five 1-inch tiles*; 1-inch by $8\frac{1}{2}$-inch strips of paper
9•4	Teaching Masters, pp. 273, 274, 279*, 281, and 282 Transparency of *Math Masters,* p. 279 Home Link Master, p. 280	base-10 blocks; slate; ruler	red and blue overhead markers; longs and cubes for overhead*
9•5	Teaching Masters, pp. 284, 285, 398, 399, and 400* Home Link Master, p. 283	tool-kit coins*; tool-kit dimes; slate	Fraction Cards
9•6	Transparency of *Math Masters,* p. 448* Home Link Master, p. 286 Teaching Masters, pp. 273*, 274*, 287, 442, and 448 *Differentiation Handbook,* p. 132	4 each of number cards 2–9; base-10 blocks*; slate	pennies or counters; half-sheet of paper; crayons; scissors; paper clips or envelope
9•7	Home Link Master, p. 288 Teaching Masters, pp. 146, 289, 399–402	tool-kit coins; dice; slate	scissors; half-sheet of paper; 2 dollar bills; 20 dimes; 40 pennies; quarter-sheets of paper*; straightedge*
9•8	Home Link Master, p. 290 Teaching Masters, pp. 291, 292, and 448	slate; dice; 4 each of number cards 2–9	counters*; half-sheet of paper; play money*; calculator; 12 counters
9•9	Home Link Master, p. 293 Teaching Masters, pp. 294 and 448	4 each of number cards 2–9	blank paper; counters; index cards*; lined paper; dictionary; calculator
9•10	Teaching Masters, pp. 27, 80, 273, 274, 295–300, 302 Home Link Master, p. 301	base-10 blocks; triangle pattern blocks; tool-kit coins*; number cards 0–9; die; slate; spring scale	half-sheet of paper; green, red, and blue crayons; $8\frac{1}{2}$" by 11" paper; scissors; centimeter ruler; 2 books of equal thickness; small objects varying in weight; kitchen scale*; Pattern-Block Template; play money
9•11	Teaching Masters, pp. 303, 305, 398, 430, 441, and 449 Transparency of *Math Masters,* p. 303* Home Link Master, p. 304	base-10 blocks*; slate; 24-pin circular geoboards; rubberbands	red and green overhead markers*; straightedge and pencil; seven 3" by 5" index cards cut in half; 8 pennies; scissors
9•12	Teaching Masters, pp. 306, 308–311, and 398 Transparency of *Math Masters,* p. 306* Home Link Master, p. 307	base-10 blocks*	overhead base-10 blocks*; red, green, and blue erasable markers*; calculator; half-sheets of paper
9•13	Home Link Master, p. 312 Teaching Masters, pp. 313 and 314	2 each of number cards 0–10; slate	display thermometer*; calculator; Class Data Pad*
9•14	Assessment Masters, pp. 187–191 Home Link Masters, pp. 315–318	slate	straightedge; Fraction Cards; counters

*Denotes optional materials

Mathematical Background

The discussion below highlights the major content ideas presented in Unit 9 and helps establish instructional priorities.

Multiplication and Division with Multiples of 10, 100, and 1,000

(Lesson 9◆1)

Much mental arithmetic and the most meaningful multiplication and division algorithms depend on quick and correct responses to problems, such as $30 \times 50 = 1{,}500$ and $300 \div 20 = 15$. These kinds of problems were introduced in Unit 7. With frequent practice in Mental Math and Reflexes and Math Boxes, children should have little trouble solving them.

Just stating a problem in a certain way is often a key to its solution. For example, it may help to think of 30×50 as "30 fifties," or to rephrase $300 \div 20$ as *How many twenties are in 300?* or *By what number must I multiply 20 to get 300?*

Everyday Mathematics uses the abbreviation "30 [50s]" for the phrase "30 fifties." You will find it helpful to have shorthand for such expressions, although you or the children may want to invent your own.

Transitions from Mental Math to Formal Algorithms (Lesson 9◆2)

In *Second Grade Everyday Mathematics,* time was devoted to solving addition and subtraction problems by informal and mental math procedures in preparation for children's invention of their own algorithms. Because it is more difficult to invent an algorithm for multiplication than for addition or subtraction, it is unlikely that children will invent a multiplication algorithm of their own. Still, mental arithmetic and work with concrete materials can pave the way for more formal and systematic procedures. As children mentally solve the problems in this lesson, allow plenty of time for them to share their solution strategies.

See Section 16.3 of the *Teacher's Reference Manual* for more information on transitioning from mental math to formal algorithms.

Explorations: Whole-Number Multiplication, Geoboard Areas, Fractions of Fractions (Lesson 9◆3)

In Exploration A, children model multiplication with base-10 blocks. They use as few longs and cubes as possible to build array models for 1-digit times 2-digit multiplication. The longs represent the tens partial products and the cubes represent the ones partial products. All children should complete this Exploration before Lesson 9-4.

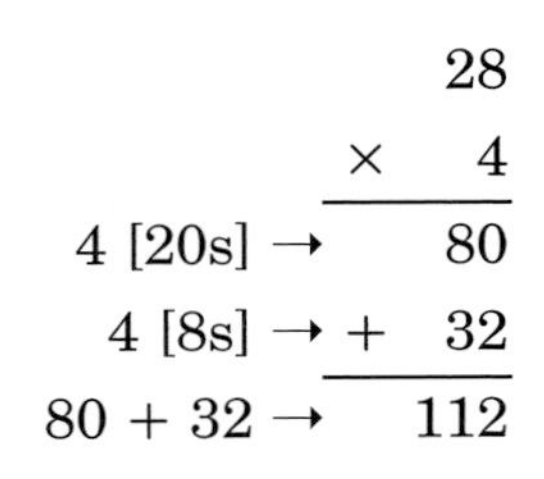

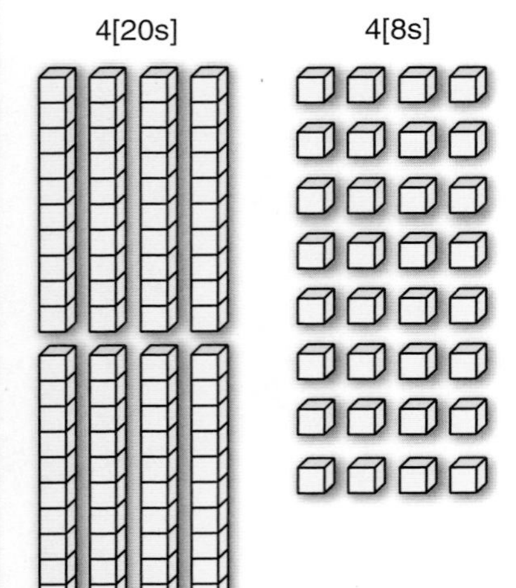

A "Low-Stress" Multiplication Algorithm (Lesson 9◆4)

The introduction of a partial-products algorithm for multiplication by 1-digit numbers is tied closely to Exploration A.

Once the algorithm has been introduced, children should practice multiplication by 1-digit numbers on a regular basis for the rest of the school year. While calculators are used more and more often in place of paper-and-pencil computation, especially with more complex problems, this algorithm provides useful practice with basic facts and their extensions and also builds "number sense" for products. The same approach is followed in extending the partial-products algorithm to 2-digit multipliers in Lessons 9-10–9-12.

To learn more about the partial-products algorithm, see Section 11.2.3 of the *Teacher's Reference Manual.*

Products with Money Amounts (Lesson 9◆5)

Lesson 9-5 is an extension of Lesson 7-7, in which children referred to a Stock-Up Sale poster to estimate the costs of several of the same item. In Lesson 9-5, children refer to a similar poster to find exact costs using the partial-products algorithm. You may find that children are even more comfortable using the partial-products algorithm with dollars-and-cents amounts than with whole numbers.

Project Note

The focus of this lesson is to apply the partial-products algorithm to money amounts.
For enrichment, see Algorithm Project 4 on page A15 to teach U.S. traditional multiplication of decimals using money.

Factors of a Whole Number (Lesson 9◆6)

A surprising amount of mathematics is based on whole number factors of whole numbers, especially on factors that are prime numbers. For our present purposes, whole number factors of whole numbers offer another look at the relationship between multiplication and division, while providing additional practice with the basic multiplication and division facts. A new game, *Factor Bingo,* is introduced to give children practice identifying the factors of whole numbers.

Multidigit Quotients (Lessons 9◆7 and 9◆8)

The work with whole number factors in Lesson 9-6 serves as a transition to Lessons 9-7 and 9-8, in which children solve division problems with multidigit quotients through hands-on activities. Lesson 9-7 presents problems that involve equal sharing. In Lesson 9-8, children solve problems about equal groupings, and they interpret remainders. These activities are exploratory; no attempt at an algorithmic solution is made at this time. More formal work with division algorithms is deferred until fourth grade.

To learn more about division algorithms, see Section 11.2.4 of the *Teacher's Reference Manual.*

The Lattice Method of Multiplication (Lesson 9◆9)

The lattice method, which was used hundreds of years ago, is presented as an alternative multiplication algorithm. Aside from its historical interest, it is fun to use. Children see that there is more than one way to find a product. The lattice method is easy to use, which makes it a good algorithm, and provides children with additional practice with the multiplication facts.

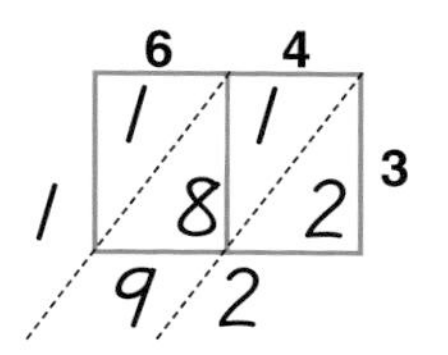

The lattice method

Some children may find it difficult to draw neat and regular lattices. To alleviate this problem, provide copies of lattices on *Math Masters,* pages 310 and 311.

See Section 11.2.3 of the *Teacher's Reference Manual* for additional information about the lattice method of multiplication.

Explorations: Array Multiplication, Equilateral Triangles, Strength of Paper (Lesson 9◆10)

All children should complete Exploration D (modeling multiplication with base-10 blocks and arrays) before proceeding to Lessons 9-11 and 9-12.

Products of 2-Digit Numbers (Lessons 9◆11 and 9◆12)

Previous work with modeling of multiplication is used to extend the partial-products algorithm, first to 2-digit numbers multiplied by multiples of 10, and then to products of any 2-digit numbers.

See Section 11.2.3 of the *Teacher's Reference Manual* to learn more about the partial-products multiplication algorithm.

Project Note

To teach U.S. traditional multiplication, see Algorithm Project 3.

Positive and Negative Numbers (Lesson 9◆13)

In this lesson, positive and negative numbers are used to represent numerical information with reference to a zero point. Children find distances between pairs of points represented by positive and negative numbers in a reference frame, and they solve problems that involve moving from a fixed place to another place. In *Third Grade Everyday Mathematics,* such problems are solved intuitively with the help of pictorial representations, especially a thermometer (regarded as a number line).

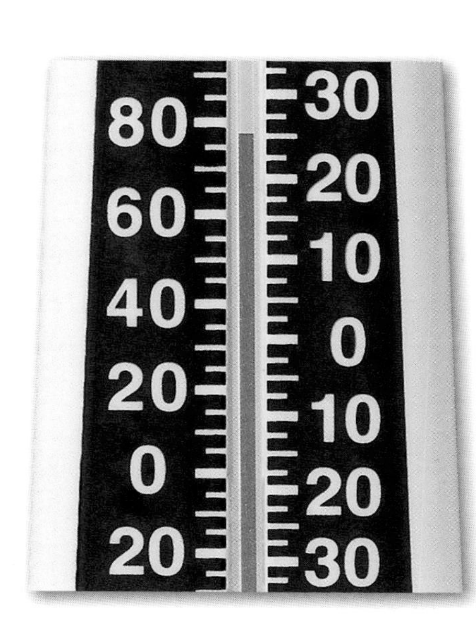

See the *Teacher's Reference Manual,* Section 9.4, for additional information about positive and negative numbers.

9·1 Multiply and Divide with Multiples of 10, 100, and 1,000

Objective To guide children as they multiply and divide with multiples of 10, 100, and 1,000.

Technology Resources www.everydaymathonline.com

ePresentations

eToolkit

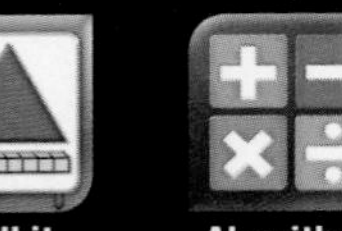
Algorithms Practice

EM Facts Workshop Game™

Family Letters

Assessment Management

Common Core State Standards

Curriculum Focal Points

Interactive Teacher's Lesson Guide

1 Teaching the Lesson

Key Concepts and Skills

- Find multiples of 10, 100, and 1,000. [Number and Numeration Goal 3]
- Compare and order numbers. [Number and Numeration Goal 6]
- Use multiplication facts to solve problems. [Operations and Computation Goal 3]
- Solve number sentences involving the symbols ×, ÷, and =. [Patterns, Functions, and Algebra Goal 2]

Key Activities

Children make up and solve multiplication and division number stories about animal weights. Children find products and quotients involving multiples of 10, 100, and 1,000.

Ongoing Assessment: Informing Instruction See page 715.

Ongoing Assessment: Recognizing Student Achievement Use journal page 206. [Number and Numeration Goal 3]

Materials

Math Journal 2, pp. 204–206
Math Masters, p. 406
slate ◆ blank transparency (optional)

2 Ongoing Learning & Practice

Playing *Name That Number*
Student Reference Book, pp. 299 and 300
per group: 4 each of number cards 0–10 and 1 each of number cards 11–20 (from the Everything Math Deck, if available)
Children use two or more operations to find equivalent names for numbers.

Math Boxes 9·1
Math Journal 2, p. 207
Children practice and maintain skills through Math Box problems.

Home Link 9·1
Math Masters, p. 267
Children practice and maintain skills through Home Link activities.

3 Differentiation Options

READINESS

Extending Multiplication Fact Patterns
Math Masters, p. 268
per partnership: base-10 blocks (longs, flats, and big cubes)
Children explore patterns in multiples of 10, 100, and 1,000.

EXTRA PRACTICE

Minute Math+
Minute Math®+, pp. 128 and 131
Children solve number stories involving multiplication and division.

ELL SUPPORT

Writing Multiplication and Division Number Stories
Children write multiplication and division number stories.

Advance Preparation

Post the Guide to Solving Number Stories poster (*Math Masters,* page 406).

***Teacher's Reference Manual,* Grades 1–3** pp. 193–195

Getting Started

Mathematical Practices
SMP1, SMP2, SMP3, SMP4, SMP5, SMP6, **SMP7**
Content Standards
3.OA.3, 3.OA.6, 3.OA.8, 3.NBT.3

Mental Math and Reflexes

Pose problems like the following. Children answer on their slates:

●○○ How much are 7 [30s]? 210

What number is 50 times as much as 6? 300

How many 9s equal 540? 60

●●○ How much are 70 [30s]? 2,100

What number is 50 times as much as 60? 3,000

How many 90s make 5,400? 60

●●● How much are 30 [700s]? 21,000

What number is 60 times as much as 500? 30,000

How many 60s make 54,000? 900

Math Message

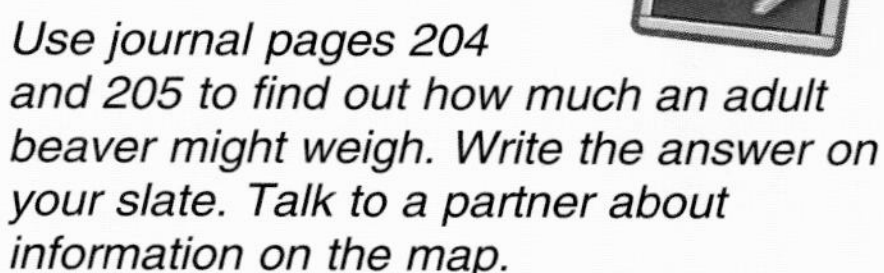

Use journal pages 204 and 205 to find out how much an adult beaver might weigh. Write the answer on your slate. Talk to a partner about information on the map.

1 Teaching the Lesson

Interactive whiteboard-ready ePresentations are available at www.everydaymathonline.com to help you teach the lesson.

▶ Math Message Follow-Up

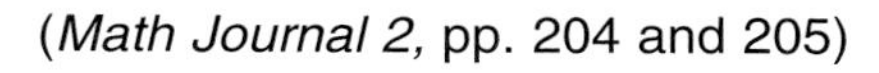

(*Math Journal 2,* pp. 204 and 205)

According to the Adult Weights of North American Animals poster, a normal weight for a beaver is from 20 to 56 lb. Remind children that the abbreviation for pounds is lb. Any weight within this range is a correct response to the Math Message. Have children briefly share their observations from the poster.

NOTE The word *range* is used here to mean the series of numbers between two given numbers. Children should not confuse this meaning with the data landmark *range,* which means the difference between the largest (maximum) and the smallest (minimum) numbers in a set of data. To support English language learners, write *range* on the board twice with examples of both meanings.

Ask children to name other animals on the poster and to tell their normal adult weight ranges. Have children give numbers within these ranges. For example, the weight range for an arctic fox is 7 lb to 20 lb. Ask: *Could an arctic fox weigh 15 lb?* yes *22 lb?* no

▶ Modeling How to Solve Multiplication and Division Number Stories

WHOLE-CLASS ACTIVITY

(*Math Journal 2,* pp. 204 and 205; *Math Masters,* p. 406)

Explain that the class will solve multiplication and division number stories. Refer children to the Guide for Solving Number Stories poster (*Math Masters,* page 406) and the animal posters in their journals (*Math Journal 2,* pages 204 and 205). Write the following problem on the board or transparency. *Which animal could weigh 30 times as much as a 50-pound sea otter?*

Student Page

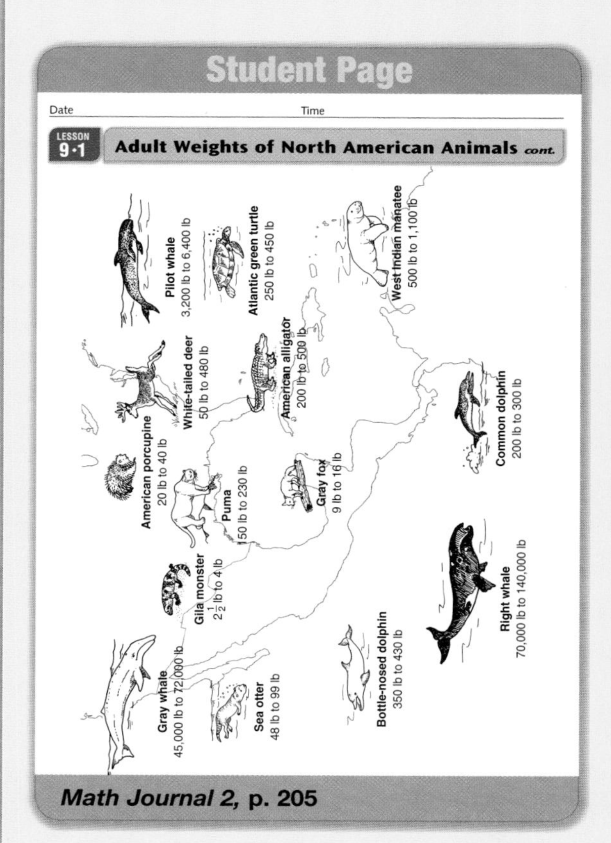

Math Journal 2, p. 205

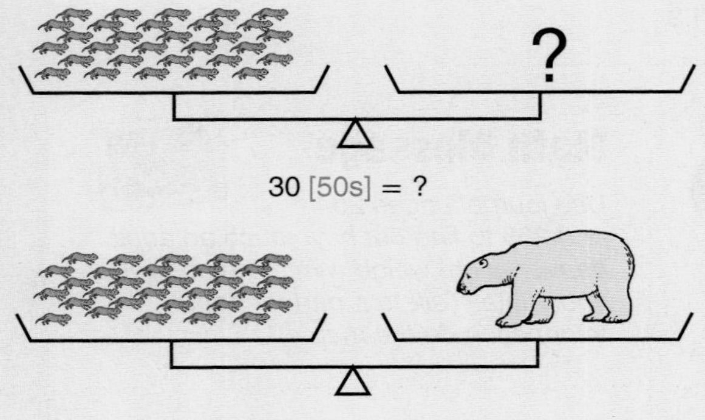

30 [50s] = 1,500

One polar bear weighs as much as 30 sea otters.

Teaching Aid Master

Name ______ Date ______ Time ______

Guide to Solving Number Stories

1. **What do you understand from the story?**
   - Read the story. What do you want to find out?
   - What do you know?
2. **What will you do?**
   - Add?
   - Subtract?
   - Multiply?
   - Divide?
   - Draw a picture?
   - Make tallies?
   - Use counters or base-10 blocks?
   - Use a number grid or number line?
   - Make a table?
   - Draw a diagram?
   - Write a number model?
3. **Answer the question.**
   - Solve the problem. Record your work.
   - Write the answer with the units.
4. **Check.**
   - Does your answer make sense? How do you know?

***Math Masters*, p. 406**

1. *What do you understand from the story? Think:*
   - What do you want to find out? Which animal could weigh 30 times as much as the sea otter?
   - What information do you know from reading the story? A sea otter weighs 50 lb. There is an animal that weighs about 30 times as much as a sea otter.
2. *What could you do to find which animal weighs about 30 times as much as the sea otter?* You could multiply 30 times 50 lb and then find an animal that weighs about that much.
   - Write a number model to represent the story. Possible number models: $? = 30 \times 50$; $30 \times 50 = ?$

NOTE Remind children that they can use either a question mark or a letter for the unknown quantity in a number model.

3. *Answer the question.* 30 times 50 lb is 1,500 lb. A polar bear could weigh from 650 to 1,750 lb; and 1,500 lb is in that range.

Allow time for children to write solution strategies on the board and explain them to the class. Possible strategies may include: I added 50 ten times to get 500 and then added 500 three times to get 1,500; I know that $50 \times 30 = 1,500$ is an extension of the basic fact $5 \times 3 = 15$; I added 30 fifty times to get 1,500.

4. *Does your answer make sense? How do you know?* Sample answer: I know that 10 sea otters weigh 500 lb. 30 sea otters would weigh 3 times that amount, about 1,500 lb; which is in the weight range for polar bears.
   - Does your answer make the number model true? yes Write a summary number model on the board: $1,500 = 30 \times 50$.

Write the following problem on the board or transparency: *How many 50-pound sea otters together would weigh about 1 ton? (1 ton = 2,000 lb)*

1. *What do you understand from the story? Think:*
   - What do you want to find out? The number of 50-pound sea otters whose total weight would be 2,000 lb
   - What information do you know from reading the story? A sea otter weighs 50 lb. An unknown number of sea otters weigh 2,000 lb.
2. *What could you do to find the number of 50-pound sea otters whose total weight would be 2,000 pounds?* Children may think of this problem in terms of multiplication (What number times 50 equals 2,000?) or division (How much is 2,000 divided by 50?).
   - Write a number model for the story. Possible number models: $? \times 50 = 2,000$; $2,000 \div 50 = ?$
3. *Answer the question.* 50 times 40 is 2,000, so forty 50-pound sea otters together weigh a ton.

Allow time for children to share solution strategies. Possible strategies may include: I know the basic fact $4 \times 5 = 20$. $40 \times 50 = 2,000$ and $2,000 \div 50 = 40$ are extensions of the basic fact. From the first story, I knew that 30 sea otters were 1,500 lb and that 10 sea otters were 500 lb, so I added and found that 40 sea otters weigh 2,000 lb.

4. *Does your answer make sense? How do you know?* Possible answer: One sea otter weighs 50 lb, so two weigh 100 lb. There are ten 100s in 1,000 and twenty 100s in 2,000, so 40 sea otters weigh 2,000 lb.

   - Does your answer make the number model true? yes Write a summary number model on the board: $40 \times 50 = 2,000$.

Writing and Solving Number Stories with Multiples of 10, 100, and 1,000

(*Math Journal 2,* pp. 204 and 205)

Use the Adult Weights of North American Animals poster as a basis for multiplication and division number stories. Choose any numbers that fall within the weight ranges. Record the problems on the board.

Suggestions:

- Which animal could weigh about 10 times as much as a 34-pound American porcupine? Harp seal, northern fur seal, American alligator, white-tailed deer, Atlantic green turtle, or black bear
- Which animal could weigh about 30 times as much as a 5-pound snowshoe hare? Puma or white-tailed deer
- How many 300-pound northern fur seals weigh as much as a 6,000-pound pilot whale? 20
- How many 80-pound white-tailed deer weigh as much as a 560-pound black bear? 7

Invite children to tell their own multiplication and division number stories for the class to solve.

Ongoing Assessment: Informing Instruction

Watch for children who tell addition or subtraction number stories. Accept and solve these types of problems, but continue to model multiplication and division number stories, emphasizing that multiplication is a way to find the total number of things when equal groups are put together.

Adjusting the Activity

Pose problems that require two steps. *Suggestion:*

Which animal could weigh about 1,000 times as much as the combined weight of a 75-pound sea otter and a 45-pound sea otter? Right whale

AUDITORY ◆ KINESTHETIC ◆ TACTILE ◆ VISUAL

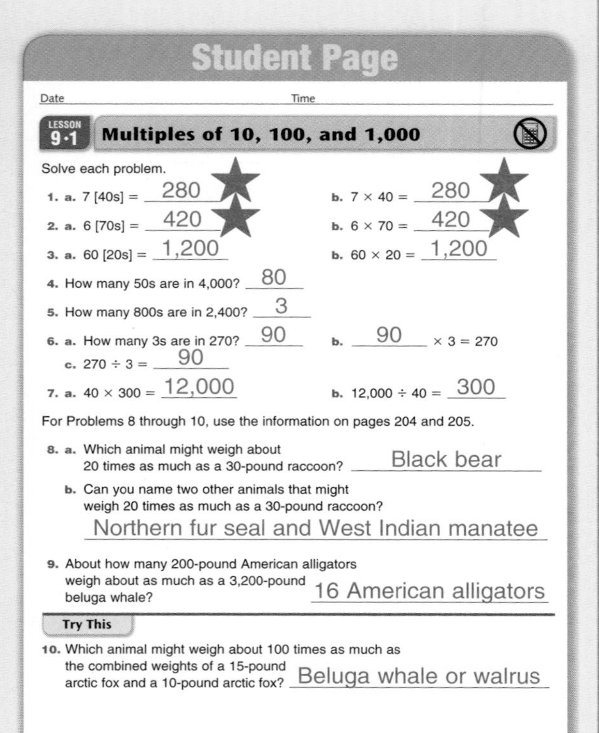
Student Page

Date ______ Time ______

LESSON 9·1 **Multiples of 10, 100, and 1,000**

Solve each problem.

1. a. 7 [40s] = 280 ★ b. 7 × 40 = 280 ★
2. a. 6 [70s] = 420 ★ b. 6 × 70 = 420 ★
3. a. 60 [20s] = 1,200 b. 60 × 20 = 1,200
4. How many 50s are in 4,000? 80
5. How many 800s are in 2,400? 3
6. a. How many 3s are in 270? 90 b. 90 × 3 = 270
   c. 270 ÷ 3 = 90
7. a. 40 × 300 = 12,000 b. 12,000 ÷ 40 = 300

For Problems 8 through 10, use the information on pages 204 and 205.

8. a. Which animal might weigh about 20 times as much as a 30-pound raccoon? Black bear
   b. Can you name two other animals that might weigh 20 times as much as a 30-pound raccoon? Northern fur seal and West Indian manatee
9. About how many 200-pound American alligators weigh about as much as a 3,200-pound beluga whale? 16 American alligators

Try This

10. Which animal might weigh about 100 times as much as the combined weights of a 15-pound arctic fox and a 10-pound arctic fox? Beluga whale or walrus

Math Journal 2, p. 206

▶ Finding Products and Quotients Involving Multiples of 10, 100, and 1,000

INDEPENDENT ACTIVITY

(*Math Journal 2,* pp. 204–206)

Children complete journal page 206. Circulate and assist as necessary.

Ongoing Assessment: Recognizing Student Achievement

Journal page 206 Problems 1 and 2 ★

Use **journal page 206, Problems 1 and 2** to assess children's progress toward solving problems involving multiples of 10, 100, and 1,000. Children are making adequate progress if they are able to complete Problems 1 and 2. Some children may be able to solve problems involving multiples of 100 and 1,000.

[Number and Numeration Goal 3]

Links to the Future

In this lesson, children make up and solve multiplication and division number stories involving multidigit numbers. Many children will use basic facts, multiples of 10, and mental math to solve these problems. However, using and explaining strategies for solving number stories involving multiplication of multidigit whole numbers by a 2-digit whole number is a Grade 4 Goal. Using and explaining strategies for solving number stories involving division of multidigit whole numbers is a Grade 5 Goal.

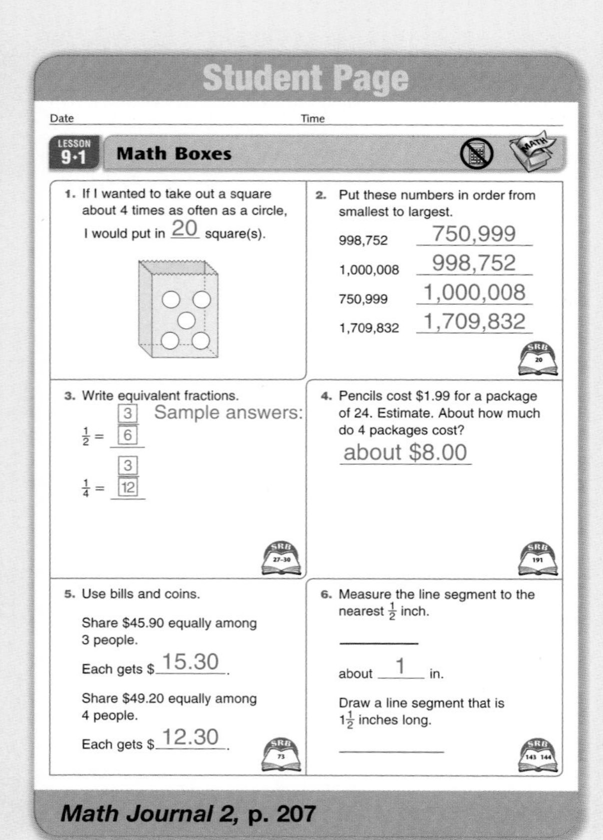
Student Page

Date ______ Time ______

LESSON 9·1 **Math Boxes**

1. If I wanted to take out a square about 4 times as often as a circle, I would put in 20 square(s).
2. Put these numbers in order from smallest to largest.
   998,752 — 750,999
   1,000,008 — 998,752
   750,999 — 1,000,008
   1,709,832 — 1,709,832
3. Write equivalent fractions. Sample answers:
   $\frac{1}{2} = \frac{3}{6}$
   $\frac{1}{4} = \frac{3}{12}$
4. Pencils cost $1.99 for a package of 24. Estimate. About how much do 4 packages cost? about $8.00
5. Use bills and coins.
   Share $45.90 equally among 3 people. Each gets $15.30.
   Share $49.20 equally among 4 people. Each gets $12.30.
6. Measure the line segment to the nearest $\frac{1}{2}$ inch.
   about 1 in.
   Draw a line segment that is $1\frac{1}{2}$ inches long.

Math Journal 2, p. 207

2 Ongoing Learning & Practice

▶ Playing *Name That Number*

SMALL-GROUP ACTIVITY

(*Student Reference Book,* pp. 299 and 300)

Children play *Name That Number.* They use two or more operations to find equivalent names for numbers. For game instructions, see Lesson 1-6 or pages 299 and 300 in the *Student Reference Book.*

▶ Math Boxes 9·1

INDEPENDENT ACTIVITY

(*Math Journal 2,* p. 207)

Mixed Practice Math Boxes in this lesson are paired with Math Boxes in Lesson 9-3. The skill in Problem 6 previews Unit 10 content.

Writing/Reasoning Have children write an answer to the following: *Explain how you solved Problem 4.* Sample answer: $1.99 is close to $2.00. I multiplied $2.00 × 4 to get $8.00.

▶ Home Link 9•1

 INDEPENDENT ACTIVITY

(*Math Masters,* p. 267)

Home Connection Children solve whole-number riddles.

3 Differentiation Options

READINESS

 PARTNER ACTIVITY

 5–15 Min

▶ Extending Multiplication Fact Patterns

(*Math Masters,* p. 268)

To explore patterns in multiples of 10, 100, and 1,000, have children complete *Math Masters,* page 268. Children can model the problems with base-10 longs, flats, and big cubes.

 SMALL-GROUP ACTIVITY

▶ *Minute Math+*

5–15 Min

To offer children more experience with multiplication and division number stories, see the following pages in *Minute Math+*:

Number Stories: pp. 128 and 131.

ELL SUPPORT

 SMALL-GROUP ACTIVITY

 15–30 Min

To provide language support for multiplication and division, have children write multiplication and division number stories for others to solve. Also provide them with opportunities to write a paragraph describing how they solved a particular problem. Provide English language learners with feedback on their mathematical writing and offer them multiple opportunities to revise their writing. This activity will support not only their problem-solving efforts, but also their communication skills.

NOTE Remind children to continue to record the sunrise, sunset, and length of day in their journals on pages 279–281. They should also continue to record the national high and low temperatures on journal page 175 and then graph the temperature range on journal page 177.

Name ______ Date ______ Time ______

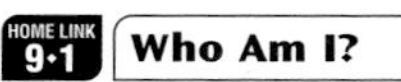

Family Note The problems in this Home Link involve children solving whole-number riddles. Your child will use place-value concepts, number sense, and computation skills to solve the riddles. To provide practice with basic and extended facts, multiplication fact practice is added at the bottom of this Home Link.

Please return this Home Link to school tomorrow.

In each riddle, I am a different whole number. Use the clues to find out who I am.

1. **Clue 1:** I am greater than 30 and less than 40. **Clue 2:** The sum of my digits is less than 5. **Who am I?** 31
2. **Clue 1:** I am greater than 15 and less than 40. **Clue 2:** If you double me, I become a number that ends in 0. **Clue 3:** $\frac{1}{5}$ of me is equal to 5. **Who am I?** 25
3. **Clue 1:** I am less than 100. **Clue 2:** The sum of my digits is 4. **Clue 3:** Half of me is an odd number. **Who am I?** 22
4. **Clue 1:** If you multiply me by 2, I become a number greater than 20 and less than 40. **Clue 2:** If you multiply me by 6, I end in 8. **Clue 3:** If you multiply me by 4, I end in 2. **Who am I?** 13 or 18
5. **Clue 1:** Double my tens digit to get my ones digit. **Clue 2:** Double me and I am less than 50. **Who am I?** 12 or 24

Practice

Solve.

6. $8 \times 7 =$ 56; $80 \times 7 =$ 560; $800 \times 7 =$ 5,600
7. $5 \times 4 =$ 20; $5 \times 40 =$ 200; $50 \times 400 =$ 20,000

***Math Masters,* p. 267**

Name ______ Date ______ Time ______

LESSON 9•1 **Extending Multiplication Fact Patterns**

Fill in the missing numbers.

1. $1 \times 10 =$ 10; $2 \times 10 =$ 20; $3 \times 10 =$ 30; $4 \times 10 =$ 40; $5 \times 10 =$ 50
   $1 \times 100 =$ 100; $2 \times 100 =$ 200; $3 \times 100 =$ 300; $4 \times 100 =$ 400; $5 \times 100 =$ 500
2. $6 \times 100 =$ 600; $7 \times 100 =$ 700; $8 \times 100 =$ 800; $9 \times 100 =$ 900
   $6 \times 1{,}000 =$ 6,000; $7 \times 1{,}000 =$ 7,000; $8 \times 1{,}000 =$ 8,000; $9 \times 1{,}000 =$ 9,000
3. 1 [10] = 10; 2 [10s] = 20; 7 [10s] = 70; 5 [10s] = 50; 8 [10s] = 80
   1 [100] = 100; 2 [100s] = 200; 7 [100s] = 700; 5 [100s] = 500; 8 [100s] = 800
4. Explain how you can use the patterns above to find the answer to 8 [1,000s].
   Sample answer: I know that 8 [1s] are 8. 8 [1,000s] are 1,000 times as much, or 8,000. I know that 8 [10s] are 80 and 8 [100s] are 800; so 8 [1,000s] must be 8,000.

Try This

5. $10 \times 100 =$ 1,000; $10 \times 1{,}000 =$ 10,000
   10 [100s] = 1,000; 10 [1,000s] = 10,000

***Math Masters,* p. 268**

9•2 Using Mental Math to Multiply

Objective To guide children as they use mental math to multiply 1-digit numbers by multidigit numbers.

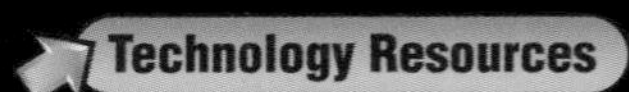

www.everydaymathonline.com

ePresentations

eToolkit

Algorithms Practice

EM Facts Workshop Game™

Family Letters

Assessment Management

Common Core State Standards

Curriculum Focal Points

Interactive Teacher's Lesson Guide

1 Teaching the Lesson

Key Concepts and Skills

- Use place-value concepts to calculate products. [Number and Numeration Goal 1]
- Use strategies to solve 1-digit by multidigit multiplication problems. [Operations and Computation Goal 4]
- Make reasonable estimates for problems involving multiplication and repeated addition. [Operations and Computation Goal 5]
- Use a multiplication/division diagram to show multiples of equal groups. [Operations and Computation Goal 6]
- Describe and apply the Associative Property of Multiplication; apply the Distributive Property of Multiplication over Addition. [Patterns, Functions, and Algebra Goal 4]

Key Activities

Children devise and practice strategies for mentally multiplying 1-digit numbers by multidigit numbers.

Ongoing Assessment: Informing Instruction See page 720.

Ongoing Assessment: Recognizing Student Achievement Use journal page 208. [Operations and Computation Goal 4]

Materials

Math Journal 2, pp. 204, 205, and 208
Home Link 9•1
slate

2 Ongoing Learning & Practice

Making Up and Solving Poster Stories
Math Journal 2, pp. 204, 205, and 209
Children make up and solve multiplication and division number stories.

Math Boxes 9•2
Math Journal 2, p. 210
Children practice and maintain skills through Math Box problems.

Home Link 9•2
Math Masters, p. 269
Children practice and maintain skills through Home Link activities.

3 Differentiation Options

READINESS

Using Multiplication/Division Diagrams
Math Masters, p. 270
Children use multiplication/division diagrams to model equal-grouping problems.

ENRICHMENT

Solving an Allowance Problem
Math Masters, p. 271
Children calculate weekly allowances according to three different plans.

Advance Preparation

You may want to draw a multiplication/division diagram on the board.

***Teacher's Reference Manual,* Grades 1–3** pp. 227, 228

Getting Started

Mathematical Practices
SMP1, SMP2, **SMP3,** SMP4, SMP5, SMP6, SMP8
Content Standards
3.OA.1, 3.OA.3, **3.OA.5,** 3.OA.8, **3.NBT.3,** 3.NF.2, 3.NF.2a, 3.NF.2b

Mental Math and Reflexes

FACTS PRACTICE

Pose problems like the following.
Children answer on slates.

●○○	●●○	●●●
4 [70s] 280	50 [4s] 200	80 [90s] 7,200
40 [70s] 2,800	50 [40s] 2,000	800 [900s] 720,000
400 [70s] 28,000	500 [40s] 20,000	8,000 [900s] 7,200,000

Math Message

Could 6 adult harp seals weigh less than 1 ton? Could they weigh more than 1 ton? (1 ton = 2,000 lb.) Use the information on pages 204 and 205 in your journal. Record your answers on your slate.

Home Link 9·1 Follow-Up

Briefly go over the answers to the riddles.

1 Teaching the Lesson

▶ Math Message Follow-Up

WHOLE-CLASS DISCUSSION

(*Math Journal 2,* pp. 204 and 205)

The answer to both questions is *yes*. Have children share solution strategies. Have them write number models for their strategies on the board.

▷ Because a harp seal could weigh between 200 and 396 lb, 6 seals could weigh as little as 1,200 lb (6×200 lb = 1,200 lb, which is less than 2,000 lb).

▷ Because the maximum weight (396 lb) is about twice the minimum weight (200 lb), 6 seals could weigh about 2,400 lb ($2 \times 1,200$ lb = 2,400 lb, which is greater than 2,000 lb).

▷ Because 396 is close to 400, 6×396 is close to 6×400, or 2,400, which is greater than 2,000 lb.

▷ Some children may have used repeated addition to solve the problem.

Pose similar problems from the Adult Weights of North American Animals poster and write them on the board. Children put their thumbs up to show an answer of *yes* and down to show an answer of *no*. They share solution strategies after each problem. *Suggestions:*

- Could 9 mountain goats weigh more than 1 ton? Yes; thumbs up Less than 1 ton? Yes; thumbs up
- Could 4 polar bears weigh more than 1 ton? Yes; thumbs up Less than 1 ton? No; thumbs down
- Could 7 white-tailed deer weigh more than 2 tons? No; thumbs down
- Could 8 beluga whales weigh more than 10 tons? Yes; thumbs up Less than 10 tons? Yes; thumbs up
- Could 25 snowshoe hares weigh more than 100 lb? Yes; thumbs up Less than 100 lb? Yes; thumbs up

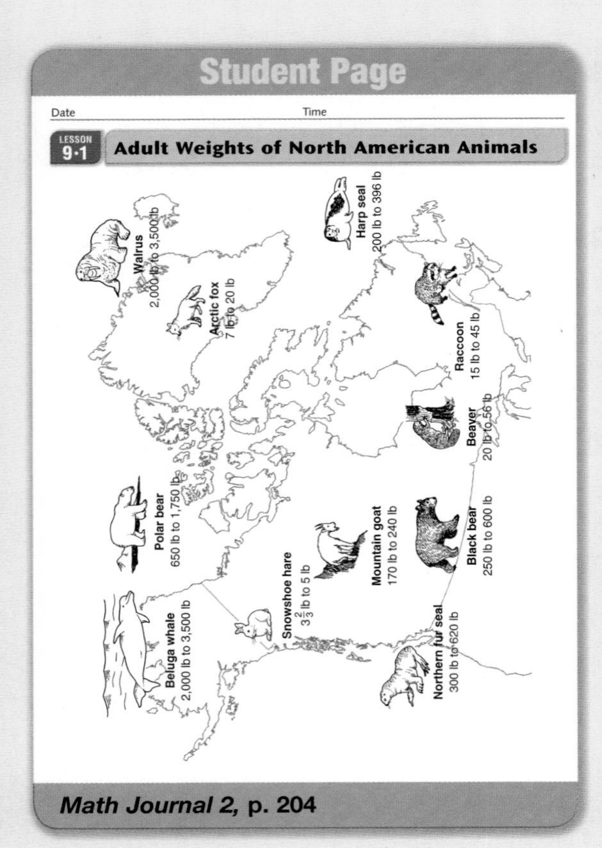

NOTE The Distributive Property of Multiplication over Addition relates multiplication to a sum of numbers by distributing a factor over the terms in the sum. For any numbers *a*, *b*, and *c*, $a(b + c) = (a \times b) + (a \times c)$. The Associative Property of Multiplication states that three numbers can be multiplied in any order without changing the product. For any three numbers *a*, *b*, and *c*, $(a \times b) \times c = a \times (b \times c)$.

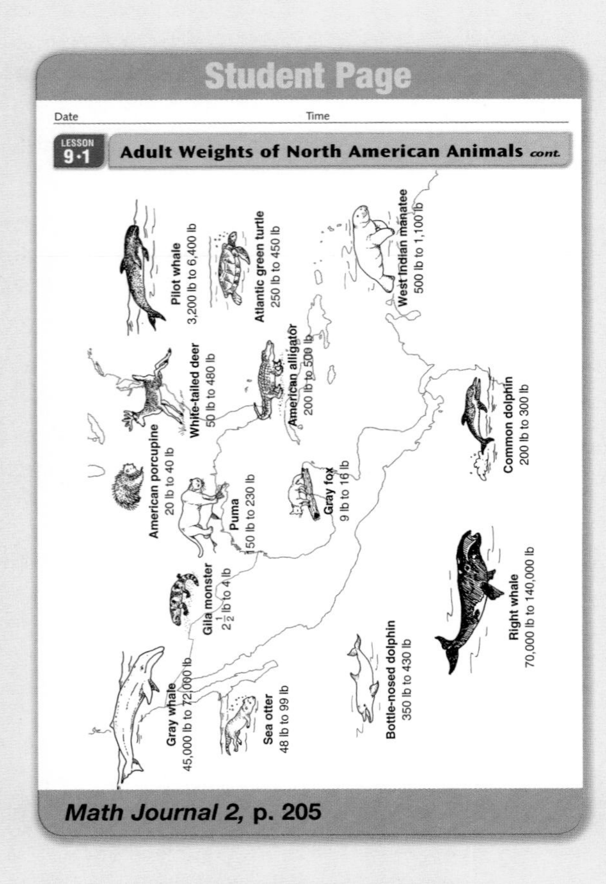

Explain that children will use mental math to solve problems involving animal weights.

Ongoing Assessment: Informing Instruction

Watch for children who are having difficulty converting tons to pounds. If this step is preventing children from focusing on the problems, give the target weight in pounds.

▶ Multiplying 1-Digit Numbers By Multidigit Numbers Mentally

WHOLE-CLASS ACTIVITY

(*Math Journal 2,* pp. 204 and 205)

Start with a problem based on the Adult Weights of North American Animals poster on journal pages 204 and 205.

Example:

- How much do six 15-pound raccoons weigh? 90 lb

Draw a multiplication/division diagram on the board. Ask children to tell you where to write the given information in the diagram, and write ? for the information to be found.

number of animals	pounds per animal	pounds in all
6	15	?

Have children find the answer—preferably mentally, but they may use paper or a slate to keep track of their thinking. They share solution strategies. Encourage them to use the language of multiples (*6 [15s]* rather than *6 times 15*) as they explain their strategies.

Possible strategies:

- Think of 6×15 as $6 \times (10 + 5)$. Use the Distributive Property of Multiplication over Addition: $6 \times (10 + 5) = (6 \times 10) + (6 \times 5) = 60 + 30 = 90$.
- Think of 6×15 as $(3 \times 2) \times 15$. Use the Associative Property of Multiplication: $(3 \times 2) \times 15 = 3 \times (2 \times 15) = 3 \times 30 = 90$. Another way to represent this thinking process: Double 15 to get 30 and 3 [30s] are 90.

Pose additional problems. Draw and fill in a diagram for each problem and ask for the solution. Be sure children share strategies before going on to the next problem. If necessary give children hints to get them started, but not until they have had ample opportunity to devise strategies on their own.

Once a child has shared a strategy, encourage other children to try it. This validates the child who suggested the strategy and offers the rest of the children the opportunity to expand their repertoire of strategies.

Suggestions:

- How much do six 45-pound raccoons weigh? 270 lb

Possible strategies: Some children might reason that since 45 is 3 times as much as 15, 6 [45s] are 3 times as much as 90, or 270. Others may apply the Distributive Property of Multiplication over Addition and reason that $6 \times 45 = 6 \times (40 + 5)$. Then, 6 [40s] are 240 and 6 [5s] are 30, so 6 [45s] are 240 + 30, or 270.

Still others may apply the Associative Property of Multiplication and think of 6 as 3×2. Next, double 45 (or 2 [45s]) to obtain 90 and then triple 90 (or 3 [90s]) to obtain 270 pounds. One way to represent this thinking process is $6 \times 45 = (3 \times 2) \times 45 = 3 \times (2 \times 45) = 3 \times 90 = 270$.

NOTE At this time, children are not expected to use the terms *distributive property* or *associative property.* They should, however, begin to develop an understanding that numbers in computations can be factored, grouped, and/or renamed in different ways to make computations easier to solve.

- How much do five 180-pound pumas weigh? 900 lb

Possible strategies: 5 [100s] plus 5 [80s] = 500 + 400 = 900; or 5 [200s] minus 5 [20s] = 1,000 − 100 = 900.

Pose problems without a context and ask for strategies.

Problems	Possible strategies
$6 \times 13 = ?$ 78	6 [10s] plus 6 [3s] = 60 + 18 = 78; or 6 [15s] minus 6 [2s] = 90 − 12 = 78
$9 \times 49 = ?$ 441	9 [50s] minus 9 [1s] = 450 − 9 = 441; or 9 [40s] plus 9 [9s] = 360 + 81 = 441; or 10 [49s] minus 1 [49] = 490 − 49 = 441
$7 \times 32 = ?$ 224	7 [30s] plus 7 [2s] = 210 + 14 = 224
$4 \times 26 = ?$ 104	4 [25s] plus 4 [1s] = 100 + 4 = 104; or 4 [20s] plus 4 [6s] = 80 + 24 = 104
$2 \times 950 = ?$ 1,900	2 [1,000s] minus 2 [50s] = 2,000 − 100 = 1,900; or 2 [900s] plus 2 [50s] = 1,800 + 100 = 1,900

▶ Practicing Mental Math Strategies

INDEPENDENT ACTIVITY

(*Math Journal 2,* p. 208)

Children complete journal page 208. Circulate and ask children to share their strategies.

Ongoing Assessment: Recognizing Student Achievement

Journal page 208 Problem 1

Use **journal page 208, Problem 1** to assess children's progress toward using strategies to solve problems involving multiplication of 2-digit numbers by a 1-digit number. Children are making adequate progress if they successfully complete Problem 1 and explain the strategy they used. Some children may complete other problems on the page successfully.

[Operations and Computation Goal 4]

Student Page

Date ______ Time ______

LESSON 9·2 **Mental Multiplication**

Solve these problems in your head. Use a slate and chalk, or pencil and paper, to help you keep track of your thinking. For some of the problems, you will need to use the information on journal pages 204 and 205.

1. Could 5 arctic foxes weigh 100 pounds? Yes
   Less than 100 pounds? Yes
   Explain the strategy you used.
   Sample answer: I multiplied 5 × 20 to get 100 pounds, which is the maximum weight. I multiplied 5 × 7 to get 35 pounds, which is the minimum weight.
2. Could 12 harp seals weigh more than 1 ton? Yes Less than 1 ton? No
   Explain the strategy that you used. Sample answer:
   I found the minimum weight by multiplying 12 × 200 to get 2,400 pounds, which is more than 1 ton.
3. How much do eight 53-pound white-tailed deer weigh? 424 pounds
   Explain the strategy that you used. Sample answer:
   I know that 53 is 50 + 3. I multiplied 8 × 50 and 8 × 3. I added the products and got 424.
4. How much do six 87-pound sea otters weigh? 522 pounds
5. How much do seven 260-pound Atlantic green turtles weigh? 1,820 pounds
6. $6 \times 54 =$ 324
7. 1,000 $= 4 \times 250$
8. $2 \times 460 =$ 920
9. 960 $= 3 \times 320$

Math Journal 2, p. 208

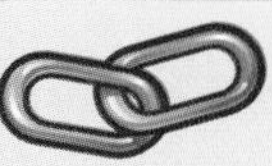

Links to the Future

Because children's mental math procedures often anticipate more formal algorithms, it is important to provide them with opportunities to devise their own strategies before presenting formal algorithms. Formal multiplication algorithms will be presented in Lessons 9-4, 9-9, 9-11, and 9-12.

Student Page

Date Time

LESSON 9·2 **Number Stories**

Use the Adult Weights of North American Animals poster on *Math Journal 2*, pages 204 and 205. Make up multiplication and division number stories. Ask a partner to solve your number stories.

1. Answers vary.

Answer:

2.

Answer:

3.

Answer:

Math Journal 2, p. 209

2 Ongoing Learning & Practice

Making Up and Solving Poster Stories

(*Math Journal 2,* pp. 204, 205, and 209)

Partners make up stories for each other to solve on journal page 209. Encourage them to make up stories that use multiplication and division. You might want to use some of these stories at various times as Mental Math and Reflexes problems.

Math Boxes 9·2

(*Math Journal 2,* p. 210)

Mixed Practice Math Boxes in this lesson are paired with Math Boxes in Lesson 9-4. The skill in Problem 6 previews Unit 10 content.

Writing/Reasoning Have children write an answer to the following: *Explain how you figured out which numbers to write on the number line in Problem 5.* Sample answer: I knew that halfway between 0 and $\frac{2}{3}$ on the number line was $\frac{1}{3}$. I counted by thirds to find the missing numbers: 0, $\frac{1}{3}$, $\frac{2}{3}$, $\frac{3}{3}$, $\frac{4}{3}$.

Home Link 9·2

(*Math Masters,* p. 269)

Home Connection Children practice multiplication facts and fact extensions to reinforce work in this lesson, as well as to prepare for the partial-products algorithm in Lesson 9-4.

Student Page

Date Time

LESSON 9·2 **Math Boxes**

1. Nicky has $806 in the bank. Andrew has $589. How much more money does Nicky have than Andrew?
$ 217

2. Write the numbers.
5 tens 9 ones
50 + 9 Total: 59
3 tens 8 ones
30 + 8 Total: 38

3. $\frac{1}{2}$ hour = 30 minutes
$1\frac{1}{2}$ hours = 90 minutes
2 hours = 120 minutes
$1\frac{1}{4}$ hours = 75 minutes
3 hours = 180 minutes

4. Draw a shape with a perimeter of 14 units.
Sample answer:
What is the area of the shape? 6 square units

5. Fill in the missing numbers. Use fractions.
0, $\frac{1}{3}$, $\frac{2}{3}$, 1, or $\frac{3}{3}$, $1\frac{1}{3}$, or $\frac{4}{3}$

6. Circle the most appropriate unit.
length of a calculator: (inches) feet miles
weight of an adult: ounces (pounds) tons
amount of gas in a car: cups pints (gallons)

Math Journal 2, p. 210

3 Differentiation Options

READINESS

SMALL-GROUP ACTIVITY

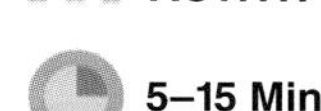

5–15 Min

▶ Using Multiplication/ Division Diagrams

(*Math Masters,* p. 270)

To explore using multiplication/division diagrams to model equal groups problems with multiples of 10, have children fill in the diagrams and solve the problems on *Math Masters,* page 270.

ENRICHMENT

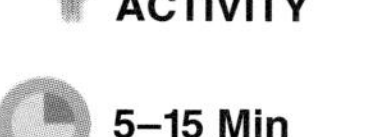

INDEPENDENT ACTIVITY

5–15 Min

PROBLEM SOLVING

▶ Solving an Allowance Problem

(*Math Masters,* p. 271)

To apply their understanding of multidigit multiplication, have children calculate weekly allowances according to three different plans.

Teaching Master

Name Date Time

LESSON 9·2 **Using Multiplication/Division Diagrams**

For each number story, complete the multiplication/division diagram, write a number model, and answer the question.

1. Tiffany keeps her button collection in a case with 10 shelves. On each shelf there are 16 buttons. How many buttons are in Tiffany's collection?

Number model: $10 \times 16 = ?$

Answer: 160 buttons (unit)

number of shelves	buttons per shelf	buttons in all
10	16	?

2. Rashida walks her neighbor's dog every day. She gets paid $20.00 every week. If Rashida saves her money for 30 weeks, how much money would she have?

Number model: $30 \times \$20 = ?$

Answer: $600 (unit)

number of weeks	dollars per week	dollars in all
30	$20	?

3. The third grade class helped plant 4 tulip gardens at school. 50 tulip bulbs fit into each garden. How many tulip bulbs were planted?

Number model: $4 \times 50 = ?$

Answer: 200 bulbs (unit)

number of gardens	bulbs per garden	bulbs in all
4	50	?

Try This

4. There were 2,000 books collected in the book drive. Each class received 200 books. How many classes received books?

Number model: $2{,}000 \div 200 = ?$ or $? \times 200 = 2{,}000$

Answer: 10 classes (unit)

number of classes	books per class	books in all
?	200	2,000

Math Masters, p. 270

Home Link Master

Name Date Time

HOME LINK 9·2 **Multiplication Facts and Extensions**

Family Note Help your child practice multiplication facts and their extensions. Observe as your child creates fact extensions, demonstrating further understanding of multiplication.

Please return this Home Link to school tomorrow.

Solve each problem.

1. a. 8 [7s] = 56, or 8 × 7 = 56
   b. 8 [70s] = 560, or 8 × 70 = 560
   c. How many 8s in 56? 7
   d. How many 8s in 560? 70
   e. How many 7s in 56? 8
   f. How many 70s in 560? 8
2. a. 9 [7s] = 63, or 9 × 7 = 63
   b. 9 [70s] = 630, or 9 × 70 = 630
   c. How many 9s in 63? 7
   d. How many 9s in 630? 70
   e. How many 7s in 63? 9
   f. How many 70s in 630? 9
3. a. 8 [5s] = 40, or 8 × 5 = 40
   b. 8 [50s] = 400, or 8 × 50 = 400
   c. How many 8s in 400? 50
   d. How many 80s in 4,000? 50
   e. How many 50s in 400? 8
   f. How many 50s in 4,000? 80
4. Write a multiplication fact you are trying to learn. Then use your fact to write some fact extensions like those above. Sample answer:

9 × 5 = 45 9 [5s] = 45

9 [50s] = 450 9 × 50 = 450

How many 9s in 45? 5 How many 5s in 45? 9

How many 9s in 450? 50 How many 50s in 450? 9

Math Masters, p. 269

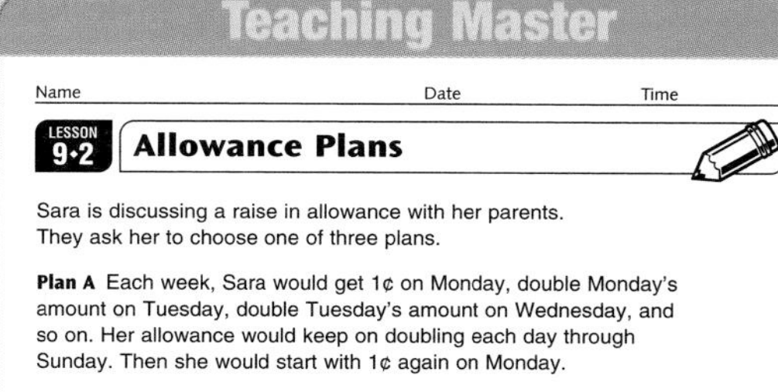

Teaching Master

Name Date Time

LESSON 9·2 **Allowance Plans**

Sara is discussing a raise in allowance with her parents. They ask her to choose one of three plans.

Plan A Each week, Sara would get 1¢ on Monday, double Monday's amount on Tuesday, double Tuesday's amount on Wednesday, and so on. Her allowance would keep on doubling each day through Sunday. Then she would start with 1¢ again on Monday.

Plan B Sara would get 32¢ on Sunday, Monday, Wednesday, and Friday of each week. She would get nothing on Tuesday, Thursday, and Saturday.

Plan C Sara would get 16¢ on each day of each week.

Which plan should Sara choose to get the most money? Plan B

Show your work on the back of this page. Explain how you found your answer. Use number sentences in your explanation. Sample answer:

For Plan A, Sara would get $0.01 + $0.02 + $0.04 + $0.08 + $0.16 + $0.32 + $0.64 = $1.27. For Plan B, she would get $0.32 × 4 = $1.28. For Plan C, she would get $0.16 × 7 = $1.12. Sara gets the most money from Plan B.

Try This Sample answer:

For the plan you chose, how much money would Sara earn in a year?

Since Sara makes $1.28 each week and there are 52 weeks in one year, I would multiply $1.28 by 52 to get $66.56.

Math Masters, p. 271

9•3 Exploring Arrays, Areas, and Fractions

Explorations

Objectives To provide opportunities for children to model multiplication with base-10 blocks, explore area relationships, and find fractions of fractions.

Technology Resources www.everydaymathonline.com

ePresentations

eToolkit

Algorithms Practice

EM Facts Workshop Game™

Family Letters

Assessment Management

Common Core State Standards

Curriculum Focal Points

Interactive Teacher's Lesson Guide

1 Teaching the Lesson

Key Concepts and Skills

- Explore fraction multiplication using paper folding. [Number and Numeration Goal 2]
- Use arrays to model multiplication. [Operations and Computation Goal 6]
- Count unit squares to find the total area covered in an array model of a multidigit multiplication problem. [Measurement and Reference Frames Goal 2]
- Draw rectangles and squares with given areas. [Measurement and Reference Frames Goal 2]

Key Activities

Exploration A: Children make arrays with base-10 blocks to model partial products.

Exploration B: Children explore the relationship between area and lengths of sides in rectangles and squares.

Exploration C: Children fold rectangles to find fractions of fractions.

Ongoing Assessment: Informing Instruction See page 727.

Materials

Home Link 9•2
transparency of *Math Masters,* p. 273 ◆ base-10 longs and cubes ◆ slate ◆ quarter-sheets of paper

Exploration A: Per group:
Math Journal 2, p. 211
Math Masters, pp. 272–274
at least 32 cubes and 18 longs ◆ red and blue crayons

Exploration B: Per person:
Math Journal 2, p. 212
Math Masters, p. 275; p. 415 (optional)
7 × 7 geoboard and rubber bands ◆ pennies (optional)

Exploration C: Per group:
Math Masters, pp. 276 and 277
crayons ◆ scissors ◆ paper ◆ tape (or glue)

2 Ongoing Learning & Practice

Comparing Fractions with Fraction Strips
five 1-inch by $8\frac{1}{2}$-inch strips of paper

Math Boxes 9•3
Math Journal 2, p. 213

Ongoing Assessment: Recognizing Student Achievement
Use Math Boxes, Problem 1.
[Data and Chance Goal 4]

Home Link 9•3
Math Masters, p. 278

3 Differentiation Options

READINESS

Finding All Possible Areas
Math Masters, p. 418
per partnership: five 1-inch tiles or square pattern blocks ◆ scissors

EXTRA PRACTICE

Minute Math+
Minute Math®+, pp. 43 and 75

Advance Preparation

Make an array grid for each group of children by gluing or taping together copies of *Math Masters,* pages 273 and 274. Place a pile of longs and cubes next to the Math Message. Cut five 1-inch by $8\frac{1}{2}$-inch strips of paper for each child. Have extra strips available in case of mistakes.

***Teacher's Reference Manual,* Grades 1–3** pp. 158, 159

Getting Started

Mathematical Practices
SMP1, SMP2, SMP3, SMP4, SMP5, **SMP6,** SMP7, **SMP8**
Content Standards
3.OA.3, 3.NBT.2, 3.NBT.3, 3.NF.3, **3.NF.3d, 3.MD.5b, 3.MD.7a, 3.MD.7b, 3.MD.7c, 3.MD.7d, 3.MD.8**

Mental Math and Reflexes

Pose the following multiplication and division number stories. Children write their answers on slates.

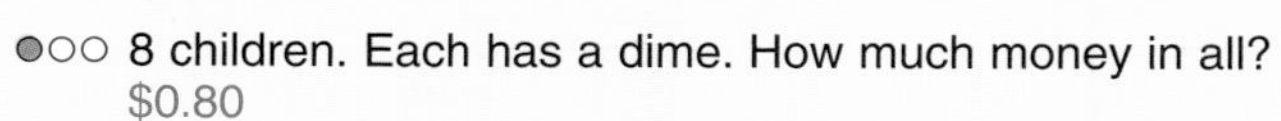

●○○ 8 children. Each has a dime. How much money in all? $0.80

5 children. Each has 8 crayons. How many crayons in all? 40 crayons

●●○ 6 flowers. 7 petals on each flower. How many petals in all? 42 petals

9 oranges. 4 seeds per orange. How many seeds in all? 36 seeds

●●● 7 children share 63 pennies equally. How many pennies per child? 9 pennies

32 chairs in 4 equal rows. How many chairs in each row? 8 chairs

Math Message

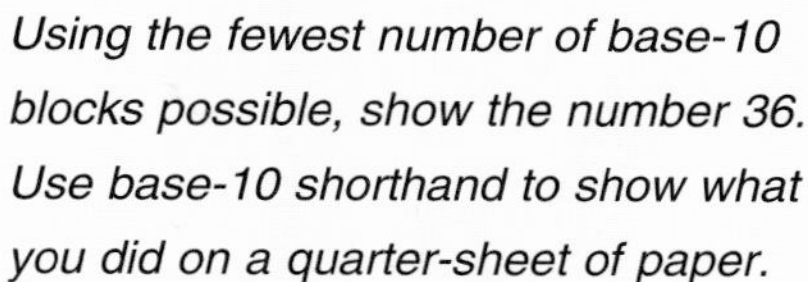

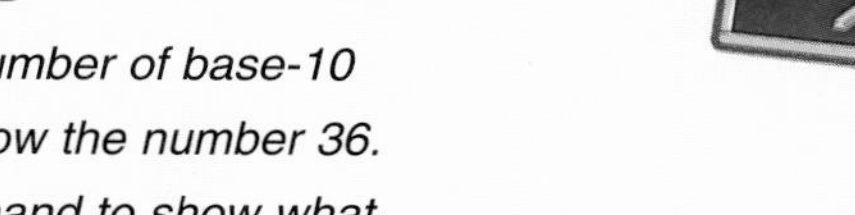

Using the fewest number of base-10 blocks possible, show the number 36. Use base-10 shorthand to show what you did on a quarter-sheet of paper.

Home Link 9·2 Follow-Up

Review answers as necessary. Have partners share their responses to Problem 4.

1 Teaching the Lesson

▶ Math Message Follow-Up

WHOLE-CLASS DISCUSSION

The fewest number of blocks to show 36 is 3 longs and 6 cubes. Pose follow-up questions as needed. For example: *How would I show 56 with the fewest number of blocks possible?* 5 longs and 6 cubes *What did I add to 36 to get to 56?* 2 longs, or 20 Continue as time allows.

▶ Modeling Multiplication with Base-10 Blocks

WHOLE-CLASS ACTIVITY

(*Math Masters,* p. 273)

Model the array multiplication activity for the class before moving children into groups to complete the Explorations. Display a transparency of *Math Masters,* page 273. Section off a portion of the grid that is 8 squares high and 14 squares wide (8-by-14).

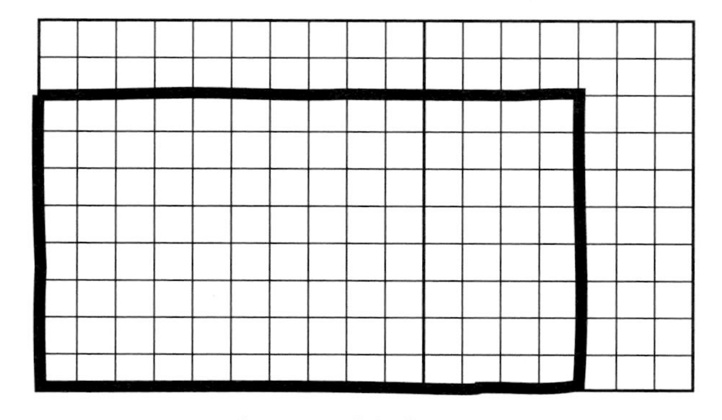

Array model of 8 by 14

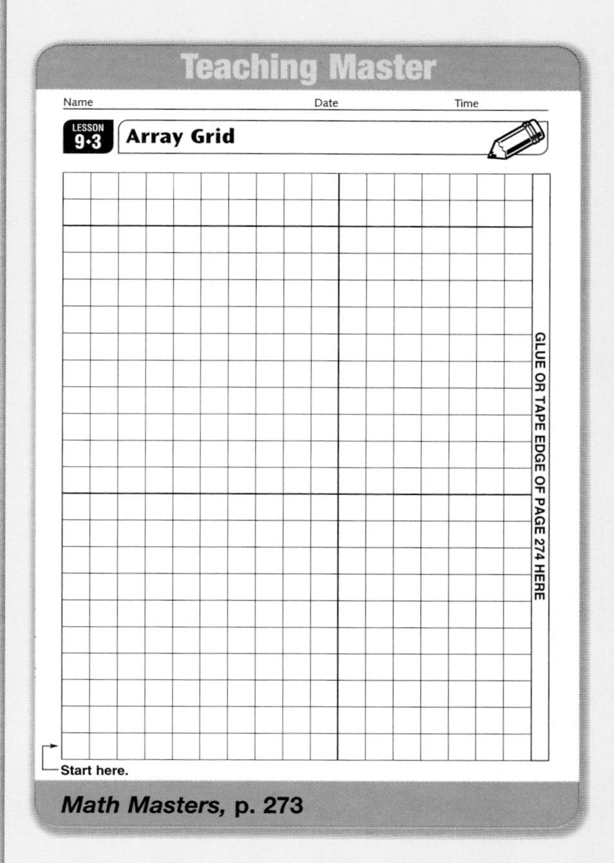

Math Masters, p. 273

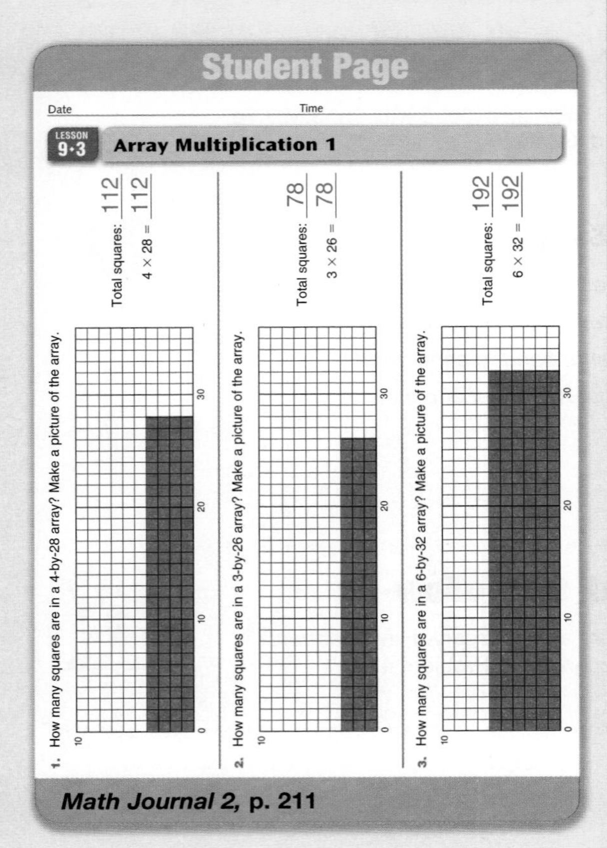
Student Page

Date Time

LESSON 9·3 **Array Multiplication 1**

1. How many squares are in a 4-by-28 array? Make a picture of the array.
Total squares: 112
$4 \times 28 =$ 112

2. How many squares are in a 3-by-26 array? Make a picture of the array.
Total squares: 78
$3 \times 26 =$ 78

3. How many squares are in a 6-by-32 array? Make a picture of the array.
Total squares: 192
$6 \times 32 =$ 192

Math Journal 2, p. 211

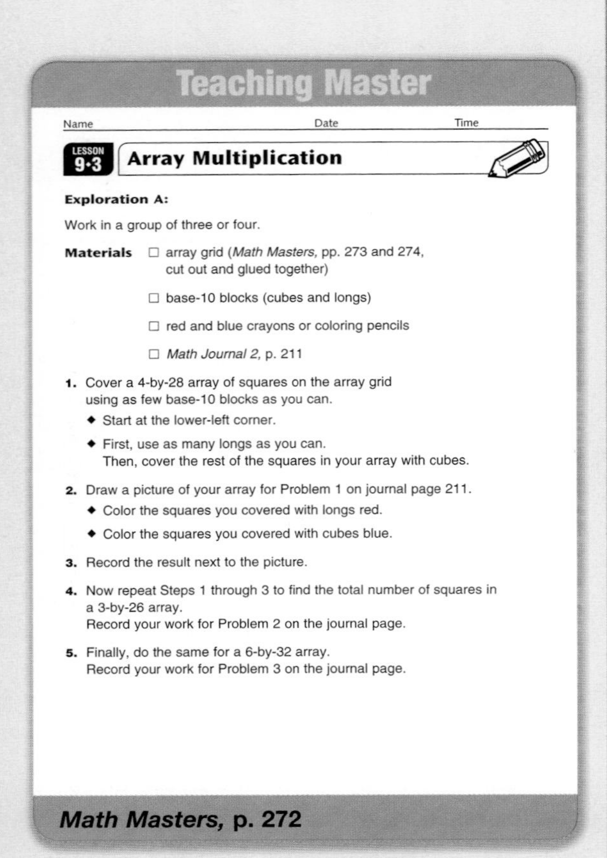
Teaching Master

Name Date Time

LESSON 9·3 **Array Multiplication**

Exploration A:

Work in a group of three or four.

Materials
- ☐ array grid (*Math Masters,* pp. 273 and 274, cut out and glued together)
- ☐ base-10 blocks (cubes and longs)
- ☐ red and blue crayons or coloring pencils
- ☐ *Math Journal 2,* p. 211

1. Cover a 4-by-28 array of squares on the array grid using as few base-10 blocks as you can.
   - Start at the lower-left corner.
   - First, use as many longs as you can. Then, cover the rest of the squares in your array with cubes.
2. Draw a picture of your array for Problem 1 on journal page 211.
   - Color the squares you covered with longs red.
   - Color the squares you covered with cubes blue.
3. Record the result next to the picture.
4. Now repeat Steps 1 through 3 to find the total number of squares in a 3-by-26 array. Record your work for Problem 2 on the journal page.
5. Finally, do the same for a 6-by-32 array. Record your work for Problem 3 on the journal page.

Math Masters, p. 272

Ask: *Starting in the lower-left corner, how could I cover this 8-by-14 area with the fewest number of base-10 blocks possible?* With 8 longs and 32 cubes Encourage children to use as many longs as possible (before cubes).

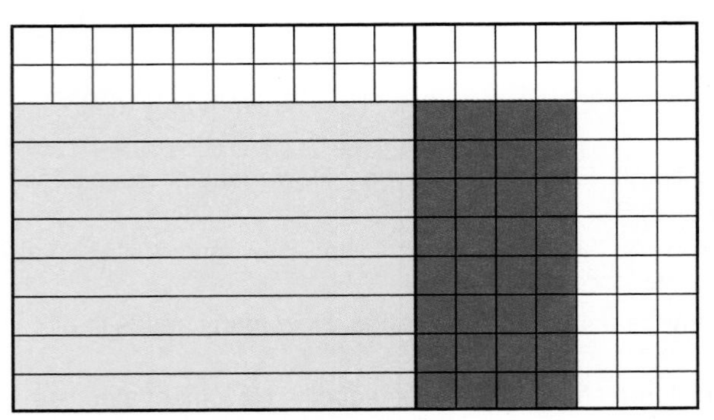
Base-10 block model of $8 \times 14 = 112$

Ask: *In the 8-by-14 array, how many squares did I cover with longs and cubes?* There are 112 squares. 8 longs $= 8 \times 10 = 80$; 32 cubes $= 32 \times 1 = 32$; $80 + 32 = 112$ *What is 8×14?* 112

Move the class into exploration groups. Plan to spend most of your time with Exploration A groups.

▶ Exploration A: Array Multiplication

SMALL-GROUP ACTIVITY

(*Math Journal 2,* p. 211; *Math Masters,* pp. 272–274)

Children follow the directions on *Math Masters,* page 272 and complete journal page 211. They cover a 4-by-28 array with as few base-10 blocks as possible. 4 rows, each with 2 longs and 8 cubes Then they record the result on the journal page using a red crayon or pencil to color the squares covered by longs and a blue crayon or pencil to color the squares covered by cubes. Children also record the total number of squares covered and complete the corresponding number model. Then they repeat these steps for a 3-by-26 array and a 6-by-32 array.

NOTE At the end of this lesson, collect the grids and store them for use in later lessons in this unit.

▶ Exploration B: Finding Geoboard Areas

INDEPENDENT ACTIVITY

(*Math Journal 2,* p. 212; *Math Masters,* pp. 275 and 415)

The directions for this Exploration are on *Math Masters,* page 275. Children explore the relationship between area and lengths of sides in rectangles and squares. They should use geoboards with at least 7 rows of 7 pins. If such geoboards are not available, children can use Geoboard Dot Paper (*Math Masters,* page 415).

Children form or draw pairs of rectangles or squares whose areas are 6, 12, and 16 square units and record the lengths of the sides of each in the table on journal page 212.

Ongoing Assessment: Informing Instruction

Watch for children who have difficulty finding the length of the sides because they are counting the pegs instead of the spaces. Have them place a penny in between the pegs of the figure and count the pennies. Emphasize that they are counting the *distance* from one peg to the next.

Next, children investigate whether they can form a rectangle or square whose area is an odd number of square units. They can; for example, a square with sides 3 units long has an area of 9 square units; a rectangle with sides 5 units and 3 units long has an area of 15 square units. Children continue if time allows.

As a follow-up, children look for a pattern or rule in their tables and try to apply this rule in solving an area problem without using a geoboard. The most likely rule is: The area of a square or rectangle is equal to the product of the lengths of two adjacent sides.

▶ Exploration C: Finding Fractions of Fractions of Regions

SMALL-GROUP ACTIVITY

(*Math Masters,* pp. 276 and 277)

Children work in groups of three or four to explore fraction multiplication by folding rectangles. See *Math Masters,* page 276 for directions. Children cut out rectangles on *Math Masters,* page 277, fold and color them, and complete number models for problems such as $\frac{1}{2}$ of $\frac{1}{4}$.

After they are finished, each group writes a report and uses some of the rectangles to illustrate their results. They look for a rule to help them solve similar problems (without folding rectangles). Then they use their rule to solve additional problems, checking their solutions by folding rectangles.

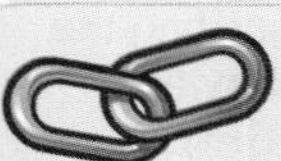

Links to the Future

The activity in Exploration C is a beginning exposure to fraction multiplication. Solving problems and number stories involving the multiplication of fractions is a Grade 5 Goal.

Student Page

Date Time

LESSON 9·3 **Geoboard Areas**

Record your results in this table.

Geoboard Areas		
Area	Longer Sides	Shorter Sides
12 square units ✓	4 units	3 units
12 square units ✓	6 units	2 units
6 square units	3 units	2 units
6 square units ✓	6 units	1 unit
16 square units	8 units	2 units
16 square units ✓	4 units	4 units
Sample answers:		
21 square units	7 units	3 units
9 square units	3 units	3 units
15 square units ✓	5 units	3 units

1. Study your table. Can you find a pattern? The area of a square or rectangle is equal to the product of the length multiplied by the width.

2. Find the lengths of the sides of a rectangle or square whose area is 30 square units without using the geoboard or geoboard dot paper. Make or draw the shape to check your answer. Sample answer: 6 units by 5 units

3. Make check marks in your table next to the rectangles and squares whose perimeters are 14 units and 16 units.

Math Journal 2, p. 212

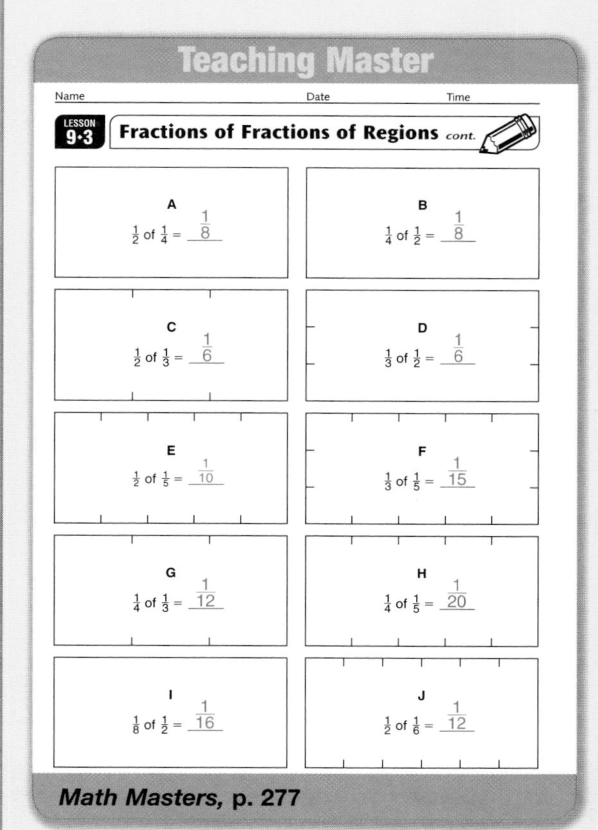
Teaching Master

Name Date Time

LESSON 9·3 **Fractions of Fractions of Regions** *cont.*

A: $\frac{1}{2}$ of $\frac{1}{4}$ = $\frac{1}{8}$

B: $\frac{1}{4}$ of $\frac{1}{2}$ = $\frac{1}{8}$

C: $\frac{1}{2}$ of $\frac{1}{3}$ = $\frac{1}{6}$

D: $\frac{1}{3}$ of $\frac{1}{2}$ = $\frac{1}{6}$

E: $\frac{1}{2}$ of $\frac{1}{5}$ = $\frac{1}{10}$

F: $\frac{1}{3}$ of $\frac{1}{5}$ = $\frac{1}{15}$

G: $\frac{1}{4}$ of $\frac{1}{3}$ = $\frac{1}{12}$

H: $\frac{1}{4}$ of $\frac{1}{5}$ = $\frac{1}{20}$

I: $\frac{1}{8}$ of $\frac{1}{2}$ = $\frac{1}{16}$

J: $\frac{1}{2}$ of $\frac{1}{6}$ = $\frac{1}{12}$

Math Masters, p. 277

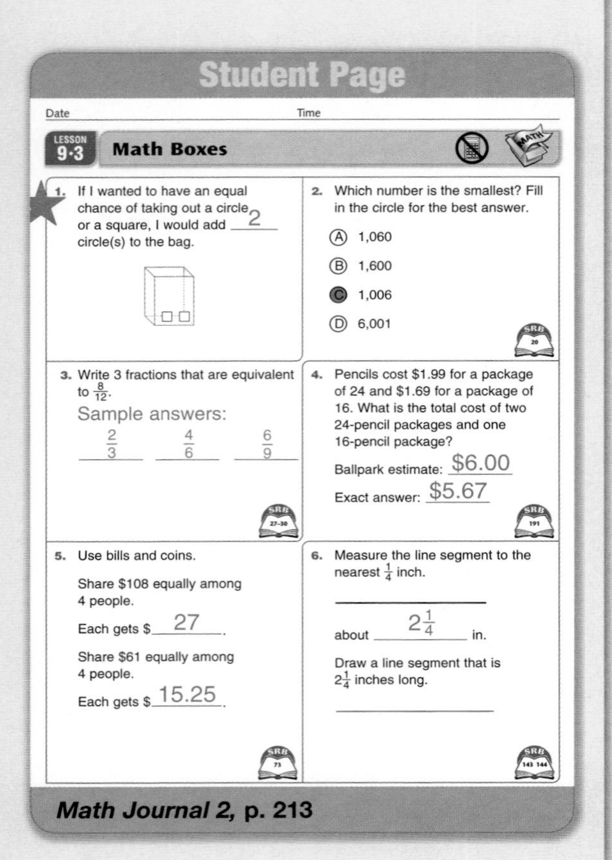
Student Page

Date Time

LESSON 9·3 **Math Boxes**

1. If I wanted to have an equal chance of taking out a circle or a square, I would add 2 circle(s) to the bag.

2. Which number is the smallest? Fill in the circle for the best answer.
   (A) 1,060
   (B) 1,600
   (C) 1,006
   (D) 6,001

3. Write 3 fractions that are equivalent to $\frac{8}{12}$.
   Sample answers: $\frac{2}{3}$ $\frac{4}{6}$ $\frac{6}{9}$

4. Pencils cost $1.99 for a package of 24 and $1.69 for a package of 16. What is the total cost of two 24-pencil packages and one 16-pencil package?
   Ballpark estimate: $6.00
   Exact answer: $5.67

5. Use bills and coins.
   Share $108 equally among 4 people.
   Each gets $ 27.
   Share $61 equally among 4 people.
   Each gets $ 15.25.

6. Measure the line segment to the nearest $\frac{1}{4}$ inch.
   about $2\frac{1}{4}$ in.
   Draw a line segment that is $2\frac{1}{4}$ inches long.

Math Journal 2, p. 213

Home Link Master

Name Date Time

HOME LINK 9·3 **Multiplication Number Stories**

Family Note Your child's class is beginning to solve multidigit multiplication and division problems. Although we have practiced multiplication and division with multiples of 10, we have been doing most of our calculating mentally. Encourage your child to explain a solution strategy for each of the problems below.

Please return this Home Link to school tomorrow.

1. How many 30-pound raccoons would weigh about as much as a 210-pound harp seal? 7 raccoons
2. How much would an alligator weigh if it weighed 10 times as much as a 50-pound sea otter? 500 lb
3. How many 20-pound arctic foxes would weigh about as much as a 2,000-pound beluga whale? 100 arctic foxes
4. Each porcupine weighs 30 pounds. A black bear weighs as much as 20 porcupines. How much does the black bear weigh? 600 lb
5. A bottle-nosed dolphin could weigh twice as much as a 200-pound common dolphin. How much could the bottle-nosed dolphin weigh? 400 lb

Try This

6. How many 2,000-pound beluga whales would weigh as much as one 120,000-pound right whale? 60 beluga whales

Math Masters, p. 278

2 Ongoing Learning & Practice

▶ Comparing Fractions with Fraction Strips

Children work in partnerships to explore comparing fractions with fraction strips. Distribute 5 strips of paper to each child (see *Advance Preparation*). Explain that each strip is a whole or ONE. Have children fold one strip into two equal parts and label each part with $\frac{1}{2}$. Then have them fold a different strip into four equal parts and label each part with $\frac{1}{4}$. In the same manner, fold each of the remaining strips into eighths, thirds, and sixths, labeling each strip with the appropriate unit fractions.

Have the children use their fraction strips to compare pairs of fractions. On a half sheet, they write number sentences using >, =, and < to describe the relationship between the two fractions.

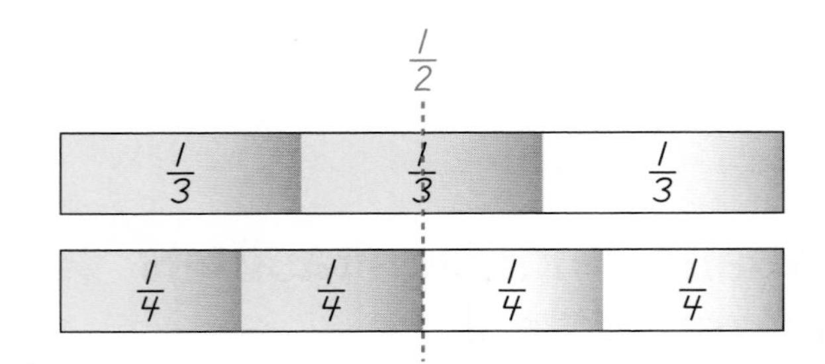

▶ Math Boxes 9·3

(*Math Journal 2,* p. 213)

Mixed Practice Math Boxes in this lesson are paired with Math Boxes in Lesson 9-1. The skill in Problem 6 previews Unit 10 content.

Ongoing Assessment: Recognizing Student Achievement

Math Boxes Problem 1

Use **Math Boxes, Problem 1** to assess children's progress toward predicting the outcome of an experiment. Children are making adequate progress if they are able to complete Problem 1 successfully. Some children may be able to determine the number of circles to add to the bag so that the chances of taking out a circle would be about three times more than taking out a square.

[Data and Chance Goal 4]

▶ Home Link 9·3

(*Math Masters,* p. 278)

Home Connection Children solve number stories that involve multiplying and dividing with multiples of 10.

3 Differentiation Options

READINESS

SMALL-GROUP ACTIVITY

▶ Finding All Possible Areas

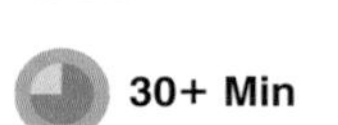

30+ Min

(*Math Masters,* p. 418)

To explore different shapes with the same area, have children use five 1-inch tiles or pattern-block squares to build all of the possible shapes with an area of five square inches. The tiles must line up along sides (not just touching corners) and not overlap. These shapes are called pentominoes. Have children record their shapes on one-inch grid paper (*Math Masters,* page 418). Have them check to be sure that each shape is unique and cannot be flipped to get an already recorded shape.

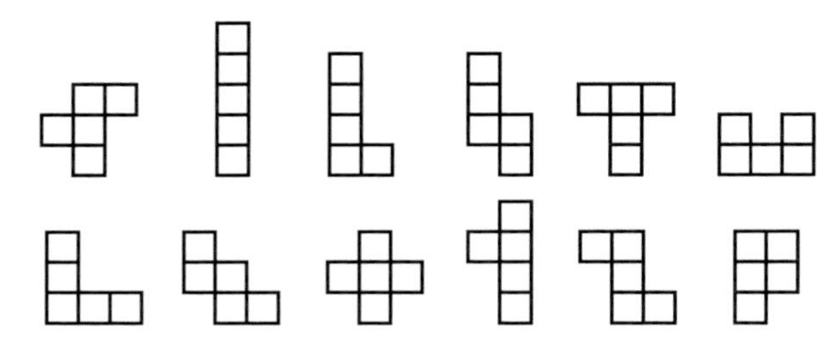

Shapes are not actual size.

When they have found all twelve configurations, have children describe the different shapes they have made and each shape's area. 5 square inches To extend the activity to include perimeter, have children find the perimeter of each shape. The perimeter of the first 11 shapes is 12 in.; the perimeter of the final shape is 10 in. If time permits, have them work to assemble their twelve shapes into one large rectangle. Have them cut out the twelve pentominoes so they can work on different configurations for the large rectangle. Once it is made, they can figure out the area of the large rectangle. 60 square inches

EXTRA PRACTICE

SMALL-GROUP ACTIVITY

▶ *Minute Math+*

5–15 Min

To offer children more experience with fractions and multiplying with multiples of 10, see the following pages in *Minute Math+*:

Measurement: p. 75

Operations: p. 43

Teaching Aid Master

Name Date Time

One-Inch Grid

Math Masters, p. 418

9•4 A Multiplication Algorithm

Objective To guide children as they multiply 1-digit numbers by multidigit numbers using a partial-products algorithm.

Technology Resources www.everydaymathonline.com

ePresentations

eToolkit

Algorithms Practice

EM Facts Workshop Game™

Family Letters

Assessment Management

Common Core State Standards

Curriculum Focal Points

Interactive Teacher's Lesson Guide

1 Teaching the Lesson

Key Concepts and Skills

- Apply place-value concepts to find partial products.
  [Number and Numeration Goal 1]
- Use the partial-products algorithm to solve problems.
  [Operations and Computation Goal 4]
- Use arrays to model multiplication.
  [Operations and Computation Goal 6]
- Apply the Distributive Property of Multiplication over Addition to find partial products.
  [Patterns, Functions, and Algebra Goal 4]

Key Activities

Children refer to their work in Exploration A of the previous lesson as they learn the partial-products algorithm.

Ongoing Assessment: Recognizing Student Achievement
Use journal page 214.
[Operations and Computation Goal 4]

Key Vocabulary

algorithm ◆ partial-products algorithm

Materials

Math Journal 2, pp. 211 and 214
Student Reference Book, pp. 68 and 69
Home Link 9•3
Math Masters, pp. 273 and 274; p. 279 (optional)
transparency of *Math Masters,* p. 279 ◆ base-10 blocks ◆ slate ◆ red and blue overhead markers ◆ longs and cubes for overhead (optional)

2 Ongoing Learning & Practice

Measuring and Drawing Accurately

Math Journal 2, p. 215
ruler
Children measure pictures and line segments and draw line segments to the nearest $\frac{1}{2}$ inch, $\frac{1}{4}$ inch, or $\frac{1}{2}$ centimeter.

Math Boxes 9•4

Math Journal 2, p. 216
Children practice and maintain skills through Math Box problems.

Home Link 9•4

Math Masters, p. 280
Children practice and maintain skills through Home Link activities.

3 Differentiation Options

READINESS

Multiplying with Base-10 Blocks

Math Masters, p. 281
per partnership: base-10 blocks (longs and cubes)
Children model equal groups with base-10 blocks to solve multiplication problems.

ENRICHMENT

Finding Sums Using Multiplication

Math Masters, p. 282
Children use count-by patterns and multiplication to find the sum of whole numbers in a series.

Advance Preparation

***Teacher's Reference Manual,* Grades 1–3** pp. 108–111

Getting Started

Mathematical Practices
SMP1, **SMP2, SMP3,** SMP4, SMP5, SMP6, SMP7
Content Standards
3.OA.3, 3.OA.5, 3.NBT.2, 3.MD.5b, 3.MD.7a, 3.MD.7b, 3.MD.7c, 3.MD.7d

Mental Math and Reflexes

Write the following problems on the board one at a time, varying in horizontal and vertical orientation. Children write only the answers on slates. Have a few children share their strategies with the class.

Suggestions:

●○○	●●○	●●●
60 + 20 + 2 82	50 + 35 + 12 97	810 + 71 + 11 892
40 + 8 + 30 78	34 + 40 + 24 98	630 + 72 + 36 738
80 + 40 + 14 134	150 + 39 + 2 191	480 + 56 + 38 574

Math Message

A farmer planted 4 rows of tomato plants with 28 plants in each row. How many tomato plants in all? Write your answer on your slate. Talk to a partner about how you solved the problem.

Home Link 9·3 Follow-Up

Briefly review answers. Have volunteers share solution strategies.

1 Teaching the Lesson

▶ Math Message Follow-Up

Children share strategies for multiplying 4 by 28. Possible strategies: (4 × 20) + (4 × 8) = 80 + 32 = 112; or (4 × 30) − (4 × 2) = 120 − 8 = 112. Some children may have used repeated addition to solve.

		28
		× 4
4 [20s]	→	80
4 [8s]	→	+ 32
80 + 32	→	112

Example of partial-products multiplication algorithm

▶ Introducing a Multiplication Algorithm

(*Math Journal 2,* p. 211; *Math Masters,* pp. 273, 274, and 279; *Student Reference Book,* pp. 68 and 69)

In Exploration A in the previous lesson, children made arrays with base-10 blocks, using as few blocks as possible. They recorded the results by coloring the squares in a grid. In this lesson, those same arrays are used to introduce a multiplication algorithm. Use an overhead projector and overhead base-10 blocks, (or regular base-10 blocks) to build the arrays from the Exploration. Children can refer to the arrays they recorded on journal page 211 while you model the procedure on the overhead with red and blue markers on a transparency of *Math Masters,* page 279.

Begin by multiplying 4 times 28 on the board. (*See margin.*)

It is recommended that you proceed from left to right; that is, calculate 4 [20s] first, and then 4 [8s]. Be careful to use the actual multiples when describing the steps. For example, say *4 [20s]* or *4 times 20,* not *4 times 2.*

Teaching Master

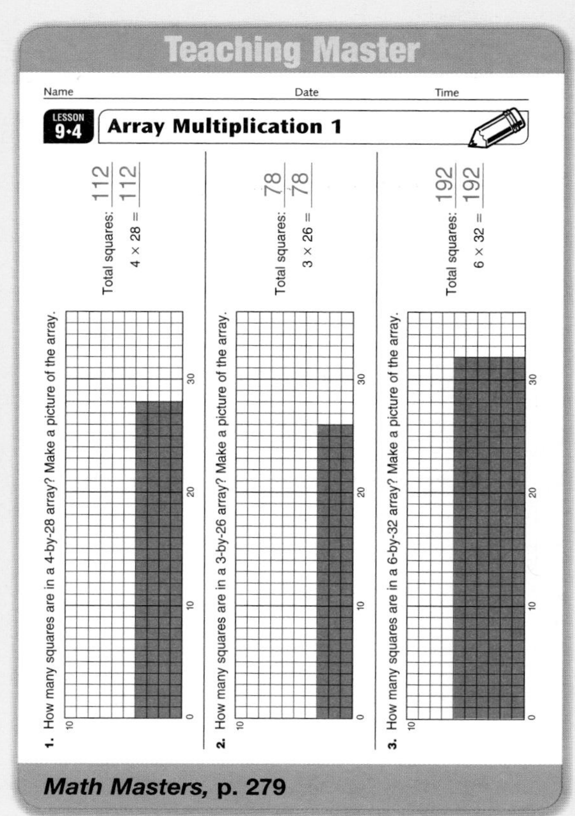

Name Date Time

LESSON 9·4 **Array Multiplication 1**

1. How many squares are in a 4-by-28 array? Make a picture of the array.
Total squares: 112
4 × 28 = 112

2. How many squares are in a 3-by-26 array? Make a picture of the array.
Total squares: 78
3 × 26 = 78

3. How many squares are in a 6-by-32 array? Make a picture of the array.
Total squares: 192
6 × 32 = 192

***Math Masters,* p. 279**

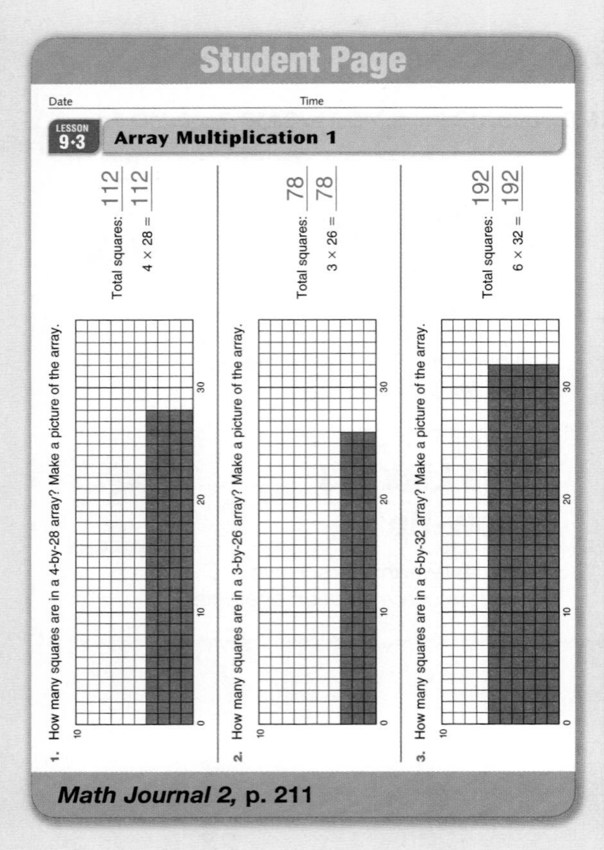
Math Journal 2, p. 211

Remind the class that an **algorithm** is a step-by-step procedure for computation that works every time when followed correctly. Tell children that the procedure you just demonstrated is called the **partial-products algorithm.** To support English language learners, explain that *partial* means *a part of something.* In the partial-products algorithm, the tens partial product and the ones partial product are found and then added to find the whole product. As you discuss the meaning, circle the partial products with colored chalk.

Next, you and the children match each part of the 4-by-28 array with a partial product. If you use an overhead projector and base-10 blocks, make 4 rows with 2 longs (4 [20s]) and 8 cubes (4 [8s]) in each row.

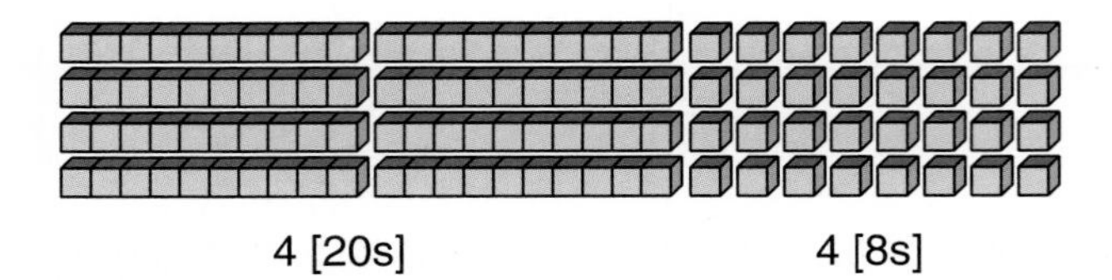

You also may refer children to the array diagram on journal page 211 as you use the markers to color the transparency as described below.

- There are 20 red squares in each of 4 rows (4 [20s]), so there are 80 red squares in all.
- There are 8 blue squares in each of 4 rows (4 [8s]), so there are 32 blue squares in all.
- There are 112 red and blue squares (80 + 32) in all in the array.

With the children's help, use the partial-products algorithm to solve the other problems on journal page 211. Again, match each part of the array with a partial product. Then have children use the algorithm to solve additional 1-digit × 2-digit problems, as needed.

Suggestions:

- 6 × 23 138
- 9 × 15 135
- 5 × 36 180

Children may read about the partial-products multiplication method on pages 68 and 69 in their *Student Reference Books.*

NOTE Multiplying from left to right has certain advantages:

- Since reading also proceeds from left to right, it is a natural way for children to work through a problem.
- It is good practice for estimating the magnitude of an answer or judging its reasonableness.

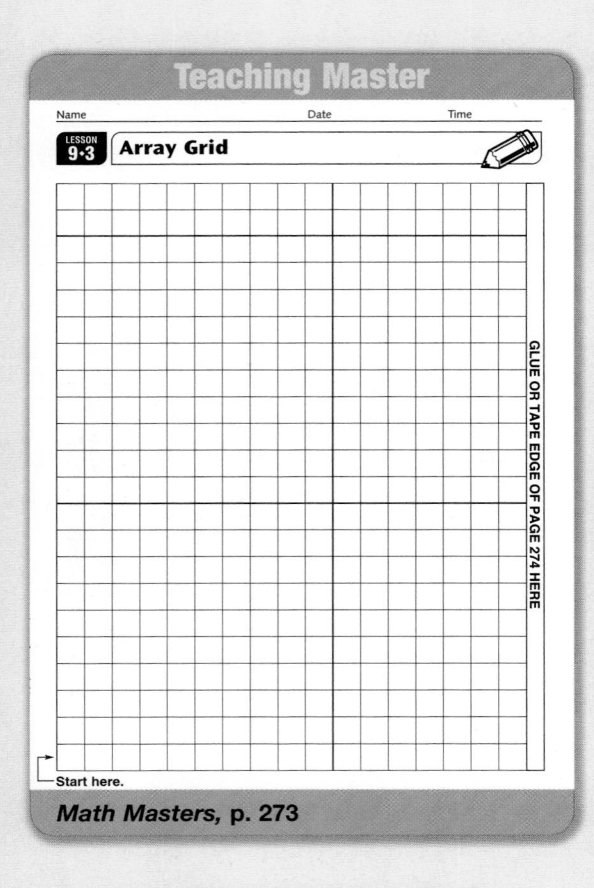
Math Masters, p. 273

Adjusting the Activity

Have children use the Array Grid (*Math Masters,* pages 273 and 274) to model the problems with base-10 blocks. Children count the blocks and match them to a partial product. Then they count the total number of blocks.

AUDITORY • KINESTHETIC • TACTILE • VISUAL

Extend the algorithm to 3-digit factors (see examples below). Be sure to include problems in which the 3-digit factor contains a 0 in the ones or tens place.

	362
	× 3
3 [300s] →	900
3 [60s] →	180
3 [2s] →	+ 6
900 + 180 + 6 →	1,086

	306
	× 4
4 [300s] →	1,200
4 [0s] →	0
4 [6s] →	+ 24
1,200 + 0 + 24 →	1,224

▶ Using an Algorithm to Multiply 1-Digit Numbers by Multidigit Numbers

(*Math Journal 2,* p. 214)

Children work to find products of 1-digit numbers and multidigit numbers. If a disagreement arises over an answer, encourage partners to discuss their strategies with each other and try the problem again. Circulate and assist as necessary.

Ongoing Assessment: Recognizing Student Achievement

Journal page 214 Problem 1

Use **journal page 214, Problem 1** to assess children's progress toward using strategies to solve multiplication problems. Children are making adequate progress if they are able to solve Problem 1 using any strategy including doubling, paper-and-pencil, base-10 blocks, and so on. Some children may be able to use the partial-products algorithm to solve the problems on the page.

[Operations and Computation Goal 4]

Adjusting the Activity

Encourage children to solve the problems by writing the partial products. They may also display the number model (for example, 4 [300s] → 1,200).

AUDITORY • KINESTHETIC • TACTILE • VISUAL

NOTE The partial-products algorithm is an application of the Distributive Property of Multiplication over Addition. For example, in the problem 3 × 362, 362 is decomposed into 300 + 60 + 2. 300, 60, and 2 are each multiplied by 3. The partial products are then added to find the whole product.

$$\begin{aligned} 3 \times 362 &= 3 \times (300 + 60 + 2) \\ &= (3 \times 300) + (3 \times 60) + (3 \times 2) \\ &= 900 + 180 + 6 \\ &= 1{,}086 \end{aligned}$$

The distributive property can be applied to any number of addends.

Student Page

Date Time

LESSON 9·4 **Using the Partial-Products Algorithm**

Multiply. Compare your answers with a partner. If you disagree, discuss your strategies with each other. Then try the problem again.

Example 7 × 46

46
× 7
7 [40s]→ 280
7 [6s]→ + 42
280 + 42→ 322

1. 34 × 2

34
× 2
2 [30s]→ 60
2 [4s]→ + 8
60 + 8→ 68

2. 83 × 5

83
× 5
5 [80s]→ 400
5 [3s]→ + 15
400 + 15→ 415

3. 55 × 6

55
× 6
6 [50s]→ 300
6 [5s]→ + 30
300 + 30→ 330

4. 214 × 7

214
× 7
7 [200s]→ 1,400
7 [10s]→ 70
7 [4s]→ + 28
1,498

5. 403 × 5

403
× 5
5 [400s]→ 2,000
5 [3s]→ + 15
2,015

***Math Journal 2,* p. 214**

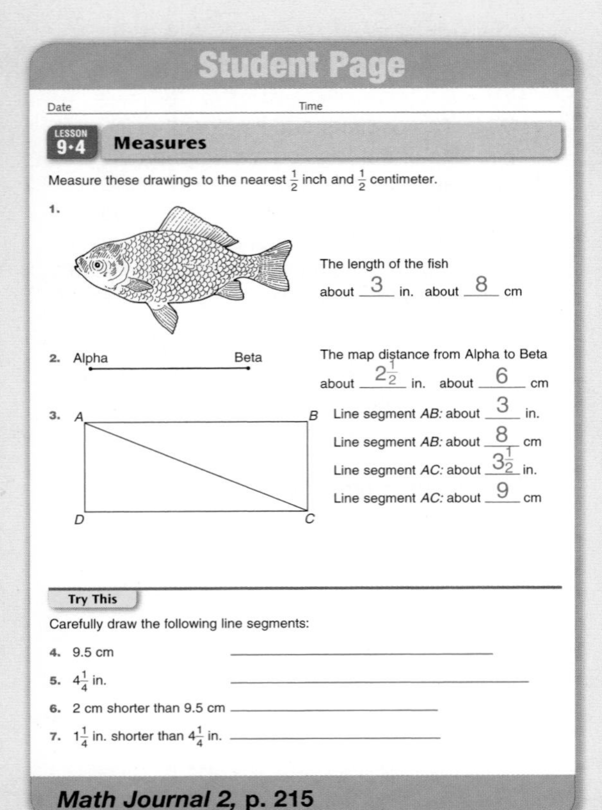
Student Page

Date Time

LESSON 9·4 **Measures**

Measure these drawings to the nearest $\frac{1}{2}$ inch and $\frac{1}{2}$ centimeter.

1. The length of the fish about 3 in. about 8 cm

2. Alpha ——— Beta
The map distance from Alpha to Beta about $2\frac{1}{2}$ in. about 6 cm

3. Line segment *AB*: about 3 in.
Line segment *AB*: about 8 cm
Line segment *AC*: about $3\frac{1}{2}$ in.
Line segment *AC*: about 9 cm

Try This

Carefully draw the following line segments:

4. 9.5 cm
5. $4\frac{1}{4}$ in.
6. 2 cm shorter than 9.5 cm
7. $1\frac{1}{4}$ in. shorter than $4\frac{1}{4}$ in.

Math Journal 2, p. 215

2 Ongoing Learning & Practice

▶ Measuring and Drawing Accurately

INDEPENDENT ACTIVITY

(*Math Journal 2,* p. 215)

Children record measurements to the nearest $\frac{1}{2}$ inch and $\frac{1}{2}$ cm. They draw line segments to the nearest $\frac{1}{4}$ inch or $\frac{1}{2}$ centimeter.

▶ Math Boxes 9·4

INDEPENDENT ACTIVITY

(*Math Journal 2,* p. 216)

Mixed Practice Math Boxes in this lesson are paired with Math Boxes in Lesson 9-2. The skill in Problem 6 previews Unit 10 content.

▶ Home Link 9·4

INDEPENDENT ACTIVITY

(*Math Masters,* p. 280)

Home Connection Children use the partial-products algorithm.

Student Page

Date Time

LESSON 9·4 **Math Boxes**

1. Morgan earned \$252 shoveling snow. Casey earned \$228. How much more money did Morgan earn? Fill in the circle for the best answer.
   (A) \$24 (B) \$26 (C) \$470 (D) \$480

2. Write the numbers.
   5 hundreds 6 tens 4 ones
   500 + 60 + 4
   Total: 564
   3 hundreds 2 tens 9 ones
   300 + 20 + 9
   Total: 329

3. 120 seconds = 2 minutes
   28 days = 4 weeks
   6 months = $\frac{1}{2}$ year
   18 months = $1\frac{1}{2}$ years

4. The length of the longer side is 8 units.
   The length of the shorter side is 4 units.
   The area of the rectangle is 32 square units.

5. Fill in the missing numbers on the number line.
   $\frac{3}{4}$, 1, $1\frac{1}{4}$, $1\frac{2}{4}$, or $1\frac{1}{2}$, $1\frac{3}{4}$

6. Circle the unit you would use to measure each item.
   weight of journal: (ounce) pound ton
   length of football field: inch (yard) mile
   length of paperclip: (cm) meter kilometer

Math Journal 2, p. 216

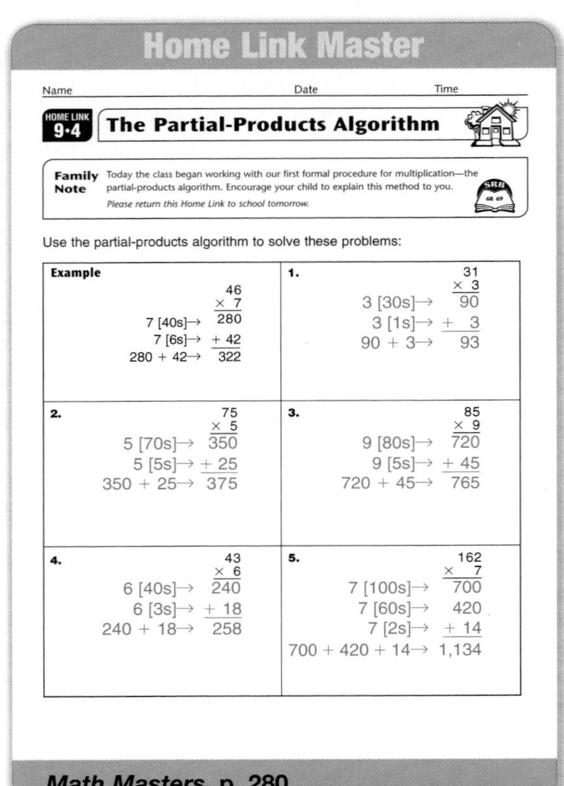
Home Link Master

Name Date Time

HOME LINK 9·4 **The Partial-Products Algorithm**

Family Note Today the class began working with our first formal procedure for multiplication—the partial-products algorithm. Encourage your child to explain this method to you.
Please return this Home Link to school tomorrow.

Use the partial-products algorithm to solve these problems:

Example	**1.**
46 × 7 7 [40s]→ 280 7 [6s]→ + 42 280 + 42→ 322	31 × 3 3 [30s]→ 90 3 [1s]→ + 3 90 + 3→ 93
2. 75 × 5 5 [70s]→ 350 5 [5s]→ + 25 350 + 25→ 375	**3.** 85 × 9 9 [80s]→ 720 9 [5s]→ + 45 720 + 45→ 765
4. 43 × 6 6 [40s]→ 240 6 [3s]→ + 18 240 + 18→ 258	**5.** 162 × 7 7 [100s]→ 700 7 [60s]→ 420 7 [2s]→ + 14 700 + 420 + 14→ 1,134

Math Masters, p. 280

3 Differentiation Options

READINESS

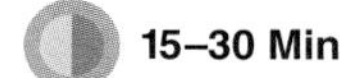

▶ Multiplying with Base-10 Blocks

(*Math Masters,* p. 281)

To explore multiplication using a concrete model, have children model multiple groups of a 2-digit number with base-10 blocks. Children then count the 10s and 1s to find the total number of blocks and record their work on *Math Masters,* page 281.

ENRICHMENT

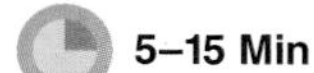

▶ Finding Sums Using Multiplication

(*Math Masters,* p. 282)

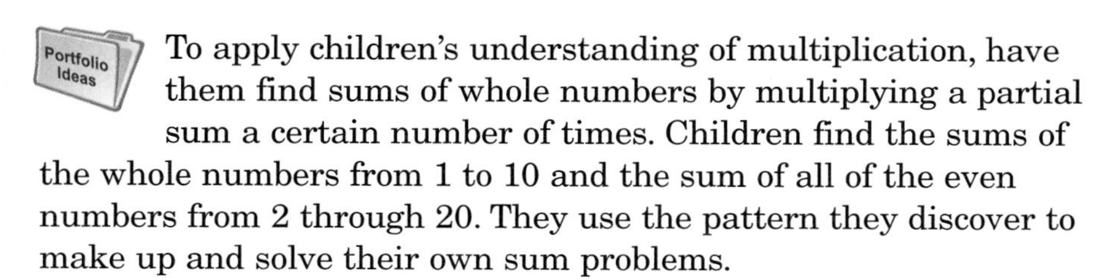

To apply children's understanding of multiplication, have them find sums of whole numbers by multiplying a partial sum a certain number of times. Children find the sums of the whole numbers from 1 to 10 and the sum of all of the even numbers from 2 through 20. They use the pattern they discover to make up and solve their own sum problems.

Teaching Master

Name Date Time

LESSON 9·4 **Number Patterns**

1. Suppose you were asked to find the sum of all of the whole numbers from 1 through 10. These addends make a count-by-1s pattern.
   A number model for this problem could look like this:

   1 + 2 + 3 + 4 + 5 + 6 + 7 + 8 + 9 + 10 = 55

   There are several ways you can find the sum. Here is one way:

   1 + 10 = 11
   2 + 9 = 11
   3 + 8 = 11
   4 + 7 = 11
   5 + 6 = 11

   1 + 2 + 3 + 4 + 5 + 6 + 7 + 8 + 9 + 10

   How many 11s in all? 5
   The sum of the whole numbers from 1 through 10 is 5 × 11 = 55.

2. Use the same method to find the sum in this count-by-2s pattern:

   2 + 4 + 6 + 8 + 10 + 12 + 14 + 16 + 18 + 20 = 110

   2 + 20 = 22 4 + 18 = 22 6 + 16 = 22
   8 + 14 = 22 10 + 12 = 22

   How many 22s in all? 5
   So the sum of the even numbers 2 through 20 is 5 × 22 = 110.

3. Make up your own count-by-3s pattern of addends. Then find the sum.
   Sample answer:
   3 + 6 + 9 + 12 + 15 + 18 + 21 + 24 = 108 3 + 24 = 27
   6 + 21 = 27 9 + 18 = 27 12 + 15 = 27 4 × 27 = 108

Math Masters, p. 282

Teaching Master

Name Date Time

LESSON 9·4 **Base-10 Block Multiplication**

1. Use longs and cubes to show 6 groups of 32.
   Count the number of longs.
   Count the number of cubes.
   Record your counts here:
   I have 18 ten(s), which is the same as 180.
   I have 12 one(s), which is the same as 12.
   Total: 192
   Number model: 6 × 32 = 192

2. Use longs and cubes to show 5 groups of 27.
   Count the number of longs.
   Count the number of cubes.
   Record your counts here:
   I have 10 ten(s), which is the same as 100.
   I have 35 one(s), which is the same as 35.
   Total: 135
   Number model: 5 × 27 = 135

3. Make up your own. Use longs and cubes to show ____ groups of ____.
   Answers vary.
   Count the number of longs.
   Count the number of cubes.
   Record your counts here:
   I have ____ ten(s), which is the same as ____.
   I have ____ one(s), which is the same as ____.
   Total: ____
   Number model: ____ × ____ = ____

Math Masters, p. 281

9•5 Buying at the Stock-Up Sale

Objective To guide children as they multiply using mental math and the partial-products algorithm.

www.everydaymathonline.com

ePresentations

eToolkit

Algorithms Practice

EM Facts Workshop Game™

Family Letters

Assessment Management

Common Core State Standards

Curriculum Focal Points

Interactive Teacher's Lesson Guide

1 Teaching the Lesson

Key Concepts and Skills

- Apply place-value concepts to find partial products.
  [Number and Numeration Goal 1]
- Use multiplication facts to make estimates and calculate partial products.
  [Operations and Computation Goal 3]
- Use the partial-products algorithm to multiply 1-digit by multidigit numbers.
  [Operations and Computation Goal 4]
- Make reasonable estimates.
  [Operations and Computation Goal 5]

Key Activities

Children make up and solve problems about costs of multiple items advertised on the Stock-Up Sale posters.

Materials

Math Journal 2, p. 217
Student Reference Book, pp. 216 and 217
Home Link 9•4
Math Masters, pp. 399 and 400 (optional)
slate ◆ tool-kit coins (optional)

2 Ongoing Learning & Practice

Playing *Fraction Top-It*
Student Reference Book, p. 287
Math Masters, p. 398
per partnership: 1 deck of Fraction Cards
Children practice comparing fractions.

Ongoing Assessment: Recognizing Student Achievement
Use an Exit Slip (*Math Masters,* page 398).
[Number and Numeration Goal 6]

Math Boxes 9•5
Math Journal 2, p. 218
Children practice and maintain skills through Math Box problems.

Home Link 9•5
Math Masters, p. 283
Children practice and maintain skills through Home Link activities.

3 Differentiation Options

READINESS

Estimating Costs
Math Masters, p. 284; p. 399 (from Part 1)
Student Reference Book, pp. 216 and 217
tool-kit dimes
Children estimate the money they need to make purchases at the Stock-Up Sale.

ENRICHMENT

Solving Multistep Number Stories
Student Reference Book, pp. 216 and 217
Math Masters, p. 285
Children estimate and solve multistep number stories.

Advance Preparation

Copy and cut apart the play money on *Math Masters,* pages 399 and 400 (optional).

***Teacher's Reference Manual,* Grades 1–3** p. 190

Getting Started

Mathematical Practices
SMP1, SMP2, SMP3, **SMP4,** SMP5, SMP6, SMP7
Content Standards
3.OA.3, 3.OA.7, **3.OA.8, 3.NBT.1, 3.NBT.2,** 3.NF.3, 3.NF.3d

Mental Math and Reflexes

Have children practice quick recall of basic multiplication facts. *Suggestions:*

●○○ 6×6 36 7×7 49 8×8 64 9×9 81

●●○ 4×8 32 6×8 48 7×8 56 9×8 72

●●● 40×9 360 600×7 4,200 70×80 5,600 60×900 54,000

Math Message

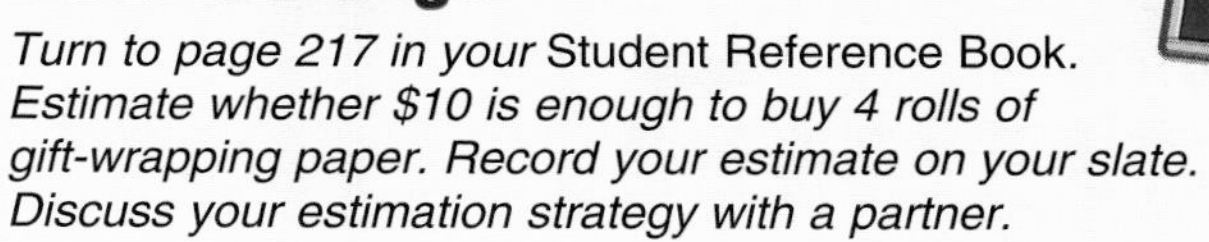

Turn to page 217 in your Student Reference Book. *Estimate whether $10 is enough to buy 4 rolls of gift-wrapping paper. Record your estimate on your slate. Discuss your estimation strategy with a partner.*

Home Link 9·4 Follow-Up

Briefly review answers. Have volunteers model the partial-products algorithm for some of the problems.

1 Teaching the Lesson

▶ Math Message Follow-Up

(*Student Reference Book,* p. 217; *Math Masters,* pp. 399 and 400)

Discuss children's answers. Possible estimation strategies:

▷ Change $2.35 to a close-but-easier amount, such as $2.50. $4 \times \$2.50 = \$10.00$ (double $2.50 twice). $10 would be enough to buy 4 rolls if they were $2.50 per roll. Because $2.50 is more than $2.35, the cost of 4 rolls at $2.35 is less than $10.

▷ Round $2.35 to the nearest $0.10, which is $2.40. $4 \times \$2.00 = \$8.00$, and $4 \times \$0.40 = \$1.60$. Therefore, $4 \times \$2.40 = \$9.60$. Because $2.40 is more than $2.35, the cost is less than $10.

Remind children that many problems can be solved with estimation instead of exact calculation. An efficient estimation strategy requires simple mental math and gives an answer that is reasonably close to the exact answer.

Have children work in small groups to find the exact cost, using mental math or an algorithm. $9.40 Take time to have children share strategies. *For example:*

$4 \times \$2.00 = \$8.00$

$4 \times \$0.30 = \$1.20$

$4 \times \$0.05 = \$0.20$

$\$8.00 + \$1.20 + \$0.20 = \$9.40$

Adjusting the Activity

Provide dollar bills (*Math Masters,* pages 399 and 400) and tool-kit coins for children to use as they act out the problems.

AUDITORY ◆ KINESTHETIC ◆ TACTILE ◆ VISUAL

Student Page

Data Bank

Stock-Up Sale Poster #2

Greeting Cards Box of 12 **$3.29** 5 or More Sale: *You pay $2.63 per box*	Bath Soap **$0.88** 5 or More Sale: *You pay $0.65 per bar*	Gift Wrapping Paper **$2.35** per roll 5 or More Sale: *You pay $1.86 per roll*
Toothbrush **$1.38** 5 or More Sale: *You pay $1.13 per brush*	Garbage Bags **$3.75** 5 or More Sale: *You pay $3.18 per box*	Night Light Bulbs 2-Pack **$0.96** 5 or More Sale: *You pay $0.76 per pack*
Glue **$1.15** 5 or More Sale: *You pay $0.94 per bottle*	Construction Paper **$0.67** per pad 5 or More Sale: *You pay $0.54 per pad*	Shoelaces **$1.27** per pair 5 or More Sale: *You pay $1.08 per pair*

***Student Reference Book,* p. 217**

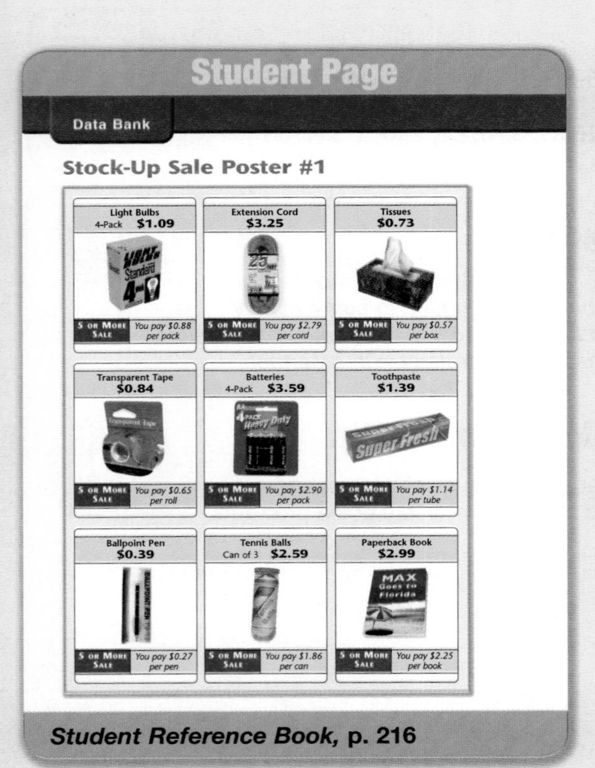

Student Page

Data Bank

Stock-Up Sale Poster #1

Light Bulbs 4-Pack $1.09	Extension Cord $3.25	Tissues $0.73
5 or More Sale: You pay $0.88 per pack	5 or More Sale: You pay $2.79 per cord	5 or More Sale: You pay $0.57 per box
Transparent Tape $0.84	Batteries 4-Pack $3.59	Toothpaste $1.39
5 or More Sale: You pay $0.65 per roll	5 or More Sale: You pay $2.90 per pack	5 or More Sale: You pay $1.14 per tube
Ballpoint Pen $0.39	Tennis Balls Can of 3 $2.59	Paperback Book $2.99
5 or More Sale: You pay $0.27 per pen	5 or More Sale: You pay $1.86 per can	5 or More Sale: You pay $2.25 per book

Student Reference Book, p. 216

NOTE Explain to children that stores often encourage customers to spend more by reducing the price of an item purchased in bulk. Stores make up for the lower profit per item by selling more items.

NOTE Some children might use mental arithmetic to find the exact answer, thinking of the solution as: $5 \times \$0.10 = \$0.50$; $\$15 - \$0.50 = \$14.50$; $\$20 - \$14.50 = \$5.50$. Praise this strategy; however, since the focus of this lesson is on the partial-products algorithm, make sure to emphasize the strategy described in this activity.

▶ Applying the Partial-Products Algorithm

(*Student Reference Book,* pp. 216 and 217)

Various items are advertised on the two Stock-Up Sale Posters. You or the children use the given prices to suggest number stories that can be solved in two steps. Prior to solving each number story, have children estimate the answer. Next they represent the number story with a number model and use a letter for the unknown quantity and parentheses to show the first calculation. Then they find the answer using the partial-products algorithm (Lesson 9-4) with dollars and cents. For the first few stories, write the problems on the board while the children suggest the number models for the partial products.

For example: *How much change would you receive if you bought 5 packs of batteries at the stock-up sale price and paid with a $20 bill?* (Story examples are based on *Student Reference Book,* pages 216 and 217.)

Remind children of the Guide to Solving Number Stories on *Math Masters,* page 406.

- What do you want to find out? The amount of change you would receive from $20
- What do you know from reading the story and looking at the Stock-Up Sale Poster? 5 packs of batteries are purchased and each pack costs the sale price of $2.90.

Ask partners to work together to estimate the answer. After a few minutes, discuss children's answers. One possible estimation strategy is to round $2.90 to the nearest dollar, which is $3.00. $\$3.00 \times 5$ is $15.00. The difference between $20.00 and $15.00 is $5, so the answer to the number story should be about $5.

Explain that because the number story asks for the amount of change, we need to calculate to find the exact answer. Ask: *Will the exact answer be more or less than $5?* More, because we rounded the price of one pack of batteries up to $3.

- What is a first step to solve the problem? Find the cost of 5 packs of batteries.
- How might you do this? Multiply $\$2.90 \times 5$. Write $\$2.90 \times 5$ on the board.
- What symbols can we use in the number model to show that this is the first step? Add parentheses around $\$2.90 \times 5$.
- What is the second step? Subtract that product from $20.00.
- How can we write this step? Indicate the first step using parentheses, then subtract from $20. Write the step on the board: $\$20 - (\$2.90 \times 5)$. Since we want to find the amount of *change,* use C for the unknown quantity in the open sentence: $\$20 - (\$2.90 \times 5) = C$.

Links to the Future

At this time, children are not expected to know the conventional order of operations, so parentheses tell them which operation comes first. Understanding that grouping symbols can be used to affect the order in which operations are carried out is a Grade 3 Grade-Level Goal. Describing and applying the conventional order of operations is a Grade 6 Grade-Level Goal.

Take a few minutes to reconnect each expression in the number model with the problem situation. *What is $20?* The amount of money used to pay for the batteries *What is $2.90?* The cost of 1 pack of batteries *Why are we multiplying $2.90 by 5?* To find the cost of 5 packs of batteries

Because the calculation in parentheses is solved first, write the multiplication problem on the board. Ask children to suggest number models for the partial products.

	$2.90
	× 5
5 [$2.00s]→	10.00
5 [$0.90s]→	+ 4.50
	$14.50

Ask: *Is $14.50 the answer to the number story?* no *Why?* $14.50 tells how much 5 packs of batteries cost, but we still need to find out how much change is left from $20. *What is the second step?* Subtract $14.50 from $20. Have children complete the calculation: $20 – $14.50 = $5.50.

- What is the answer to the number story? You would get $5.50 change.
- Does your answer make sense? yes
- How do you know? Sample answers: Before I solved for the exact answer, I estimated the change to be about $5. $5.50 is close to $5; I know my answer has to be less than $20 because some of the money was spent on batteries.
- Does your answer make the number model true? yes Write a summary number model on the board: $20 – ($2.90 × 5) = $5.50.

Pose another number story: *How much would it cost to buy 5 pads of construction paper and 1 bottle of glue?*

- What do you want to find out? The total cost of the construction paper and 1 bottle of glue
- What do you know from reading the story and looking at the poster? I know that if you buy 5 or more pads you get the stock-up sale price. One pad of construction paper at the sale price is $0.54 and 1 bottle of glue at the regular price costs $1.15.

A possible number model for the story is ($0.54 × 5) + $1.15 = *T*.

- What is the answer? The total cost is $3.85.

As needed, continue to suggest number stories involving two or more steps to solve with the class.

Student Page

Date ______ Time ______

LESSON 9·5 Shopping at the Stock-Up Sale

Use the Stock-Up Sale Posters on pages 216 and 217 in the *Student Reference Book.* Solve each number story below. There is no sales tax.

For each problem:

- Estimate the answer.
- Write a number model with parentheses to show which step is first. Use a letter to show what you want to find out.
- Solve for the exact answer.
- Show your work.

workspace

1. Jeff bought 5 toothbrushes and 1 tube of toothpaste. What is the total cost? Sample answer:
   Estimate: The total cost is about $7.40.
   Number model: (5 × $1.13) + $1.39 = *T*
   Answer: $7.04
   Does your answer make sense? Explain.
   Sample answer: Yes, my estimate was about $7.40 and my answer was $7.04. They are close.

2. Mr. De la Garza pays for 8 boxes of tissues with a $5.00 bill. How much change will he get? Sample answer:
   Estimate: He will get about $0.20.
   Number model: $5.00 – (8 × $0.57) = *C*
   Answer: $0.44
   Does your answer make sense? Explain.
   Sample answers: Yes, because the amount of change is less than what he started with; my answer is close to my estimate.

Math Journal 2, p. 217

Student Page

Games

Fraction Top-It

Materials □ 1 deck of Fraction Cards (*Math Journal 2,* Activity Sheets 5–8)

Players 2

Skill Comparing fractions

Object of the game To collect more cards.

Directions

1. Shuffle the Fraction Cards and place the deck picture-side down on the table.
2. Each player turns over a card from the top of the deck. Players compare the shaded parts of the cards. The player with the larger fraction shaded takes both cards.
3. If the shaded parts are equal, the fractions are equivalent. Each player then turns over another card. The player with the larger fraction shaded takes all the cards from both plays.
4. The game is over when all cards have been taken from the deck. The player with more cards wins.

Examples Players turn over a $\frac{3}{4}$ card and a $\frac{4}{6}$ card.
The $\frac{3}{4}$ card has a larger shaded area. The player holding the $\frac{3}{4}$ card takes both cards.

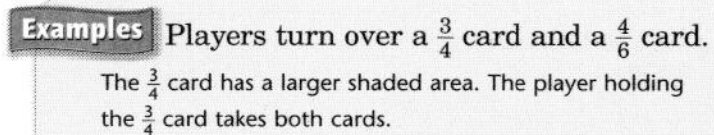

Players turn over a $\frac{1}{2}$ card and a $\frac{4}{8}$ card.
The shaded parts are equal. Each player turns over another card. The player with the larger Fraction Card takes all the cards.

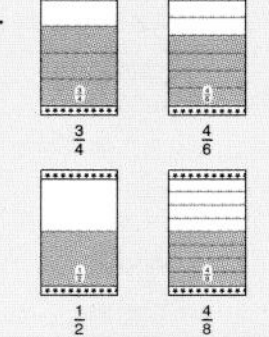

Student Reference Book, p. 287

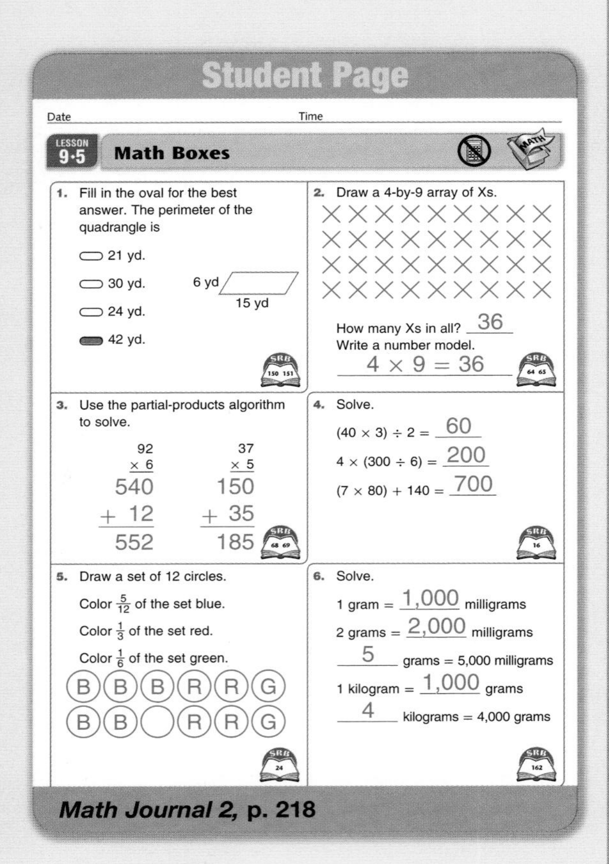
Student Page

Date Time

LESSON 9·5 Math Boxes

1. Fill in the oval for the best answer. The perimeter of the quadrangle is
- 21 yd.
- 30 yd.
- 24 yd.
- 42 yd. (filled)

6 yd
15 yd

SRB 150 151

2. Draw a 4-by-9 array of Xs.

X X X X X X X X X
X X X X X X X X X
X X X X X X X X X
X X X X X X X X X

How many Xs in all? 36
Write a number model.
$4 \times 9 = 36$

SRB 64 65

3. Use the partial-products algorithm to solve.

92×6: 540 + 12 = 552

37×5: 150 + 35 = 185

SRB 68 69

4. Solve.

$(40 \times 3) \div 2 =$ 60

$4 \times (300 \div 6) =$ 200

$(7 \times 80) + 140 =$ 700

SRB 16

5. Draw a set of 12 circles.

Color $\frac{5}{12}$ of the set blue.

Color $\frac{1}{3}$ of the set red.

Color $\frac{1}{6}$ of the set green.

B B B R R G
B B _ R R G

SRB 24

6. Solve.

1 gram = 1,000 milligrams

2 grams = 2,000 milligrams

5 grams = 5,000 milligrams

1 kilogram = 1,000 grams

4 kilograms = 4,000 grams

SRB 162

Math Journal 2, p. 218

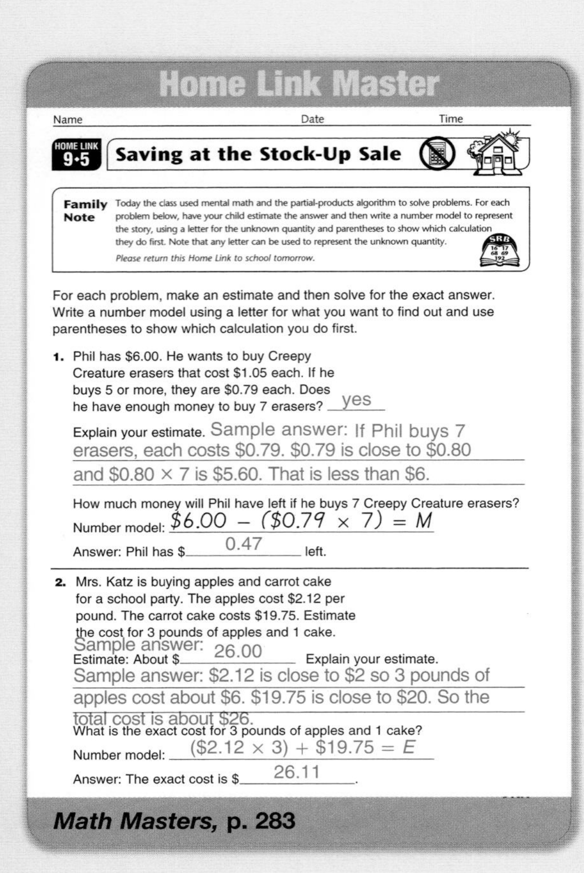
Home Link Master

Name Date Time

HOME LINK 9·5 Saving at the Stock-Up Sale

Family Note Today the class used mental math and the partial-products algorithm to solve problems. For each problem below, have your child estimate the answer and then write a number model to represent the story, using a letter for the unknown quantity and parentheses to show which calculation they do first. Note that any letter can be used to represent the unknown quantity.

Please return this Home Link to school tomorrow.

SRB 16 17 68 69 172

For each problem, make an estimate and then solve for the exact answer. Write a number model using a letter for what you want to find out and use parentheses to show which calculation you do first.

1. Phil has \$6.00. He wants to buy Creepy Creature erasers that cost \$1.05 each. If he buys 5 or more, they are \$0.79 each. Does he have enough money to buy 7 erasers? yes

Explain your estimate. Sample answer: If Phil buys 7 erasers, each costs \$0.79. \$0.79 is close to \$0.80 and \$0.80 × 7 is \$5.60. That is less than \$6.

How much money will Phil have left if he buys 7 Creepy Creature erasers?

Number model: $\$6.00 - (\$0.79 \times 7) = M$

Answer: Phil has \$ 0.47 left.

2. Mrs. Katz is buying apples and carrot cake for a school party. The apples cost \$2.12 per pound. The carrot cake costs \$19.75. Estimate the cost for 3 pounds of apples and 1 cake.

Estimate: About \$ Sample answer: 26.00 Explain your estimate.
Sample answer: \$2.12 is close to \$2 so 3 pounds of apples cost about \$6. \$19.75 is close to \$20. So the total cost is about \$26.

What is the exact cost for 3 pounds of apples and 1 cake?

Number model: $(\$2.12 \times 3) + \$19.75 = E$

Answer: The exact cost is \$ 26.11.

Math Masters, p. 283

▶ Solving Stock-Up Sale Stories

PARTNER ACTIVITY

PROBLEM SOLVING

(*Math Journal 2,* p. 217; *Student Reference Book,* pp. 216 and 217)

Children work together in partnerships to solve 2-step problems on journal page 217 using the information on pages 216 and 217 in the *Student Reference Book.* Children write the number models using a letter variable for the unknown quantity.

2 Ongoing Learning & Practice

▶ Playing *Fraction Top-It*

PARTNER ACTIVITY

(*Student Reference Book,* p. 287; *Math Masters,* p. 398)

Children practice comparing fractions by playing *Fraction Top-It.* For game instructions, see Lesson 8-6 or page 287 in the *Student Reference Book.* Have children use an Exit Slip to record at least five rounds using the symbols >, <, and = to compare the fraction pairs.

Ongoing Assessment: Recognizing Student Achievement

Exit Slip

Use an **Exit Slip** (*Math Masters,* page 398) to assess children's progress toward comparing fractions. Children are making adequate progress if they are able to record at least 5 pairs of fractions with the appropriate comparison symbols. Some children may be able to compare the fractions without using Fraction Cards.

[Number and Numeration Goal 6]

▶ Math Boxes 9·5

INDEPENDENT ACTIVITY

(*Math Journal 2,* p. 218)

Mixed Practice Math Boxes in this lesson are paired with Math Boxes in Lesson 9-7. The skill in Problem 6 previews Unit 10 content.

▶ Home Link 9·5

INDEPENDENT ACTIVITY

PROBLEM SOLVING

(*Math Masters,* p. 283)

Home Connection Children use mental math or the partial-products algorithm to solve multiplication number stories.

3 Differentiation Options

READINESS

PARTNER ACTIVITY

▶ Estimating Costs

5–15 Min

(*Math Masters,* p. 284; *Student Reference Book,* pp. 216 and 217)

To provide experience with estimating money amounts, have children determine the number of dollar bills and dimes they need to make purchases. Use the Stock-Up Sale posters on pages 216 and 217 in the *Student Reference Book.* Children record their work on *Math Masters,* page 284.

ENRICHMENT

PARTNER ACTIVITY

▶ Solving Multistep Number Stories

15–30 Min

(*Student Reference Book,* pp. 216 and 217; *Math Masters,* p. 285)

To provide children with experience with multistep number stories, have them use information from the Stock-Up Sale Posters on *Student Reference Book,* pages 216 and 217 to solve stories on *Math Masters,* page 285. For each story, have children estimate and then solve. Explain that when writing number models for number stories with more than two steps, more than one set of parentheses is sometimes needed. For example, consider the following story: *Compare the cost of buying 4 paperback books to the cost of buying 5 paperback books.* A possible number model could be ($2.99 × 4) – ($2.25 × 5) = *D*. The calculations for the costs of 4 books at the regular price and 5 books at the sale price must be done before subtracting to find the difference.

NOTE It is also acceptable for children to write a series of number models for number stories with more than two steps.

Teaching Master

Name Date Time

LESSON 9·5 **Dollars and Dimes**

Use the Stock-Up Sale posters on pages 216 and 217 in your *Student Reference Book.* Suppose that you have only dollars and dimes. Write the least amount of money you could use to buy each item.

Use dollars and dimes to help you.

Items to Be Purchased	Dollars and Dimes Needed
Example: 1 box of 12 Greeting Cards Price: $3.29	3 dollars 3 dimes Total: $ 3.30
1 roll of Gift-Wrapping Paper Price: $2.35	2 dollars 4 dimes Total: $ 2.40
1 roll of Transparent Tape Price: $0.84	0 dollars 9 dimes Total: $ 0.90
1 box of Tissues Price: $0.73	0 dollars 8 dimes Total: $ 0.80
1 Paperback Book Price: $2.99	3 dollars 0 dimes Total: $ 3.00

Math Masters, p. 284

Algorithm Project The focus of this lesson is to apply the partial-products algorithm to money amounts. For enrichment, see Algorithm Project 4 on page A15 to teach U.S. traditional multiplication of decimals using money.

Teaching Master

Name Date Time

LESSON 9·5 **Solving Multistep Number Stories**

Use the Stock-Up Sale Posters on pages 216 and 217 in the *Student Reference Book.* For each problem below, make an estimate and then solve the number story. There is no sales tax.

1. How much more do 5 boxes of garbage bags cost than 3 boxes of garbage bags?

   Estimate: About $ 3 Explain your estimate. Sample answer: If I buy 5 boxes, I pay $3.18 for each box; if I buy 3 boxes, I pay $3.75 for each box. $3.18 is close to $3 and $3.75 is close to $4. $3 × 5 = $15 and $4 × 3 = $12. The difference is about $3.

   Sample answer: Number model: (5 × $3.18) – (3 × $3.75) = *D*

   Solve. Show your work on the back of the page.

   Answer: 5 boxes cost $ 4.65 more than 3 boxes.

2. How much more does it cost to buy 5 rolls of wrapping paper than 2 rolls of wrapping paper?

   Estimate: About $ 2.50 Explain your estimate. Sample answer: If I buy 5 rolls, each roll costs $1.86. If I buy 3 rolls, each roll costs $2.35. I know that $1.86 is close to $2 and $2.35 is close to $2.50, so $2 × 5 = $10 and $2.50 × 3 = $7.50. The difference will be about $2.50.

   Sample answer: Number model: (5 × $1.86) – (3 × $2.35) = *D*

   Solve. Show your work on the back of the page.

   Answer: 5 rolls cost $ 2.25 more than 3 rolls.

Math Masters, p. 285

9•6 Factors of a Whole Number

Objective To guide children as they identify whole-number factors of whole numbers.

Technology Resources www.everydaymathonline.com

ePresentations

eToolkit

Algorithms Practice

EM Facts Workshop Game™

Family Letters

Assessment Management

Common Core State Standards

Curriculum Focal Points

Interactive Teacher's Lesson Guide

1 Teaching the Lesson

Key Concepts and Skills

- Use multiplication facts to solve problems. [Operations and Computation Goal 3]
- Use multiplication facts to find whole-number factors of a whole number. [Operations and Computation Goal 3]
- Use arrays to model whole-number factors of a whole number. [Operations and Computation Goal 6]

Key Activities

Children identify factors of whole numbers, reinforcing the link between multiplication and division; they play *Factor Bingo* to practice identifying factors.

Ongoing Assessment: Recognizing Student Achievement Use Mental Math and Reflexes. [Number and Numeration Goal 2]

Key Vocabulary

factors

Materials

Math Journal 2, p. 219
Student Reference Book, pp. 285 and 286
Home Link 9•5
Math Masters, p. 448
transparency of *Math Masters,* p. 448 (optional) ◆ per group: 4 each of number cards 2–9 (from the Everything Math Deck, if available) ◆ pennies or other counters ◆ slate ◆ half-sheet of paper

2 Ongoing Learning & Practice

Using the Partial-Products Algorithm

Math Journal 2, p. 220
Math Masters, pp. 273 and 274 (optional)
base-10 blocks (optional)
Children practice the partial-products algorithm.

Ongoing Assessment: Informing Instruction See page 746.

Math Boxes 9•6

Math Journal 2, p. 221
Children practice and maintain skills through Math Box problems.

Home Link 9•6

Math Masters, p. 286
Children practice and maintain skills through Home Link activities.

3 Differentiation Options

READINESS

Playing *Array Bingo*

Student Reference Book, p. 273
Math Masters, p. 442
per partnership: paper clips or envelopes ◆ scissors
Children explore fractions using an array model.

ENRICHMENT

Playing *Finding Factors*

Math Masters, p. 287
per partnership: 2 different-colored counters, 2 different-colored crayons
Children apply their understanding of factors.

ELL SUPPORT

Building a Math Word Bank

Differentiation Handbook, p. 132
Children add the term *factor* to their Math Word Banks.

Getting Started

Mathematical Practices
SMP1, SMP2, SMP4, SMP5, **SMP6,** SMP7
Content Standards
3.OA.2, 3.OA.3, 3.OA.5, 3.OA.7

Mental Math and Reflexes 

Have children find fractions of whole numbers, using counters if necessary. They record their answers on half-sheets of paper. Share strategies after solving problems. *Suggestions:*

●○○ $\frac{1}{2}$ of 20 10
$\frac{1}{4}$ of 12 3

●●○ $\frac{1}{3}$ of 18 6
$\frac{2}{3}$ of 21 14

●●● $\frac{2}{3}$ of 45 30
$\frac{5}{8}$ of 16 10

Math Message

You want to pack 24 bottles of juice into full cartons. Each carton holds 4 bottles. Can you pack all 24 bottles into cartons so none are left over?

Home Link 9·5 Follow-Up

Have children share strategies for making estimates and solving the problems.

Ongoing Assessment: Recognizing Student Achievement

Use **Mental Math and Reflexes** to assess children's progress toward using concrete materials to model common fractions. Children are making adequate progress if they successfully complete Levels ●○○ and ●●○ problems. Some children may complete Level ●●● problems successfully.

[Number and Numeration Goal 2]

1 Teaching the Lesson

▶ Math Message Follow-Up

Have children model the solution by making an array with counters or by drawing it on slates. For example, if they make rows of 4 counters, each row represents a full carton. There will be 6 rows. Arrays help children visualize factors as the rows and columns that make up the array for a number. Building arrays is a good beginning for work in later grades with prime, composite, and square numbers.

6 full cartons with 4 bottles each

Ask: *How many full cartons are there?* 6 *Are there any leftover bottles?* No Explain to children that one way to think about the problem is to ask, "How many 4s are there in 24?"

Pose the same problem to the class, but vary the number of bottles that a full carton will hold: 6 bottles? 9 bottles? 10 bottles? 12 bottles? Have children model each situation with an array of counters. For 6 bottles, there are 4 rows of 6 counters. For 9 bottles, 2 rows have 9 counters, but the last row will be short 3 counters, so this number does not work.

Ask: *What other sizes of cartons can be used to pack 24 bottles so none are left over?* Help children see that 24 bottles can be packed into full cartons that hold 1, 2, 3, 4, 6, 8, 12, or 24 bottles. The numbers 1, 2, 3, 4, 6, 8, 12, and 24 are called **factors** of 24. To support English language learners, write *factor* on the board. Ask volunteers to come to the board to draw different arrays representing 24.

NOTE Although a factor may be a whole number, decimal, or a fraction, the lessons in *Third Grade Everyday Mathematics* involve whole-number factors only.

Ask children to describe the factors of 24 in their own words. Record their key ideas on the board. Possible responses: The factors of 24 are whole numbers that can be multiplied to get 24; they are the numbers of rows or columns in arrays for 24; they are whole numbers that will divide 24 without leaving a remainder.

▶ Identifying Factors of a Whole Number

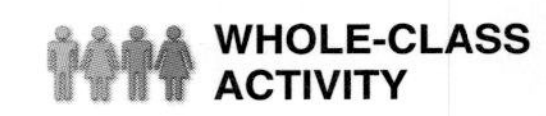

Pose a problem similar to the Math Message, and ask children to solve it. They may use counters or drawings. Record their solutions in a table on the board. List the numbers and factors in the table in sequential order so the children can better identify patterns.

For example: There are 15 bottles.

- Can they fill cartons that hold 3 bottles each? Yes Is 3 a factor of 15? Yes
- Can they fill cartons that hold 4 bottles each? No Is 4 a factor of 15? No
- What other sizes of cartons could you use? 1, 5, 15 Are these also factors of 15? Yes

Repeat with other whole numbers; however, omit mention of cartons and bottles. Ask children to identify factors of numbers and record the answers in the table. Arrays might help children get mental images of factors.

Number	Factors
15	1, 3, 5, 15
16	1, 2, 4, 8, 16
17	1, 17
18	1, 2, 3, 6, 9, 18
19	1, 19
20	1, 2, 4, 5, 10, 20

Ask children to make observations about the table. Guide children with questions such as the following:

- Which numbers have exactly 2 factors? 17 and 19
- What is another whole number *not* in the table that has only 2 factors? Sample answers: 3, 5, 7, 11
- Which numbers have 2 as a factor? 16, 18, and 20
- Which numbers in the table have the most factors? 18 and 20
- Which numbers have an even number of factors? 15, 17, 18, 19, and 20
- Which number has an odd number of factors? 16
- Which number is a factor of all whole numbers? 1
- Is every whole number a factor of itself? Yes

Adjusting the Activity

ELL

To support English language learners, point out the difference between *a number with 2 factors* and *a number with 2 as a factor.*

AUDITORY ◆ KINESTHETIC ◆ TACTILE ◆ VISUAL

▶ Introducing *Factor Bingo*

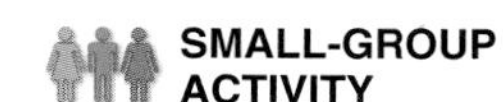

SMALL-GROUP ACTIVITY

(*Math Journal 2,* p. 219; *Math Masters,* p. 448; *Student Reference Book,* pp. 285 and 286)

Discuss the rules for *Factor Bingo* on pages 285 and 286 in the *Student Reference Book*. You might want to make an overhead transparency of *Math Masters,* page 448 and play a demonstration game with the class.

▶ Playing *Factor Bingo*

SMALL-GROUP ACTIVITY

(*Math Journal 2,* p. 219; *Math Masters,* p. 448)

Make sure the children understand the rules before completing their boards. Children use the *Factor Bingo* Game Mat on journal page 219 or make up a new one on *Math Masters,* page 448. After several games, some children may discover that certain numbers have more factors than others. Their chances of winning are then enhanced by a judicious choice and placement of numbers. When children complete play, hold a discussion about good board numbers (ones that have several factors between 2 and 9) and impossible board numbers (numbers that do not have factors between 2 and 9).

Adjusting the Activity

Have children remove the 2 and 5 cards from their decks. Distribute additional blank copies of *Math Masters,* page 448 and ask children to complete a new game mat. Have them discuss why they selected the numbers and locations they did.

AUDITORY ◆ KINESTHETIC ◆ TACTILE ◆ VISUAL

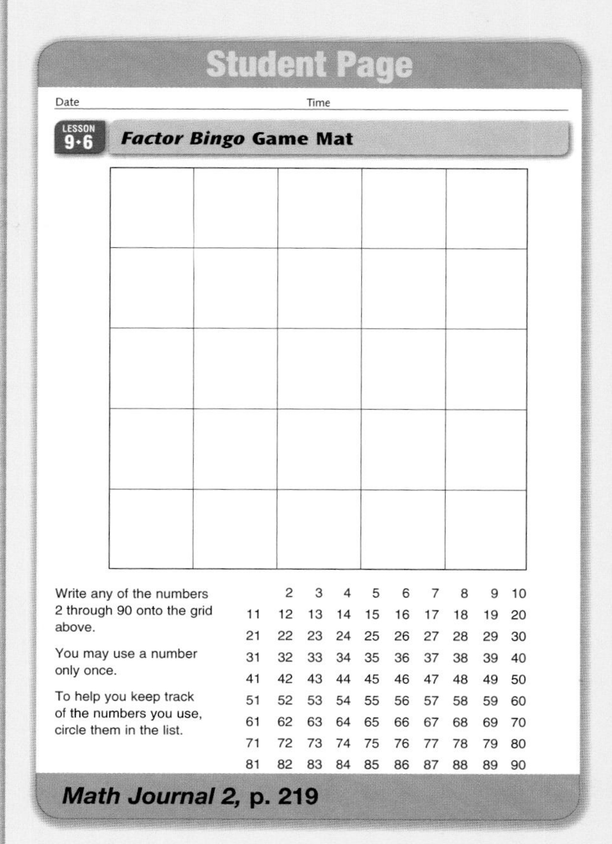

Student Page

Date Time

LESSON 9·6 ***Factor Bingo* Game Mat**

Write any of the numbers 2 through 90 onto the grid above.

You may use a number only once.

To help you keep track of the numbers you use, circle them in the list.

	2	3	4	5	6	7	8	9	10
11	12	13	14	15	16	17	18	19	20
21	22	23	24	25	26	27	28	29	30
31	32	33	34	35	36	37	38	39	40
41	42	43	44	45	46	47	48	49	50
51	52	53	54	55	56	57	58	59	60
61	62	63	64	65	66	67	68	69	70
71	72	73	74	75	76	77	78	79	80
81	82	83	84	85	86	87	88	89	90

Math Journal 2, p. 219

Math Journal 2, p. 219 is identical to *Math Masters,* p. 448.

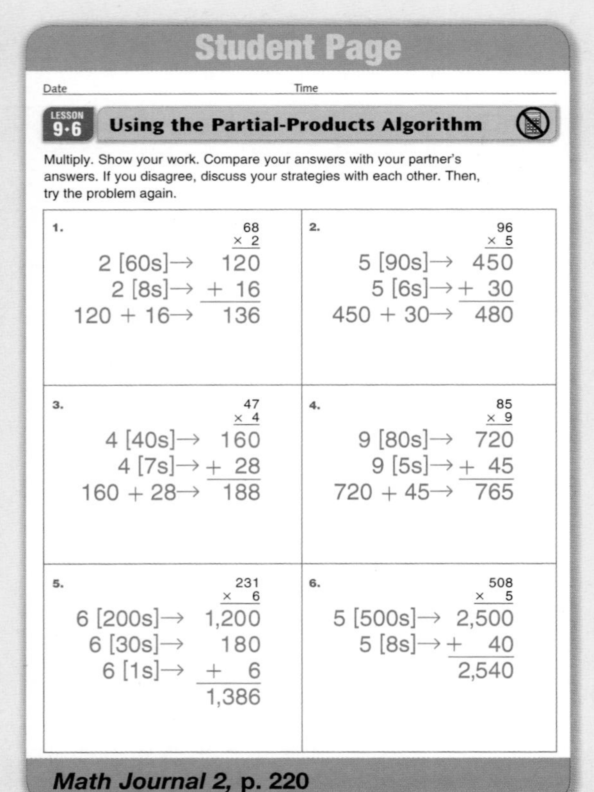
Student Page

Date Time

LESSON 9·6 **Using the Partial-Products Algorithm**

Multiply. Show your work. Compare your answers with your partner's answers. If you disagree, discuss your strategies with each other. Then, try the problem again.

1.
```
                  68
                 × 2
2 [60s] →       120
 2 [8s] →     +  16
120 + 16 →      136
```

2.
```
                  96
                 × 5
5 [90s] →       450
 5 [6s] →     +  30
450 + 30 →      480
```

3.
```
                  47
                 × 4
4 [40s] →       160
 4 [7s] →     +  28
160 + 28 →      188
```

4.
```
                  85
                 × 9
9 [80s] →       720
 9 [5s] →     +  45
720 + 45 →      765
```

5.
```
                  231
                  × 6
6 [200s] →      1,200
 6 [30s] →        180
  6 [1s] →      +   6
                1,386
```

6.
```
                  508
                  × 5
5 [500s] →      2,500
  5 [8s] →      +  40
                2,540
```

Math Journal 2, p. 220

NOTE The partial-products algorithm is an application of the Distributive Property of Multiplication over Addition. At this time, children are not expected to use the term *distributive property.* They should, however, begin to develop an understanding of the property as they use the partial-products algorithm.

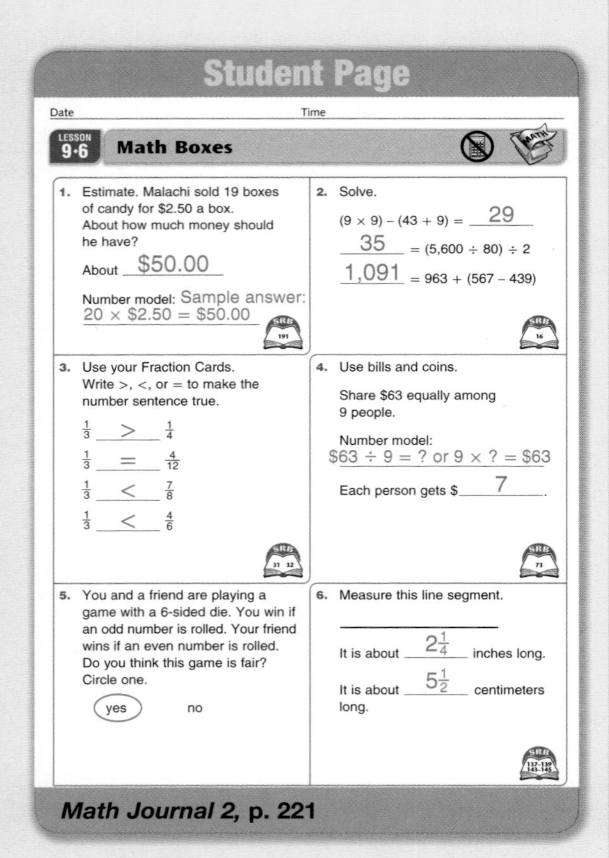
Student Page

Date Time

LESSON 9·6 **Math Boxes**

1. Estimate. Malachi sold 19 boxes of candy for $2.50 a box. About how much money should he have?
About $50.00
Number model: Sample answer: 20 × $2.50 = $50.00

2. Solve.
(9 × 9) − (43 + 9) = 29
35 = (5,600 ÷ 80) ÷ 2
1,091 = 963 + (567 − 439)

3. Use your Fraction Cards. Write >, <, or = to make the number sentence true.
$\frac{1}{3}$ > $\frac{1}{4}$
$\frac{1}{3}$ = $\frac{4}{12}$
$\frac{1}{3}$ < $\frac{7}{8}$
$\frac{1}{3}$ < $\frac{4}{6}$

4. Use bills and coins.
Share $63 equally among 9 people.
Number model: $63 ÷ 9 = ? or 9 × ? = $63
Each person gets $7.

5. You and a friend are playing a game with a 6-sided die. You win if an odd number is rolled. Your friend wins if an even number is rolled. Do you think this game is fair? Circle one.
(yes) no

6. Measure this line segment.
It is about $2\frac{1}{4}$ inches long.
It is about $5\frac{1}{2}$ centimeters long.

Math Journal 2, p. 221

2 Ongoing Learning & Practice

▶ Using the Partial-Products Algorithm

(*Math Journal 2,* p. 220; *Math Masters,* pp. 273 and 274)

Children use the partial-products algorithm to find products of 1-digit numbers and multidigit numbers on journal page 220.

Ongoing Assessment: Informing Instruction

Watch for children who are unsure of using the partial-products algorithm. Have them use the Array Grid (*Math Masters,* pages 273 and 274) and base-10 blocks to model the problems. Then have them write number models for each partial product. *For example:*

```
                    29
                   × 4
4 [20]s     →       80
4 [9]s      →     + 36
80 + 36     →      116
```

▶ Math Boxes 9·6

(*Math Journal 2,* p. 221)

Mixed Practice Math Boxes in this lesson are paired with Math Boxes in Lesson 9-8. The skill in Problem 6 previews Unit 10 content.

Portfolio Ideas

Writing/Reasoning Have children write an answer to the following: *Explain how you decided if the game in Problem 5 was fair.* Sample answer: A 6-sided die has an equal number of even and odd numbers, so players have an equal chance of rolling a winning number.

▶ Home Link 9·6

(*Math Masters,* p. 286)

Home Connection Children find all possible arrangements of 18 chairs in equal rows. They list all of the whole-number factors of 18 and tell someone at home how finding the chair arrangements can help them list the factors.

3 Differentiation Options

READINESS

▶ Playing *Array Bingo*

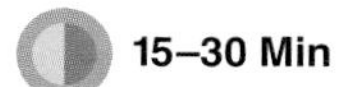

(*Student Reference Book,* p. 273; *Math Masters,* p. 442)

To explore factors using an array model, have children play *Array Bingo.* Children cut apart the *Array Bingo* cards on *Math Masters,* page 442. Discuss the rules for *Array Bingo* on page 273 in the *Student Reference Book,* and have children play in pairs. When finished, have children clip their *Array Bingo* cards together (or place them in an envelope) to store in their tool kits.

ENRICHMENT

▶ Playing *Finding Factors*

15–30 Min

(*Math Masters,* p. 287)

To apply their understanding of factors, have children play *Finding Factors* on *Math Masters,* page 287. When they have completed a few rounds of the game, have children discuss their strategies.

ELL SUPPORT

▶ Building a Math Word Bank

5–15 Min

(*Differentiation Handbook,* p. 132)

To provide language support for multiplication, have children use the Word Bank template on *Differentiation Handbook,* page 132. Ask children to write the term *factor,* draw a picture representing the word, and write other related words. See the *Differentiation Handbook* for more information.

Home Link Master

Name ______ Date ______ Time ______

HOME LINK 9·6 **Arrays and Factors**

Family Note Discuss with your child all the ways to arrange 18 chairs in equal rows. Then help your child use this information to list the factors of 18 (pairs of numbers whose product is 18).
Please return this Home Link to school tomorrow.

SRB 64-67

Work with someone at home.
The third-grade class is putting on a play. Children have invited 18 people. Gilda and Harvey are in charge of arranging the 18 chairs. They want to arrange them in rows with the same number of chairs in each row, with no chairs left over.

Yes or no: Can they arrange the chairs in ...	If yes, how many chairs in each row?
1 row? yes	18 chairs
2 rows? yes	9 chairs
3 rows? yes	6 chairs
4 rows? no	____ chairs
5 rows? no	____ chairs
6 rows? yes	3 chairs
7 rows? no	____ chairs
8 rows? no	____ chairs
9 rows? yes	2 chairs
10 rows? no	____ chairs
18 rows? yes	1 chairs

List all the factors of the number 18. (*Hint:* 18 has exactly 6 factors.)
1 18 2
9 3 6

How does knowing all the ways to arrange 18 chairs in equal rows help you find the factors of 18? Tell someone at home.
Sample answer: When 18 chairs are arranged in equal rows, the number of rows and the number of chairs in each row are factors of 18.

Math Masters, p. 286

Teaching Master

Name ______ Date ______ Time ______

LESSON 9·6 ***Finding Factors***

Materials ☐ 2 different-colored counters, 2 different-colored crayons
☐ *Finding Factors* gameboard (see below)

Players 2

Object of the Game To shade five products in a row, column, or diagonal

Directions

1. Player A places a counter on one of the factors in the Factor Strip at the bottom of the gameboard.
2. Player B places a second counter on one of the factors in the Factor Strip. (Two counters can cover the same factor.) Now that two factors are covered, Player B wins the square that is the product of the two factors. Player B shades this square with his or her color.
3. Player A moves either **one** of the counters to a new factor on the Factor Strip. If the product of the two covered factors has not been shaded, Player A shades this square with his or her color and wins the square.
4. Play continues until 5 squares in a row, column, or diagonal are shaded in the same color.

1	2	3	4	5	6
7	8	9	10	12	14
15	16	18	20	21	24
25	27	28	30	32	35
36	40	42	45	48	49
54	56	63	64	72	81

Factor Strip

1	2	3	4	5	6	7	8	9

Math Masters, p. 287

9•7 Sharing Money

Objective To guide children as they share whole-dollar amounts equally.

www.everydaymathonline.com

ePresentations

eToolkit

Algorithms Practice

EM Facts Workshop Game™

Family Letters

Assessment Management

Common Core State Standards

Curriculum Focal Points

Interactive Teacher's Lesson Guide

1 Teaching the Lesson

Key Concepts and Skills

- Model money exchanges with manipulatives.
  [Number and Numeration Goal 1]
- Solve equal-sharing division stories involving money amounts.
  [Operations and Computation Goal 6]

Key Activities

Children solve problems about sharing whole-dollar amounts equally in preparation for more formal division procedures.

Ongoing Assessment: Informing Instruction See page 750.

Materials

Math Journal 2, p. 222
Home Link 9•6
Math Masters, pp. 399–402
tool-kit coins ◆ scissors ◆ half-sheet of paper ◆ slate ◆ quarter-sheet of paper (optional)

2 Ongoing Learning & Practice

Comparing Fractions

Math Journal 2, p. 191
straightedge (optional)
Children use number lines to compare fractions.

Math Boxes 9•7

Math Journal 2, p. 223
Children practice and maintain skills through Math Box problems.

Ongoing Assessment: Recognizing Student Achievement
Use Math Boxes, Problem 5.
[Number and Numeration Goal 2]

Home Link 9•7

Math Masters, p. 288
Children practice and maintain skills through Home Link activities.

3 Differentiation Options

READINESS

Trading Money

Math Masters, p. 146 (one per player)
per partnership: 2 dollar bills, 20 dimes, and 40 pennies; 2 dice
Children trade money to practice finding equivalent coin and bill values.

ENRICHMENT

Sharing Money Equally

Math Masters, p. 289
Children solve a problem with equal shares of money.

Advance Preparation

Each partnership will need six $100 bills, forty $10 bills, and forty-eight $1 bills. Copy *Math Masters,* pages 399–402. Have children cut the bills apart.

***Teacher's Reference Manual,* Grades 1–3** pp. 111–113

Getting Started

Mathematical Practices
SMP1, SMP2, **SMP4,** SMP5, SMP6, SMP7
Content Standards
3.OA.2, 3.OA.3, 3.OA.7, **3.NF.3d**

Mental Math and Reflexes

Children write fractions on their slates and show whether each fraction is greater than $\frac{1}{2}$ (thumbs-up), equal to $\frac{1}{2}$ (fists), or less than $\frac{1}{2}$ (thumbs-down).

●○○ $\frac{1}{4}$ less than $\frac{1}{2}$, thumbs-down
$\frac{3}{6}$ equal to $\frac{1}{2}$, fist

●●○ $\frac{3}{8}$ less than $\frac{1}{2}$, thumbs-down
$\frac{7}{8}$ greater than $\frac{1}{2}$, thumbs-up

●●● $\frac{2}{3}$ greater than $\frac{1}{2}$, thumbs-up
$\frac{3}{5}$ greater than $\frac{1}{2}$, thumbs-up

Math Message

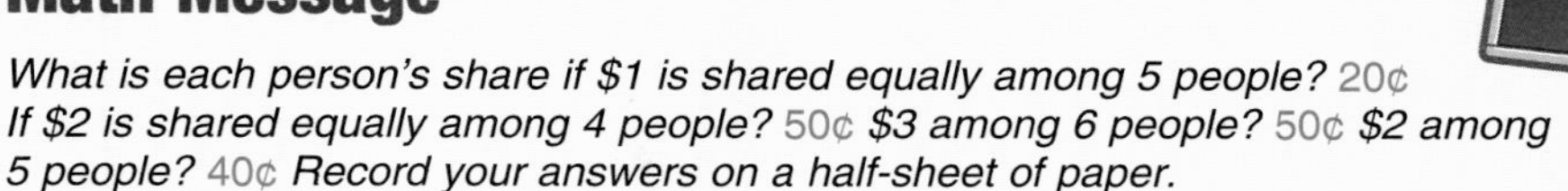

What is each person's share if $1 is shared equally among 5 people? 20¢ *If $2 is shared equally among 4 people?* 50¢ *$3 among 6 people?* 50¢ *$2 among 5 people?* 40¢ *Record your answers on a half-sheet of paper.*

Home Link 9·6 Follow-Up

Ask volunteers to draw arrays with 18 dots on the board. Ask someone to explain how knowing all of the ways to arrange 18 chairs in equal rows can help them name the factors of 18. When 18 chairs are arranged in rows with the same number of chairs in each row with no chairs left over, the number of rows and the number of chairs in each row are factors of 18. Knowing the different arrays for 18 visually shows the factors of 18.

1 Teaching the Lesson

▶ Math Message Follow-Up

WHOLE-CLASS DISCUSSION

Children share their solutions and strategies. Possible strategies for $1 shared by 5 people include:

▷ There are 5 [20s] in 100 so there are five $0.20 in $1.00.

▷ Change the dollars to cents and divide: $1 = 100¢, and 100¢ divided equally among 5 people is 20¢ apiece.

▷ Change the dollars to dimes and divide: $1 = 10 dimes, and 10 dimes divided equally among 5 people is 2 dimes, or 20¢ apiece.

▶ Sharing Play Money

WHOLE-CLASS ACTIVITY

(*Math Journal 2,* p. 222; *Math Masters,* pp. 399–402)

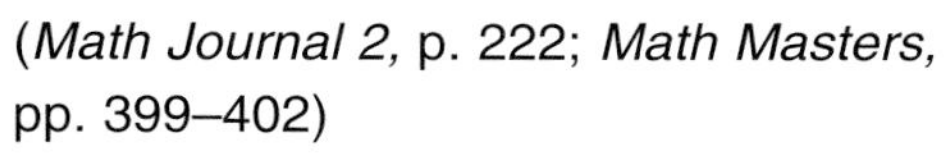

Children work with partners. Have them turn to journal page 222. Work through Problems 1 and 2 with the class, while children use $100, $10, and $1 bills to represent the amounts being shared.

Adjusting the Activity

ELL

Provide children with quarter-sheets of paper to use as a model for how many groups they need. For example, if 5 people are sharing a dollar, children use 5 quarter-sheets of paper to model dividing the dollar into 5 equal shares.

AUDITORY ◆ KINESTHETIC ◆ TACTILE ◆ VISUAL

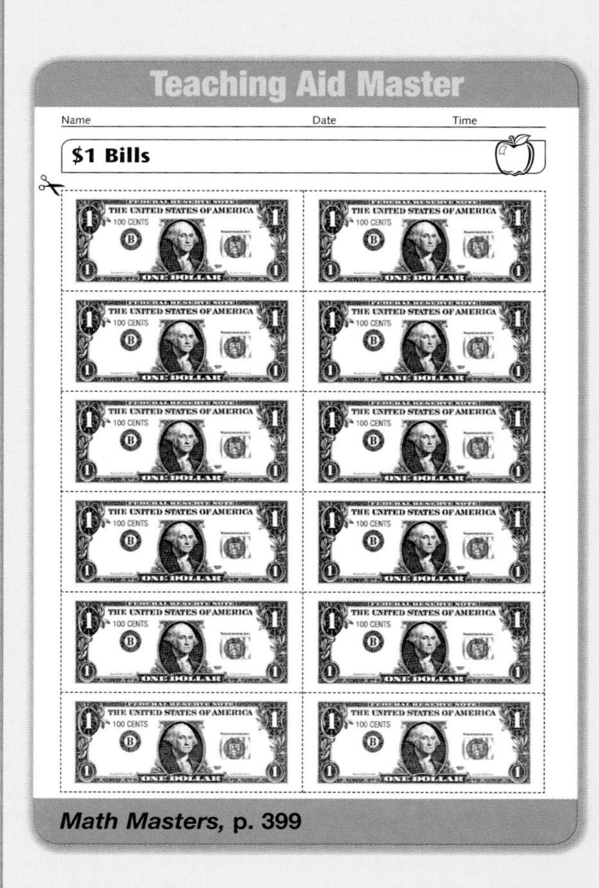

Math Masters, p. 399

Student Page

Date Time

LESSON 9·7 **Sharing Money**

Work with a partner. Put your play money in a bank for both of you to use.

1. If $54 is shared equally by 3 people, how much does each person get?
   a. Number model: $54 ÷ 3 = ?
   b. How many $10 bills does each person get? 1 $10 bill(s)
   c. How many dollars are left to share? $ 24.00
   d. How many $1 bills does each person get? 8 $1 bill(s)
   e. Answer: Each person gets $ 18.00.
2. If $71 is shared equally by 5 people, how much does each person get?
   a. Number model: $71 ÷ 5 = ?
   b. How many $10 bills does each person get? 1 $10 bill(s)
   c. How many dollars are left to share? $ 21.00
   d. How many $1 bills does each person get? 4 $1 bill(s)
   e. How many $1 bills are left over? 1 $1 bill(s)
   f. If the leftover $1 bill(s) are shared equally, how many cents does each person get? $ 0.20
   g. Answer: Each person gets $ 14.20.
3. $84 ÷ 3 = $ 28.00
4. $75 ÷ 6 = $ 12.50
5. $181 ÷ 4 = $ 45.25
6. $617 ÷ 5 = $ 123.40

Math Journal 2, p. 222

Ongoing Assessment: Informing Instruction

Watch for children who have trouble with problems in which a share involves dollars *and* cents. Have them exchange the leftover $1 bills for coins and divide the coins into equal shares.

NOTE The solution to a division problem often consists of the quotient and a remainder. Because such results are not entirely analogous to the results obtained with the other operations, the equal sign has been replaced with an arrow in division number models with remainders. When children learn to express quotients with fractions or decimals, *Everyday Mathematics* will use the traditional form; for example, $12 \div 5 = 2.4$ or $2\frac{2}{5}$.

Problem 1: Share $54 equally among 3 people.

Have the class read aloud Problem 1 on journal page 222. Discuss what you want to find out and what you know from the problem. Remind children that the division operation can be used to solve equal-sharing problems. Ask a volunteer to write a division number model for the story on the board while the rest of the children write it in their journals. $54 ÷ 3 = ?

▷ To solve, have partners place five $10 bills and four $1 bills on the table and set the rest of the bills aside. They make three piles with the same amount in each pile. After they put a $10 bill in each pile, there are still two $10 bills and four $1 bills left to share. Because the $10 bills cannot be distributed equally among the three piles, children exchange them for twenty $1 bills. Now there are twenty-four $1 bills to be shared, or eight $1 bills per pile. Each pile now has one $10 bill and eight $1 bills, or $18 total.

▷ Children record these transactions on page 222.

Ask: *Does your answer make sense?* yes *How do you know?* Sample answer: I know that $54 is close to $60 and $60 ÷ 3 is $20. Since $20 is close to $18, my answer makes sense. Write a summary number model on the board: $54 ÷ 3 = $18.

Problem 2: Share $71 equally among 5 people.

▷ Have children read aloud Problem 2. Discuss what you want to find out and what you know from the problem. Ask children to write a number model for the story in their journals while you write it on the board. $71 ÷ 5 = ?

▷ To solve, partners take seven $10 bills and one $1 bill and make 5 equal piles with one $10 bill in each. There are two $10 bills and one $1 bill left over. They exchange the two $10 bills for twenty $1 bills and distribute them among the five piles, or four $1 bills per pile. If they cannot decide what to do with the remaining $1 bill, remind them of the first Math Message problem. (When $1 is divided among 5 people, each person gets 20¢.) Thus, each person's share is $14.20.

Ask: *Does your answer make sense?* yes *How do you know?* Sample answer: I know that $71 is close to $70. If I think of $70 as $60 + $10, I know that there are five $12 in 60 and five $2 in 10. So, there are five $14 in 70, which is very close to five $14.20 in $71. Write a summary number model on the board: $71 ÷ 5 = $14.20.

Pose the following questions: *What if 71¢ had been shared equally among 5 people? What would each person's share have been?* 14¢ *Could the leftover penny have been shared equally?* no *What is a number model for this problem?* 71¢ ÷ 5 → 14¢ R1¢ The number model is read "71 cents divided by 5 is 14 cents with a remainder of 1 cent."

▶ Solving Division Problems

(*Math Journal 2,* p. 222)

PARTNER ACTIVITY

Children model the remaining equal-sharing problems (Problems 3 through 6) on journal page 222 with play money and complete the number models. Children will check their answers to Problems 3 through 6 with a calculator in the next lesson, so postpone a class discussion of these problems until then.

Links to the Future

Many children will be able to divide, with the use of manipulatives, whole-dollar amounts that can be shared equally, but remainders may confuse some children. The activities in this lesson are laying a foundation for more formal division work in fourth grade. Solving problems involving the division of multidigit whole numbers with remainders is a Grade 5 Goal.

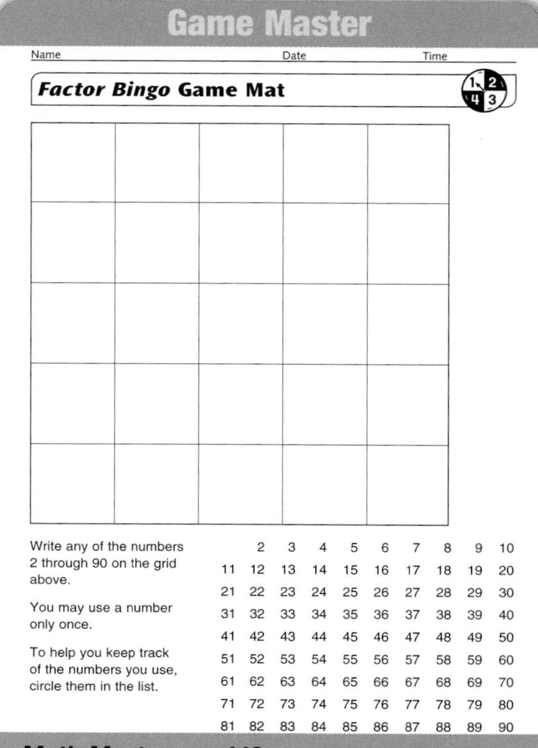

Game Master

Name Date Time

Factor Bingo Game Mat

Write any of the numbers 2 through 90 on the grid above.

You may use a number only once.

To help you keep track of the numbers you use, circle them in the list.

2	3	4	5	6	7	8	9	10
11	12	13	14	15	16	17	18	19	20
21	22	23	24	25	26	27	28	29	30
31	32	33	34	35	36	37	38	39	40
41	42	43	44	45	46	47	48	49	50
51	52	53	54	55	56	57	58	59	60
61	62	63	64	65	66	67	68	69	70
71	72	73	74	75	76	77	78	79	80
81	82	83	84	85	86	87	88	89	90

Math Masters, p. 448

2 Ongoing Learning & Practice

▶ Comparing Fractions

(*Math Journal 2,* p. 191)

INDEPENDENT ACTIVITY

To provide children with practice using number lines to compare fractions, have them turn to their Fraction Number-Line Poster on journal page 191. Have children locate $\frac{1}{3}$ and $\frac{1}{4}$ on the poster and determine which of the two fractions is larger and explain how they know. Sample answer: I know that $\frac{1}{3}$ is larger than $\frac{1}{4}$ because when I look at the number lines, I see that $\frac{1}{3}$ is to the right of $\frac{1}{4}$. If needed, children can place a straightedge vertically on the poster next to one of the two fractions to determine if it's less than, equal to, or greater than the other fraction. Have them write a number sentence using >, =, and < to describe the relationship between each pair of fractions. Continue with other fraction pairs.

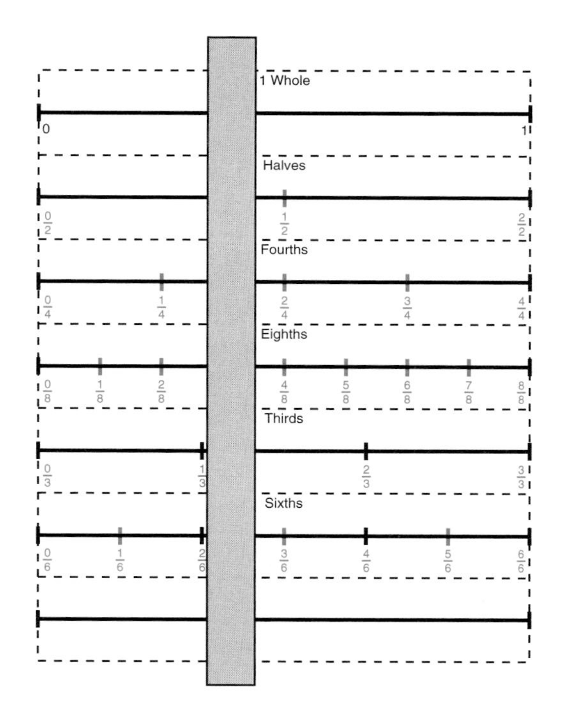

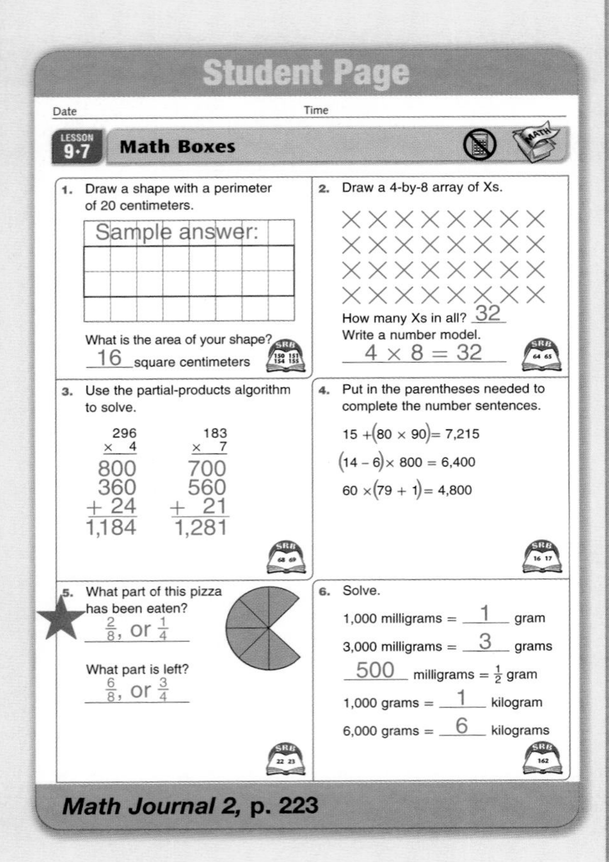

Student Page

Date Time

LESSON 9·7 **Math Boxes**

1. Draw a shape with a perimeter of 20 centimeters.
Sample answer:
What is the area of your shape? 16 square centimeters

2. Draw a 4-by-8 array of Xs.
XXXXXXXX
XXXXXXXX
XXXXXXXX
XXXXXXXX
How many Xs in all? 32
Write a number model. $4 \times 8 = 32$

3. Use the partial-products algorithm to solve.

$$\begin{array}{r} 296 \\ \times\ 4 \\ \hline 800 \\ 360 \\ +\ 24 \\ \hline 1{,}184 \end{array} \qquad \begin{array}{r} 183 \\ \times\ 7 \\ \hline 700 \\ 560 \\ +\ 21 \\ \hline 1{,}281 \end{array}$$

4. Put in the parentheses needed to complete the number sentences.
$15 + (80 \times 90) = 7{,}215$
$(14 - 6) \times 800 = 6{,}400$
$60 \times (79 + 1) = 4{,}800$

5. What part of this pizza has been eaten? $\frac{2}{8}$, or $\frac{1}{4}$
What part is left? $\frac{6}{8}$, or $\frac{3}{4}$

6. Solve.
1,000 milligrams = 1 gram
3,000 milligrams = 3 grams
500 milligrams = $\frac{1}{2}$ gram
1,000 grams = 1 kilogram
6,000 grams = 6 kilograms

Math Journal 2, p. 223

▶ Math Boxes 9·7

INDEPENDENT ACTIVITY

(*Math Journal 2*, p. 223)

Mixed Practice Math Boxes in this lesson are paired with Math Boxes in Lesson 9-5. The skill in Problem 6 previews Unit 10 content.

Writing/Reasoning Have children write an answer to the following: *Explain how you could equally share the leftover pizza from Problem 5 among 4 people.* Sample answer: Each person can have one complete piece and half of another piece, giving each person $1\frac{1}{2}$ pieces.

Ongoing Assessment: Recognizing Student Achievement

Math Boxes Problem 5 

Use **Math Boxes, Problem 5** to assess children's progress in solving problems involving fractional parts of a region. Children are making adequate progress if they are able to solve Problem 5. Some children may be able to record 2 or more equivalent fractions to answer each question.

[Number and Numeration Goal 2]

▶ Home Link 9·7

(*Math Masters*, p. 288)

Home Connection Children solve an equal-sharing problem involving money.

Home Link Master

Name Date Time

HOME LINK 9·7 **Sharing Money with Friends**

Family Note In class we are thinking about division, but we have not yet introduced a procedure for division. We will work with formal division algorithms in *Fourth Grade Everyday Mathematics.* Encourage your child to solve the following problems in his or her own way and to explain the strategy to you. These problems provide an opportunity to develop a sense of what division means and how it works. Sometimes it helps to model problems with bills and coins or with pennies, beans or other counters that stand for coins and bills.

Please return this Home Link to school tomorrow.

1. Four friends want to share \$77. They have 7 ten-dollar bills and 7 one-dollar bills. They can go to the bank to get smaller bills and coins if they need to.
   a. Number model: $\$77 \div 4 = ?$
   b. How many \$10 bills could each friend get? 1
      How many \$10 bills would be left over? 3
   c. Of the remaining money, how many \$1 bills could each friend get? (Remember, you can exchange larger bills for smaller ones.) 9
   d. How many \$1 bills would be left over? 1
   e. If the leftover money is shared equally, how many cents does each friend get? \$0.25
   f. Answer: Each friend gets a total of \$ 19.25.

Practice

Use the partial-products method to solve these problems. Show your work.

2. $21 \times 2 = 42$
3. $48 \times 4 = 192$
4. $63 \times 5 = 315$

Math Masters, p. 288

3 Differentiation Options

READINESS

5–15 Min

▶ Trading Money

(*Math Masters,* p. 146)

To provide experience with money exchanges, have children make dollar-dime-penny trades in the *Money Trading Game*. Children make their trades on the Place-Value Mat on *Math Masters,* page 146.

Money Trading Game

You will need 2 dollar bills, 20 dimes, 40 pennies, 2 dice, and one Place-Value Mat per player. Each player begins with 1 dollar on his or her Place-Value Mat. The bank should have 20 dimes and 40 pennies.

Directions:

Take turns. On each turn, a player does the following:

1. Roll the dice and find the sum of the dice.
2. Return that number of cents to the bank. Make exchanges when needed.
3. The player not rolling the dice checks on the accuracy of the transactions.
4. The first player to clear his or her Place-Value Mat wins the game.

ENRICHMENT

5–15 Min

▶ Sharing Money Equally

(*Math Masters,* p. 289)

To apply children's understanding of equal shares, have them figure out how many people can go to the magic show for $25. Children record their work on *Math Masters,* page 289. Have children explain their strategies for solving the problems. Discuss why they think the last problem might be a Try This. Sample answer: It was harder to answer because there was money left over.

Teaching Master

Name Date Time

LESSON 5•8 **Place-Value Mat**

Pennies Hundredths Cubes ($0.01, 0.01)	
Dimes Tenths Longs ($0.10, 0.1)	
Dollars Ones Flats ($1.00, 1)	

Math Masters, p. 146

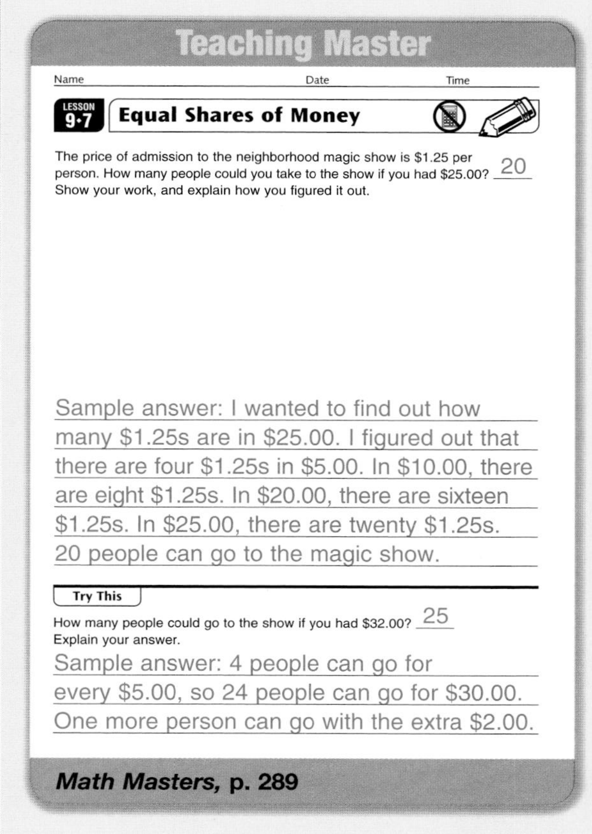

Teaching Master

Name Date Time

LESSON 9•7 **Equal Shares of Money**

The price of admission to the neighborhood magic show is $1.25 per person. How many people could you take to the show if you had $25.00? 20
Show your work, and explain how you figured it out.

Sample answer: I wanted to find out how many $1.25s are in $25.00. I figured out that there are four $1.25s in $5.00. In $10.00, there are eight $1.25s. In $20.00, there are sixteen $1.25s. In $25.00, there are twenty $1.25s. 20 people can go to the magic show.

Try This

How many people could go to the show if you had $32.00? 25
Explain your answer.

Sample answer: 4 people can go for every $5.00, so 24 people can go for $30.00. One more person can go with the extra $2.00.

Math Masters, p. 289

9•8 Broken-Calculator Division

Objective To guide children as they explore computational strategies for division and interpret remainders.

Technology Resources www.everydaymathonline.com

ePresentations

eToolkit

Algorithms Practice

EM Facts Workshop Game™

Family Letters

Assessment Management

Common Core State Standards

Curriculum Focal Points

Interactive Teacher's Lesson Guide

1 Teaching the Lesson

Key Concepts and Skills

- Interpret calculator displays for remainders in equal-sharing and equal-grouping problems.
  [Operations and Computation Goal 6]
- Use equal sharing to solve division number stories.
  [Operations and Computation Goal 6]

Key Activities

Children divide numbers using the division keys on a calculator and interpret the calculator display. They devise ways of dividing numbers using a calculator without using the division key and solve division number stories with remainders.

Ongoing Assessment: Informing Instruction See pages 756 and 757.

Materials

Math Journal 2, pp. 222 and 224
Home Link 9•7
calculator ◆ slate ◆ half-sheet of paper ◆ play money (optional) ◆ counters (optional)

2 Ongoing Learning & Practice

Playing *Factor Bingo*
Math Masters, p. 448 (one per player)
Student Reference Book pp. 285 and 286
per partnership: 4 each of number cards 2–9 (from the Everything Math Deck, if available), 24 counters
Children apply their understanding of factors.

Math Boxes 9•8
Math Journal 2, p. 225
Children practice and maintain skills through Math Box problems.

Ongoing Assessment: Recognizing Student Achievement
Use Math Boxes, Problem 2.
[Patterns, Functions, and Algebra Goal 3]

Home Link 9•8
Math Masters, p. 290
Children practice and maintain skills through Home Link activities.

3 Differentiation Options

READINESS

Picturing Division
Math Masters, p. 291
Children use a visual model to explore equal-sharing and equal-grouping problems.

ENRICHMENT

Solving Division Number Stories
Math Masters, p. 292
Children solve division number stories and express the remainders as fractions.

ELL SUPPORT

Using Calculators to Solve Division Problems
calculator
Children discuss calculator keys they press to solve division problems.

Advance Preparation

***Teacher's Reference Manual,* Grades 1–3** pp. 23–29

Getting Started

Mathematical Practices
SMP1, SMP2, SMP3, SMP4, SMP5, **SMP6**
Content Standards
3.OA.3, 3.NBT.2

Mental Math and Reflexes

Children record answers to fraction number stories on their slates. Encourage children to draw or use counters as needed. *Suggestions:*

●○○ Troy read 8 books over the summer. $\frac{7}{8}$ of the books were mysteries. How many mysteries did Troy read? 7 mysteries

●●○ Perry saved 20 coins. $\frac{2}{5}$ of them were dimes. $\frac{1}{4}$ of them were quarters. $\frac{3}{10}$ of the coins were nickels. The rest were pennies. How many of each coin did Perry save? 8 dimes, 5 quarters, 6 nickels and 1 penny

●●● The guests at Tory and Marissa's birthday party ate 10 slices of pie. If each pie had six slices, what fraction of pies was eaten? $\frac{10}{6}$, or $1\frac{4}{6}$, or $1\frac{2}{3}$ pies

Math Message

Solve Problems 3 through 6 on journal page 222 using your calculator. On a half-sheet of paper, write the answers the calculator displays. Compare with your answers on the journal page.

Home Link 9·7 Follow-Up

Briefly go over the answers. Have children share strategies for solving Problem 1.

1 Teaching the Lesson

▶ Math Message Follow-Up

WHOLE-CLASS DISCUSSION

(*Math Journal 2,* p. 222)

In discussing calculator answers to Problems 3 through 6 on journal page 222, point out that the calculator display must be interpreted to fit the situation. For example, the calculator display for 75 ÷ 6 is 12.5 (a number with one decimal place), but the answer to \$75 ÷ 6 is \$12.50 (a number with two decimal places).

Adjusting the Activity

ELL

When using calculators, it is important to discuss the meaning of each calculator entry. Ask questions such as: *What does [number] stand for? What does [number] represent? Why are you dividing? What does the answer represent? What does the answer mean? What are the units?*

AUDITORY ◆ KINESTHETIC ◆ TACTILE ◆ VISUAL

Ask children to solve the following problem with their calculators:

- A farmer wants to pack 246 eggs into egg cartons that hold a dozen eggs each. How many full cartons will she have?

Remind children that they must divide 246 by 12 to find how many 12s there are in 246. When this is done on a calculator, the display shows 20.5. Ask: *In this problem, what does 20.5 stand for?* Cartons of eggs *Is 20.5 cartons the answer to the problem?* No. 20.5 is between 20 and 21, so there are 20 full cartons with some eggs left over. Some children assume that the 5 after the decimal point is the remainder or the number of eggs left over. Clarify that this is not the case.

NOTE Some calculators have a key that gives the answer to a division problem as a whole number and a remainder. If this key is used, the answer to 75 ÷ 6 is 12 with a remainder of 3. When the calculator display is interpreted to fit the situation, the remainder of 3 represents \$3. \$75 ÷ 6 is \$12 with \$3 left over. \$3 can be evenly divided by 6, resulting in \$0.50. Another answer to \$75 ÷ 6 is \$12.50.

Student Page

Date Time

LESSON 9·7 **Sharing Money**

Work with a partner. Put your play money in a bank for both of you to use.

1. If \$54 is shared equally by 3 people, how much does each person get?
   a. Number model: \$54 ÷ 3 = ?
   b. How many \$10 bills does each person get? 1 \$10 bill(s)
   c. How many dollars are left to share? \$ 24.00
   d. How many \$1 bills does each person get? 8 \$1 bill(s)
   e. Answer: Each person gets \$ 18.00.
2. If \$71 is shared equally by 5 people, how much does each person get?
   a. Number model: \$71 ÷ 5 = ?
   b. How many \$10 bills does each person get? 1 \$10 bill(s)
   c. How many dollars are left to share? \$ 21.00
   d. How many \$1 bills does each person get? 4 \$1 bill(s)
   e. How many \$1 bills are left over? 1 \$1 bill(s)
   f. If the leftover \$1 bill(s) are shared equally, how many cents does each person get? \$ 0.20
   g. Answer: Each person gets \$ 14.20.
3. \$84 ÷ 3 = \$ 28.00
4. \$75 ÷ 6 = \$ 12.50
5. \$181 ÷ 4 = \$ 45.25
6. \$617 ÷ 5 = \$ 123.40

Math Journal 2, p. 222

Adjusting the Activity

Pose the following question: *How many eggs are left over?* 6 *Possible strategies:* 0.5 is another name for $\frac{1}{2}$, and a half-full carton of eggs contains 6 eggs. 20 full cartons of eggs contain $20 \times 12 = 240$ eggs. That leaves 6 unpacked eggs ($246 - 240 = 6$).

AUDITORY ♦ KINESTHETIC ♦ TACTILE ♦ VISUAL

As time permits, pose and discuss additional problems in which children must interpret the calculator display. *Suggestions:*

- There are 263 pencils. A box holds 50 pencils. How many full boxes of pencils are there? 5 boxes
- A bus holds 36 people. 155 people are going on a field trip. How many buses are needed? 5 buses

Ongoing Assessment: Informing Instruction

For the bus problem, the calculator display will show 4.3055555. Watch for children who think this is a big number. Direct their attention to the decimal point and the whole number to the left of the decimal point.

▶ Exploring Strategies for Finding Quotients

SMALL-GROUP ACTIVITY

Ask children to pretend that the division key on each calculator is broken. How would they use their broken calculators to solve the following problem?

- A farmer packs 576 eggs into cartons that hold a dozen eggs each. How many full cartons does she pack?

Ask each group to write a brief report describing the strategies they used to solve the problem. Bring the class together to share strategies. *Possible strategies:*

▷ Clear the calculator and enter 576. Subtract 12 over and over until the display shows a number less than 12 (in this case, 0). Keep a tally of the number of times 12 is subtracted. This tally gives the number of full cartons. 48

▷ Clear the calculator and enter 576. Subtract 120 (the number of eggs in 10 full cartons) over and over until the display shows a number less than 120 (in this case, 96). Keep a tally of the number of times 120 is subtracted. This tally gives the number of tens of cartons. 4 tens = 40 Subtract 12 from the number in the display until the display shows a number less than 12. This gives the number of additional full cartons. 8. Add 40 + 8 to get 48 cartons.

▷ Use repeated estimates for the number multiplied by 12 to get 576. The repeated-estimates strategy is often referred to as guess-and-check. *For example:*

$25 \times 12 = 300$—too small

$40 \times 12 = 480$—too small

$50 \times 12 = 600$—too large, but close

$48 \times 12 = 576$—right on target!

Pose additional broken-calculator problems as necessary for the groups to solve. *Suggestions:*

- A baker packs 315 hamburger buns into packages of 8. How many full packages does he have? 39
  How many leftover buns? 3
- The cafeteria manager plans to serve 78 cartons of yogurt for lunch. The cartons come in packages of 6. How many 6-carton packages must be purchased? 13

▶ Solving Division Number Stories with Remainders

PARTNER ACTIVITY

(*Math Journal 2,* p. 224)

Partners use their calculators to solve the division problems on journal page 224. Explain to children that they can use the division key on Problems 1 through 3, but they will pretend it is broken in Problems 4 and 5. When children finish, have volunteers explain how they interpreted the calculator display for each problem and how they solved Problems 4 and 5 without using the division key.

Adjusting the Activity

ELL

When you introduce the idea of the broken calculator to English language learners, it should be clear that you are pretending it is broken. Explain that children will be asked to solve some problems without using certain calculator keys.

AUDITORY ◆ KINESTHETIC ◆ TACTILE ◆ VISUAL

Ongoing Assessment: Informing Instruction

Watch for children who need support in implementing a strategy for solving the division problems. Encourage them to draw pictures to illustrate the problems. (*See margin.*)

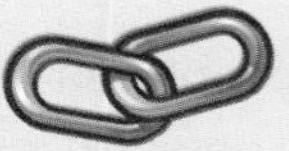

Links to the Future

The activities in this lesson are an early exposure to interpreting remainders. Some children will need more practice before they develop a full understanding of division concepts. Expressing the remainder as a whole number or fraction appropriate to the context of the problem is a Grade 5 Goal.

Student Page

Date Time

LESSON 9•8 **Division with Remainders**

Solve the problems below. Remember that you will have to decide what the remainder means in order to answer the questions. You may use your calculator, counters, play money, or pictures.

1. Ruth is buying soda for a party. There are 6 cans in a pack. She needs 44 cans. How many 6-packs will she buy? 8 6-packs
2. Paul is buying tickets to the circus. Each ticket costs $7. He has $47. How many tickets can he buy? 6 tickets
3. Héctor is standing in line for the roller coaster. There are 33 people in line. Each roller coaster car holds 4 people. How many cars are needed to hold 33 people? 9 cars

Pretend that the division key on your calculator is broken. Solve the following problems:

4. Regina is building a fence around her dollhouse. She is making each fence post 5 inches tall. The wood she bought is 36 inches long. How many fence posts does each piece of wood make? 7 posts
   Explain how you found your answer.
   Sample answer: I subtracted 10 (2 posts) as many times as I could. Then I subtracted 5 as many times as I could.
5. Missy, Ann, and Herman found a $10 bill. They want to share the money equally. How much money will each person get? $3.33
   Explain how you found your answer. Sample answer:
   I subtracted 3 from 10 three times. That left 1. or $1.00.
   I subtracted .30 from 1. three times. That left .1 or $0.10.
   I subtracted .03 from .1 three times. That left .01 or $.01.

Math Journal 2, p. 224

A picture of Problem 1 on journal page 224

7 [6s] = 42

Ruth needs 2 more cans to make 44. She must buy eight 6-packs.

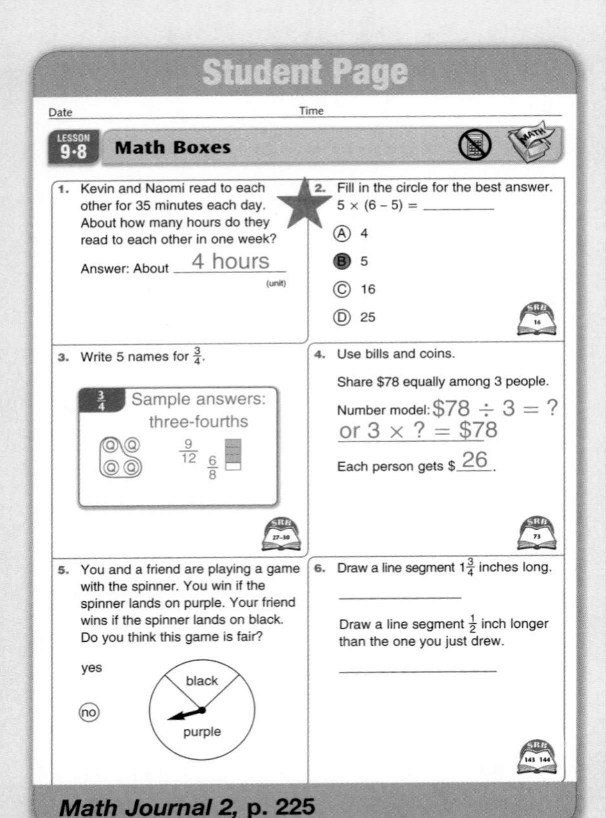
Student Page

Date Time

LESSON 9·8 **Math Boxes**

1. Kevin and Naomi read to each other for 35 minutes each day. About how many hours do they read to each other in one week?
Answer: About 4 hours (unit)

2. Fill in the circle for the best answer.
$5 \times (6 - 5) =$ ______
Ⓐ 4
Ⓑ 5
Ⓒ 16
Ⓓ 25

3. Write 5 names for $\frac{3}{4}$.
Sample answers: three-fourths $\frac{9}{12}$ $\frac{6}{8}$

4. Use bills and coins.
Share \$78 equally among 3 people.
Number model: $\$78 \div 3 = ?$ or $3 \times ? = \$78$
Each person gets \$ 26.

5. You and a friend are playing a game with the spinner. You win if the spinner lands on purple. Your friend wins if the spinner lands on black. Do you think this game is fair?
yes
no
black
purple

6. Draw a line segment $1\frac{3}{4}$ inches long.
Draw a line segment $\frac{1}{2}$ inch longer than the one you just drew.

Math Journal 2, p. 225

2 Ongoing Learning & Practice

▶ Playing *Factor Bingo*

(*Math Masters,* p. 448; *Student Reference Book,* pp. 285 and 286)

This game was introduced in Lesson 9-6. Have children make new game boards on *Math Masters,* page 448. If necessary, review the rules for the game on pages 285 and 286 in the *Student Reference Book.*

▶ Math Boxes 9·8

INDEPENDENT ACTIVITY

(*Math Journal 2,* p. 225)

Mixed Practice Math Boxes in this lesson are paired with Math Boxes in Lesson 9-6. The skill in Problem 6 previews Unit 10 content.

Ongoing Assessment: Recognizing Student Achievement

Math Boxes Problem 2 

Use **Math Boxes, Problem 2** to assess children's progress toward understanding that parentheses affect the order of operations. Children are making adequate progress if they successfully complete Problem 2. Some children may be able to write and solve their own number sentences with parentheses.

[Patterns, Functions, and Algebra Goal 3]

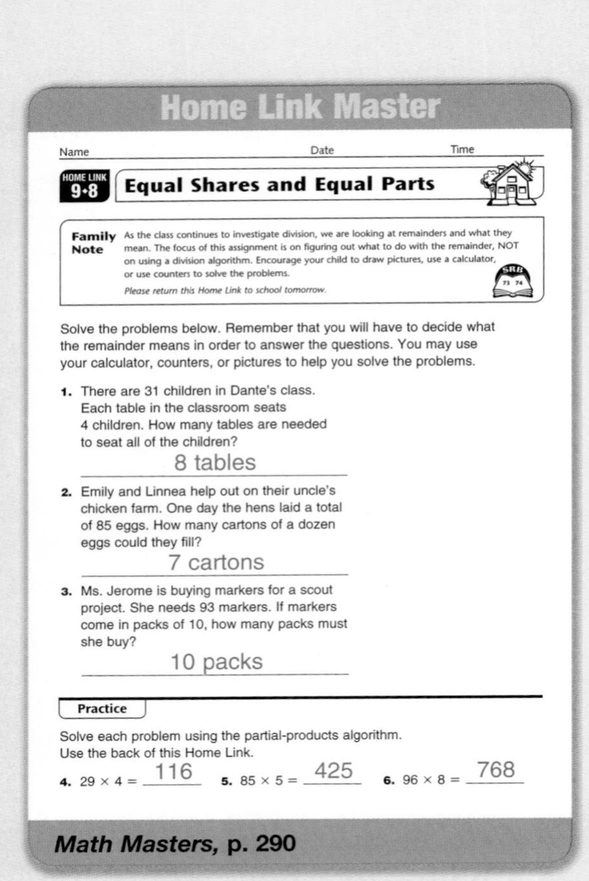
Home Link Master

Name Date Time

HOME LINK 9·8 **Equal Shares and Equal Parts**

Family Note As the class continues to investigate division, we are looking at remainders and what they mean. The focus of this assignment is on figuring out what to do with the remainder, NOT on using a division algorithm. Encourage your child to draw pictures, use a calculator, or use counters to solve the problems.

Please return this Home Link to school tomorrow.

Solve the problems below. Remember that you will have to decide what the remainder means in order to answer the questions. You may use your calculator, counters, or pictures to help you solve the problems.

1. There are 31 children in Dante's class. Each table in the classroom seats 4 children. How many tables are needed to seat all of the children?
8 tables

2. Emily and Linnea help out on their uncle's chicken farm. One day the hens laid a total of 85 eggs. How many cartons of a dozen eggs could they fill?
7 cartons

3. Ms. Jerome is buying markers for a scout project. She needs 93 markers. If markers come in packs of 10, how many packs must she buy?
10 packs

Practice

Solve each problem using the partial-products algorithm. Use the back of this Home Link.

4. $29 \times 4 =$ 116
5. $85 \times 5 =$ 425
6. $96 \times 8 =$ 768

Math Masters, p. 290

▶ Home Link 9·8

INDEPENDENT ACTIVITY

(*Math Masters,* p. 290)

Home Connection Children solve number stories about dividing quantities into equal parts and interpreting remainders.

3 Differentiation Options

READINESS

INDEPENDENT ACTIVITY

▶ Picturing Division

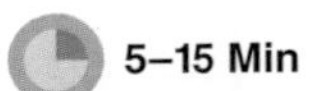

(*Math Masters,* p. 291)

To explore equal-sharing and equal-grouping problems using a visual model, have children illustrate the solution to division problems. Children record their work on *Math Masters,* page 291.

ENRICHMENT

PARTNER ACTIVITY

5–15 Min

Solving Division Number Stories

(*Math Masters,* p. 292)

To apply children's understanding of remainders, have them solve division problems and express the remainders as fractions on *Math Masters,* page 292. Have children share solution strategies. For Problem 2, children might draw 4 pizzas and divide each into 8 equal slices. They would shade 3 of the pizzas (for 24 slices) and one of the slices in the fourth pizza (for a total of 25 shaded slices). Point out that to serve everyone, the class will need to order 4 pizzas.

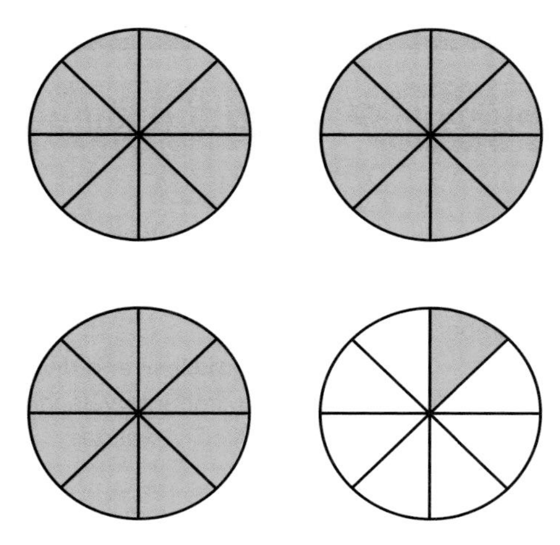

4 pizzas are needed to serve 25 people.

ELL SUPPORT

SMALL-GROUP ACTIVITY

5–15 Min

Using Calculators to Solve Division Problems

To provide support for solving division problems with a calculator, discuss the keys that are pressed and the resulting displays. For example, pose the following problem: A bus holds 36 people. 162 people are going on a field trip. How many buses are needed?

After the children have solved the problem, ask the following questions:

- What keys did you press on the calculator to solve the problem? 162 (÷) 36 (=)
- What number did you see in the display? 4.5
- What does the 4 represent? The number of buses carrying 36 people
- How many people will the 4 buses hold? $36 \times 4 = 144$
- How many more people will need a seat? $162 - 144 = 18$
- Where will these 18 sit? On the fifth bus

Teaching Master

Name Date Time

LESSON 9•8 **Picturing Division**

For each problem—

- Draw a picture.
- Answer the question.
- Explain what you did with what was left over.

1. There are 18 children in art class. If 4 children can sit at each table, how many tables do they need?

Picture:

Answer: They need 5 tables.

Explanation: Sample answer: There are 4 children at each of the 4 tables. 2 children are left over, so they need 5 tables.

2. Hot dogs come in packages of 8. If José is having a birthday party and needs 20 hot dogs, how many packages must he buy?

Picture:

Answer: He must buy 3 packages.

Explanation: Sample answer: 2 packages have 16 hot dogs—$8 \times 2 = 16$. 3 packages have 24 hot dogs—$8 \times 3 = 24$. José must buy 3 packages of hot dogs.

Math Masters, **p. 291**

Teaching Master

Name Date Time

LESSON 9•8 **Pizza with Remainders**

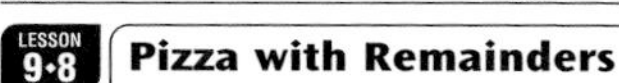

The third-grade class is having a pizza party. The class expects 22 children, 1 teacher, and 2 parents. Each pizza will be divided into 8 equal slices.

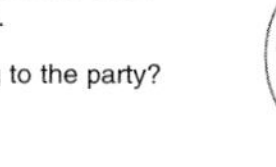

1. In all, how many people are coming to the party? 25 people

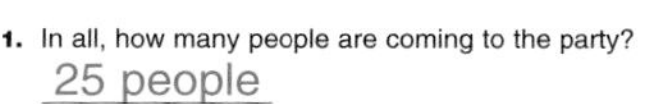

2. Suppose that each person who comes to the party will eat 1 slice of pizza.
   a. How many whole pizzas will the people eat? 3 pizzas
   b. How many additional slices will be needed? 1 slice
   c. What fractional part of a whole pizza is that? $\frac{1}{8}$
   d. Is that more or less than half of a whole pizza? Less than $\frac{1}{2}$
   e. How many whole pizzas should the teacher order? 4 whole pizzas
3. Suppose instead that each person will eat 2 slices of pizza.
   a. How many slices of pizza will the people eat? 50 slices
   b. How many whole pizzas will the people eat? 6 whole pizzas
   c. How many additional slices will be needed? 2 extra slices
   d. What fractional part of a whole pizza is that? $\frac{2}{8}$
   e. How many whole pizzas should the teacher order? 7 pizzas
4. Lakeisha brought 2 granola bars to the party. She decided to share them equally with her 3 best friends. What fractional part of a granola bar did she and her friends get? $\frac{1}{2}$

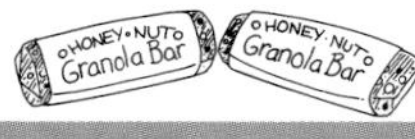

Math Masters, **p. 292**

9•9 Lattice Multiplication

Objective To introduce the lattice method of multiplication.

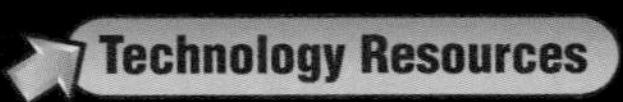

www.everydaymathonline.com

ePresentations | eToolkit | Algorithms Practice | EM Facts Workshop Game™ | Family Letters | Assessment Management | Common Core State Standards | Curriculum Focal Points | Interactive Teacher's Lesson Guide

1 Teaching the Lesson

Key Concepts and Skills

- Use addition facts to solve lattice multiplication problems.
  [Operations and Computation Goal 1]
- Use multiplication facts to solve lattice multiplication problems.
  [Operations and Computation Goal 3]
- Explore a strategy for solving problems involving multiplication of 1-digit by multidigit numbers.
  [Operations and Computation Goal 4]

Key Activities

Children explore lattice multiplication as an alternative method for multiplying multidigit numbers.

Ongoing Assessment: Informing Instruction See pages 762 and 763.

Key Vocabulary

lattice multiplication

Materials

Math Journal 2, pp. 226 and 227
Student Reference Book, pp. 70–72
Home Link 9•8
calculator ◆ blank paper ◆ counters (optional) ◆ index cards (optional)

2 Ongoing Learning & Practice

Playing *Factor Bingo*
Math Masters, p. 448
Student Reference Book, pp. 285 and 286
per partnership: 4 each of number cards 2–9 (from the Everything Math Deck, if available) ◆ 12 counters per player
Children practice identifying factors.

Math Boxes 9•9
Math Journal 2, p. 228
Children practice and maintain skills through Math Box problems.

Ongoing Assessment: Recognizing Student Achievement
Use Math Boxes, Problem 5.
[Geometry Goal 2]

Home Link 9•9
Math Masters, p. 293
Children practice and maintain skills through Home Link activities.

3 Differentiation Options

ENRICHMENT

Multiplying and Dividing Multiples of 10 in Music
Math Masters, p. 294
dictionary
Children multiply and divide multiples of 10 using time intervals in the musical composition *Vexations.*

EXTRA PRACTICE

Practicing Partial Products
Math Journal 2, p. 227
lined paper
Children practice multiplication using the partial-products algorithm.

Advance Preparation

***Teacher's Reference Manual,* Grades 1–3** pp. 109, 110

Getting Started

Mathematical Practices
SMP2, SMP3, **SMP5,** SMP6, SMP7, SMP8
Content Standards
3.OA.7, 3.NBT.2

Mental Math and Reflexes

Pose calculator puzzles such as the following:

	Enter	Change to	How?
●○○	8	32	× 4
	20	4	÷ 5
●●○	12	48	× 4
	72	9	÷ 8
●●●	35	140	× 4
	224	28	÷ 8

Math Message

Solve without a calculator. Show your work on paper.

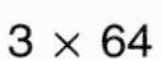

3 × 64

5 × 713

7 × 376

Home Link 9·8 Follow-Up

Have children share their solution strategies. They may include modeling the problems with pictures or counters.

1 Teaching the Lesson

▶ Math Message Follow-Up

WHOLE-CLASS DISCUSSION

Quickly review the answers. 192; 3,565; 2,632 Have children save their work for reference in the following activity.

▶ Exploring the Lattice Method of Multiplication

WHOLE-CLASS ACTIVITY

ELL

COMPUTATION PRACTICE

(*Math Journal 2,* p. 226; *Student Reference Book,* pp. 70–72)

This activity exposes children to an alternate algorithm for multiplication. It also provides an opportunity for cooperative problem solving.

Divide the class into groups of two or three, and call children's attention to the problems in Column A on journal page 226. Point out that these problems are the same ones they solved in the Math Message but that the method used to solve them is one that children might not have seen before. Ask groups to try to figure out how this method works. Once children think they understand how to use it, have them try to solve the problems in Column B using that method.

After everyone has had time to work the problems, bring the class together to share their discoveries. Note that Problem 3 involves renaming. Ask: *Can someone explain what to do if a diagonal sum is a 2-digit number?* Write the ones digit of the sum, and then add the tens digit to the sum in the next diagonal.

Student Page

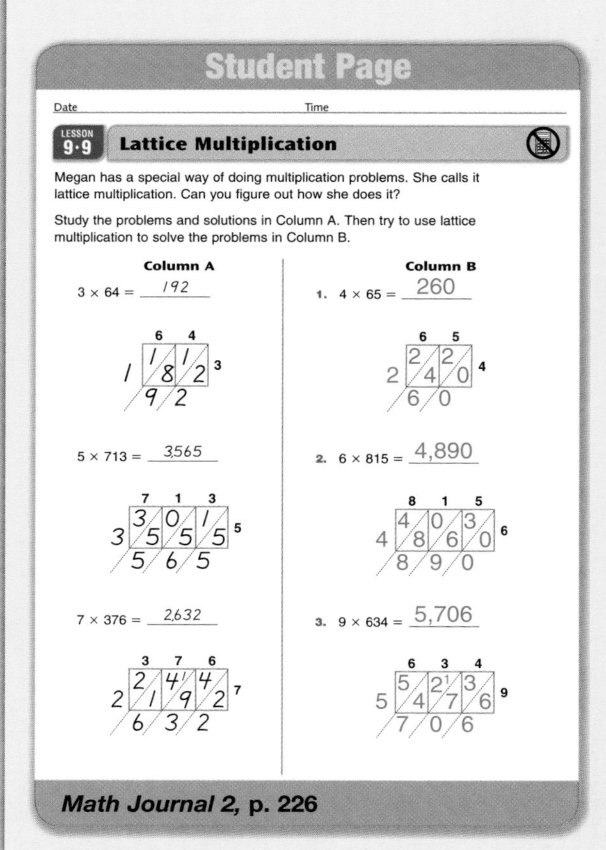

Date Time

LESSON 9·9 **Lattice Multiplication**

Megan has a special way of doing multiplication problems. She calls it lattice multiplication. Can you figure out how she does it?

Study the problems and solutions in Column A. Then try to use lattice multiplication to solve the problems in Column B.

Column A

3 × 64 = 192

5 × 713 = 3565

7 × 376 = 2,632

Column B

1. 4 × 65 = 260

2. 6 × 815 = 4,890

3. 9 × 634 = 5,706

***Math Journal 2,* p. 226**

NOTE Many people view lattice multiplication as a trick. However, if you look carefully, place value is evident within the lattice.

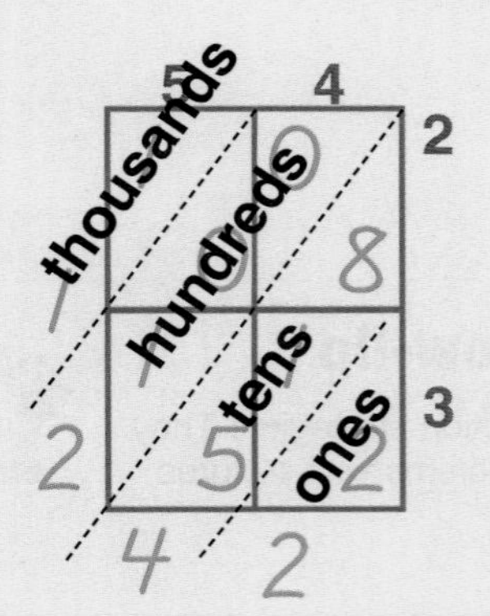

Explain to the class that this method of finding products is called **lattice multiplication.** To support English language learners, discuss the meanings of the word *lattice* and write *lattice multiplication* on the board. A lattice is a structure that has crossed strips that are used as a screen. In math, a lattice is a box with squares and diagonals that is used for multiplication.

To multiply using the lattice method:

1. Write the factors on the outside of the grid, one across the top and one down the right side.
2. Multiply each digit in one factor by each digit in the other factor.
3. Add the numbers inside the lattice within each diagonal. If the sum on a diagonal exceeds 9, the excess 10s are added in the next diagonal.

Ongoing Assessment: Informing Instruction

Watch for children who confuse the numbers in the lattice. Have them use one or more of the following strategies:

- Use an index card to mark their place as they add along each diagonal.

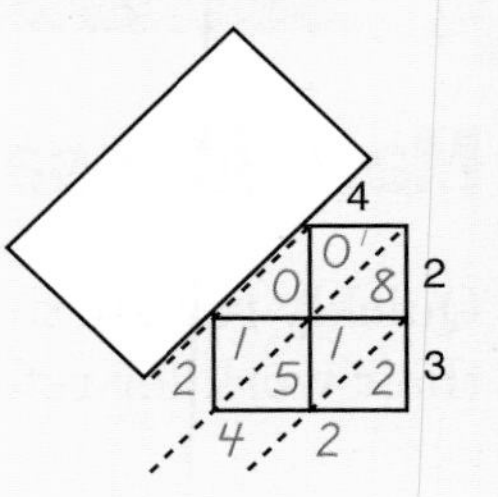

- Cross out the factors of the problem before adding so those numbers are not accidentally added along with the numbers within the grid.

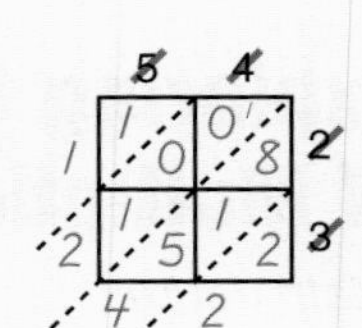

- Try this alternative:

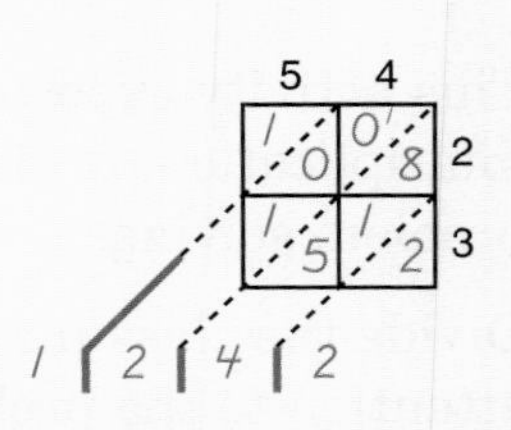

Children should not be required to learn this method, but they should try it. If they like it, they should not be discouraged from using it. Having choices among algorithms is important. Given those choices, most children will choose the ones that work best for them. Have children read more about the lattice multiplication method on pages 70–72 in the *Student Reference Book.*

▶ Practicing Lattice Multiplication

PARTNER ACTIVITY

(*Math Journal 2,* p. 227)

Children work with a partner to complete journal page 227. Circulate and assist as necessary.

Ongoing Assessment: Informing Instruction

Watch for children who make mistakes as they work their way through the lattice method. Check to see whether their mistakes are a result of incorrect fact recall or confusion about the steps.

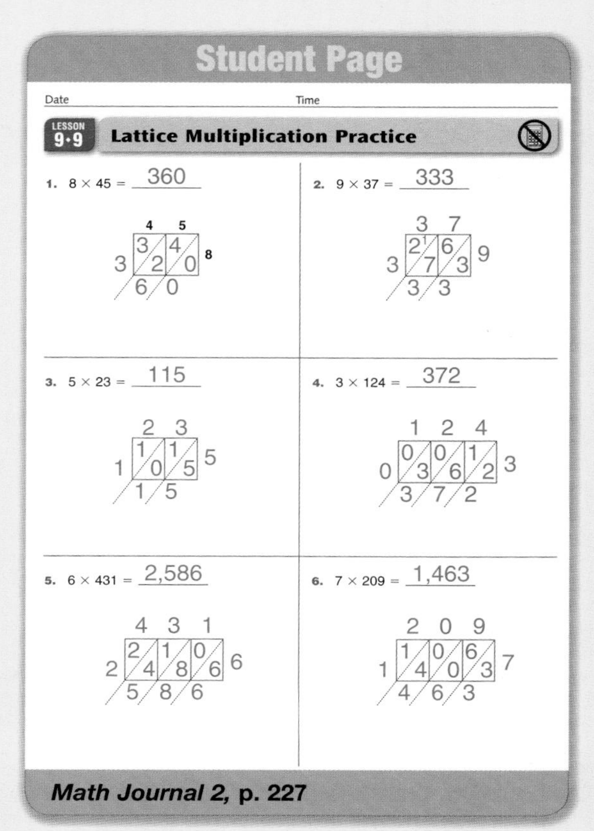

Student Page

Date Time

LESSON 9•9 **Lattice Multiplication Practice**

1. 8 × 45 = 360
2. 9 × 37 = 333
3. 5 × 23 = 115
4. 3 × 124 = 372
5. 6 × 431 = 2,586
6. 7 × 209 = 1,463

Math Journal 2, p. 227

2 Ongoing Learning & Practice

▶ Playing *Factor Bingo*

PARTNER ACTIVITY

(*Math Masters,* p. 448; *Student Reference Book,* pp. 285 and 286)

Children play *Factor Bingo* to practice identifying factors. This game was introduced in Lesson 9-6. If necessary, review the rules for the game on pages 285 and 286 in the *Student Reference Book.*

Student Page

Games

Factor Bingo

Materials □ number cards 2–9 (4 of each)
□ 1 *Factor Bingo* game mat for each player (*Math Masters,* p. 448)
□ 12 counters for each player

Players 2 to 4

Skill Finding factors of a number

Object of the game To get 5 counters in a row, column, or diagonal; or to get 12 counters anywhere on the game mat.

Directions

1. Fill in your own game mat. Choose 25 different numbers from the numbers 2 through 90.
2. Write each number you choose in exactly 1 square on your game mat grid. Be sure to mix the numbers up as you write them on the grid; they should not all be in order. To help you keep track of the numbers you use, circle them in the list below the game mat.
3. Shuffle the number cards and place them number-side down on the table. Any player can turn over the top card. This top card is the "factor."
4. Players check their grids for a number that has the card number as a factor. Players who find such a number cover the number with a counter. A player may place only 1 counter on the grid for each card that is turned over.
5. Turn over the next top card and continue in the same way. You call out "Bingo!" and win the game if you are the first player to get 5 counters in a row, column, or diagonal. You also win if you get 12 counters anywhere on the game mat.
6. If all the cards are used before someone wins, shuffle the cards again and continue playing.

Student Reference Book, p. 285

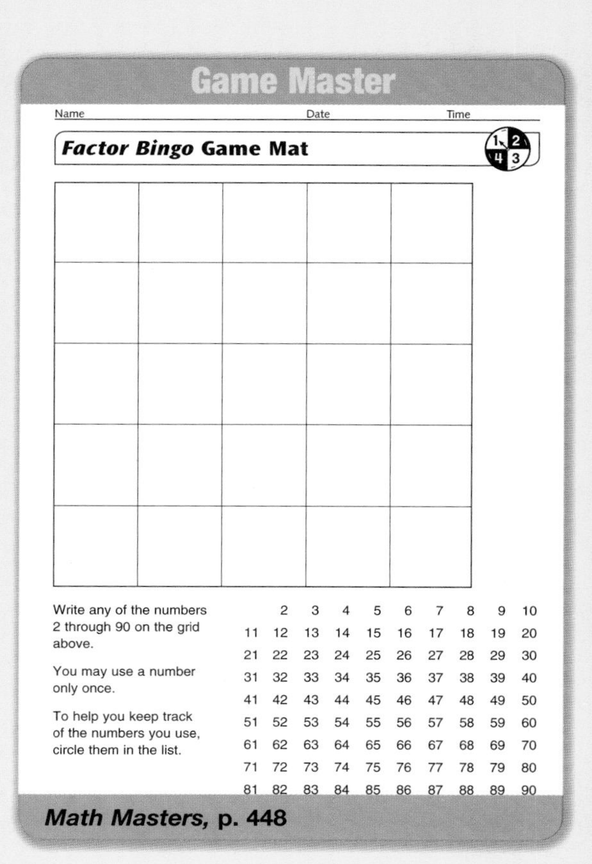

Game Master

Name Date Time

***Factor Bingo* Game Mat**

Write any of the numbers 2 through 90 on the grid above.

You may use a number only once.

To help you keep track of the numbers you use, circle them in the list.

2	3	4	5	6	7	8	9	10
11	12	13	14	15	16	17	18	19	20
21	22	23	24	25	26	27	28	29	30
31	32	33	34	35	36	37	38	39	40
41	42	43	44	45	46	47	48	49	50
51	52	53	54	55	56	57	58	59	60
61	62	63	64	65	66	67	68	69	70
71	72	73	74	75	76	77	78	79	80
81	82	83	84	85	86	87	88	89	90

Math Masters, p. 448

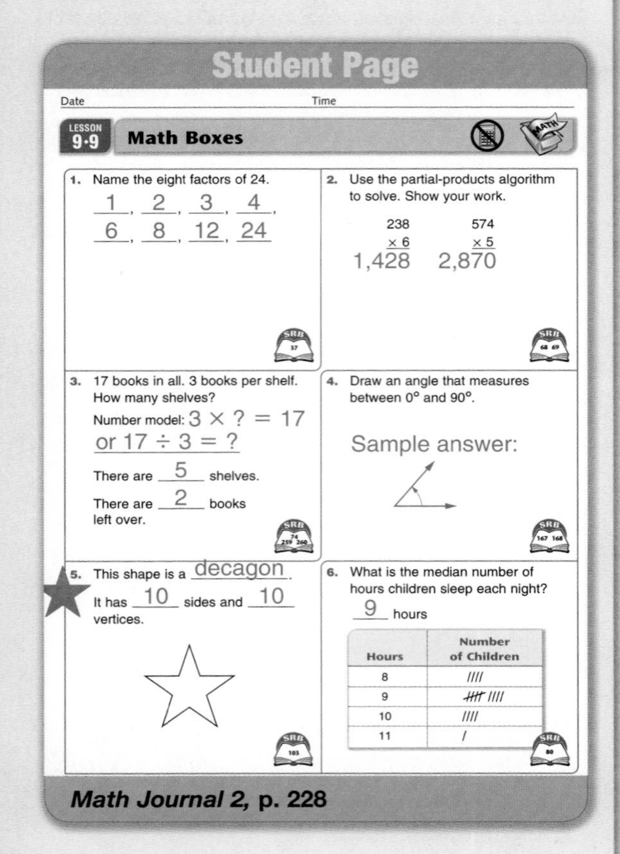

Student Page
Date
Time
LESSON 9·9
Math Boxes
1. Name the eight factors of 24.
1, 2, 3, 4,
6, 8, 12, 24
2. Use the partial-products algorithm to solve. Show your work.
238 × 6
1,428
574 × 5
2,870
3. 17 books in all. 3 books per shelf. How many shelves?
Number model: 3 × ? = 17 or 17 ÷ 3 = ?
There are 5 shelves.
There are 2 books left over.
4. Draw an angle that measures between 0° and 90°.
Sample answer:
5. This shape is a decagon.
It has 10 sides and 10 vertices.
6. What is the median number of hours children sleep each night?
9 hours
Hours
Number of Children
8
9
10
11
Math Journal 2, p. 228

Math Boxes 9·9

(*Math Journal 2,* p. 228)

Mixed Practice Math Boxes in this lesson are linked with Math Boxes in Lessons 9-11 and 9-13. The skill in Problem 6 previews Unit 10 content.

Writing/Reasoning Have children write an answer to the following: *Explain how you found all the factors for 24 in Problem 1.* Sample answer: I drew all the arrays for 24 and wrote a number model for each array. The factors for the number models are all factors for 24.

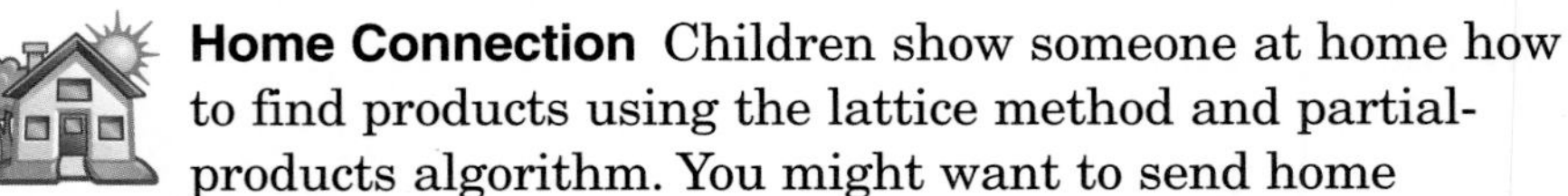

Ongoing Assessment: Recognizing Student Achievement

Math Boxes Problem 5

Use **Math Boxes, Problem 5** to assess children's progress toward identifying and describing plane figures. Children are making adequate progress if they record the number of vertices and sides correctly. Some children may identify the shape correctly.

[Geometry Goal 2]

Home Link 9·9

INDEPENDENT ACTIVITY

(*Math Masters,* p. 293)

Home Connection Children show someone at home how to find products using the lattice method and partial-products algorithm. You might want to send home the *Student Reference Book*, which includes descriptions of these methods.

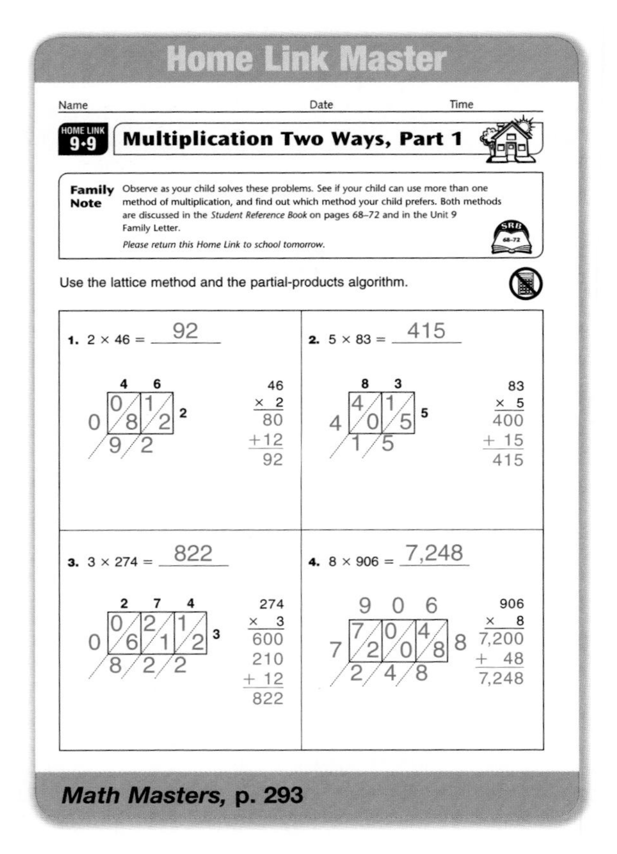

Home Link Master
Name
Date
Time
HOME LINK 9·9
Multiplication Two Ways, Part 1
Family Note
Observe as your child solves these problems. See if your child can use more than one method of multiplication, and find out which method your child prefers. Both methods are discussed in the Student Reference Book on pages 68–72 and in the Unit 9 Family Letter.
Please return this Home Link to school tomorrow.
Use the lattice method and the partial-products algorithm.
1. 2 × 46 = 92
46 × 2 = 80 + 12 = 92
2. 5 × 83 = 415
83 × 5 = 400 + 15 = 415
3. 3 × 274 = 822
274 × 3 = 600 + 210 + 12 = 822
4. 8 × 906 = 7,248
906 × 8 = 7,200 + 48 = 7,248
Math Masters, p. 293

3 Differentiation Options

ENRICHMENT

INDEPENDENT ACTIVITY

15–30 Min

▶ Multiplying and Dividing Multiples of 10 in Music

(*Math Masters,* p. 294)

Portfolio Ideas

To apply children's understanding of multiplication, have them solve problems related to the musical composition *Vexations* on *Math Masters,* page 294. When they have finished the page have children share their strategies for solving the problem. Encourage them to discuss the computation as well as the conversions between the units.

EXTRA PRACTICE

15–30 Min

▶ Practicing Partial Products

(*Math Journal 2,* p. 227)

To offer children more experience with the partial-products algorithm, have children solve the problems on journal page 227 using the partial-products algorithm. They record their work on a sheet of paper and check their answers with a partner.

Planning Ahead

For Exploration F in Lesson 9-10, you will need to gather small objects in varying weights (paper clips, rubber bands, straws, pencils, crayons, erasers, calculators, and so on).

Teaching Master

Name Date Time

LESSON 9•9 **Mathematics in Music**

The French composer Erik Satie lived from 1866 to 1925. He wrote a piece of music called *Vexations,* in which the same tune is played 840 times in a row without stopping. It takes about 30 seconds to play this tune once.

1. About how many minutes would it take to play all of *Vexations* without stopping? about 420 minutes
2. How many hours is that? 7 hours
3. Suppose someone played the whole piece 4 times without stopping. Could this be done in 1 day? No
4. How many times a day could the whole piece be played without stopping? 3 times
5. Look up the meaning of *vexation* in a dictionary. Explain why you think Satie gave the piece of music that name.
Sample answer: It is probably an extremely annoying piece to listen to.

Math Masters, p. 294

9•10 Exploring Arrays, Equilateral Triangles, and Strength of Paper

Explorations

Objective To provide opportunities for children to explore 2-digit multiplication, number patterns, and the rigidity of triangles.

Technology Resources www.everydaymathonline.com

ePresentations

eToolkit

Algorithms Practice

EM Facts Workshop Game™

Family Letters

Assessment Management

Common Core State Standards

Curriculum Focal Points

Interactive Teacher's Lesson Guide

1 Teaching the Lesson

Key Concepts and Skills

- Use arrays to model multiplication. [Number and Numeration Goal 6]
- Collect and organize data in a table. [Data and Chance Goal 1]
- Model and compare polygons. [Geometry Goal 2]
- Describe number patterns. [Patterns, Functions, and Algebra Goal 1]

Key Activities

Exploration D: Children make arrays with base-10 blocks to model partial products in problems involving 2-digit multiples of 10 and other 2-digit numbers.

Exploration E: Children figure out and record the number of equilateral triangles inside larger equilateral triangles and look for patterns.

Exploration F: Children test the effect of folding on the strength of paper.

Key Vocabulary

equilateral triangle

Materials

Home Link 9•9

slate ◆ base-10 blocks ◆ half-sheet of paper

Exploration D: Per group:
Math Journal 2, pp. 229 and 230
Math Masters, pp. 273, 274, 295, and 296
green, red, and blue crayons ◆ 4 flats, 25 longs, 28 cubes

Exploration E: Per partnership:
Math Masters, pp. 297–299
Pattern-Block Template ◆ triangle pattern blocks ◆ paper

Exploration F: Per group:
Math Masters, p. 300
$8\frac{1}{2}$" by 11" sheet of paper ◆ scissors ◆ centimeter ruler ◆ 2 books of equal thickness ◆ paper ◆ small objects varying in weight ◆ spring or kitchen scale

2 Ongoing Learning & Practice

Sharing Money
Math Journal 2, p. 231
per partnership: at least 2 each of number cards 0–9 (from the Everything Math Deck, if available), six-sided die, play money and tool-kit coins (optional)

Math Boxes 9•10
Math Journal 2, p. 232

Ongoing Assessment: Recognizing Student Achievement
Use Math Boxes, Problem 5.
[Measurement and Reference Frames Goal 1]

Home Link 9•10
Math Masters, p. 301

3 Differentiation Options

ENRICHMENT
Finding Patterns with Triangular Numbers
Math Masters, p. 302

EXTRA PRACTICE
Frames-and-Arrows Problems
Math Masters, p. 27 or 80

Getting Started

Mathematical Practices
SMP1, SMP2, SMP4, SMP5, SMP6, **SMP7**
Content Standards
3.MD.2, 3.MD.5b, 3.MD.7a, 3.MD.7b, 3.MD.7c, 3.MD.7d

Mental Math and Reflexes

Pose problems like the following. Children answer on slates.

●○○ 4 [8s] 32
40 [8s] 320
400 [8s] 3,200

●●○ 9 [70s] 630
90 [70s] 6,300
900 [70s] 63,000

●●● 80 [50s] 4,000
800 [50s] 40,000
8,000 [50s] 400,000

Continue as time allows.

Math Message

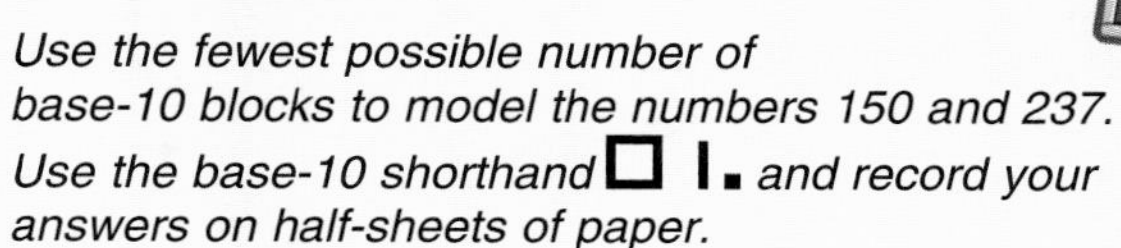

Use the fewest possible number of base-10 blocks to model the numbers 150 and 237. Use the base-10 shorthand □ | ▪ and record your answers on half-sheets of paper.

Home Link 9·9 Follow-Up

Briefly review answers. Have partners discuss which multiplication algorithm they prefer.

1 Teaching the Lesson

▶ Math Message Follow-Up

WHOLE-CLASS DISCUSSION

With the fewest blocks possible, 150 is displayed with 1 flat and 5 longs. 237 is displayed with 2 flats, 3 longs, and 7 cubes.

Pose follow-up questions as needed. For example:

Ask: *How could I show 270 with the fewest number of blocks possible?* 2 flats, 7 longs

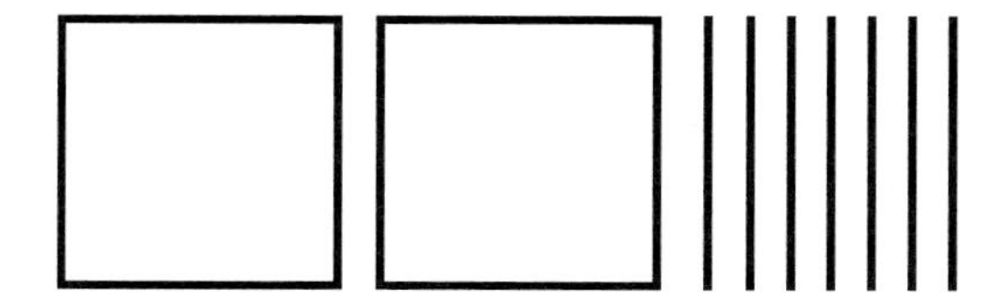

389? 3 flats, 8 longs, 9 cubes

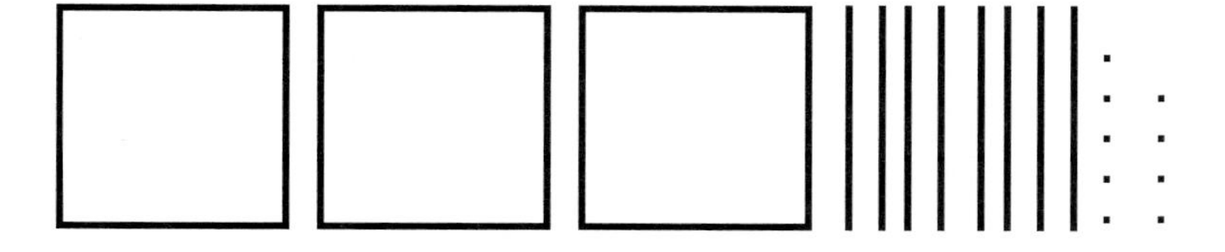

306? 3 flats, 6 cubes

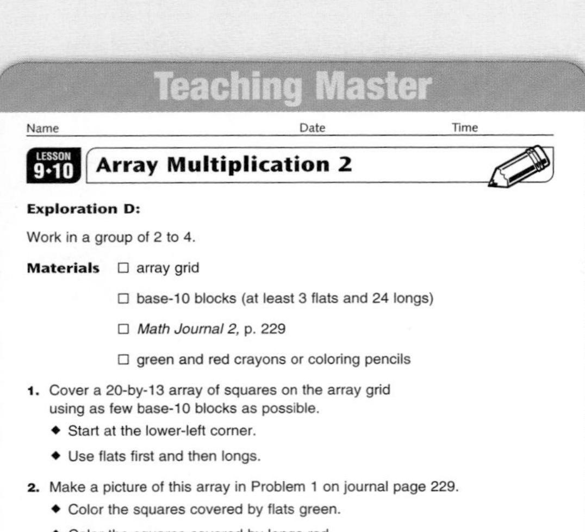
Teaching Master

Name Date Time

LESSON 9·10 **Array Multiplication 2**

Exploration D:

Work in a group of 2 to 4.

Materials
- ☐ array grid
- ☐ base-10 blocks (at least 3 flats and 24 longs)
- ☐ *Math Journal 2,* p. 229
- ☐ green and red crayons or coloring pencils

1. Cover a 20-by-13 array of squares on the array grid using as few base-10 blocks as possible.
   - Start at the lower-left corner.
   - Use flats first and then longs.
2. Make a picture of this array in Problem 1 on journal page 229.
   - Color the squares covered by flats green.
   - Color the squares covered by longs red.
3. Record the result next to the picture.
4. Cover an 18-by-30 array of squares on the array grid using as few base-10 blocks as possible.
   - Start at the lower-left corner.
   - Use flats first and then longs.
5. Make a picture of this array in Problem 2 on journal page 229.
   - Color the squares covered by flats green.
   - Color the squares covered by longs red.
6. Record the result next to the picture.

Math Masters, **p. 295**

▶ Exploration D: Modeling Multiplication with Arrays and Base-10 Blocks

SMALL-GROUP ACTIVITY

(*Math Journal 2,* pp. 229 and 230; *Math Masters,* pp. 273, 274, 295 and 296)

This Exploration is an extension of Exploration A in Lesson 9-3. Instructions are given on *Math Masters,* pages 295 and 296; work is recorded on journal pages 229 and 230. All children should do this Exploration, as these activities are followed up in Lessons 9-11 and 9-12. Plan to work with the children as they rotate through this Exploration.

In Array Multiplication 2, children use flats and longs to model partial products in multiplication of 2-digit numbers by 2-digit multiples of 10. In Array Multiplication 3, children use flats, longs, and cubes to model partial products in multiplication of 2-digit numbers. They cover squares on the array grid (*Math Masters,* pages 273 and 274) with as few blocks as possible. On journal pages 229 and 230, children use a green crayon to represent the squares covered by flats, red to represent the squares covered by longs, and blue to represent the squares covered by cubes.

Adjusting the Activity

Have children record their results by first outlining areas with the correct colors and then filling them in.

AUDITORY • KINESTHETIC • TACTILE • VISUAL

Student Page

Date Time

LESSON 9·10 **Array Multiplication 2**

1. How many squares are in a 20-by-13 array? Total squares = 260
   20 × 13 = 260

2. How many squares are in an 18-by-30 array? Total squares = 540
   18 × 30 = 540

Math Journal 2, **p. 229**

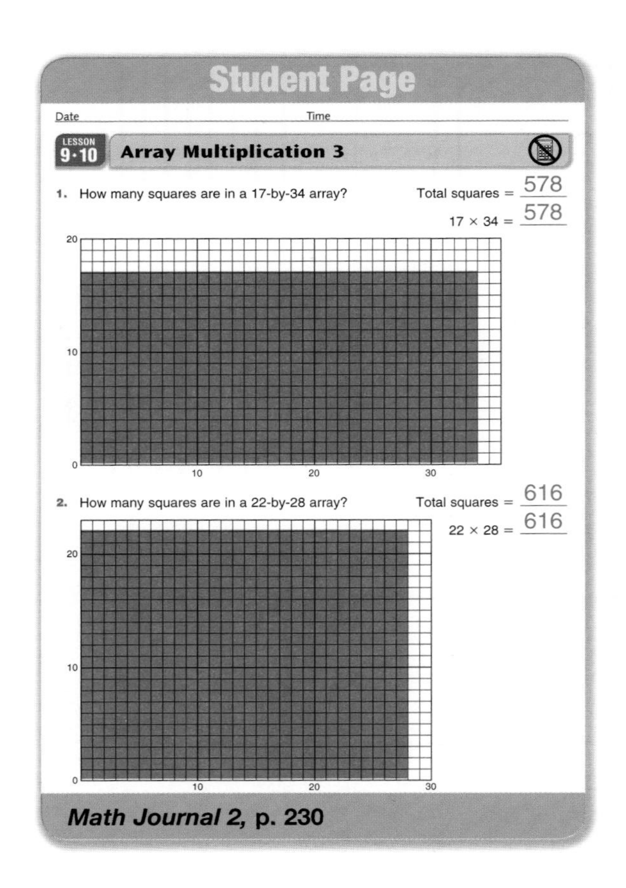
Student Page

Date Time

LESSON 9·10 **Array Multiplication 3**

1. How many squares are in a 17-by-34 array? Total squares = 578
   17 × 34 = 578

2. How many squares are in a 22-by-28 array? Total squares = 616
   22 × 28 = 616

Math Journal 2, **p. 230**

Exploration E: Finding Number Patterns by Building Equilateral Triangles

PARTNER ACTIVITY

(*Math Masters,* pp. 297–299)

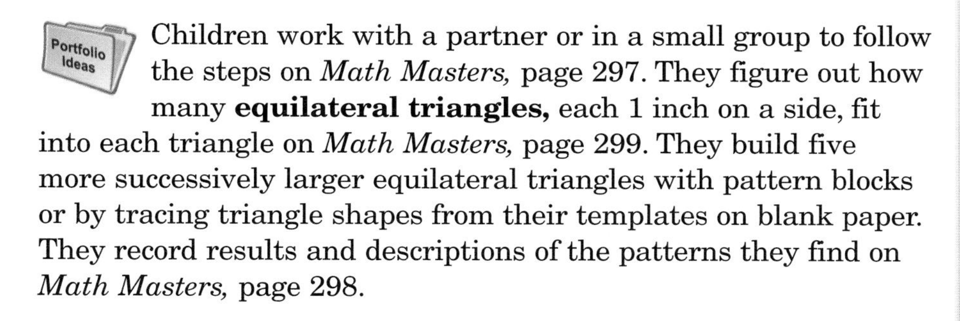

Portfolio Ideas

Children work with a partner or in a small group to follow the steps on *Math Masters,* page 297. They figure out how many **equilateral triangles,** each 1 inch on a side, fit into each triangle on *Math Masters,* page 299. They build five more successively larger equilateral triangles with pattern blocks or by tracing triangle shapes from their templates on blank paper. They record results and descriptions of the patterns they find on *Math Masters,* page 298.

Exploration F: Building Bridges and Testing Their Strength

SMALL-GROUP ACTIVITY

(*Math Masters,* p. 300)

Science Link Children work in small groups to build bridges out of equal-size rectangles. They place small objects on the bridges to test how much weight they can hold before collapsing. Then they use a spring or kitchen scale to weigh in grams the objects that each bridge holds and record their findings. (See a sample record sheet on *Math Masters,* page 300.) Children do not fold the first rectangle before testing its strength. They test a second rectangle for strength after folding it fanlike 8 or 9 times. They test a third rectangle's strength after folding it fanlike 12 to 14 times.

When most children are finished, bring the class together to compare results. Ask: *Do the sizes of the folds affect how much the bridge holds?* Sample answer: Yes. The smaller the folds, the stronger the bridge. *What shapes do you see in the fan-folded rectangles?* Sample answer: Triangle shapes Discuss that the strength of the folded bridges has to do with the rigidity of triangles.

Ask children to recall their experiments with straw polygons. They were able to change the shape of other polygons by pushing or pulling at one of the corners, but they could not change the shapes of triangles. This rigidity gives the fan-folded bridges their strength.

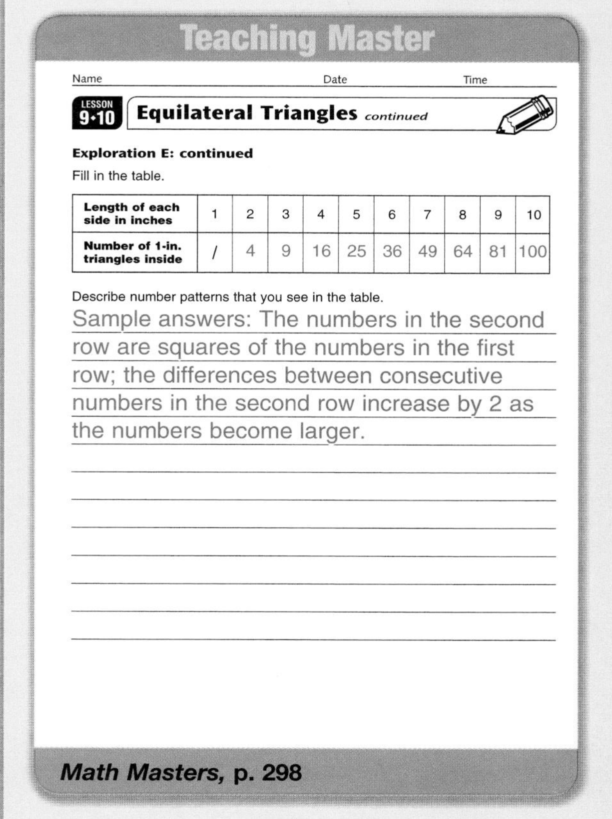

Teaching Master

Name Date Time

LESSON 9·10 **Equilateral Triangles** *continued*

Exploration E: continued

Fill in the table.

Length of each side in inches	1	2	3	4	5	6	7	8	9	10
Number of 1-in. triangles inside	1	4	9	16	25	36	49	64	81	100

Describe number patterns that you see in the table.

Sample answers: The numbers in the second row are squares of the numbers in the first row; the differences between consecutive numbers in the second row increase by 2 as the numbers become larger.

Math Masters, p. 298

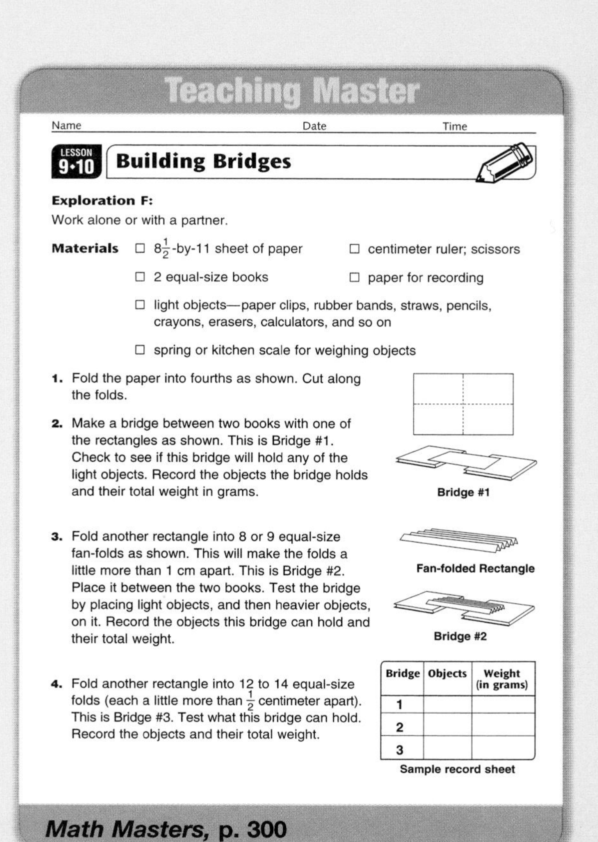

Teaching Master

Name Date Time

LESSON 9·10 **Building Bridges**

Exploration F:

Work alone or with a partner.

Materials
- ☐ $8\frac{1}{2}$-by-11 sheet of paper
- ☐ centimeter ruler; scissors
- ☐ 2 equal-size books
- ☐ paper for recording
- ☐ light objects—paper clips, rubber bands, straws, pencils, crayons, erasers, calculators, and so on
- ☐ spring or kitchen scale for weighing objects

1. Fold the paper into fourths as shown. Cut along the folds.
2. Make a bridge between two books with one of the rectangles as shown. This is Bridge #1. Check to see if this bridge will hold any of the light objects. Record the objects the bridge holds and their total weight in grams.
3. Fold another rectangle into 8 or 9 equal-size fan-folds as shown. This will make the folds a little more than 1 cm apart. This is Bridge #2. Place it between the two books. Test the bridge by placing light objects, and then heavier objects, on it. Record the objects this bridge can hold and their total weight.
4. Fold another rectangle into 12 to 14 equal-size folds (each a little more than $\frac{1}{2}$ centimeter apart). This is Bridge #3. Test what this bridge can hold. Record the objects and their total weight.

Bridge	Objects	Weight (in grams)
1		
2		
3		

Sample record sheet

Math Masters, p. 300

Student Page

Date ______ Time ______

LESSON 9·10 **Sharing Money**

Work with a partner.

Materials ☐ number cards 0–9 (at least 2 of each)
☐ 1 die
☐ $10 bills, $1 bills, and tool-kit coins (optional)

Draw 2 number cards. Form a 2-digit number to show how much money will be shared. Roll 1 die to show how many friends will share the money. Fill in the blanks below. Answers vary.

1. $______ is shared equally by ______ friends.
   a. Number model: ______
   b. How many $10 bills does each friend get? ______
   c. How many $1 bills does each friend get? ______
   d. How many $1 bills are left over? ______
   e. If the leftover money is shared equally, how many cents does each friend get? ______
   f. Each friend gets a total of $______.

Repeat. Draw the next 2 cards. Roll the die. Fill in the blanks below.

2. $______ is shared equally by ______ friends.
   a. Number model: ______
   b. How many $10 bills does each friend get? ______
   c. How many $1 bills does each friend get? ______
   d. How many $1 bills are left over? ______
   e. If the leftover money is shared equally, how many cents does each friend get? ______
   f. Each friend gets a total of $______.

Math Journal 2, p. 231

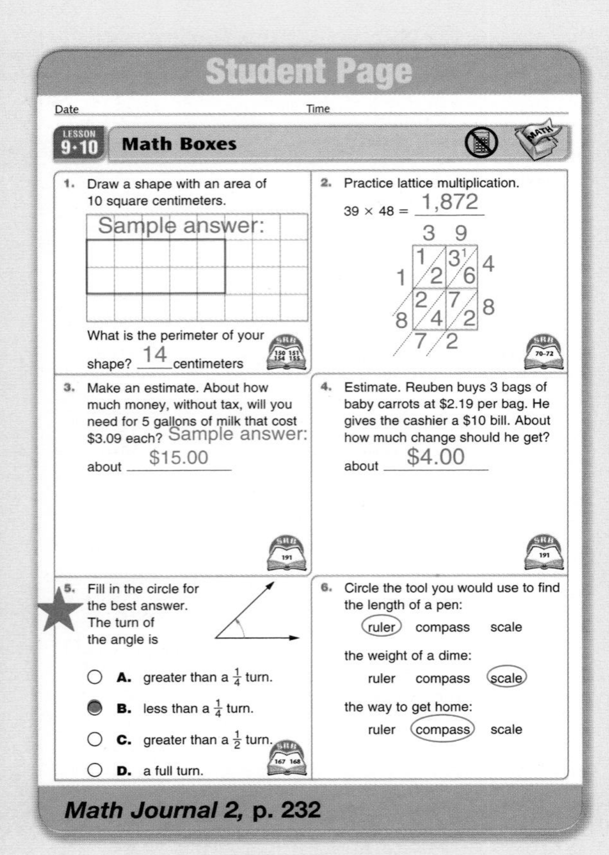
Student Page

Date ______ Time ______

LESSON 9·10 **Math Boxes**

1. Draw a shape with an area of 10 square centimeters. Sample answer:
   What is the perimeter of your shape? 14 centimeters
2. Practice lattice multiplication.
   39 × 48 = 1,872
3. Make an estimate. About how much money, without tax, will you need for 5 gallons of milk that cost $3.09 each? Sample answer:
   about $15.00
4. Estimate. Reuben buys 3 bags of baby carrots at $2.19 per bag. He gives the cashier a $10 bill. About how much change should he get?
   about $4.00
5. Fill in the circle for the best answer. The turn of the angle is
   A. greater than a $\frac{1}{4}$ turn.
   B. less than a $\frac{1}{4}$ turn. (filled)
   C. greater than a $\frac{1}{2}$ turn.
   D. a full turn.
6. Circle the tool you would use to find the length of a pen:
   (ruler) compass scale
   the weight of a dime:
   ruler compass (scale)
   the way to get home:
   ruler (compass) scale

Math Journal 2, p. 232

2 Ongoing Learning & Practice

▶ Sharing Money

(*Math Journal 2,* p. 231)

Portfolio Ideas

Children shuffle the 0–9 number cards, take the two top cards, and form a 2-digit number. This number represents the amount of money to be shared. Next, children roll a die. This determines the number of people who will share the money. Children record the problems, number models, and their answers on journal page 231.

▶ Math Boxes 9·10

INDEPENDENT ACTIVITY

(*Math Journal 2,* p. 232)

Mixed Practice Math Boxes in this lesson are paired with Math Boxes in Lesson 9-12. The skill in Problem 6 previews Unit 10 content.

Ongoing Assessment: Recognizing Student Achievement

Math Boxes Problem 5

Use **Math Boxes, Problem 5** to assess children's ability to describe angle rotations. Children are making adequate progress if they are able to complete Problem 5 successfully. Some children may be able to draw the other three angles as described.

[Measurement and Reference Frames Goal 1]

▶ Home Link 9·10

(*Math Masters,* p. 301)

Home Connection Children show someone at home how to find products using the lattice method and the partial-products algorithm.

3 Differentiation Options

ENRICHMENT

PARTNER ACTIVITY

15–30 Min

▶ Finding Patterns with Triangular Numbers

(*Math Masters,* p. 302)

To further explore number patterns, have children identify patterns in triangular numbers. They record their work on *Math Masters,* page 302.

EXTRA PRACTICE

INDEPENDENT ACTIVITY

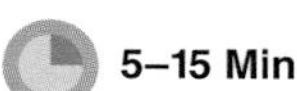

5–15 Min

▶ Frames-and-Arrows Problems

(*Math Masters,* p. 27 or 80)

Algebraic Thinking To offer children more practice with number patterns, have them make up and solve one- or two-rule Frames-and-Arrows problems. They record their work on *Math Masters,* page 27 or 80. Encourage children to trade problems with a partner and then solve.

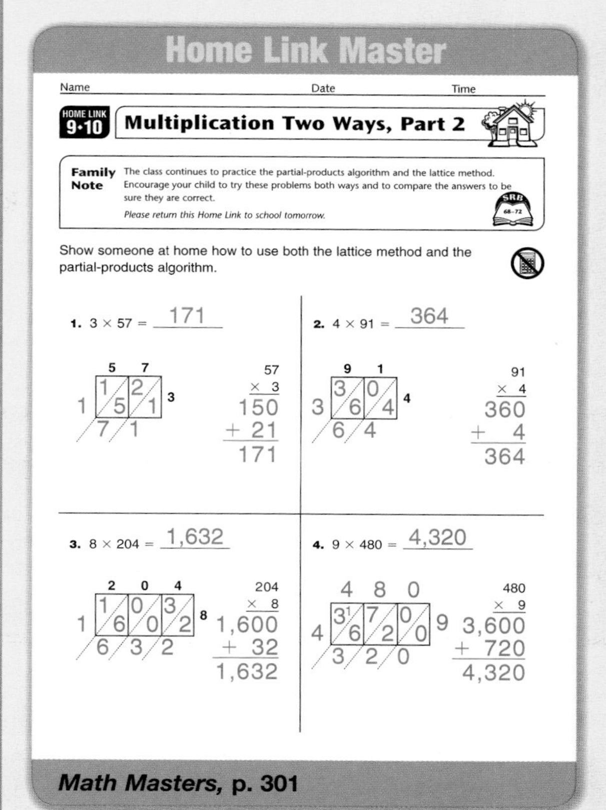

Home Link Master

Name Date Time

HOME LINK 9·10 **Multiplication Two Ways, Part 2**

Family Note The class continues to practice the partial-products algorithm and the lattice method. Encourage your child to try these problems both ways and to compare the answers to be sure they are correct.

Please return this Home Link to school tomorrow.

SRB 68–72

Show someone at home how to use both the lattice method and the partial-products algorithm.

1. $3 \times 57 =$ 171
   57 × 3: 150 + 21 = 171

2. $4 \times 91 =$ 364
   91 × 4: 360 + 4 = 364

3. $8 \times 204 =$ 1,632
   204 × 8: 1,600 + 32 = 1,632

4. $9 \times 480 =$ 4,320
   480 × 9: 3,600 + 720 = 4,320

Math Masters, p. 301

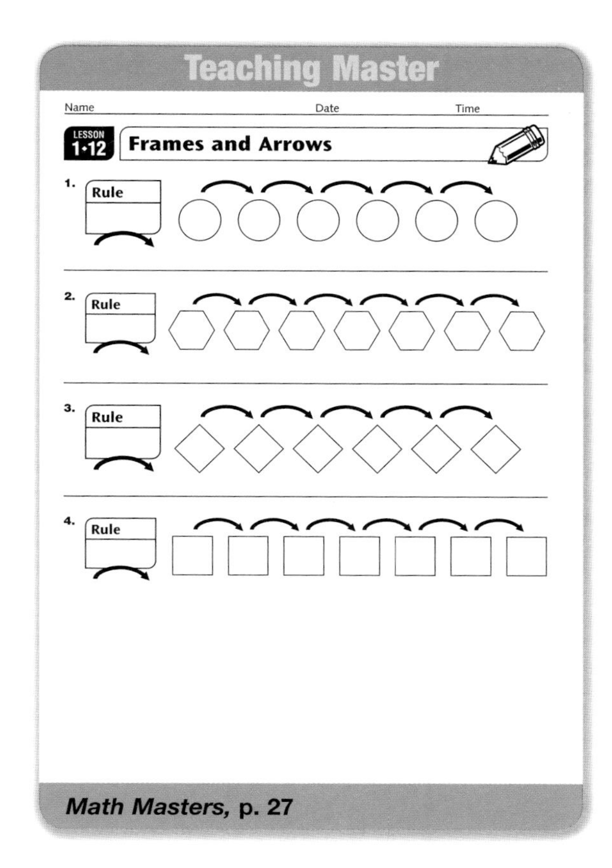

Teaching Master

Name Date Time

LESSON 1·12 **Frames and Arrows**

1. Rule
2. Rule
3. Rule
4. Rule

Math Masters, p. 27

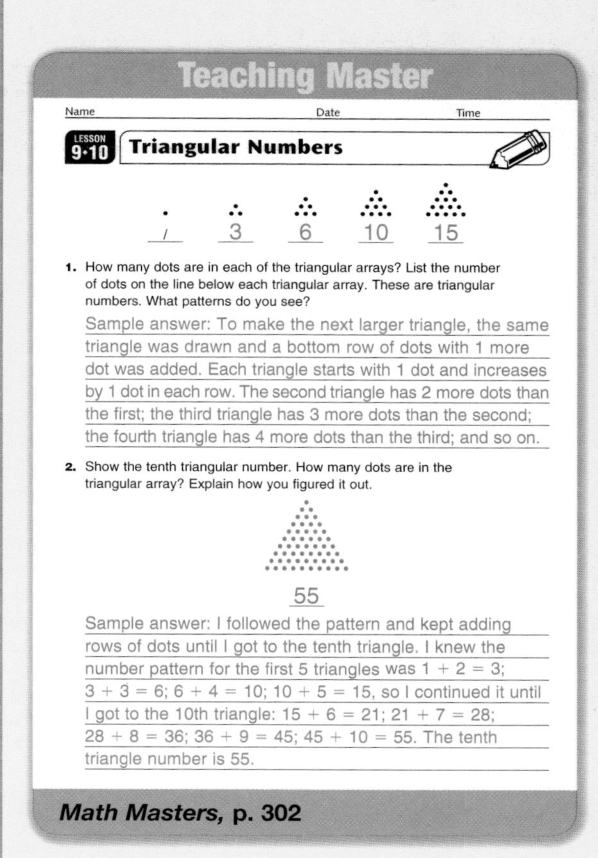

Teaching Master

Name Date Time

LESSON 9·10 **Triangular Numbers**

1 3 6 10 15

1. How many dots are in each of the triangular arrays? List the number of dots on the line below each triangular array. These are triangular numbers. What patterns do you see?

   Sample answer: To make the next larger triangle, the same triangle was drawn and a bottom row of dots with 1 more dot was added. Each triangle starts with 1 dot and increases by 1 dot in each row. The second triangle has 2 more dots than the first; the third triangle has 3 more dots than the second; the fourth triangle has 4 more dots than the third; and so on.

2. Show the tenth triangular number. How many dots are in the triangular array? Explain how you figured it out.

   55

   Sample answer: I followed the pattern and kept adding rows of dots until I got to the tenth triangle. I knew the number pattern for the first 5 triangles was 1 + 2 = 3; 3 + 3 = 6; 6 + 4 = 10; 10 + 5 = 15, so I continued it until I got to the 10th triangle: 15 + 6 = 21; 21 + 7 = 28; 28 + 8 = 36; 36 + 9 = 45; 45 + 10 = 55. The tenth triangle number is 55.

Math Masters, p. 302

9•11 Products of 2-Digit Numbers, Part 1

Objective To guide children as they extend the partial-products method to products of 2-digit numbers and 2-digit multiples of 10.

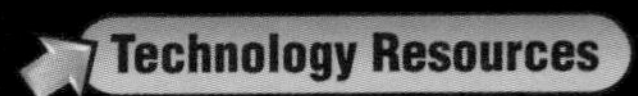

www.everydaymathonline.com

ePresentations

eToolkit

Algorithms Practice

EM Facts Workshop Game™

Family Letters

Assessment Management

Common Core State Standards

Curriculum Focal Points

Interactive Teacher's Lesson Guide

1 Teaching the Lesson

Key Concepts and Skills

- Apply place-value concepts to find partial products.
  [Number and Numeration Goal 1]
- Use addition to add partial products.
  [Operations and Computation Goal 2]
- Use multiplication facts to calculate partial products.
  [Operations and Computation Goal 3]
- Use base-10 blocks and array models to find products of 2-digit by 2-digit multiples of 10.
  [Operations and Computation Goal 6]

Key Activities

Children use Exploration D from the preceding lesson as a beginning point to extend the partial-products algorithm to products of 2-digit numbers and 2-digit multiples of 10.

Ongoing Assessment: Informing Instruction See page 774.

Materials

Math Journal 2, pp. 229 and 233
Home Link 9•10
Math Masters, p. 303
transparency of *Math Masters,* p. 303 (optional) ◆ slate ◆ red and green overhead markers (optional) ◆ base-10 blocks (optional)

Playing *Angle Race*
Math Masters, pp. 398, 430 (optional), and 441
Student Reference Book, pp. 271 and 272
per partnership: 24-pin circular geoboard and 15 rubber bands or *Math Masters,* p. 430, straightedge, and pencil
Children practice recognizing angle measures.

Ongoing Assessment: Recognizing Student Achievement
Use an Exit Slip (*Math Masters,* page 398).
[Measurement and Reference Frames Goal 1]

Math Boxes 9•11
Math Journal 2, p. 234
Children practice and maintain skills through Math Box problems.

Home Link 9•11
Math Masters, p. 304
Children practice and maintain skills through Home Link activities.

3 Differentiation Options

READINESS

Extending Basic Facts
Math Masters, p. 449
Student Reference Book, pp. 293 and 294
per partnership: 7 index cards cut in half ◆ scissors ◆ 8 pennies per child
Children play an extended facts version of *Multiplication Bingo.*

ENRICHMENT

Finding an Error in Lattice Multiplication
Math Masters, p. 305
Children identify an error in lattice multiplication.

Advance Preparation

For *Angle Race* in Part 2, children may use a 24-pin circular geoboard and rubberbands. For the optional Enrichment activity in Part 3, make one copy of *Math Masters,* page 305 for every two children.

***Teacher's Reference Manual,* Grades 1–3** pp. 108, 109

Getting Started

Mathematical Practices
SMP1, SMP2, **SMP3,** SMP4, SMP5, SMP6, SMP7, **SMP8**
Content Standards
3.OA.3, **3.OA.5, 3.NBT.2, 3.NBT.3, 3.MD.5b, 3.MD.7a, 3.MD.7b, 3.MD.7c, 3.MD.7d**

Mental Math and Reflexes

Have children record factors of numbers on slates.

Suggestions:

●○○ 6 1, 2, 3, 6
7 1, 7

●●○ 8 1, 2, 4, 8
14 1, 2, 7, 14

●●● 20 1, 2, 4, 5, 10, 20
28 1, 2, 4, 7, 14, 28

Math Message

Write the problems on your slate and solve them.

7 × 23 = ____ 161

70 × 23 = ____ 1,610

4 × 362 = ____ 1,448

40 × 362 = ____ 14,480

Home Link 9·10 Follow-Up

Briefly review answers. Before collecting the Home Links, have children circle the multiplication method in each box that they like the best.

1 Teaching the Lesson

▶ Math Message Follow-Up

Children share solution strategies. Some may have solved the first problem in each pair using the lattice method of multiplication, while others may have used the partial-products algorithm. The partial-products algorithm is shown below.

$$\begin{array}{rcr} & & 23 \\ & & \underline{\times \quad 7} \\ 7\ [20s] & \rightarrow & 140 \\ 7\ [3s] & \rightarrow & \underline{+\ 21} \\ 140 + 21 & \rightarrow & 161 \end{array}$$

$$\begin{array}{rcr} & & 362 \\ & & \underline{\times \quad 4} \\ 4\ [300s] & \rightarrow & 1{,}200 \\ 4\ [60s] & \rightarrow & 240 \\ 4\ [2s] & \rightarrow & \underline{+ \quad 8} \\ 1{,}200 + 240 + 8 & \rightarrow & 1{,}448 \end{array}$$

For the problem 70 × 23, some children may reason that because 7 × 23 = 161 and 70 is 10 times 7, the product of 70 and 23 must be 10 times 161, or 1,610. Similar reasoning can be applied to 4 × 362 1,448 and 40 × 362. 14,480

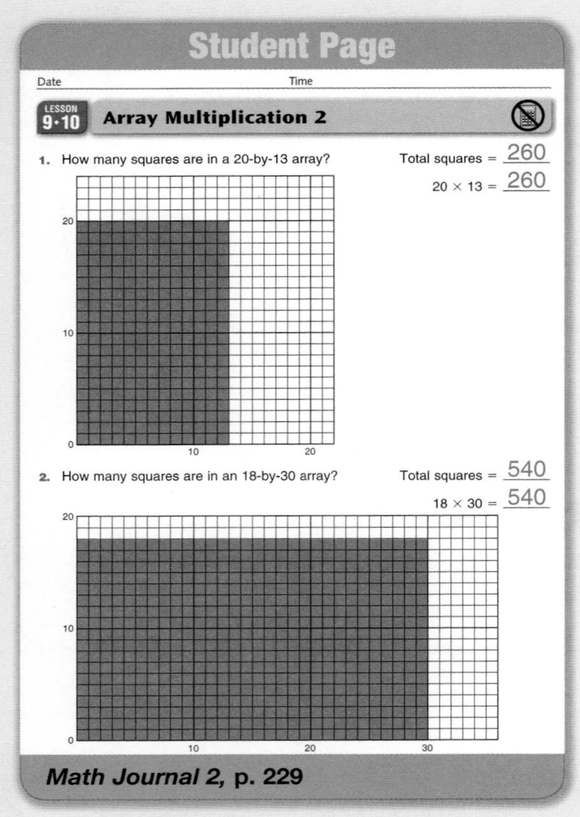
Student Page

Date Time

LESSON 9·10 **Array Multiplication 2**

1. How many squares are in a 20-by-13 array? Total squares = 260

20 × 13 = 260

2. How many squares are in an 18-by-30 array? Total squares = 540

18 × 30 = 540

Math Journal 2, p. 229

Math Masters, page 303 is a duplicate of *Math Journal 2,* page 229.

Ongoing Assessment: Informing Instruction

Watch for children who need further support with partial products of 1-digit and multidigit numbers. Consider having them write out the multidigit number in expanded notation before multiplying. For example, in 7 × 23, 23 can be written as 2 tens 3 ones, or 20 + 3. The multiplication then becomes 7 × 20 and 7 × 3.

▶ Extending the Partial-Products Algorithm

COMPUTATION PRACTICE

(*Math Journal 2,* p. 229; *Math Masters,* p. 303)

Use a transparency or copy of *Math Masters,* page 303 to model the partial-products algorithm. Ask children to turn to the first array on journal page 229. On the board, show how to find the total number of squares in the array using the partial-products algorithm.

		13
		× 20
20 [10s]	→	200
20 [3s]	→	+ 60
200 + 60	→	260

Children refer to the array diagram in their journals and match each part of the diagram with a partial product as you do the same at the board.

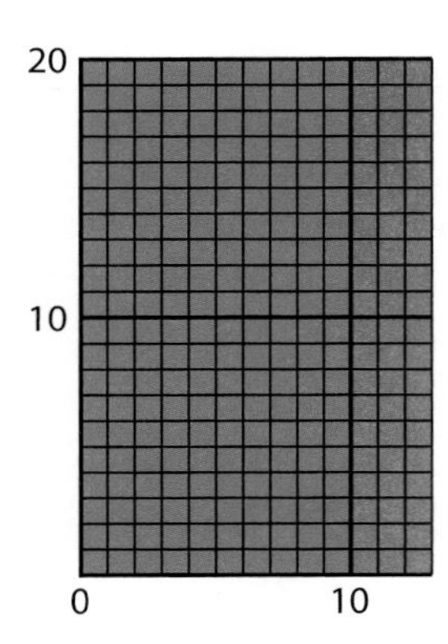

- There are 10 green squares in each of 20 rows, so there are 200 green squares (20 [10s]) in all.
- There are 3 red squares in each of 20 rows, so there are 60 red squares (20 [3s]) in all.
- There are 260 green and red squares (200 + 60) in the array.

With the children's help, use the algorithm to solve the second problem on the journal page.

		30
		× 18
10 [30s]	→	300
8 [30s]	→	+ 240
300 + 240	→	540

Again, children match each part of the diagram on journal page 229 with the worked-out problem as you do the same at the overhead. Remind children to use the actual multiples when describing the steps in multiplication. For example, they should say *8 [30s]* or *8 times 30,* not *8 times 3.*

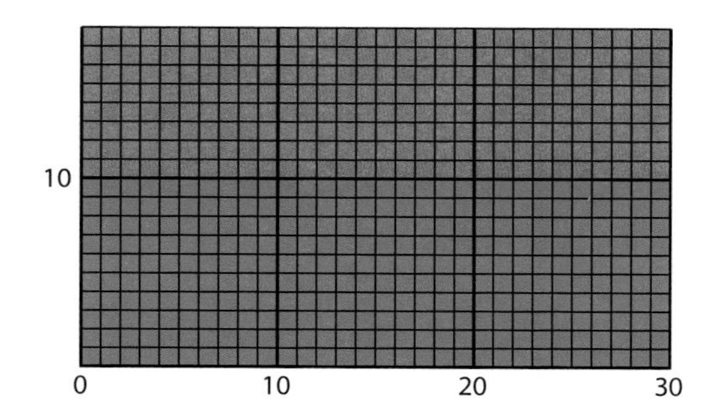

Give children additional problems of this type, as needed, such as: 40 × 17 680, 16 × 50 800, and 30 × 21 630.

Links to the Future

The activities in this lesson extend the partial-products algorithm to products of 2-digit numbers and 2-digit multiples of 10. Solving problems involving the multiplication of multidigit whole numbers by a 2-digit number is a Grade 4 Goal.

▶ Using the Partial-Products Algorithm

(*Math Journal 2,* p. 233)

Circulate and assist as children complete journal page 233.

Adjusting the Activity

Have children write out the number models for each partial product—for example, 20 [30s] → 600. Have them use base-10 blocks to model the problems.

AUDITORY ◆ KINESTHETIC ◆ TACTILE ◆ VISUAL

Student Page

Date Time

LESSON 9·11 **Multiplication with Multiples of 10**

Multiply. Compare your answers with a partner. If you disagree, discuss your strategies with each other. Then try the problem again.

Example: 30 × 26 20 [30s] → 600 6 [30s] → + 180 780	**1.** 70 × 18 700 + 560 1,260
2. 88 × 40 3,200 + 320 3,520	**3.** 60 × 35 1,800 + 300 2,100
4. 80 × 44 3,200 + 320 3,520	**5.** 90 × 63 5,400 + 270 5,670

Math Journal 2, p. 233

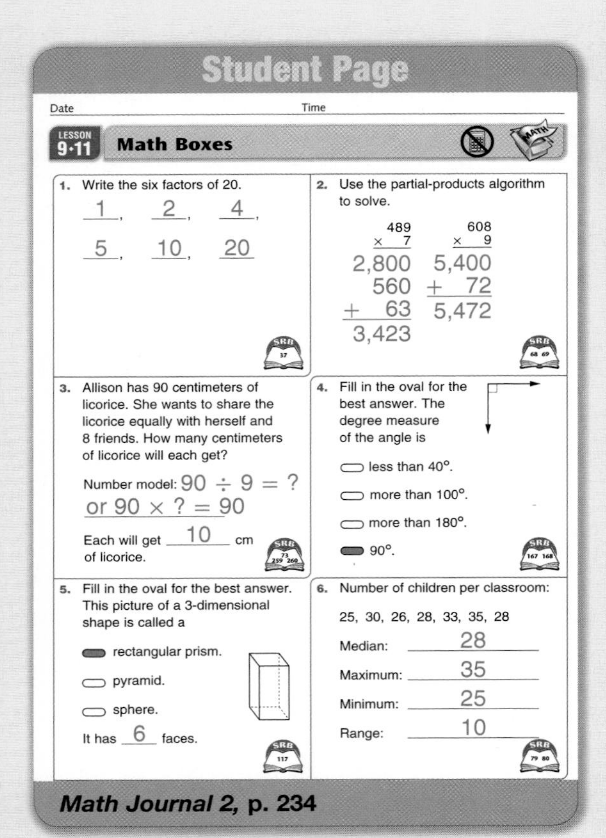
Student Page

Date ____ Time ____

LESSON 9·11 **Math Boxes**

1. Write the six factors of 20.
 1, 2, 4,
 5, 10, 20

2. Use the partial-products algorithm to solve.

489	608
× 7	× 9
2,800	5,400
560	+ 72
+ 63	5,472
3,423	

3. Allison has 90 centimeters of licorice. She wants to share the licorice equally with herself and 8 friends. How many centimeters of licorice will each get?
 Number model: 90 ÷ 9 = ? or 90 × ? = 90
 Each will get 10 cm of licorice.

4. Fill in the oval for the best answer. The degree measure of the angle is
 - less than 40°.
 - more than 100°.
 - more than 180°.
 - ● 90°.

5. Fill in the oval for the best answer. This picture of a 3-dimensional shape is called a
 - ● rectangular prism.
 - pyramid.
 - sphere.

 It has 6 faces.

6. Number of children per classroom:
 25, 30, 26, 28, 33, 35, 28
 Median: 28
 Maximum: 35
 Minimum: 25
 Range: 10

Math Journal 2, p. 234

Home Link Master

Name ____ Date ____ Time ____

HOME LINK 9·11 **2-Digit Multiplication: Two Ways**

Family Note Your child's class continues to practice the partial-products algorithm and the lattice method, now with 2-digit numbers and 2-digit multiples of 10.
Please return this Home Link to school tomorrow.

Use the lattice method and the partial-products algorithm.

1. 20 × 38 = 760
2. 50 × 17 = 850
3. 90 × 62 = 5,580

38	17	62
× 20	× 50	× 90
600	500	5,400
+160	+350	+ 180
760	850	5,580

Practice

On the back of this page, use your favorite method to solve these problems.

4. 40 × 28 = 1,120
5. 60 × 35 = 2,100

Math Masters, p. 304

2 Ongoing Learning & Practice

▶ Playing *Angle Race*

PARTNER ACTIVITY

(*Math Masters,* pp. 398, 430, and 441; *Student Reference Book,* pp. 271 and 272)

See pages 271 and 272 in the *Student Reference Book,* or Lesson 6-9, for game directions. Have children draw and describe their last angle rotation on an Exit Slip (*Math Masters,* page 398).

Ongoing Assessment: Recognizing Student Achievement

Exit Slip

Use an **Exit Slip** (*Math Masters,* page 398) to assess children's progress toward describing angles as records of rotations. Children are making adequate progress if they accurately describe their angle rotation using language such as *more or less than* $\frac{1}{4}$ *turn,* $\frac{1}{2}$ *turn,* or $\frac{3}{4}$ *turn.* Some children may be able to describe their angle using the correct degree measure.

[Measurement and Reference Frames Goal 1]

▶ Math Boxes 9·11

INDEPENDENT ACTIVITY

(*Math Journal 2,* p. 234)

Mixed Practice Math Boxes in this lesson are linked with Math Boxes in Lessons 9-9 and 9-13. The skill in Problem 6 previews Unit 10 content.

▶ Home Link 9·11

INDEPENDENT ACTIVITY

(*Math Masters,* p. 304)

Home Connection Children use the lattice method and the partial-products algorithm to find products of multidigit numbers and 2-digit multiples of 10.

3 Differentiation Options

READINESS

PARTNER ACTIVITY

15–30 Min

▶ Extending Basic Facts

(*Math Masters,* p. 449; *Student Reference Book,* pp. 293 and 294)

To provide experience with extended multiplication facts, have children play an extended-facts version of *Multiplication Bingo.* Have children make a set of 14 number cards by cutting 3-by-5 index cards in half and labeling them with two of each of the following numbers: 10, 20, 30, 40, 50, 60, and 100. They should use the following list of numbers for their gameboard (*Math Masters,* page 449): 100; 400; 600; 800; 900; 1,200; 1,500; 1,600; 1,800; 2,000; 2,400; 2,500; 3,000; 3,600; 5,000; 6,000. Have them follow the rules for the game on *Student Reference Book,* pages 293 and 294.

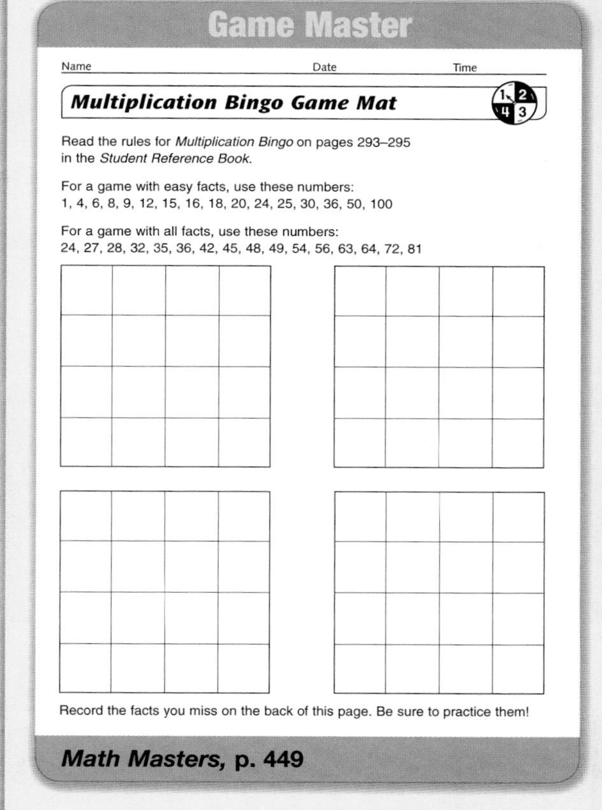

Game Master

Name Date Time

Multiplication Bingo Game Mat

Read the rules for *Multiplication Bingo* on pages 293–295 in the *Student Reference Book.*

For a game with easy facts, use these numbers:
1, 4, 6, 8, 9, 12, 15, 16, 18, 20, 24, 25, 30, 36, 50, 100

For a game with all facts, use these numbers:
24, 27, 28, 32, 35, 36, 42, 45, 48, 49, 54, 56, 63, 64, 72, 81

Record the facts you miss on the back of this page. Be sure to practice them!

Math Masters, p. 449

ENRICHMENT

5–15 Min

▶ Finding an Error in Lattice Multiplication

(*Math Masters,* p. 305)

To apply children's understanding of multiplication, have them identify and describe an error in an example of lattice multiplication. Children record their work on *Math Masters,* page 305.

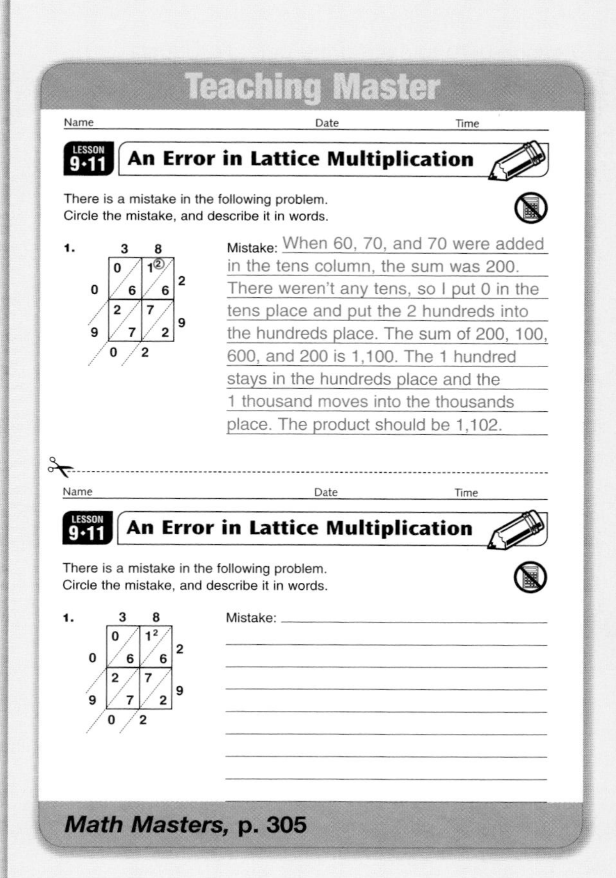

Teaching Master

Name Date Time

LESSON 9•11 **An Error in Lattice Multiplication**

There is a mistake in the following problem.
Circle the mistake, and describe it in words.

1\. Mistake: When 60, 70, and 70 were added in the tens column, the sum was 200. There weren't any tens, so I put 0 in the tens place and put the 2 hundreds into the hundreds place. The sum of 200, 100, 600, and 200 is 1,100. The 1 hundred stays in the hundreds place and the 1 thousand moves into the thousands place. The product should be 1,102.

Name Date Time

LESSON 9•11 **An Error in Lattice Multiplication**

There is a mistake in the following problem.
Circle the mistake, and describe it in words.

1\. Mistake:

Math Masters, p. 305

9•12 Products of 2-Digit Numbers, Part 2

Objective To guide children as they extend the partial-products algorithm to products of any two 2-digit numbers.

www.everydaymathonline.com

ePresentations

eToolkit

Algorithms Practice

EM Facts Workshop Game™

Family Letters

Assessment Management

Common Core State Standards

Curriculum Focal Points

Interactive Teacher's Lesson Guide

1 Teaching the Lesson

Key Concepts and Skills

- Apply place-value concepts to find partial products.
  [Number and Numeration Goal 1]
- Use addition to add partial products.
  [Operations and Computation Goal 2]
- Use multiplication facts to calculate partial products.
  [Operations and Computation Goal 3]
- Use base-10 blocks and arrays to model multiplication.
  [Operations and Computation Goal 6]

Key Activities

Children use the arrays they created in Lesson 9•10 to extend the partial-products algorithm to any two 2-digit numbers.

Ongoing Assessment: Informing Instruction See pages 780 and 781.

Materials

Math Journal 2, pp. 230 and 235
Home Link 9•11
Math Masters, p. 306
transparency of *Math Masters,* p. 306 (optional) ◆ half-sheet of paper ◆ red, green, and blue erasable markers (optional) ◆ base-10 blocks (optional) ◆ overhead base-10 blocks (optional)

2 Ongoing Learning & Practice

Playing *Beat the Calculator* (Multiplication)
Math Journal 2, p. 282
Student Reference Book, p. 279
per group: calculator
Children practice multiplication facts.

Ongoing Assessment: Recognizing Student Achievement
Use an Exit Slip (*Math Masters,* page 398).
[Operations and Computation Goal 3]

Math Boxes 9•12
Math Journal 2, p. 236
Children practice and maintain skills through Math Box problems.

Home Link 9•12
Math Masters, p. 307
Children practice and maintain skills through Home Link activities.

3 Differentiation Options

ENRICHMENT
Exploring Egyptian Multiplication
Math Masters, pp. 308 and 309
Children explore the Egyptian multiplication algorithm.

EXTRA PRACTICE
Using the Lattice Method
Math Journal 2, p. 235
Math Masters, pp. 310 and 311
Children practice the lattice method with 2-digit numbers.

ELL SUPPORT
Using a Graphic Organizer
Differentiation Handbook, p. 34
Children use a graphic organizer from the *Differentiation Handbook.*

Advance Preparation

***Teacher's Reference Manual,* Grades 1–3** pp. 108, 109

Getting Started

Mathematical Practices
SMP1, **SMP2, SMP3, SMP4,** SMP5, SMP6, SMP7

Content Standards
3.OA.3, 3.OA.4, **3.OA.5,** 3.OA.7, **3.NBT.2, 3.NBT.3, 3.MD.5b, 3.MD.7a, 3.MD.7b, 3.MD.7c, 3.MD.7d**

Mental Math and Reflexes

Write the following problems on the board. Have children use mental math to solve.

●○○ 5 [70s] 350
30 [6s] 180
40 [2s] 80

●●○ 80 [50s] 4,000
60 [90s] 5,400
70 [80s] 5,600

●●● 70 [400s] 28,000
3,000 [80s] 240,000
90 [7,000s] 630,000

Math Message

Write these problems on a half sheet. Solve and show your work.

$20 \times 34 =$ ____ 680

$70 \times 48 =$ ____ 3,360

Home Link 9+11 Follow-Up

Partners share methods for solving Problems 4 and 5. Briefly review answers.

1 Teaching the Lesson

▶ Math Message Follow-Up

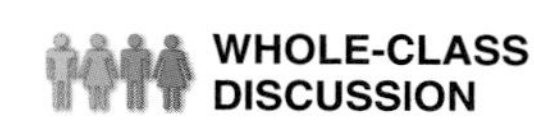

Algorithm Project The focus of this lesson is the partial-products algorithm. To teach U.S. traditional multiplication, see Algorithm Project 3 on page A10.

Children share solution strategies. The partial-products algorithms are written below.

```
                    34
                  × 20
20 [30s]   →       600
20 [4s]    →      + 80
600 + 80   →       680
```

```
                    48
                  × 70
70 [40s]      →  2,800
70 [8s]       →  + 560
2,800 + 560   →  3,360
```

NOTE *Math Masters,* page 306 is a duplicate of *Math Journal 2,* page 230.

▶ Extending the Partial-Products Algorithm

(*Math Journal 2,* p. 230; *Math Masters,* p. 306)

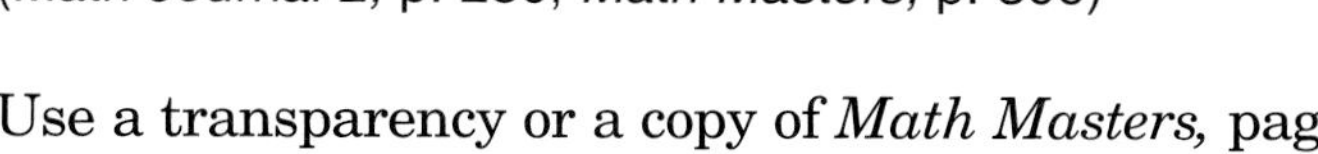

Use a transparency or a copy of *Math Masters,* page 306 to model the partial-products algorithm. Ask children to turn to the first array on journal page 230. Show them how to find the total number of squares in the array using the partial-products algorithm.

```
                             34
                           × 17
10 [30s]              →     300
10 [4s]               →      40
7 [30s]               →     210
7 [4s]                →    + 28
300 + 40 + 210 + 28   →     578
```

NOTE Encourage children to add the partial products mentally. They may think 300 plus 200 is 500. 500 plus 40 is 540. 540 plus 10 is 550. 550 plus 20 is 570. 570 plus 8 is 578.

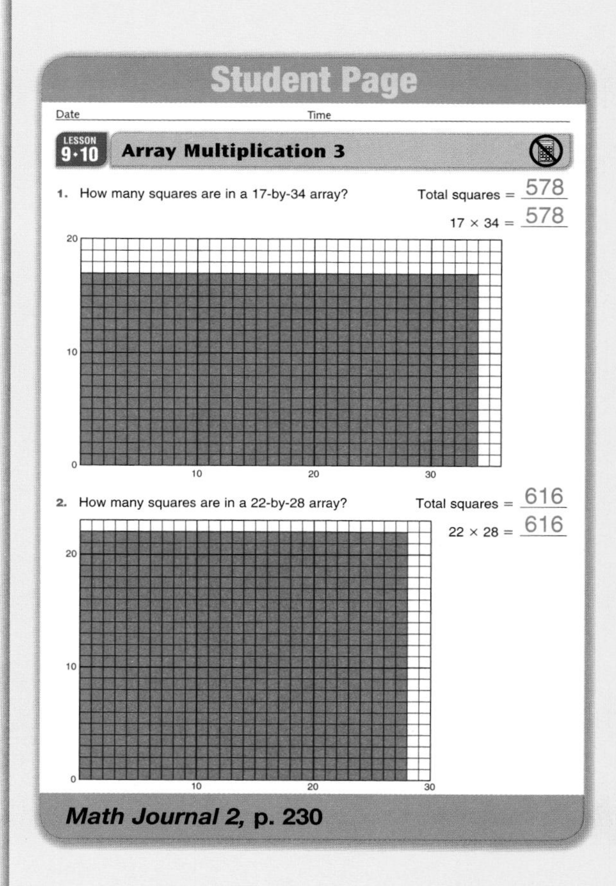

Student Page

Date Time

LESSON 9•10 **Array Multiplication 3**

1. How many squares are in a 17-by-34 array? Total squares = 578

$17 \times 34 =$ 578

2. How many squares are in a 22-by-28 array? Total squares = 616

$22 \times 28 =$ 616

Math Journal 2, p. 230

$$\begin{array}{r} 34 \\ \times\ 17 \\ \hline 30 \times 10 \\ 30 \times 7 \\ 7 \times 4 \\ 10 \times 4 \end{array}$$

NOTE When using the partial-products algorithm to multiply 2-digit numbers, children are applying the Distributive Property of Multiplication over Addition two times.
For example:

$17 \times 34 = 17 \times (30 + 4)$
$= (17 \times 30) + (17 \times 4)$
$= [(10 + 7) \times 30] + [(10 + 7) \times 4]$
$= (10 \times 30) + (7 \times 30) + (10 \times 4) + (7 \times 4)$
$= 300 + 210 + 40 + 28$
$= 578$

The diagram to the right provides a visual representation of the partial products in 34×17.

Adjusting the Activity

ELL

Have children draw lines connecting each pair of digits as they multiply. Explain that the lines will form a bowtie shape if they have found all the partial products. Note that the partial products may be found in any order. (*See margin.*)

AUDITORY ◆ KINESTHETIC ◆ TACTILE ◆ VISUAL

Ongoing Assessment: Informing Instruction

Watch for children who need support with partial products of multiples of 10 and 2-digit numbers. Have them write one number in expanded notation before multiplying. For example, in 70×48, 48 would be written as 4 tens 8 ones, or $40 + 8$. The multiplication becomes 70×40 and 70×8.

Children refer to the array diagram in their journals and match each part of the diagram with a partial product as you do the same at the overhead.

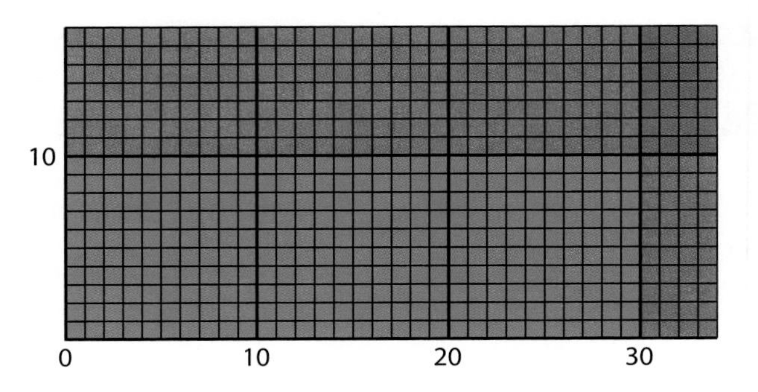

- There are 30 green squares in each of 10 rows, so there are 300 green squares (10 [30s]) in all.
- There are 4 red squares in each of the 10 rows to the right of the green squares, or 40 red squares (10 [4s]) in all.
- There are 30 red squares in each of the 7 rows above the green squares, or 210 red squares (7 [30s]) in all.
- There are 4 blue squares in each of 7 rows, or 28 blue squares (7 [4s]) in all.
- There are 578 squares (300 + 40 + 210 + 28) total in the array.

With children's help, use the algorithm to solve the second problem on the journal page.

$$\begin{array}{rcr} & & 28 \\ & & \underline{\times\ 22} \\ 20\ [20s] & \rightarrow & 400 \\ 20\ [8s] & \rightarrow & 160 \\ 2\ [20s] & \rightarrow & 40 \\ 2\ [8s] & \rightarrow & \underline{+\ 16} \\ 400 + 160 + 40 + 16 & \rightarrow & 616 \end{array}$$

Again, children match each part of the diagram with the completed problem on the board as you do the same at the overhead projector.

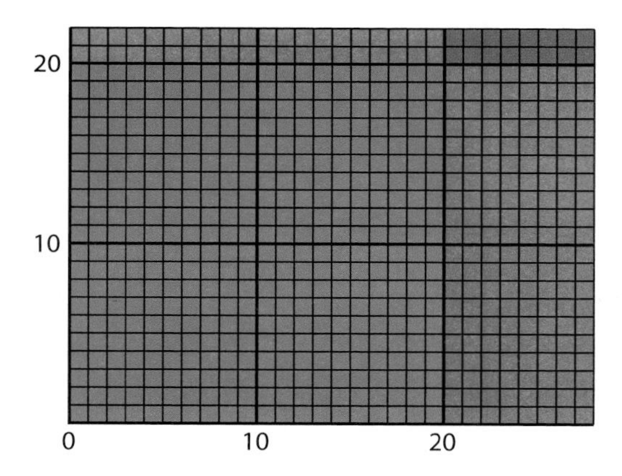

Give children additional problems of this type as needed, such as 23 × 46 1,058; 13 × 28 364; and 31 × 22 682.

Finding Products of 2-Digit Numbers

COMPUTATION PRACTICE

(*Math Journal 2,* p. 235)

Have children work with partners to solve the problems on journal page 235. Remind them to write the number model for each partial product. For example, 10 [20s] → 200 or 10 × 20 → 200. Circulate and assist as necessary.

Ongoing Assessment: Informing Instruction

Watch for children who have difficulty with partial products. Have them continue to use base-10 blocks to model the problems.

Links to the Future

Do not expect all children to master the partial-products algorithm for multiplying 2-digit numbers by 2-digit numbers at this time. Using strategies to multiply 2-digit numbers by 2-digit numbers is a Grade 4 Goal.

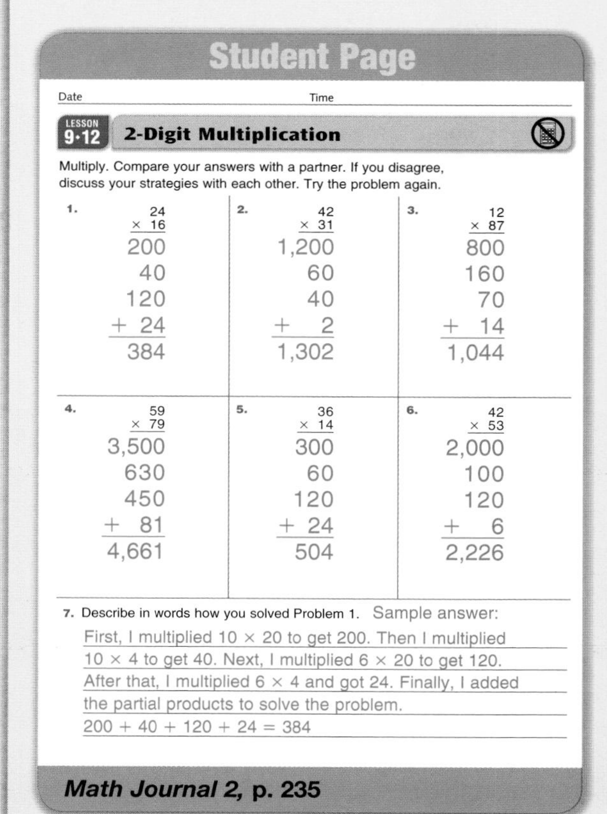

Student Page

Date Time

LESSON 9·12 **2-Digit Multiplication**

Multiply. Compare your answers with a partner. If you disagree, discuss your strategies with each other. Try the problem again.

1.	2.	3.
24 × 16: 200, 40, 120, + 24 = 384	42 × 31: 1,200, 60, 40, + 2 = 1,302	12 × 87: 800, 160, 70, + 14 = 1,044

4.	5.	6.
59 × 79: 3,500, 630, 450, + 81 = 4,661	36 × 14: 300, 60, 120, + 24 = 504	42 × 53: 2,000, 100, 120, + 6 = 2,226

7. Describe in words how you solved Problem 1. Sample answer: First, I multiplied 10 × 20 to get 200. Then I multiplied 10 × 4 to get 40. Next, I multiplied 6 × 20 to get 120. After that, I multiplied 6 × 4 and got 24. Finally, I added the partial products to solve the problem. 200 + 40 + 120 + 24 = 384

Math Journal 2, p. 235

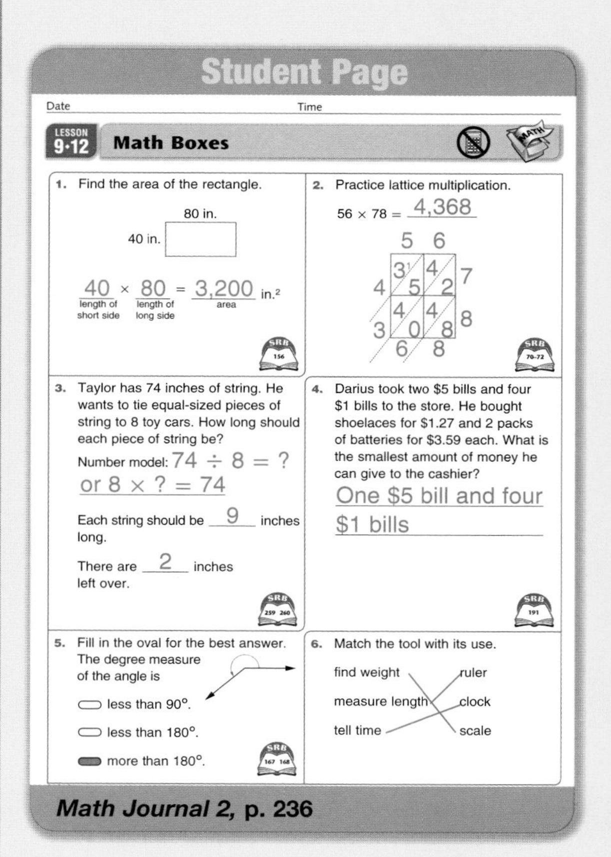

Student Page

Date Time

LESSON 9·12 **Math Boxes**

1. Find the area of the rectangle.

80 in.
40 in.

40 × 80 = 3,200 in.²
(length of short side × length of long side = area)

2. Practice lattice multiplication.

56 × 78 = 4,368

3. Taylor has 74 inches of string. He wants to tie equal-sized pieces of string to 8 toy cars. How long should each piece of string be?

Number model: 74 ÷ 8 = ? or 8 × ? = 74

Each string should be 9 inches long.

There are 2 inches left over.

4. Darius took two $5 bills and four $1 bills to the store. He bought shoelaces for $1.27 and 2 packs of batteries for $3.59 each. What is the smallest amount of money he can give to the cashier?

One $5 bill and four $1 bills

5. Fill in the oval for the best answer. The degree measure of the angle is

- less than 90°.
- less than 180°.
- more than 180°. (filled)

6. Match the tool with its use.

find weight — scale
measure length — ruler
tell time — clock

Math Journal 2, p. 236

Home Link Master

Name Date Time

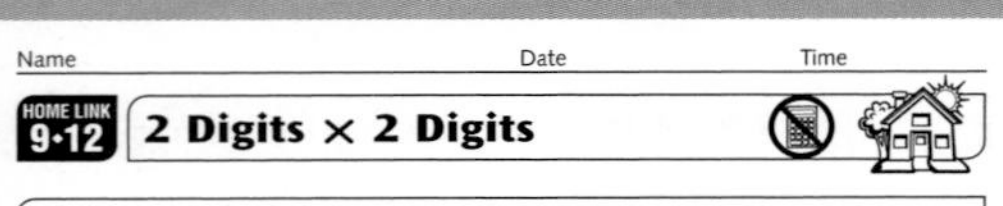

Family Note The class continues to practice the partial-products algorithm and the lattice method, now with any 2-digit numbers. Encourage your child to try these problems both ways and to compare the answers to be sure they are correct.

Please return this Home Link to school tomorrow.

Use the lattice method and the partial-products algorithm.

1. 21 × 35 = 735

	3	5	
2	0/6	1/0	
1	0/3	0/5	

$$\begin{array}{r} 35 \\ \times\ 21 \\ \hline 600 \\ 100 \\ 30 \\ +\ 5 \\ \hline 735 \end{array}$$

2. 17 × 43 = 731

$$\begin{array}{r} 43 \\ \times\ 17 \\ \hline 400 \\ 30 \\ 280 \\ +\ 21 \\ \hline 731 \end{array}$$

3. 58 × 62 = 3,596

$$\begin{array}{r} 62 \\ \times\ 58 \\ \hline 3{,}000 \\ 100 \\ 480 \\ +\ 16 \\ \hline 3{,}596 \end{array}$$

Practice

On the back of this page, use your favorite method to solve these problems.

4. 55 × 49 = 2,695 **5.** 91 × 33 = 3,003

Math Masters, p. 307

NOTE To provide an additional assessment of children's fact recall, consider administering the Facts Survey (see Lesson 7-2 for directions) in the next week or so.

Teaching Master

Name Date Time

LESSON 9·12 **Egyptian Multiplication**

With a partner, carefully study the Egyptian multiplication algorithm below. Then solve a problem using this method.

Example: 13 × 28

Step 1: Write the first factor in the first column (13). Then write 1 in the first row below the factor. Double 1 and write 2 in the row below. Continue to double the number above until you get a number that is equal to or greater than the first factor. Cross out that number if it is greater than the first factor. 16 is crossed out.

1st factor: 13	2nd factor: —
1	
2	
4	
8	
~~16~~	

Step 2: Write the second factor in the second column (28). Then write that number again in the box below. (It should be next to the 1 in the first column.) Double that number in each new line until the last number lines up with the last number of the first column (224 lines up with 8).

1st factor: 13	2nd factor: 28
1	28
2	56
4	112
8	224
~~16~~	

Step 3: Starting with the greatest number in column 1 (8), circle the numbers that add up to be the first factor (13). 8 + 4 + 1 = 13

Cross out the row of numbers that you did not use to make the first factor (2 and 56).

1st factor: 13	2nd factor: 28
(1)	28
2	~~56~~
(4)	112
(8)	224
~~16~~	

Step 4: Add the numbers in the second column that are not crossed out. 28 + 112 + 224 = 364

Answer: 13 × 28 = 364

Check the answer by solving the problem using an algorithm you already know.

1st factor: 13	2nd factor: 28
(1)	28
2	~~56~~
(4)	112
(8)	224
~~16~~	

Math Masters, p. 308

2 Ongoing Learning & Practice

▶ Playing *Beat the Calculator* (Multiplication)

(*Math Journal 2,* p. 282; *Student Reference Book,* p. 279)

Children develop automaticity with multiplication facts by playing *Beat the Calculator.* Have children use the Multiplication Fact Power Table, journal page 282, to record the facts whose products they provide correctly when playing the role of the Brain. Have the Caller select facts from the shaded portion of the table. For Fact Power Table directions, see Lesson 4-5. For game directions, see page 279 in the *Student Reference Book.* Remind children to fill in the product when they have 3 check marks for a fact.

Ongoing Assessment: Recognizing Student Achievement

Use an **Exit Slip** (*Math Masters,* page 398) to assess children's progress toward demonstrating automaticity with multiplication facts through 10 × 10. Children record the facts from the Multiplication Fact Power Table for which they recorded at least one check mark. Children are making adequate progress if they record over half of the facts from the shaded portion of the table. Some children may record most of the facts.

[Operations and Computation Goal 3]

▶ Math Boxes 9·12

(*Math Journal 2,* p. 236)

Mixed Practice Math Boxes in this lesson are paired with Math Boxes in Lesson 9-10. The skill in Problem 6 previews Unit 10 content.

Writing/Reasoning Have children write an answer to the following: *Explain how you decided which bills Darius could give the cashier in Problem 4.* Sample answer: The total amount Darius needs to give the cashier is $8.45. The smallest amount of money he can give the cashier is $9.00: one $5 bill and four $1 bills.

▶ Home Link 9·12

(*Math Masters,* p. 307)

Home Connection Children find the product of two 2-digit numbers using the lattice method and the partial-products algorithm.

3 Differentiation Options

ENRICHMENT

Exploring Egyptian Multiplication

15–30 Min

(*Math Masters,* pp. 308 and 309)

To further explore multiplication, have children study an ancient Egyptian algorithm for multiplication on *Math Masters,* page 308 and use the algorithm to solve another problem. They record their work on *Math Masters,* page 309.

EXTRA PRACTICE

Using the Lattice Method

5–15 Min

(*Math Journal 2,* p. 235; *Math Masters,* pp. 310 and 311)

To offer children more experience with the lattice method, have them use the lattice method to do the problems on journal page 235. You might want to give them copies of *Math Masters,* page 311 (blank 2-digit by 2-digit grids). *Math Masters,* page 310 (blank 2-digit by 3-digit grids) is available for practicing multiplication problems involving multiplying 3-digit numbers by 2-digit numbers.

ELL SUPPORT

Using a Graphic Organizer

5–15 Min

(*Differentiation Handbook,* p. 34)

To provide language support for multiplication, have children create a graphic organizer for the word *multiplication.* They should write words, numbers, symbols, or draw pictures that are related to the word *multiplication.* Have them extend the graphic organizer as appropriate. See the *Differentiation Handbook,* page 34 for more details.

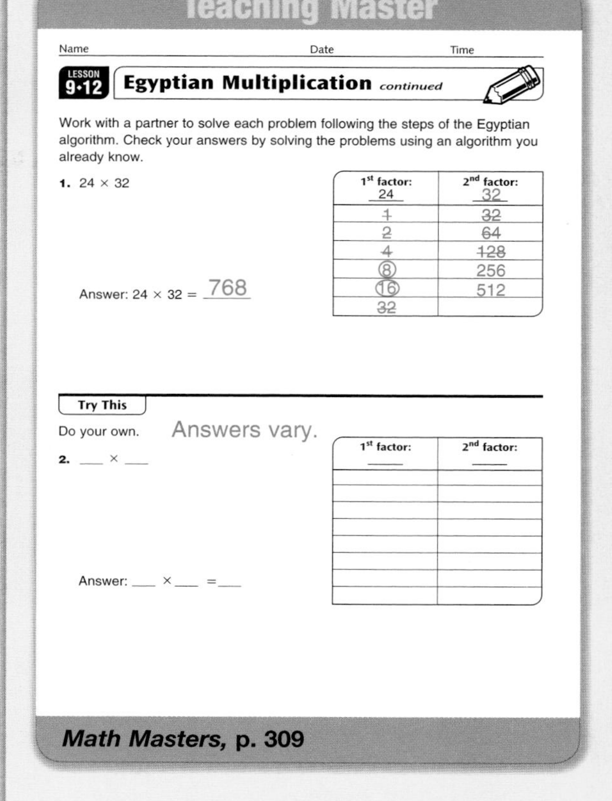

Teaching Master

Name Date Time

LESSON 9·12 **Egyptian Multiplication** *continued*

Work with a partner to solve each problem following the steps of the Egyptian algorithm. Check your answers by solving the problems using an algorithm you already know.

1. 24 × 32

1st factor: 24	2nd factor: 32
~~1~~	~~32~~
~~2~~	~~64~~
~~4~~	~~128~~
(8)	256
(16)	512
~~32~~	

Answer: 24 × 32 = 768

Try This

Do your own. Answers vary.

2. ___ × ___

1st factor: ___	2nd factor: ___

Answer: ___ × ___ = ___

Math Masters, p. 309

NOTE The lattice method was developed by the Egyptians more than 4,000 years ago and is used today in Russia, Ethiopia, the Arab world, and the Near East. Point out the location of Egypt on a world map.

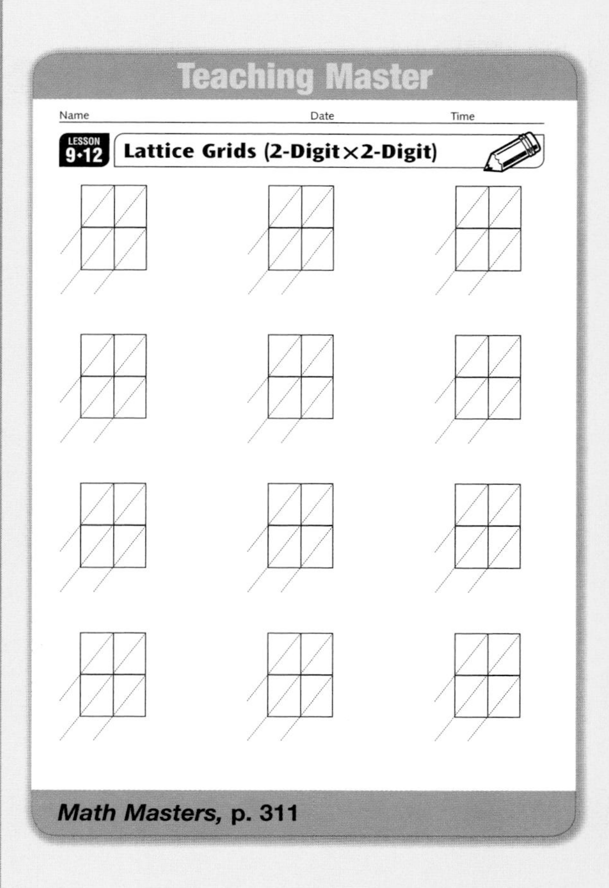

Teaching Master

Name Date Time

LESSON 9·12 **Lattice Grids (2-Digit × 2-Digit)**

Math Masters, p. 311

9·13 Positive and Negative Numbers

Objective To guide children as they investigate positive and negative numbers.

Technology Resources www.everydaymathonline.com

ePresentations

eToolkit

Algorithms Practice

EM Facts Workshop Game™

Family Letters

Assessment Management

Common Core State Standards

Curriculum Focal Points

Interactive Teacher's Lesson Guide

1 Teaching the Lesson

Key Concepts and Skills

- Compare and order positive and negative numbers.
  [Number and Numeration Goal 6]
- Solve number stories involving the addition and subtraction of positive and negative numbers.
  [Operations and Computation Goal 2]

Key Activities

Children consider two uses of positive and negative numbers: relating numbers to a zero point and recording changes. They solve number stories about positive and negative numbers.

Key Vocabulary

Fahrenheit scale ◆ degrees Fahrenheit ◆ Celsius scale ◆ degrees Celsius

Materials

Math Journal 2, p. 237
Student Reference Book, pp. 170 and 171
Home Link 9•12
calculator ◆ slate ◆ display thermometer (optional)

2 Ongoing Learning & Practice

Making a Line Plot

Student Reference Book, pp. 79–81, 89A, and 89B
Class Data Pad (optional)
Children measure their pencils and show the data by making a line plot.

Math Boxes 9•13

Math Journal 2, p. 238
Children practice and maintain skills through Math Box problems.

Ongoing Assessment: Recognizing Student Achievement
Use Math Boxes, Problem 1.
[Measurement and Reference Frames Goal 2]

Home Link 9•13

Math Masters, p. 312
Children practice and maintain skills through Home Link activities.

3 Differentiation Options

READINESS

Counting on a Number Line

Math Masters, p. 313
Children count on a number line with positive and negative numbers.

ENRICHMENT

Solving Subtraction Number Stories

Math Masters, p. 314
2 each of number cards 0–10 (from the Everything Math Deck, if available)
Children explore the importance of order in solving subtraction problems.

Advance Preparation

***Teacher's Reference Manual,* Grades 1–3** pp. 64–66

Getting Started

Mathematical Practices
SMP1, **SMP2**, SMP3, **SMP4,** SMP5, SMP6
Content Standards
3.NBT.2, 3.MD.4, 3.MD.6, **3.MD.7b**

Mental Math and Reflexes

Children skip count on their calculators. They say the counts as they press [=] on their calculators.

Suggestions:

●○○ Start at 12; count down by 4s. 12, 8, 4, 0, –4, –8, –12, ...

●●○ Start at –20; count up by 5s. –20, –15, –10, –5, 0, 5, 10, 15, 20, ...

●●● Start at –18; count up by 4s. –18, –14, –10, –6, –2, 2, 6, 10, 14, 18, ...

Math Message

Look at the thermometer on page 171 in your Student Reference Book.
Which temperature is colder, –5°C or –10°C? –10°C *+1°C or –14°C?* –14°C *How do you know?*

Home Link 9·12 Follow-Up

Have children share solution strategies for Problems 4 and 5 with a partner.
Briefly review answers.

1 Teaching the Lesson

▶ Math Message Follow-Up

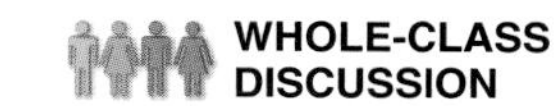

(*Student Reference Book,* pp. 170 and 171)

Discuss any disagreements about answers. Colder is further down on the temperature scale. If you have a display thermometer in the classroom, ask children to show the pairs of temperatures.

Review the two thermometer scales on page 171 in the *Student Reference Book.* The **Fahrenheit scale,** marked in **degrees Fahrenheit,** is standard in the United States for everyday use. For example, most U.S. newspapers report temperatures only in degrees Fahrenheit, so Fahrenheit is used in the class high/low temperature record. The **Celsius scale,** marked in **degrees Celsius,** is standard throughout the rest of the world for everyday use and everywhere, including the United States, for scientific work.

Note the different temperatures on each scale for the same natural phenomena: the freezing and boiling points of water, the freezing point of salt solutions, and room temperature and body temperature.

NOTE For additional practice with Fahrenheit and Celsius thermometer scales, go to www.everydaymathonline.com.

NOTE See pages 265 and 266 in the *Student Reference Book* for directions to skip counting on a calculator. When skip counting beginning with a negative number, it is necessary to enter the start number and then press the [+/–] key to make the numbers negative. For the ●●○ Mental Math and Reflexes problem, the following key sequences are needed:

TI 20: 20, [+/–], [+], 5, [=], [=], ...

Casio: 5, [+], [+], 20, [+/–], [=], [=], ...

Student Page

Reference Frames

Most thermometers have marks that are spaced 2 degrees apart.

Fahrenheit thermometer		Celsius thermometer
212°F	Water boils	100°C
98.6°F	Body temperature	37°C
70°F	Room temperature	about 20°C
32°F	Water freezes	0°C
0°F	Salt water freezes	–18°C

***Student Reference Book,* p. 171**

NOTE Locations on a reference scale that are expressed without a negative symbol are usually assumed to be positive. However, it is sometimes helpful to be more explicit by using the + symbol.

▶ Writing Temperatures above and below Zero

Help children make connections between temperatures expressed in words and temperatures expressed with numbers and units. Dictate temperatures above and below zero for children to write on their slates. For this exercise, specify that all temperatures are on the Celsius scale. *Examples:*

- Write the number and unit for 5 degrees below zero. −5°C
- Write the number and unit for 8 degrees above zero. 8°C or +8°C

Explain that thermometers can be thought of as number lines or reference frames. Zero is a reference or beginning point from which positive and negative numbers go in opposite directions. Temperatures are expressed in words as above or below zero, or with symbols as positive or negative numbers.

Adjusting the Activity

ELL

Have children think in terms of a number line. Ask questions like the following: *What is the distance (how many jumps) between +2 and −2?* 4 *What is the distance (how many jumps) between +100 and −1,000?* 1,100

AUDITORY • KINESTHETIC • TACTILE • VISUAL

▶ Using Sea Level as a Zero Point

Discuss what children know about sea level. Sea level is an agreed-upon zero point from which elevations, such as land elevations and depths of oceans, are measured. Just as with the discussion on temperatures, ask higher/lower questions. *Examples:*

- Which is lower, 100 meters above sea level or 1,000 meters below sea level? 1,000 meters below sea level
- Which is lower, 2 meters above sea level or 2 meters below sea level? 2 meters below sea level

Dictate elevations, and have children write them on their slates as positive or negative numbers. Check that children write a negative sign when needed and the appropriate unit. *Examples*:

- 977 meters below sea level −977 m
- 4,240 meters above sea level +4,240 m or 4,240 m

▶ Expressing Changes with Positive and Negative Numbers

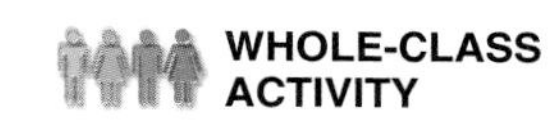

WHOLE-CLASS ACTIVITY

Changes are often expressed with positive and negative numbers. Discuss changes like the following:

- 6-pound loss: −6 lb; 6-pound gain: +6 lb
- 10°C temperature drop: −10°C; 10°C temperature rise: +10°C
- in football, gain of 6 yards: +6 yards; 15-yard penalty: −15 yards
- lose $10: −$10; find $10: +$10

Have children suggest other change situations. Record them on the board with positive and negative numbers.

You and the children then make up number stories involving comparisons. *Examples:*

- Is it better to owe $5 or to owe $10? Owe $5
- Is it easier to carry my backpack if I put in 3 lb or take out 5 lb? Take out 5 lb
- In football, is it worse for the team to get a 10-yard penalty or a 15-yard penalty? 15-yard penalty

▶ Solving Number Stories with Positive and Negative Numbers

PARTNER ACTIVITY

PROBLEM SOLVING

(*Math Journal 2,* p. 237)

Children use thermometer scales, number lines, or other tools to find answers to the problems on journal page 237. Bring the class together to share solutions and strategies.

Adjusting the Activity

Encourage children to look for patterns on the completed journal page. For example, how do you find the difference between a positive temperature and a negative temperature? Add the two numbers as though both were positive.

AUDITORY • KINESTHETIC • TACTILE • VISUAL

Links to the Future

This lesson is an early exposure to adding and subtracting positive and negative numbers. This early exposure provides a background for work with positive and negative numbers that will continue through Grades 4, 5, and 6.

Solving problems and number stories involving positive and negative numbers is a Grade 5 Goal.

Student Page

Date Time

LESSON 9·13 **Number Stories with Positive & Negative Numbers**

Solve the following problems. Use the thermometer scale, the class number line, or other tools to help.

1. The largest change in temperature in a single day took place in January 1916 in Browning, Montana. The temperature dropped 100°F that day. The temperature was 44°F when it started dropping.

   How low did it go? −56°F

2. The largest temperature rise in 12 hours took place in Granville, North Dakota, on February 21, 1918. The temperature rose 83°F that day. The high temperature was 50°F.

   What was the low temperature? −33°F

3. On January 12, 1911, the temperature in Rapid City, South Dakota, fell from 49°F at 6 A.M. to −13°F at 8 A.M.

   By how many degrees did the temperature drop in those 2 hours? 62°F

4. The highest temperature ever recorded in Verkhoyansk, Siberia, was 98°F. The lowest temperature ever recorded there was −94°F.

   What is the difference between those two temperatures? 192°

5. Write your own number story using positive and negative numbers.

   Sample answer: My cat weighed 16 lb. Then she got sick and now weighs 13 lb. What was her weight change? −3 lb.

°F 100 90 80 70 60 50 40 30 20 10 0 −10 −20 −30 −40 −50 −60 −70 −80 −90 −100

Math Journal 2, p. 237

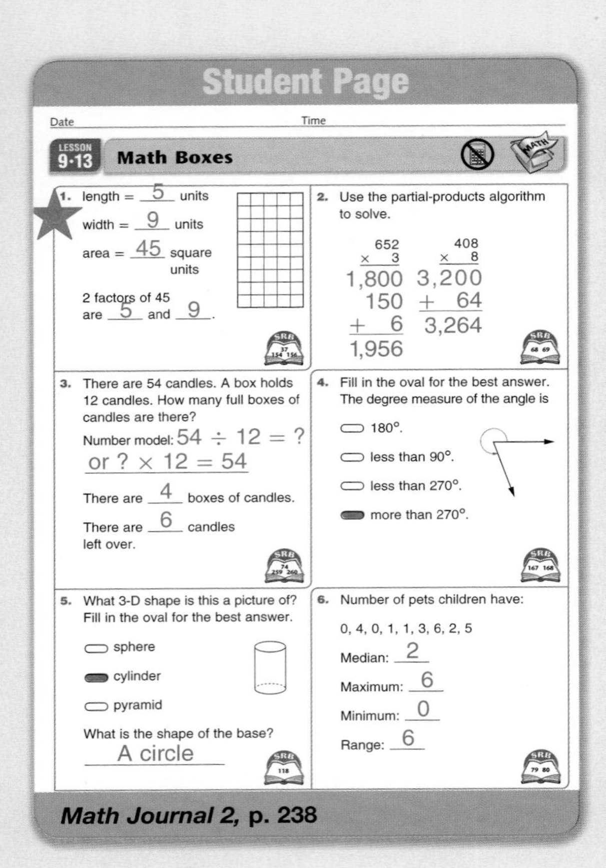
Student Page

Date Time

LESSON 9·13 **Math Boxes**

1. length = 5 units
width = 9 units
area = 45 square units
2 factors of 45 are 5 and 9.

2. Use the partial-products algorithm to solve.

652 × 3	408 × 8
1,800	3,200
150	+ 64
+ 6	3,264
1,956	

3. There are 54 candles. A box holds 12 candles. How many full boxes of candles are there?
Number model: 54 ÷ 12 = ? or ? × 12 = 54
There are 4 boxes of candles.
There are 6 candles left over.

4. Fill in the oval for the best answer. The degree measure of the angle is
- 180°.
- less than 90°.
- less than 270°.
- more than 270°. (filled)

5. What 3-D shape is this a picture of? Fill in the oval for the best answer.
- sphere
- cylinder (filled)
- pyramid

What is the shape of the base? A circle

6. Number of pets children have:
0, 4, 0, 1, 1, 3, 6, 2, 5
Median: 2
Maximum: 6
Minimum: 0
Range: 6

Math Journal 2, p. 238

2 Ongoing Learning & Practice

▶ Making a Line Plot

INDEPENDENT ACTIVITY

(*Student Reference Book,* pp. 79–81, 89A, and 89B)

Children measure the lengths of their pencils to the nearest $\frac{1}{2}$ inch and record the measures on the board or Class Data Pad. Have them copy the measures on paper and order them from shortest to longest. Then they make a line plot with the horizontal scale marked in $\frac{1}{2}$-inch units and show the data. Remind children that since no pencil is 0 inches long, the scale can begin with the shortest pencil length. Circulate to make sure that each child labels the horizontal and vertical axes and gives the line plot a title.

When most children have completed their line plots, have them identify the median, mode, maximum, minimum, and range of their data.

▶ Math Boxes 9·13

(*Math Journal 2,* p. 238)

Mixed Practice Math Boxes in this lesson are linked with Math Boxes in Lessons 9-9 and 9-11. The skill in Problem 6 previews Unit 10 content.

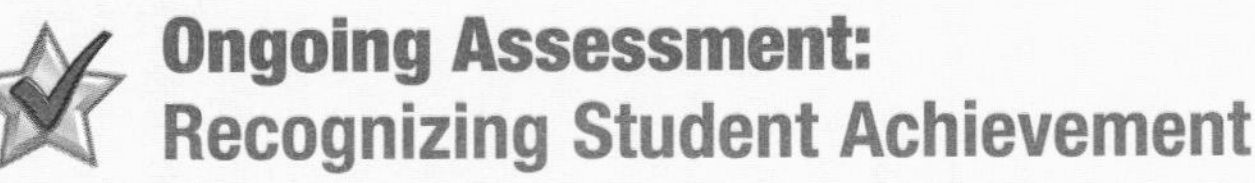

Math Boxes Problem 1

Use **Math Boxes, Problem 1** to assess children's progress toward finding the areas of rectangular shapes. Children are making adequate progress if they find the area of the rectangle. Some children may identify two factors of 45.
[Measurement and Reference Frames Goal 2]

Home Link Master

Name Date Time

HOME LINK 9·13 **Positive and Negative Temperatures**

Family Note Encourage your child to use the thermometer pictured here to answer questions about thermometer scales, temperature changes, and temperature comparisons. If you have a real thermometer, try to show your child how the mercury moves up and down.
Please return this Home Link to school tomorrow.

1. What is the coldest temperature this thermometer could show?
a. −40 °F b. −40 °C
2. What is the warmest temperature this thermometer could show?
a. 220 °F b. 104 °C
3. What temperature is 20 degrees warmer than −10°C? 10°C
4. How much colder is −9°C than 9°C? 18° colder
5. Would 30°C be a good temperature for swimming outside? Yes
For sledding? No Explain.
It would be very warm outside. 30° C is about the same as 86° F.
6. Would −6°C be a good temperature for ice-skating? Yes
For in-line skating? No Explain.
Water freezes at 0° C so there would be ice to skate on. This would be dangerous for in-line skating.

°F °C — 100 Water boils; Body Temperature; Room Temperature; 0 Water freezes; Salt solution freezes

Math Masters, p. 312

▶ Home Link 9·13

(*Math Masters,* p. 312)

Home Connection Children answer questions about thermometer scales, temperature changes, and appropriate temperatures for various activities. Point out the two scales on the thermometer (°F and °C).

3 Differentiation Options

READINESS

INDEPENDENT ACTIVITY

▶ Counting on a Number Line

5–15 Min

(*Math Masters,* p. 313)

To provide experience with finding distances between positive and negative numbers on a number line, have children practice counting on a number line. Children record their work on *Math Masters,* page 313. Have children describe the relationships they found.

ENRICHMENT

▶ Solving Subtraction Number Stories

15–30 Min

(*Math Masters,* p. 314)

To explore solving subtraction number stories have children follow the steps on *Math Masters,* page 314. When children have completed the page, discuss the patterns. Sample answers: When the numbers on the cards are the same, the difference between them is always 0. When the numbers are not the same, the differences are opposites. For example, $6 - 2 = 4$ and $2 - 6 = -4$. 4 and -4 are opposites.

Planning Ahead

For Lesson 10-1, you will need four objects of various shapes, volumes, and weights that can fit into an empty 2- or 3-pound coffee can. A good mix of objects might be a baseball, a tennis ball (or a rubber ball about the size of a tennis ball), a base-10 big cube, and an unopened 16-ounce can of food. Place a label with the name of each object on each item so that children can use consistent names when they list the items.

For the optional Readiness activity in Lesson 10-2, you will need a few rectangular prisms.

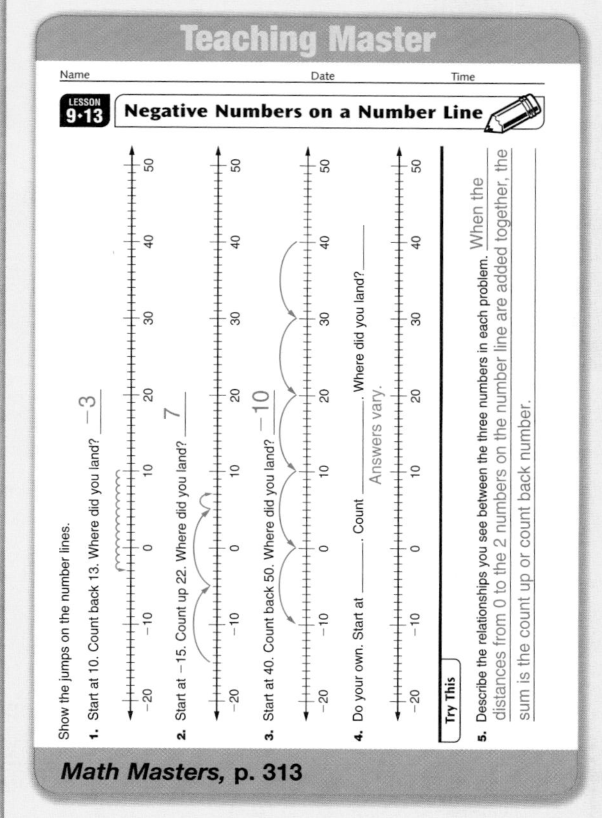

Teaching Master

Name ______ Date ______ Time ______

LESSON 9·13 **Negative Numbers on a Number Line**

Show the jumps on the number lines.

1. Start at 10. Count back 13. Where did you land? -3
2. Start at -15. Count up 22. Where did you land? 7
3. Start at 40. Count back 50. Where did you land? -10
4. Do your own. Start at ______. Count ______. Where did you land? ______ Answers vary.

Try This

5. Describe the relationships you see between the three numbers in each problem. When the distances from 0 to the 2 numbers on the number line are added together, the sum is the count up or count back number.

Math Masters, p. 313

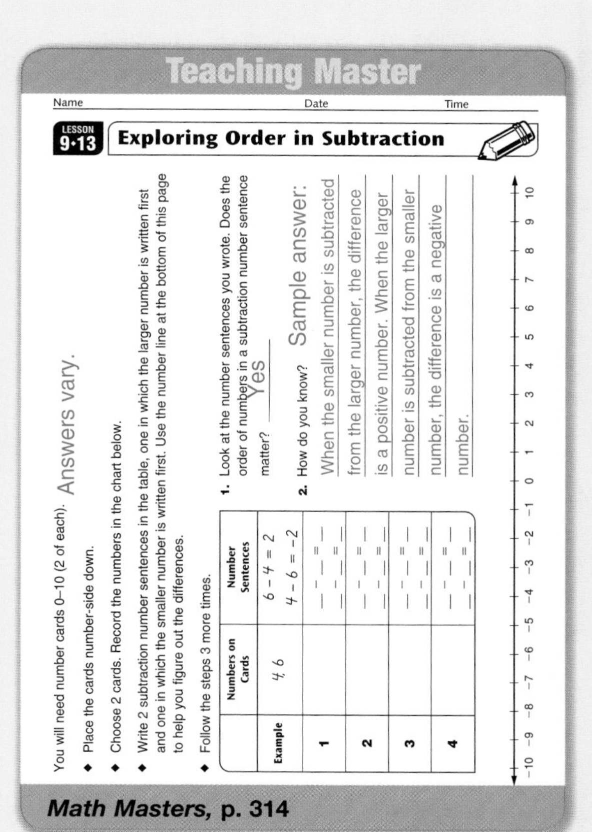

Teaching Master

Name ______ Date ______ Time ______

LESSON 9·13 **Exploring Order in Subtraction**

You will need number cards 0–10 (2 of each). Answers vary.

- Place the cards number-side down.
- Choose 2 cards. Record the numbers in the chart below.
- Write 2 subtraction number sentences in the table, one in which the larger number is written first and one in which the smaller number is written first. Use the number line at the bottom of this page to help you figure out the differences.
- Follow the steps 3 more times.

	Numbers on Cards	Number Sentences
Example	4, 6	$6 - 4 = 2$ $4 - 6 = -2$
1		___ − ___ = ___ ___ − ___ = ___
2		___ − ___ = ___ ___ − ___ = ___
3		___ − ___ = ___ ___ − ___ = ___
4		___ − ___ = ___ ___ − ___ = ___

1. Look at the number sentences you wrote. Does the order of numbers in a subtraction number sentence matter? Yes
2. How do you know? Sample answer: When the smaller number is subtracted from the larger number, the difference is a positive number. When the larger number is subtracted from the smaller number, the difference is a negative number.

Math Masters, p. 314

9•14 Progress Check 9

Objective To assess children's progress on mathematical content through the end of Unit 9.

1 Looking Back: Cumulative Assessment

Input children's data from Progress Check 9 into the **Assessment Management Spreadsheets**.

Materials

- Home Link 9•13
- *Assessment Handbook,* pp. 118–125, 187–191, 210, and 260–263
- slate; Fraction Cards; counters; straightedge

CONTENT ASSESSED	LESSON(S)	ASSESSMENT ITEMS				
		SELF	ORAL/SLATE	WRITTEN PART A	WRITTEN PART B	OPEN RESPONSE
Compare and order fractions. [Number and Numeration Goal 6]	9•2–9•4	4	2	4		
Demonstrate automaticity with multiplication facts through 10 × 10. [Operations and Computation Goal 3]	9•1, 9•2, 9•4–9•7, 9•9–9•12		3, 4	2, 3	16, 17	
Use and describe strategies to solve problems involving the multiplication of 2- and 3-digit numbers by a 1-digit number. [Operations and Computation Goal 4]	9•1–9•5, 9•9, 9•12	1–3		1–3	16, 17	✔
Make reasonable estimates for whole-number addition and subtraction problems. [Operations and Computation Goal 5]	9•3, 9•5, 9•6, 9•8, 9•10, 9•12	6	1	13–15		
Use arrays to model multiplication; use equal grouping to model division. [Operations and Computation Goal 6]	9•1, 9•2, 9•4, 9•6–9•8, 9•11–9•13		3, 4		18	
Describe and use strategies to measure the perimeter of polygons; count unit squares to find the areas of rectangles. [Measurement and Reference Frames Goal 2]	9•2–9•4, 9•7, 9•10, 9•12, 9•13	5		9–12		
Describe numeric patterns; describe rules for patterns and use them to solve problems. [Patterns, Functions, and Algebra Goal 1]	9•10					✔
Recognize that numerical expressions can have different values depending on the order of operations. [Patterns, Functions, and Algebra Goal 3]	9•5–9•8			5–8		

2 Looking Ahead: Preparing for Unit 10

Math Boxes 9•14

Home Link 9•14: Unit 10 Family Letter

Materials

- *Math Journal 2,* p. 239
- *Math Masters,* pp. 315–318

Getting Started

Math Message

Complete the Self Assessment (Assessment Handbook, page 187).

Home Link 9·13 Follow-Up

Briefly review answers. Have children share strategies for solving the problems.

1 Looking Back: Cumulative Assessment

▶ Math Message Follow-Up

INDEPENDENT ACTIVITY

(Self Assessment, *Assessment Handbook,* page 187)

The Self Assessment offers children the opportunity to reflect upon their progress.

▶ Oral and Slate Assessments

WHOLE-CLASS ACTIVITY

Problems 1 and 3 provide summative information and can be used for grading purposes. Problems 2 and 4 provide formative information that can be useful in planning future instruction.

Oral Assessment

1. Have children mentally estimate the sums of multidigit addition and subtraction problems. *Suggestions:*

   $57 + 72$ $60 + 70 = 130$; $43 + 39$ $40 + 40 = 80$;
   $98 - 23$ $100 - 20 = 80$

2. Show whether each fraction is greater than $\frac{1}{2}$ (thumbs-up), less than $\frac{1}{2}$ (thumbs-down), or equal to $\frac{1}{2}$ (fist). *Suggestions:*

   $\frac{2}{5}$ thumbs-down, less than $\frac{1}{2}$; $\frac{6}{12}$ fist, equal to $\frac{1}{2}$; $\frac{9}{10}$ thumbs-up, greater than $\frac{1}{2}$; $\frac{2}{4}$ fist, equal to $\frac{1}{2}$; $\frac{1}{6}$ thumbs-down, less than $\frac{1}{2}$

Slate Assessment

3. Tell multiplication number stories. Have children write a number model for each and then solve. *Suggestions:*

   - 9 boxes of colored pencils. 8 colored pencils in a box. How many colored pencils in all? $9 \times 8 = ?$; 72 colored pencils
   - 6 bags of marbles. 9 marbles in each bag. How many marbles in all? $6 \times 9 = ?$; 54 marbles

4. Tell division number stories. Encourage children to write a number model for each and then solve. *Suggestions:*

   - 56 candies shared equally by 7 children. How many candies per child? $56 \div 7 = ?$ or $7 \times ? = 56$; 8 candies per child
   - 47 pennies shared equally by 9 children. How many pennies per child? $47 \div 9 = ?$ or $9 \times ? = 47$; 5 pennies per child with 2 pennies left over

Assessment Master

Name Date Time

LESSON 9·14 **Self Assessment** Progress Check 9

Check one box for each skill.

Skills	I can do this on my own and can explain how to do it.	I can do this on my own.	I can do this if I get help or look at an example.
1. Solve multiplication number stories.			
2. Use partial products to solve multiplication problems.			
3. Use the lattice method to solve multiplication problems.			
4. Compare fractions using Fraction Cards.			
5. Find the area and perimeter of a shape.			
6. Estimate money amounts.			

***Assessment Handbook,* p. 187**

Assessment Master

Name Date Time

LESSON 9·14 **Written Assessment** Progress Check 9

Part A

1. How much do four 40-pound beavers weigh? 160 pounds
   Show your work.

Use partial products or the lattice method to solve.

2. 23 × 4 = 80 + 12 = 92

3. 49 × 8 = 320 + 72 = 392

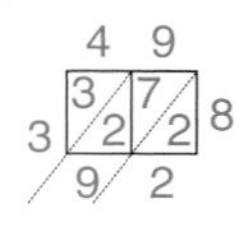

4. Put these fractions in order from smallest to largest. You may use your Fraction Cards.
   $\frac{9}{9}$ $\frac{2}{3}$ $\frac{5}{6}$ $\frac{4}{12}$ $\frac{0}{2}$

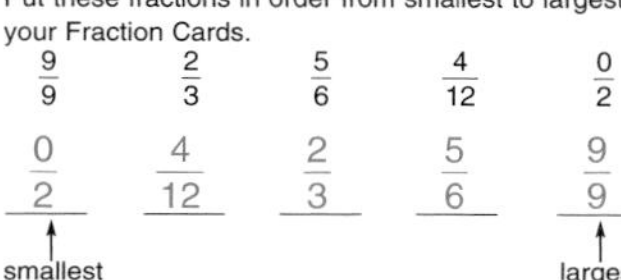

***Assessment Handbook,* p. 188**

Assessment Master

Name ______ Date ______ Time ______

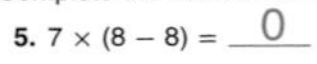

LESSON 9•14 Written Assessment *continued*

Complete the number sentences.

5. 7 × (8 − 8) = 0
6. 48 = (7 × 8) − 8
7. 7 + (3 × 9) = 34
8. 90 = (7 + 3) × 9
9. Draw a rectangle with a perimeter of 24 centimeters.

Sample answers for Problems 9–12:

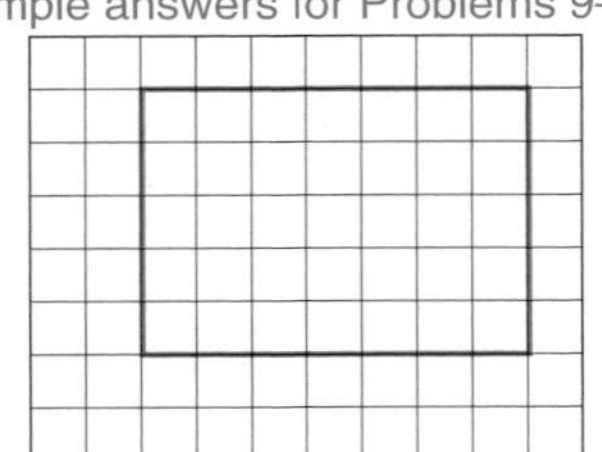

10. How do you know the perimeter is 24 cm?
My rectangle is 7 cm long and 5 cm wide. I added the lengths of the 4 sides. 7 + 7 + 5 + 5 = 24.
11. What is the area of your rectangle? 35 sq cm
12. How did you find the area?
I counted the square centimeters; I multiplied the length of the rectangle by the width of the rectangle.

Assessment Handbook, p. 189

Assessment Master

Name ______ Date ______ Time ______

LESSON 9•14 Written Assessment *continued*

Mr. Stevens has $10.00 to buy as many packs of batteries as he can. 1 pack of batteries costs $3.59. Sample answers:

13. How many packs can he buy? 2
14. About how much money will he spend? About $7.00
15. About how much change will he get back? About $3.00

Part B

16. Explain Lora's mistake in the problem below.

28
× 60
120
+ 48
168

Lora multiplied 60 times 2 instead of 60 times 20. She also multiplied 8 by 6 instead of 8 times 60.

17. Use partial products or the lattice method to solve.

37
× 28
1,036

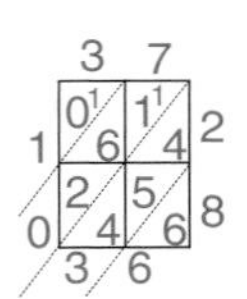

18. Marge is buying hamburger buns for the third grade picnic. She needs 90 buns. They come in packages of 8. How many packages should she buy? 12 packages

Explain how you figured out your answer.
80 buns come in 10 packages because 8 × 10 = 80. 2 more packages would make 96 buns. Marge needs 12 packages to get 90 buns. 6 buns would be left over.

Assessment Handbook, p. 190

▶ Written Assessment

(*Assessment Handbook*, pp. 188–190)

Part A Recognizing Student Achievement

Problems 1 through 15 provide summative information and may be used for grading purposes.

Problem(s)	Description
1	Solve a multidigit multiplication number story.
2, 3	Use the lattice or partial-products method to solve multidigit multiplication problems.
4	Use area models to order fractions.
5–8	Solve problems involving parentheses.
9–12	Describe and use strategies for calculating the perimeter and the area of a shape.
13–15	Make reasonable estimates.

Part B Informing Instruction

Problems 16 through 18 provide formative information that can be useful in planning future instruction.

Problem(s)	Description
16	Describe the strategy used to solve a multidigit multiplication problem.
17	Solve a multidigit multiplication problem.
18	Use equal grouping to model division.

Use the checklists on pages 261 and 263 of the *Assessment Handbook* to record results. Then input the data into the **Assessment Management Spreadsheets** to keep an ongoing record of children's progress toward Grade-Level Goals.

▶ Open Response

(*Assessment Handbook,* p. 191)

Factor Patterns

The open-response item requires children to apply skills and concepts from Unit 9 to solve a multistep problem. See the *Assessment Handbook,* pages 121–125 for rubrics and children's work samples for this problem.

2 Looking Ahead: Preparing for Unit 10

▶ Math Boxes 9•14

INDEPENDENT ACTIVITY

(*Math Journal 2,* p. 239)

Mixed Practice This Math Boxes page is a preview of content in Unit 10.

▶ Home Link 9•14: Unit 10 Family Letter

INDEPENDENT ACTIVITY

(*Math Masters,* pp. 315–318)

Home Connection The Unit 10 Family Letter provides parents and guardians with information and activities related to Unit 10 topics.

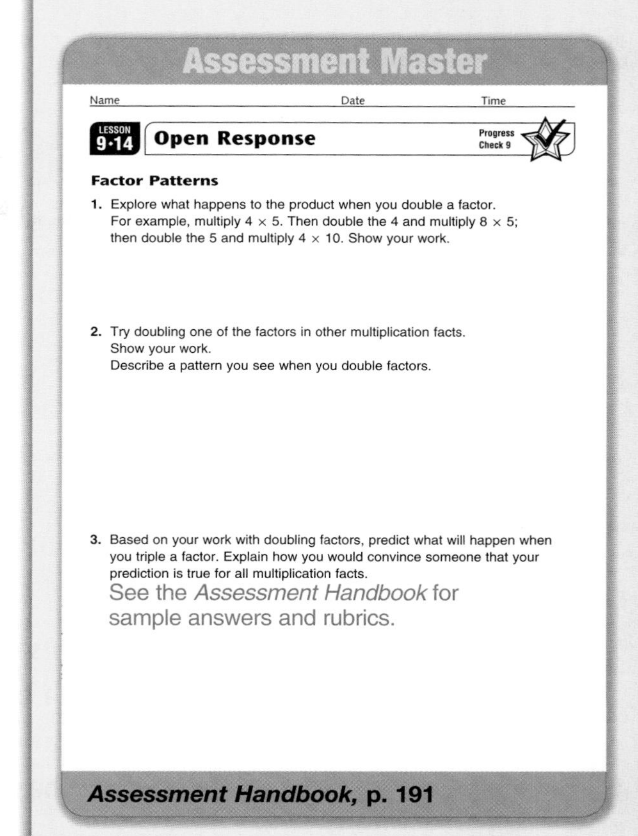

Assessment Master

Name Date Time

LESSON 9•14 **Open Response** Progress Check 9

Factor Patterns

1. Explore what happens to the product when you double a factor. For example, multiply 4 × 5. Then double the 4 and multiply 8 × 5; then double the 5 and multiply 4 × 10. Show your work.

2. Try doubling one of the factors in other multiplication facts. Show your work. Describe a pattern you see when you double factors.

3. Based on your work with doubling factors, predict what will happen when you triple a factor. Explain how you would convince someone that your prediction is true for all multiplication facts.

See the *Assessment Handbook* for sample answers and rubrics.

***Assessment Handbook,* p. 191**

Home Link Masters

Name Date Time

LESSON 9•13 **Unit 10: Family Letter**

Measurement and Data

This unit has three main objectives:

- To review and extend previous work with measures of length, weight, and capacity by providing a variety of hands-on activities and applications. These activities will provide children with experience using U.S. customary and metric units of measurement.
- To extend previous work with the median and mode of a set of data and to introduce the mean (average) of a set of data.
- To introduce two new topics: finding the volume of rectangular prisms and using ordered pairs to locate points on a coordinate grid.

Children will repeat the personal measurements they made earlier in the year so that they may record their own growth. They will display these data in graphs and tables and find typical values for the class by finding the median, mean, and mode of the data.

They will begin to work with volumes of rectangular boxes, which have regular shapes, and will also compare the volumes of several irregular objects and investigate whether there is a relationship between the weight of these objects and their volumes.

Tables of Measures	
Length	1 kilometer = 1,000 meters 1 meter = 100 centimeters 1 centimeter = 10 millimeters 1 mile = 1,760 yards 1 yard = 3 feet 1 foot = 12 inches
Weight	1 kilogram = 1,000 grams 1 gram = 1,000 milligrams 1 ton = 2,000 pounds 1 pound = 16 ounces
Volume & Capacity	1 liter = 1,000 milliliters 1 gallon = 4 quarts 1 quart = 2 pints 1 pint = 2 cups 1 cubic yard = 27 cubic feet 1 cubic foot = 1,728 cubic inches

Please keep this Family Letter for reference as your child works through Unit 10.

***Math Masters,* pp. 315–318**

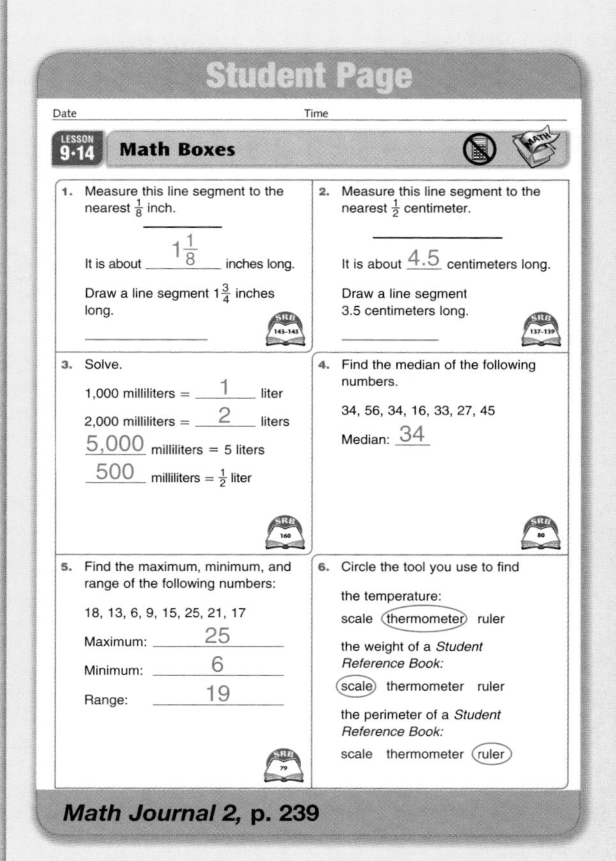

Student Page

Date Time

LESSON 9•14 **Math Boxes**

1. Measure this line segment to the nearest $\frac{1}{8}$ inch.
It is about $1\frac{1}{8}$ inches long.
Draw a line segment $1\frac{3}{4}$ inches long.
SRB 143–145

2. Measure this line segment to the nearest $\frac{1}{2}$ centimeter.
It is about 4.5 centimeters long.
Draw a line segment 3.5 centimeters long.
SRB 137–139

3. Solve.
1,000 milliliters = 1 liter
2,000 milliliters = 2 liters
5,000 milliliters = 5 liters
500 milliliters = $\frac{1}{2}$ liter
SRB 160

4. Find the median of the following numbers.
34, 56, 34, 16, 33, 27, 45
Median: 34
SRB 80

5. Find the maximum, minimum, and range of the following numbers:
18, 13, 6, 9, 15, 25, 21, 17
Maximum: 25
Minimum: 6
Range: 19
SRB 79

6. Circle the tool you use to find
the temperature:
scale (thermometer) ruler
the weight of a *Student Reference Book:*
(scale) thermometer ruler
the perimeter of a *Student Reference Book:*
scale thermometer (ruler)

***Math Journal 2,* p. 239**

Unit 10 Organizer

Measurement and Data

Overview

In this unit, children review and extend their previous work with measures of length, weight, and capacity. Measurements will be displayed in graphs and frequency tables. The emphasis on hands-on activities in this unit reflects the fact that anything that involves measures begins with the use of measuring tools.

Children will also extend previous informal work with the median and mode of a set of data and introduce the standard method of calculating the mean. These statistical measures are used to analyze and compare measurement data. Unit 10 has three main areas of focus:

- To review units, tools, and measures of weight, length, and capacity,
- To introduce the mean of a set of data, and
- To gain experience with plotting points on a coordinate grid.

Linking to the Common Core State Standards

CCSS

The content of Unit 10 addresses the Common Core State Standards for Mathematics in *Measurement and Data*. The correlation of the Common Core State Standards to the *Everyday Mathematics* Grade 3 lessons begins on page CS1.

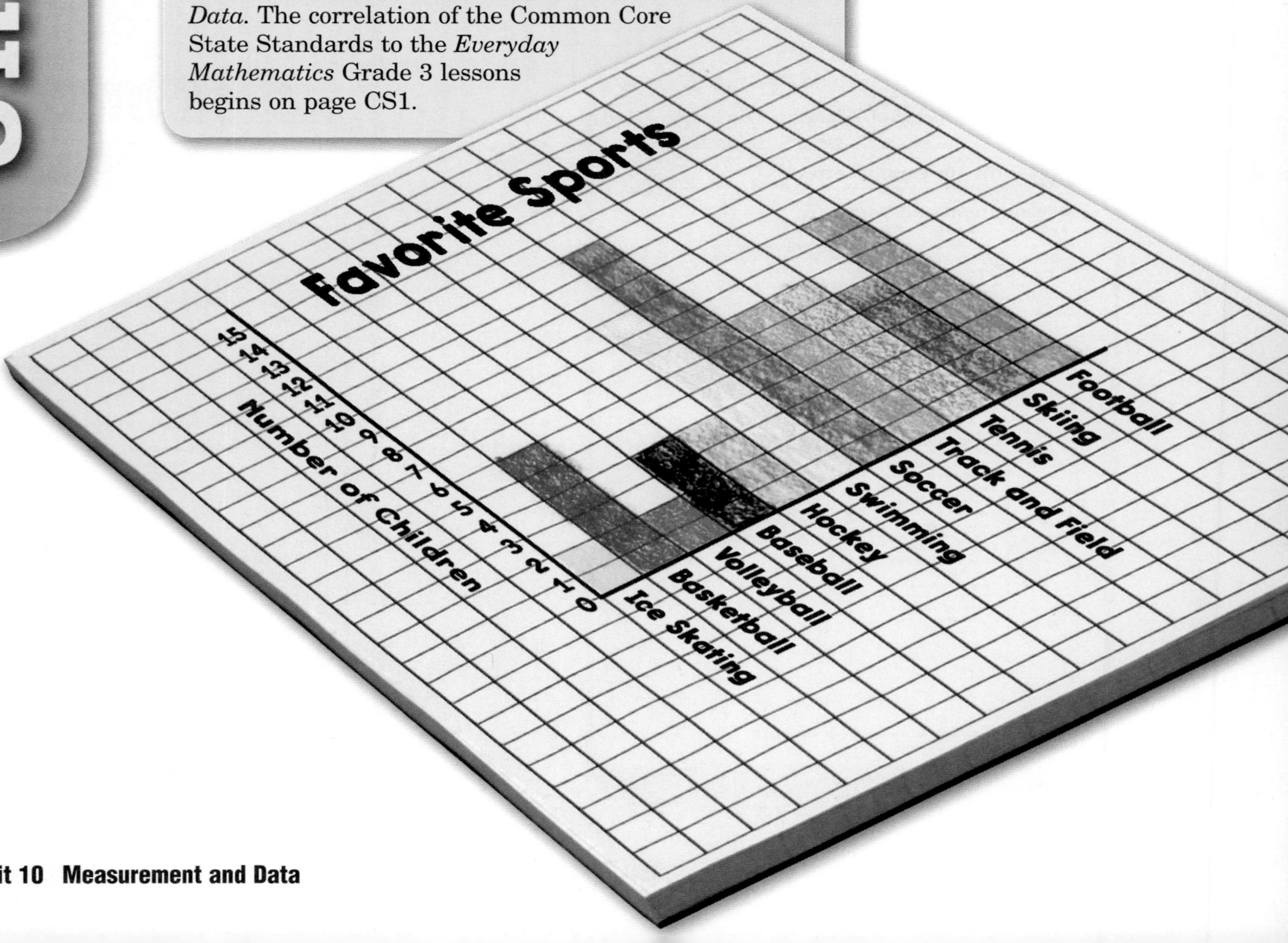

Favorite Sports

Number of Children

0 1 2 3 4 5 6 7 8 9 10 11 12 13 14 15

Ice Skating, Basketball, Volleyball, Baseball, Hockey, Swimming, Soccer, Track and Field, Tennis, Skiing, Football

Contents

*Visit www.everydaymathonline.com for Guiding Questions that support Standards for Mathematical Practice (SMPs).

Learning In Perspective

	Lesson Objectives	Links to the Past	Links to the Future
10•1	To provide a review of units, tools, and measuring length in U.S. customary and metric systems.	Measuring tools are introduced in Kindergarten. In Grade 2, children measure objects with rulers, tape measures, and metersticks/yardsticks.	Children continue to apply measurement to real-world situations beyond Grade 3.
10•2	To guide children as they explore the volume of rectangular prisms.	In previous grades, children investigate volume through informal activities.	In Grade 4, children build regular prisms using centimeter cubes and derive a formula for finding volume.
10•3	To provide a review of metric and U.S. customary units of weight; and to guide children as they examine different kinds of scales and read weights on scales.	In Kindergarten, children informally work with units of measure for weight. In Grade 2, children use standard and nonstandard tools to measure and estimate weight.	In Grade 4, children work with equivalencies for units of measure for weight.
10•4	To provide experiences ordering objects by volume, using a pan balance to measure mass, and measuring weight using various kinds of scales.	In Grade 2, children explore the concept of volume and informally work with units of measure for weight.	In Grade 4, children work with equivalencies for units of measure for linear measure, weight, and capacity. They continue to explore the concept of mass.
10•5	To explore the concept of capacity; and to demonstrate equivalencies between measures of capacity.	Children begin working informally with units of measure in Kindergarten. In Grade 2, children explore capacity through informal activities.	In Grade 4, children work with equivalencies for units of measure for linear measure, weight, and capacity.
10•6	To introduce the mean of a set of data; and to review the median of a set of data.	In Grade 2, children find the median, mode, maximum, and minimum of data sets.	Beyond Grade 3, children continue to find the mean, median, and mode when analyzing data. They determine which middle value is most useful in a given situation.
10•7	To guide children as they calculate the mean of a set of data; and to review the median of a set of data.	In Grade 2, children find the median, mode, maximum, and minimum of data sets.	Beyond Grade 3, children continue to analyze data in a variety of situations. They determine which middle value is most useful in a given situation.
10•8	To introduce the memory keys on a calculator.	Children have used calculators to skip count and to solve problems with large numbers since Kindergarten.	In Grade 4 and beyond, children continue to solve problems with calculators when appropriate.
10•9	To guide children as they make frequency tables, and as they find the median, mean, and mode of data sets.	In Kindergarten and Grade 1, children analyze the frequency of data values by tallying. In Grade 2, children find the median, mode, maximum, and minimum of data sets.	In Unit 11, children make frequency tables to organize the results of probability experiments. Beyond Grade 3, children continue to analyze data in a variety of situations.
10•10	To introduce plotting coordinates on coordinate grids.	Since Kindergarten, children have located and placed numbers on number lines.	In Grade 4, children use grid coordinates to identify regions, give directions, and describe routes on a map. In Grade 5, children plot transformations on a coordinate grid.

	Key Concepts and Skills	Grade 3 Goals*
10•1	Measure line segments to the nearest $\frac{1}{2}$ inch and $\frac{1}{2}$ centimeter.	Measurement and Reference Frames Goal 1
	Label points on a ruler.	Measurement and Reference Frames Goal 1
	Describe relationships among units of length.	Measurement and Reference Frames Goal 3
	Predict the weight of objects.	Data and Chance Goal 4
10•2	Measure length to the nearest centimeter.	Measurement and Reference Frames Goal 1
	Measure area as square units.	Measurement and Reference Frames Goal 2
	Identify parallel sides of a rectangular prism.	Geometry Goal 1
	Identify bases of a rectangular prism.	Geometry Goal 2
10•3	Compare numbers to interpret intervals.	Number and Numeration Goal 6
	Order objects by weight.	Number and Numeration Goal 6
	Check predictions of weight of objects to the actual weight of objects.	Data and Chance Goal 4
10•4	Collect and organize data in a table.	Data and Chance Goal 1
	Predict the volume of objects and test the predictions.	Data and Chance Goal 4
	Predict the weight of objects and test the predictions.	Data and Chance Goal 4
10•5	Describe relationships among measures.	Measurement and Reference Frames Goal 3
	Compare fractions.	Number and Numeration Goal 6
	Use multiplication facts to find customary-unit equivalencies.	Operations and Computation Goal 3
10•6	Order whole numbers.	Number and Numeration Goal 6
	Use data to complete a bar graph.	Data and Chance Goal 1
	Find the median and mean of data sets.	Data and Chance Goal 2
	Use graphs to ask and answer questions.	Data and Chance Goal 2
10•7	Add 2- and 3-digit numbers with a calculator.	Operations and Computation Goal 2
	Collect and organize data.	Data and Chance Goal 1
	Find the median and mean of a data set.	Data and Chance Goal 2
	Use graphs to answer questions and draw conclusions.	Data and Chance Goal 2
10•8	Use addition and subtraction facts to solve problems.	Operations and Computation Goal 1
	Use mental arithmetic to add and subtract numbers.	Operations and Computation Goal 2
	Use calculators to solve problems involving the addition and subtraction of whole numbers.	Operations and Computation Goal 2
10•9	Order whole numbers.	Number and Numeration Goal 6
	Collect and organize data to create a frequency table.	Data and Chance Goal 1
	Find the median and mode of a data set.	Data and Chance Goal 2
10•10	Order numbers on a number line.	Number and Numeration Goal 6
	Draw line segments to connect plotted points on a coordinate grid.	Geometry Goal 1

*See the Appendix for a complete list of Grade 3 Goals.

A Balanced Curriculum

Ongoing Practice

Everyday Mathematics provides numerous opportunities for ongoing practice. These activities are embedded throughout the lessons:

Mental Math and Reflexes activities promote speed and accuracy in mental computation.

Math Boxes offer mixed practice and are paired across lessons as shown in the brackets below. This makes them useful as assessment tools. The last one or two boxes on each page preview the next unit's content.

Mixed practice	[10•1, 10•3], [10•2, 10•4], [10•5, 10•7], [10•6, 10•8], [10•9, 10•10]
Mixed practice with multiple choice	10•1, 10•2, 10•6, 10•7, 10•8, 10•10
Mixed practice with writing/reasoning opportunity	10•3, 10•4, 10•5, 10•6, 10•7, 10•8, 10•9

Home Links are daily homework assignments that review the content of the lesson and often contain ongoing facts practice or computation practice.

Minute Math+ problems are offered for additional practice in Lessons 10•4, 10•5, and 10•9.

EM Facts Workshop Game provides online practice of basic facts and computation.

EXTRA PRACTICE **Extra Practice** activities are included in Lessons 10•1, 10•4, 10•5, 10•7, 10•9, and 10•10.

Practice through Games

Games are an essential component of practice in the *Everyday Mathematics* program. Games offer skills practice and promote strategic thinking. See the *Differentiation Handbook* for ways to adapt games to meet children's needs.

Lesson	Game	Skill Practiced
10•2	*Fraction Top-It*	**Comparing fractions** [NN Goals 1 and 6]
10•3	*Factor Bingo*	**Finding factors of a number** [OC Goal 3]
10•4	*Beat the Calculator* (Multiplication)	**Practicing multiplication facts** [OC Goal 3]
10•7	*Multiplication Top-It*	**Practicing multiplication facts** [OC Goal 3]
10•8, 10•10	*Memory Addition/Subtraction*	**Practicing mental addition and subtraction skills** [OC Goal 2]

[NN] Number and Numeration
[MRF] Measurement and Reference Frames
[OC] Operations and Computation
[GEO] Geometry
[DC] Data and Chance
[PFA] Patterns, Functions, and Algebra

Problem Solving 

Good problem solvers use a variety of strategies, including the following:

- Draw a picture.
- Act out the problem.
- Make a table, chart, or list.
- Look for a pattern.
- Try a simpler version of the problem.
- Make a guess and try it out.

The table below lists some of the opportunities in this unit for children to practice these strategies.

Lessons that teach *through* problem solving, not just *about* problem solving

Lesson	Activity
10•2	Find the volume of a rectangular prism.
10•3	Order four objects by weight.
10•4	Measuring mass of objects.
10•6	Find the mean and median of a set of data.
10•6	Find the median of a set of data.
10•8	Solve measurement number stories.
10•8	Solve calculator riddles.

See Chapter 18: Problem Solving in the *Teacher's Reference Manual* for more information.

The Language of Mathematics

Everyday Mathematics provides lesson-specific suggestions to help all children acquire, process, and express mathematical ideas. Throughout Unit 10, there are lesson-specific language development notes that address the needs of English language learners, indicated by ELL.

ELL SUPPORT Activities to support English language learners are in Part 3 of Lessons 10•2, 10•3, and 10•6.

The *English Learners Handbook* and the *Differentiation Handbook* have suggestions for promoting language development and acquisition of mathematics vocabulary. See Unit 10 in each handbook.

Unit 10 Vocabulary

average
capacity of a container
capacity of a scale
coordinate
coordinate grid
cubic centimeter
frequency table
height of a prism
mean
median
memory
memory keys
mode
ordered pair
plotting the point
precision
square centimeter
square inch
volume
weight

Literacy Connection

Millions to Measure, by David M. Schwartz, HarperCollins, 2003

A Fly on the Ceiling: A Math Myth, by Julie Glass, Random House, 1998

Who Sank the Boat? by Pamela Allen, Sandcastle Books, 1990

For more literacy connections, see the *Home Connection Handbook,* Grades 1–3.

Cross-Curricular Links 

Health
Lesson 10•5 Children discuss nutritional information on labels.

Social Studies
Lesson 10•10 Children learn how to use the index on a map.

Balanced Assessment

Daily Assessments

- **Recognizing Student Achievement** – A daily assessment that is included in every lesson to evaluate children's progress toward the Grade 3 Grade-Level Goals.
- **Informing Instruction** – Notes that appear throughout the unit to help anticipate children's common errors and suggest appropriate problem-solving strategies.

Lesson	Recognizing Student Achievement	Informing Instruction
10•1	Measure to the nearest $\frac{1}{2}$ inch and $\frac{1}{2}$ cm. [MRF Goal 1]	
10•2	Write decimal numbers and identify the value of the digits. [NN Goal 1]	Count cubes to find volume. Find the volume of rectangular prisms.
10•3	Demonstrate automaticity with multiplication facts through 10 × 10. [OC Goal 3]	Read scales.
10•4	Demonstrate automaticity with multiplication facts through 10 × 10. [OC Goal 3]	
10•5	Draw conclusions about data representations. [DC Goal 2]	
10•6	Complete a bar graph. [DC Goal 1]	Find the median of a data set.
10•7	Explain the meaning of *median.* [DC Goal 2]	
10•8	Predict the outcome of an experiment. [DC Goal 4]	
10•9	Solve problems involving fractional parts of sets. [NN Goal 2]	Find the mode of a data set. Find missing measurements.
10•10	Find the median of a data set. [DC Goal 2]	

[NN] Number and Numeration
[MRF] Measurement and Reference Frames
[OC] Operations and Computation
[GEO] Geometry
[DC] Data and Chance
[PFA] Patterns, Functions, and Algebra

Portfolio Opportunities

The following lessons provide opportunities to gather samples of children's mathematical writings, drawings, and creations to add balance to the assessment process: Lessons 10•2, 10•3, 10•4, 10•5, 10•6, 10•7, 10•8, 10•9, and 10•11.

See pages 16 and 17 in the *Assessment Handbook* for more information about portfolios and how to use them.

Unit Assessment

Progress Check 10 – A cumulative assessment of concepts and skills taught in Unit 10 and in previous units, providing information for evaluating children's progress and planning for future instruction. These assessments include oral/slate, written, and open-response activities, as shown below in the sample Progress Check lesson opener.

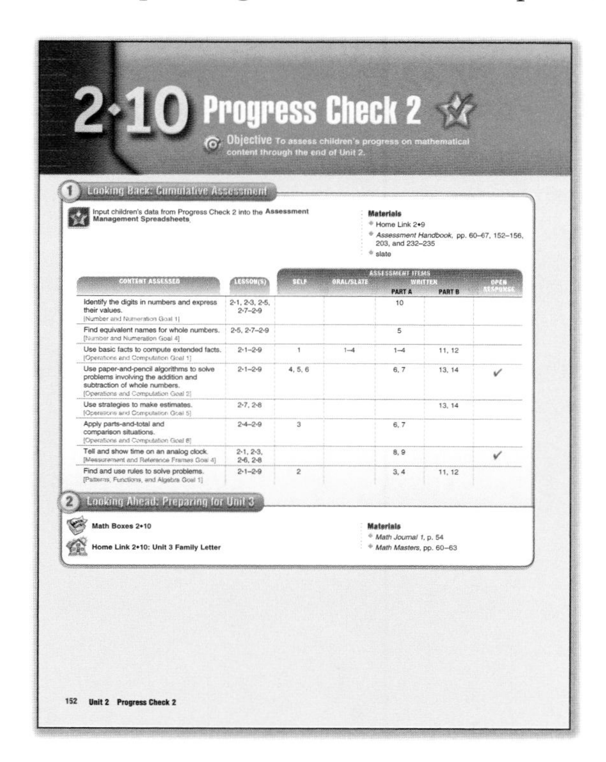

2•10 Progress Check 2

Objective To assess children's progress on mathematical content through the end of Unit 2.

1 Looking Back: Cumulative Assessment

Input children's data from Progress Check 2 into the **Assessment Management Spreadsheets**.

Materials
- Home Link 2•9
- *Assessment Handbook*, pp. 60–67, 152–156, 203, and 232–235
- slate

Content Assessed	Lesson(s)	Assessment Items: Self	Oral/Slate	Written: Part A	Written: Part B	Open Response
Identify the digits in numbers and express their values. [Number and Numeration Goal 1]	2·1, 2·3, 2·5, 2·7–2·9			10		
Find equivalent names for whole numbers. [Number and Numeration Goal 4]	2·5, 2·7–2·9			5		
Use basic facts to compute extended facts. [Operations and Computation Goal 1]	2·1–2·9	1	1–4	1–4	11, 12	
Use paper-and-pencil algorithms to solve problems involving the addition and subtraction of whole numbers. [Operations and Computation Goal 2]	2·1–2·9	4, 5, 6		6, 7	13, 14	✓
Use strategies to make estimates. [Operations and Computation Goal 5]	2·7, 2·8				13, 14	
Apply parts-and-total and comparison situations. [Operations and Computation Goal 6]	2·4–2·9	3		6, 7		
Tell and show time on an analog clock. [Measurement and Reference Frames Goal 4]	2·1, 2·3, 2·6, 2·8			8, 9		✓
Find and use rules to solve problems. [Patterns, Functions, and Algebra Goal 1]	2·1–2·9	2		3, 4	11, 12	

2 Looking Ahead: Preparing for Unit 3

Math Boxes 2•10

Home Link 2•10: Unit 3 Family Letter

Materials
- *Math Journal 1*, p. 54
- *Math Masters*, pp. 60–63

152 Unit 2 Progress Check 2

Core Assessment Resources

Assessment Handbook

- **Unit 10 Assessment Overview,** pages 126–133
- **Unit 10 Assessment Masters,** pages 192–196
- **Unit 10 Individual Profiles of Progress,** pages 264, 265, and 280
- **Unit 10 Class Checklists,** pages 266, 267, and 281
- **Math Logs,** pages 286–288
- **Exit Slip,** page 283
- **Other Student Assessment Forms,** pages 284, 285, 289, and 290

Assessment Management Spreadsheets

The Assessment Management Spreadsheets consist of the Digital Class Checklists and Individual Profile of Progress Checklists. Use them to monitor, record, and report children's progress.

Addressing All Needs

Differentiated Instruction

Adjusting the Activity – suggests adaptations that target advanced learners, English language learners, or learners who need additional instructional support.

ELL SUPPORT / **ELL** – provides lesson-specific suggestions to help English language learners understand and process the mathematical content.

READINESS – accesses children's prior knowledge or previews content that prepares children to engage in the lesson's Part 1 activities.

EXTRA PRACTICE – provides additional opportunities to apply the mathematical content of the lesson.

ENRICHMENT – enables children to apply or further explore the mathematical content of the lesson.

Lesson	Adjusting the Activity	ELL Support/ ELL	Readiness	Extra Practice	Enrichment
10•1			•	•	•
10•2		•	•		•
10•3	•	•	•		•
10•4				•	
10•5			•	•	•
10•6		•	•		•
10•7		•	•	•	•
10•8	•	•	•		•
10•9	•	•	•	•	•
10•10	•	•		•	•

Additional Resources

Differentiation Handbook
Provides ideas and strategies for differentiating instruction.
Pages 111–117

English Learners Handbook
Contains lesson-specific comprehension strategies.
Pages 96–105

Multilingual Handbook
Previews concepts and vocabulary. It is written in six languages.
Pages 191–210

Planning Tips

Multiage Classroom

Companion Lessons from Grades 2 and 4 can help you meet instructional needs of a multiage classroom. The full Scope and Sequence can be found in the Appendix.

Grade 2	4•7, 9•2–9•5	5•6, 8•2	2•8, 7•5, 9•9	2•8, 5•6, 7•5, 8•2, 9•6, 9•8, 9•9	9•6, 9•8	3•5, 7•7, 12•6	3•5, 7•7, 12•6	10•3, 10•4	7•8	
Grade 3	**10•1**	**10•2**	**10•3**	**10•4**	**10•5**	**10•6**	**10•7**	**10•8**	**10•9**	**10•10**
Grade 4	4•9, 4•10	11•4, 11•5	11•7	11•4, 11•5, 11•7	11•7	2•6	2•6		2•6	6•8

Pacing for Success

Pacing depends on a number of factors, such as children's individual needs and how long your school has been using *Everyday Mathematics*. At the beginning of Unit 10, you may want to use tools available at www.everydaymathonline.com to help you set your pace.

Home Support

Unit 10 Family Letter (English/Spanish) provides families with an overview, Do-Anytime Activities, Building Skills through Games, a list of vocabulary, and answers to the daily homework (Home Links). Family Letters in English, Spanish, and seven other languages are also available online.

Home Links are the daily homework assignments. They consist of active projects and ongoing review problems.

Home Support Resources

Home Connection Handbook
Offers ideas and reproducible masters for communicating with families. See Table of Contents for unit information.

Student Reference Book
Provides a resource for children and parents.

Pages 80, 81, 83–85, 88, 89, 89A, 89B, 137–140, 143–146, 154–156, 160–163, 165, 166, 180, 181, 246, 247, 279, 285–287, 290, 291, 297, 298

Materials

Technology Resources www.everydaymathonline.com

ePresentations

eToolkit

Algorithms Practice

EM Facts Workshop Game™

Family Letters

Assessment Management

Common Core State Standards

Curriculum Focal Points

Interactive Teacher's Lesson Guide

Lesson	Masters	Manipulative Kit	Other Items
10•1	Home Link Master, p. 320 Teaching Masters, pp. 319, 321, and 322	tape measure; meterstick; ruler; slate	Class Data Pad; trundle wheel*; half-sheets of paper; 4 objects
10•2	Teaching Masters, pp. 323, 326, and 327 Teaching Aid Master, p. 416* Home Link Masters, pp. 324 and 325 *Differentiation Handbook,* p. 133	cm cubes	model of a rectangular prism; tape; scissors; half-sheets of paper; 4 objects from Lesson 10•1; Fraction Cards; various rectangular prisms; blank paper
10•3	Home Link Master, p. 329 Game Master, p. 448 Teaching Masters, pp. 328 and 330	4 each of number cards 2–9; slate	Class Data Pad and 4 objects from Lesson 10•1; a variety of scales; counters; half-sheets of paper; liter bottle of water; 5 objects of varying weights; 5 index cards labeled with weights of objects
10•4	Teaching Masters, pp. 331, 333–335 Home Link Master, p. 332 Teaching Aid Master, p. 398	liter pitcher; slate; pan balance; base-10 blocks	counters*; 4 objects from Lesson 10•1; empty 2- or 3-lb coffee can; water; large bucket or tub; paper towels or tray; objects to weigh; bath scale; other scales; chalkboard eraser; 1-pound package of pasta; 5-lb bag of flour or sugar; nickel; liter bottle of water; paper clip; calculator
10•5	Home Link Master, p. 337 Teaching Aid Master, p. 398 Teaching Masters, pp. 336 and 338	tape measure	containers (half-pint, pint, quart, half-gallon, gallon, liter, 100mL); water; paper towels; tray; Class Data Pad from Lessons 10•1 and 10•3; food labels; half-sheet of paper; tubs of rice, dried beans, or sand; 5 containers of different sizes and shapes; funnel*; small paper cups; $\frac{1}{2}$ cup of popcorn kernels; popped popcorn from $\frac{1}{2}$ cup of kernels; scales; measuring cup
10•6	Home Link Master, p. 340 Teaching Masters, pp. 339, 341, and 342 *Differentiation Handbook,* p. 132	ruler; tool-kit pennies; dice	stick-on notes*; straightedge; counters
10•7	Home Link Master, p. 343 Teaching Masters, pp. 344 and 345 Teaching Aid Masters, pp. 398 and 437 Transparency of *Math Masters,* p. 437	4 each of number cards 0–10; slate	stick-on notes; small box; calculator; paper; counters*; crayons
10•8	Teaching Masters, pp. 347–349 Home Link Master, p. 346	slate	index card or stick-on note*; calculator
10•9	Home Link Master, p. 351 Teaching Masters, pp. 350 and 352	slate*	Class Data Pad; counters*; $8\frac{1}{2}$" by 11" sheets of paper; numbered index cards; calculator; graphing software*
10•10	Transparency of *Math Masters,* p. 438* Home Link Master, p. 353 Teaching Masters, pp. 354 and 355 Teaching Aid Masters, p. 438	geoboard and rubber bands; slate	map with index; dry-erase marker (fine point); straightedge; calculator
10•11	Assessment Masters, pp. 192–196 Home Link Masters, pp. 356–359	ruler; slate	blue and green crayons; blank paper; counters; calculator

*Denotes optional materials

Mathematical Background

The discussion below highlights the major content ideas presented in Unit 10 and helps establish instructional priorities.

Equivalent Measures and Measure Conversions

(Lessons 10•1, 10•3, and 10•5)

The importance of measure in nearly everyone's daily life is reflected in the many entries in dictionaries for the word *measure.* For example, in the American Heritage Dictionary, there are 17 entries for the noun form of *measure* (including such uses as measures in music notation) and 11 entries for its verb form. In addition, there are a few entries for the word *measurement.*

Just as counts answer the question "How many __?", measures answer the question "How much __?" where the blank represents length, weight, power, speed, energy, or volume. We use whole numbers to count objects. To measure objects, the number system must be extended to include fractions and decimals.

A measure, like a count, is always linked to a unit. In the United States, we use both U.S. customary and metric units of measure. For this reason, it is important that children become adept at using the most common units in both systems.

These lessons review units of measure in both the metric and U.S. customary systems. The focus is on equivalencies between units of measure; on the selection of the appropriate tools and units for making various measurements; and on making the actual measurements.

Lesson 10-3 also examines a variety of scales used to weigh objects ranging from those that are very light (on letter scales or diet/food scales) to those that are very large (on platform scales).

Refer to Section 14.2 of the *Teacher's Reference Manual* for additional information about measurement systems.

Metric System Units of Length	U.S. Customary System Units of Length
1 kilometer (km) = 1,000 meters (m)	1 mile (mi) = 1,760 yards (yd) = 5,280 feet (ft)
1 meter (m) = 10 decimeters (dm) = 100 centimeters (cm) = 1,000 millimeters (mm)	1 yard (yd) = 3 feet (ft) = 36 inches (in.)
1 decimeter (dm) = 10 centimeters (cm)	1 foot (ft) = 12 inches (in.)
1 centimeter (cm) = 10 millimeters (mm)	

Note

The metric system is often thought to be easy to use because it employs a base-ten number system in most of its basic physical units: meter (length), gram (mass or weight), liter (capacity), Kelvin (thermodynamic temperature, a measure of actual energy content), ampere (electric current), mole (substance), and candela (luminous intensity). These basic units are standardized by an international bureau of standards. Other metric units are multiples of these few basic units or result from combining them. (The kilometer, for example, is a multiple of a meter—1,000 meters.) Units of area and volume are obtained by multiplying lengths. Units of length combined with units of time result in units of speed (for example, meters per second).

Unit 10 Organizer

Project Note

Use Project 1, Solid Waste, to guide children as they estimate and measure the weight or volume of a week's accumulation of trash.

Volume, Capacity, and Weight

(Lessons 10•2–10•5)

Children already know from past experience that units of area are used in measuring 2-dimensional space. The names of most of these units contain explicit references to their 2-dimensionality: square inches (sq in. or in^2), square centimeters (sq cm or cm^2). Similarly, the names of many units for volume and capacity make explicit reference to their three dimensions: cubic inches (cu in. or in^3), cubic centimeters (cu cm or cm^3), and so on.

Other units for volume and capacity, such as milliliters, teaspoons, pints, quarts, and liters, are expressed without reference to dimension.

The introduction to volumes of rectangular prisms in Lesson 10-2 is entirely informal. The activities are structured so that children may begin to think intuitively of volume in terms of counting identical layers of cubes. This serves as preparation for more formal work in Grades 4–6, when the volume of a prism or cylinder is expressed as the product of the area of its base times its height.

Exploration A in Lesson 10-4 introduces a powerful and practical method for comparing the volumes of irregular objects: The objects are submerged in water, and the amounts of water displaced by the various objects are poured into a liter pitcher. (The more water displaced, the greater the volume of the object.) The volume of each object is recorded to the nearest 50mL.

By comparing the volumes and weights of the objects in this same exploration, children begin to develop an intuitive grasp of the meaning of the density of materials—a topic that will be further developed in Grades 4–6.

Please see the *Teacher's Reference Manual,* Sections 14.5 and 14.6, for more information about volume, capacity, weight, and mass.

Metric System Units of Mass (Weight)	U.S. Customary System Units of Weight
1 metric ton (t) = 1,000 kilograms (kg)	1 pound (lb) = 16 ounces (oz)
1 kilogram (kg) = 1,000 grams (g)	1 ton (T) = 2,000 pounds (lb)
1 gram (g) = 1,000 milligrams (mg)	
Units of Capacity and Volume	**Units of Capacity and Volume**
1 kiloliter (kL) = 1,000 liters (L)	1 gallon (gal) = 4 quarts (qt)
1 liter (L) = 1,000 milliliters (mL)	1 quart (qt) = 2 pints (pt)
	1 pint (pt) = 2 cups (c)
	1 cup (c) = 8 fluid ounces (fl oz)
	1 fluid ounce (fl oz) = 2 tablespoons (tbs)
	1 tablespoon (tbs) = 3 teaspoons (tsp)

Formal Methods for Finding the Mean of a Set of Data

(Lessons 10•6–10•9)

Children's first exposure to the mean of a set of data came in Lesson 3-1. There they found the mean length of shoes in the class by pacing off the shoes of 16 children on a strip of adding-machine tape and folding it into 16 equal parts. In Lesson 10-6, they extend their understanding of the concept of the mean as an average or typical value through a hands-on activity: They find the mean of a set of data by leveling off the bars in a bar graph so that each bar is the same height. Then Lesson 10-7 introduces the standard method of computing the mean (dividing the sum of the data by the number of pieces of data).

Project Note

Use Project 6, How Far Can You Go in a Million Steps? to provide opportunities to measure and estimate distances and to guide children as they work with powers of 10 and large numbers.

Lesson 10-8 introduces the use of the memory keys on calculators. Note that not all calculators have the same number of memory keys nor use the same labels on the memory keys. You will need to take this into account as you and the children work with calculators. Before you start Lesson 10-8, make sure that you know how to operate the memory keys on the calculators that children are using. See Lesson 10-8 and the *Student Reference Book* for details about memory keys on TI and Casio calculators.

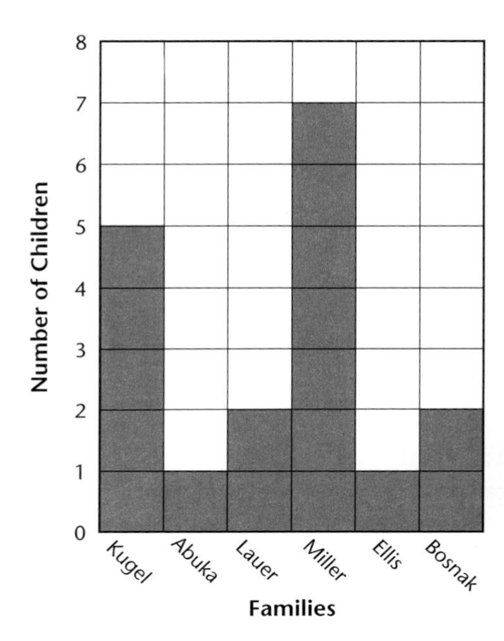

Lesson 10-9 extends the standard method of finding the mean to data recorded in a frequency table. This method involves using the memory keys on the calculator to find the sum of the data. The memory keys make it possible to reduce the number of calculator entries, thus reducing the likelihood of making keying errors.

For additional information about data analysis, see Section 12.2.4 of the *Teacher's Reference Manual.*

Coordinate Grids (Lesson 10•10)

This lesson introduces the use of ordered pairs to locate points on a coordinate grid. This is an important topic, which will be extended in later grades, as well as in high school and college mathematics courses.

Refer to Section 15.3.2 of the *Teacher's Reference Manual* for additional information about coordinate grids.

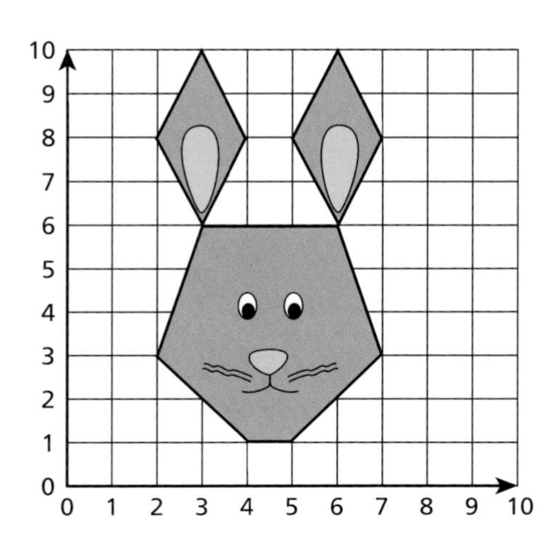

10•1 Review: Length

Objective To provide a review of units, tools, and measuring length in U.S. customary and metric systems.

ePresentations

eToolkit

Algorithms Practice

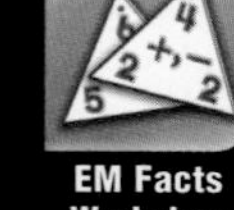
EM Facts Workshop Game™

Family Letters

Assessment Management

Common Core State Standards

Curriculum Focal Points

Interactive Teacher's Lesson Guide

1 Teaching the Lesson

Key Concepts and Skills

- Measure line segments to the nearest $\frac{1}{2}$ inch and $\frac{1}{2}$ centimeter.
  [Measurement and Reference Frames Goal 1]
- Label points on a ruler.
  [Measurement and Reference Frames Goal 1]
- Describe relationships among units of length.
  [Measurement and Reference Frames Goal 3]
- Predict the weight of objects.
  [Data and Chance Goal 4]

Key Activities

Children list and discuss measuring tools and units of length, rename U.S. customary measurements, and practice measuring in centimeters and inches. They predict the weight of objects.

Ongoing Assessment: Recognizing Student Achievement
Use journal page 240.
[Measurement and Reference Frames Goal 1]

Materials

Math Journal 2, pp. 240 and 241
Student Reference Book, pp. 137–140, 143–146, 154–156, 246, and 247
ruler ◆ Class Data Pad ◆ trundle wheel (optional) ◆ tape measure ◆ slate ◆ half-sheet of paper ◆ 4 objects placed in random order on a table

2 Ongoing Learning & Practice

Using a Multiplication Algorithm
Math Journal 2, p. 242
Children practice using a multiplication algorithm to find products.

Math Boxes 10•1
Math Journal 2, p. 243
Children practice and maintain skills through Math Box problems.

Home Link 10•1
Math Masters, p. 320
Children practice and maintain skills through Home Link activities.

3 Differentiation Options

READINESS

Completing a Story with Measures
Math Masters, p. 322
Children complete a story by filling in measurement units.

ENRICHMENT

Finding Measurements
Math Masters, p. 321
per partnership: rulers, tape measures, metersticks
Children use estimation skills to search for classroom items of given measurements.

EXTRA PRACTICE

Finding a Buried Treasure
Math Masters, p. 319
ruler
Children measure the lengths of two paths leading to a buried treasure.

Advance Preparation

For Part 1, display 4 objects. (See Planning Ahead, Lesson 9•13.)

For the optional Enrichment activity in Part 3, draw line segments that are 12 in. and 100 cm on the board.

***Teacher's Reference Manual,* Grades 1–3** p. 157

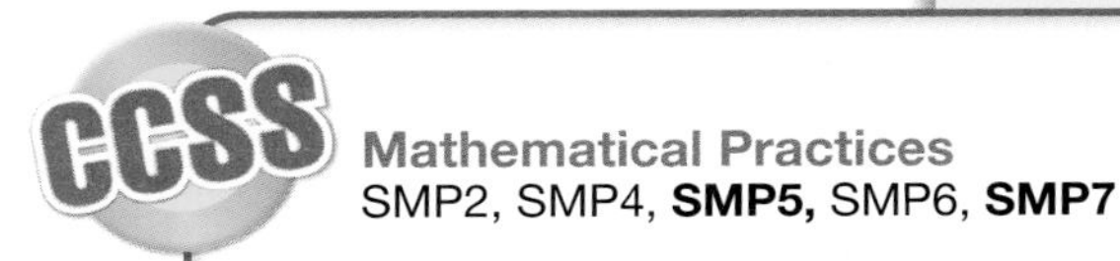

Mathematical Practices
SMP2, SMP4, **SMP5,** SMP6, **SMP7**

Getting Started

Mental Math and Reflexes

On their slates, have children solve problems like the following:

●○○ 7 [5s] 35
70 [5s] 350
70 [50s] 3,500

●●○ 80 [4s] 320
80 [40s] 3,200
80 [400s] 32,000

●●● 30 [90s] 2,700
30 [900s] 27,000
300 [900s] 270,000

Math Message

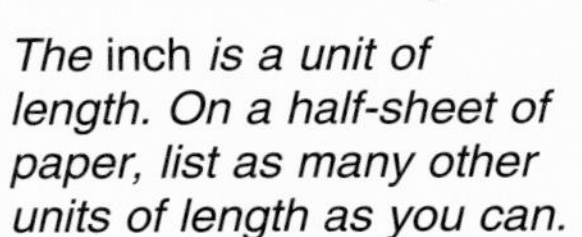

The inch is a unit of length. On a half-sheet of paper, list as many other units of length as you can.

Interactive whiteboard-ready ePresentations are available at www.everydaymathonline.com to help you teach the lesson.

1 Teaching the Lesson

▶ Math Message Follow-Up

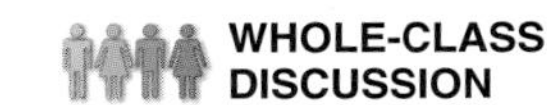

WHOLE-CLASS DISCUSSION

(*Student Reference Book,* pp. 246 and 247)

Quickly review units of length and their equivalents. Ask children to name the units in their lists as you write them in three columns on the board. Put metric units in one column and U.S. customary units in another column. If you are not sure to which system a unit belongs, or if a unit is neither metric nor U.S. customary, list it in the third column.

Metric Units	U.S. Customary Units	Other

After children have no more units to add to the list, review equivalencies between units. Record them on the Class Data Pad. (*See margin.*) Be sure to call attention to the abbreviations for the units.

Remind children that there is a table of measures on *Student Reference Book,* pages 246 and 247 and on the inside back cover of their journals.

NOTE Be sure to save these pages in the Class Data Pad. Add equivalencies as they come up in later lessons.

Metric Units
1 kilometer (km) = 1,000 meters (m)
1 meter (m) = 10 decimeters (dm)
1 meter (m) = 100 centimeters (cm)
1 meter (m) = 1,000 millimeters (mm)
1 decimeter (dm) = 10 centimeters (cm)
1 centimeter (cm) = 10 millimeters (mm)

U.S. Customary Units
1 mile (mi) = 1,760 yards (yd)
1 mile (mi) = 5,280 feet (ft)
1 yard (yd) = 3 feet (ft)
1 yard (yd) = 36 inches (in.)
1 foot (ft) = 12 inches (in.)

Class Data Pad

NOTE Remind children to continue to record the sunrise, sunset, and length of day for your location in their journals on pages 279–281. They will also continue to record the national high and low temperatures on journal page 175, and then graph the temperature range on journal pages 176 and 177.

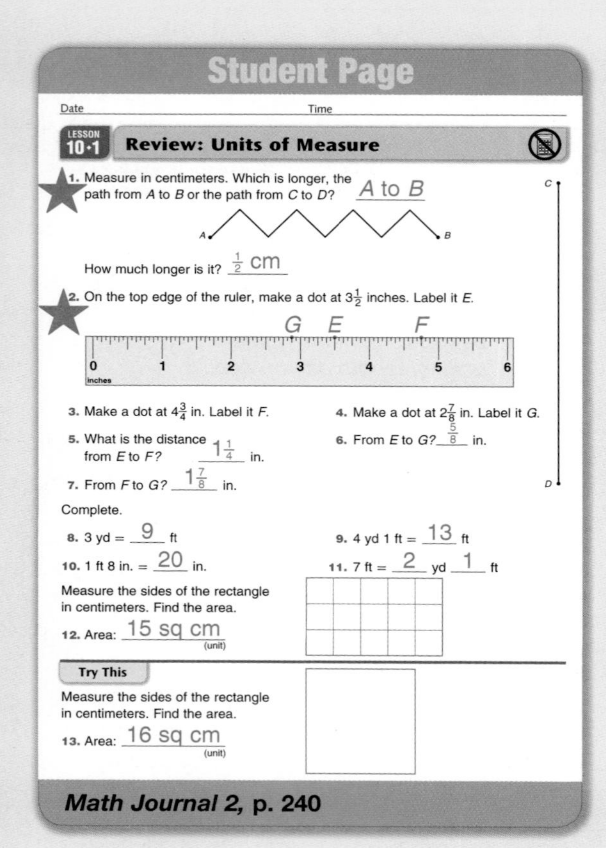
Student Page

Date Time

LESSON 10·1 **Review: Units of Measure**

1. Measure in centimeters. Which is longer, the path from *A* to *B* or the path from *C* to *D*? A to B

How much longer is it? $\frac{1}{2}$ cm

2. On the top edge of the ruler, make a dot at $3\frac{1}{2}$ inches. Label it *E*.

3. Make a dot at $4\frac{3}{4}$ in. Label it *F*.
4. Make a dot at $2\frac{7}{8}$ in. Label it *G*.
5. What is the distance from *E* to *F*? $1\frac{1}{4}$ in.
6. From *E* to *G*? $\frac{5}{8}$ in.
7. From *F* to *G*? $1\frac{7}{8}$ in.

Complete.

8. 3 yd = 9 ft
9. 4 yd 1 ft = 13 ft
10. 1 ft 8 in. = 20 in.
11. 7 ft = 2 yd 1 ft

Measure the sides of the rectangle in centimeters. Find the area.

12. Area: 15 sq cm (unit)

Try This

Measure the sides of the rectangle in centimeters. Find the area.

13. Area: 16 sq cm (unit)

Math Journal 2, p. 240

Student Page

Date Time

LESSON 10·1 **Weight and Volume**

Complete Part 1 before the start of Lesson 10-3. Answers vary.

Part 1 Order the objects on display from heaviest (1) to lightest (4). Lift them to help you guess. Record your guesses below.

1. ____ 2. ____
3. ____ 4. ____

Complete Part 2 as part of Lesson 10-3.

Part 2 Record the actual order of the objects from heaviest (1) to lightest (4). How close were your guesses?

1. ____ 2. ____
3. ____ 4. ____

Complete Parts 3 and 4 and Problems 1–3 as part of Lesson 10-4.

Part 3 Order the objects on display from largest (1) to smallest (4) volume. Record your guesses below.

1. ____ 2. ____
3. ____ 4. ____

Part 4 Record the actual order of the objects from largest (1) to smallest (4) volume. How close were your guesses?

1. ____ 2. ____
3. ____ 4. ____

1. Make a dot on the produce scale to show 1 kg. Label it *A*.
2. Make a dot on the produce scale to show $3\frac{1}{2}$ kg. Label it *B*.
3. Make a dot on the produce scale to show 2 kg, 500 g. Label it *C*.

Math Journal 2, p. 241

▶ Discussing Tools Used to Measure Distances

WHOLE-CLASS DISCUSSION

Ask children to name tools for measuring distances. Rulers, yardsticks, metersticks, tape measures Demonstrate a trundle wheel if one is available. If it is not mentioned, refer to a car's odometer. Children may also mention personal references, such as strides, shoe lengths, forearms, or hand spans. Ask children to suggest distances they might measure with each tool. Extend the discussion by asking questions such as these:

Trundle wheel

- Would it make sense to measure the distance between two cities with a yardstick? no
- How could you measure the circumference (distance around) of the lid of a jar? With a tape measure
- How could you measure the diameter of a ball? Sample answer: Place the ball on a flat surface. Hold a board on top of the ball, parallel to the flat surface. Measure the distance between the flat surface and the board. (Take this opportunity to review the meaning of parallel.) Another possibility: Measure the circumference of the ball; find $\frac{1}{3}$ of the circumference.
- How would you estimate the height of a building? Sample answer: Estimate the height of a room from floor to ceiling and then multiply that number by the number of floors.

▶ Renaming Measurements

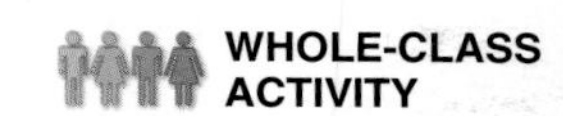
WHOLE-CLASS ACTIVITY

Ask children to find the 18-inch mark on their tape measures. Ask them to identify equivalent names for 18 inches. $1\frac{1}{2}$ feet; $\frac{1}{2}$ yard If prompting is needed, ask:

- Is 18 inches more or less than 1 foot? more How many more inches than 1 foot? 6 in. How many feet and inches are there in 18 inches? 1 ft and 6 in., or 1 ft 6 in.
- What fraction of 1 foot is 6 inches? 6 in. = $\frac{6}{12}$ ft or $\frac{1}{2}$ ft How can you rename 18 inches using a whole number and a fraction? 18 in. = $1\frac{1}{2}$ ft

Pose other renaming problems, limiting measurements to lengths on children's tape measures. For each problem, children share renaming strategies, using their tape measures to help them. *For example:*

- 2 yards is equal to how many feet? 6 ft
- 2 feet is equal to how many inches? 24 in.
- 1 meter is equal to how many centimeters? 100 cm

Give other names for the following lengths:

- 2 feet 3 inches 27 in.; $2\frac{1}{4}$ ft; $\frac{27}{36}$ yd or $\frac{3}{4}$ yd
- 15 inches 1 ft 3 in.; $1\frac{1}{4}$ ft; $\frac{15}{36}$ yd or $\frac{5}{12}$ yd
- 5 ft 60 in.; 1 yd 2 ft; $1\frac{2}{3}$ yds
- $1\frac{1}{3}$ yards 4 ft; 1 yd 1 ft; 48 in.
- $\frac{1}{2}$ meter 50 cm

Practicing Measurement Skills

INDEPENDENT ACTIVITY

(*Math Journal 2,* p. 240, *Student Reference Book,* pp. 137–140; 143–146; 154–156)

Children measure in centimeters and inches, rename linear measures using U.S. customary units, and find the areas of rectangles. Remind children to begin measuring at the 0-mark on their rulers.

Refer children to the *Student Reference Book* to review measuring in the metric and U.S. customary systems. See the following pages:

▷ Measuring Length in Centimeters and Millimeters (pages 137–139)

▷ Changing Units of Length in the Metric System (page 140)

▷ Measuring Length in Inches (pages 143–145)

▷ Changing Units of Length in the U.S. Customary System (page 146)

▷ Area (pages 154–156)

Ongoing Assessment: Recognizing Student Achievement

Journal page 240 Problems 1 and 2

Use **journal page 240, Problems 1 and 2** to assess children's progress toward measuring to the nearest $\frac{1}{2}$ inch and $\frac{1}{2}$ cm. Children are making adequate progress if they successfully complete Problems 1 and 2. Some children may successfully complete Problems 3–7 involving measures to the nearest $\frac{1}{4}$ and $\frac{1}{8}$ in.

[Measurement and Reference Frames Goal 1]

Student Page

Date Time

LESSON 10·1 **Multiplication Practice**

Use your favorite multiplication algorithm to solve the following problems. Show your work.

1. 427 × 3 = 1,281
2. 505 × 8 = 4,040
3. 20 × 90 = 1,800
4. 67 × 40 = 2,680
5. 74 × 35 = 2,590
6. 37 × 58 = 2,146

Math Journal 2, p. 242

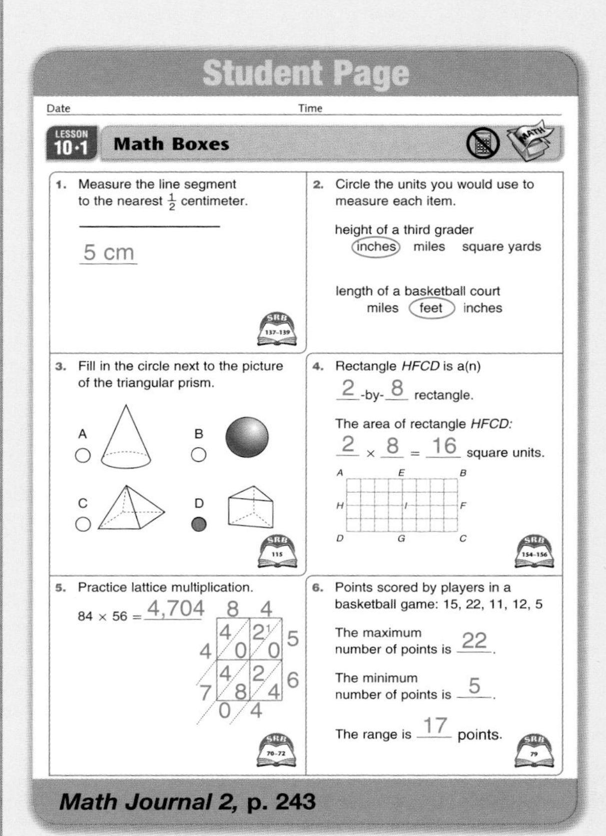

Student Page

Date Time

LESSON 10·1 **Math Boxes**

1. Measure the line segment to the nearest $\frac{1}{2}$ centimeter.
5 cm

2. Circle the units you would use to measure each item.
height of a third grader
(inches) miles square yards
length of a basketball court
miles (feet) inches

3. Fill in the circle next to the picture of the triangular prism.
A B C D (D filled)

4. Rectangle *HFCD* is a(n) 2-by-8 rectangle.
The area of rectangle *HFCD:* 2 × 8 = 16 square units.

5. Practice lattice multiplication.
84 × 56 = 4,704

6. Points scored by players in a basketball game: 15, 22, 11, 12, 5
The maximum number of points is 22.
The minimum number of points is 5.
The range is 17 points.

Math Journal 2, p. 243

Home Link Master

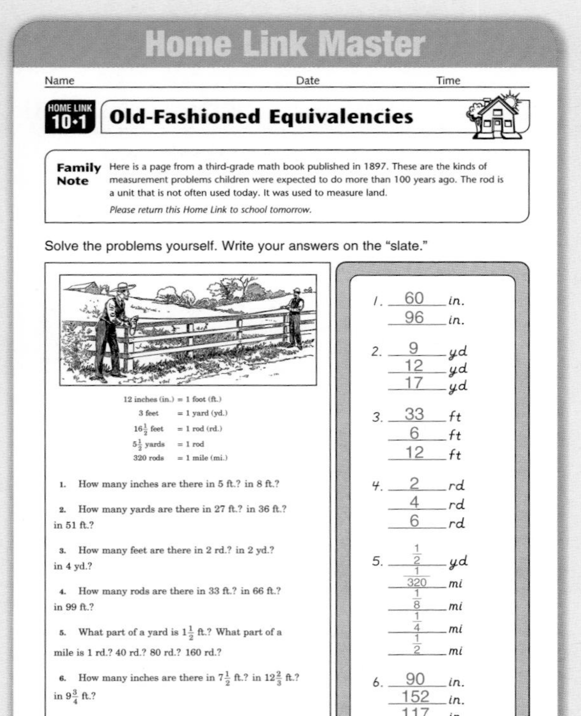
Name Date Time

HOME LINK 10•1 **Old-Fashioned Equivalencies**

Family Note Here is a page from a third-grade math book published in 1897. These are the kinds of measurement problems children were expected to do more than 100 years ago. The rod is a unit that is not often used today. It was used to measure land.

Please return this Home Link to school tomorrow.

Solve the problems yourself. Write your answers on the "slate."

12 inches (in.) = 1 foot (ft.)
3 feet = 1 yard (yd.)
$16\frac{1}{2}$ feet = 1 rod (rd.)
$5\frac{1}{2}$ yards = 1 rod
320 rods = 1 mile (mi.)

1. How many inches are there in 5 ft.? in 8 ft.?
2. How many yards are there in 27 ft.? in 36 ft.? in 51 ft.?
3. How many feet are there in 2 rd.? in 2 yd.? in 4 yd.?
4. How many rods are there in 33 ft.? in 66 ft.? in 99 ft.?
5. What part of a yard is $1\frac{1}{2}$ ft.? What part of a mile is 1 rd.? 40 rd.? 80 rd.? 160 rd.?
6. How many inches are there in $7\frac{1}{2}$ ft.? in $12\frac{2}{3}$ ft.? in $9\frac{3}{4}$ ft.?

Graded Work in Arithmetic: Third Year by S. W. Baird, 1897.

1. 60 in., 96 in.
2. 9 yd, 12 yd, 17 yd
3. 33 ft, 6 ft, 12 ft
4. 2 rd, 4 rd, 6 rd
5. $\frac{1}{2}$ yd, $\frac{1}{320}$ mi, $\frac{1}{8}$ mi, $\frac{1}{4}$ mi, $\frac{1}{2}$ mi
6. 90 in., 152 in., 117 in.

***Math Masters*, p. 320**

▶ Ordering Four Objects by Weight

INDEPENDENT ACTIVITY

(*Math Journal 2,* p. 241)

Children complete Part 1 on journal page 241 before the start of Lesson 10-3. Although the activity should take no more than 5 minutes, only one child can do it at a time. Therefore, children should start working on the activity a couple of days in advance.

NOTE These four objects will be used over the next several lessons.

2 Ongoing Learning & Practice

▶ Using a Multiplication Algorithm

INDEPENDENT ACTIVITY

(*Math Journal 2,* p. 242)

Children use paper-and-pencil multiplication algorithms to solve the problems. Children may share their answers with a partner. If there is a disagreement, encourage them to discuss their strategies with each other and try the problem again.

▶ Math Boxes 10•1

(*Math Journal 2,* p. 243)

Mixed Practice Math Boxes in this lesson are paired with Math Boxes in Lesson 10-3. The skill in Problem 6 previews Unit 11 content.

▶ Home Link 10•1

(*Math Masters,* p. 320)

Home Connection Children solve measurement problems from a textbook published in 1897. Explain that each Home Link problem has more than one answer space.

Teaching Master

Name Date Time

LESSON 10•1 **Story with Measures**

Make a list of 8 measurements of length. Use each of the following units at least once: inch, foot, yard, mile. Answers vary.

A. ________ ________ (unit) B. ________ ________ (unit)
C. ________ ________ (unit) D. ________ ________ (unit)
E. ________ ________ (unit) F. ________ ________ (unit)
G. ________ ________ (unit) H. ________ ________ (unit)

Match the letters in the story with the letters of your measures. Fill in each blank in the story with the measure that has the same letter.

This morning, after walking (A) ________ to school, I saw my friend Emma looking up into a tree. She was staring at a spot about (B) ________ above the ground. How in the world did her backpack get up there? I ran (C) ________ to my friend Henry's house. He had a stepladder (D) ________ tall. We raced back to school and set it up under the tree. I climbed up as far as I could go. If only I were (E) ________ taller, I could reach the backpack. Isaac came running with a stick that was (F) ________ long. I held it up, caught the backpack, and jiggled it free. It crashed to the ground with a thud!

Luckily, my locker is (G) ________ tall and (H) ________ wide. The ladder just fit. At the end of the day, we returned the ladder to Henry's house. Emma and I decided she was getting too big and strong to be tossing backpacks just for fun.

- Read the story. Is it silly or sensible?
- Discuss how you would change the measurements and distances to make the story more sensible.

***Math Masters*, p. 322**

3 Differentiation Options

READINESS

SMALL-GROUP ACTIVITY

▶ Completing a Story with Measures

5–15 Min

(*Math Masters,* p. 322)

To provide experience with measures of length, have children complete a story by filling in measurement units. They read the story and decide if it is silly or sensible. If it is silly (most likely), children change the measurement units or numbers to make sense. They record their work on *Math Masters,* page 322.

ENRICHMENT

PARTNER ACTIVITY

▶ Finding Measurements

15–30 Min

(*Math Masters,* p. 321)

To offer children more experience with estimation skills for measurements, have them find examples of items in the classroom that are close to given measurements. Post 12-inch and 100-centimeter line segments for children to use as references. They record their work on *Math Masters,* page 321.

EXTRA PRACTICE

INDEPENDENT ACTIVITY

▶ Finding a Buried Treasure

5–15 Min

(*Math Masters,* p. 319)

To apply children's understanding of linear measure, have them find the shorter of two paths. They measure line segments to the nearest $\frac{1}{4}$ inch on each path.

Planning Ahead

Collect several different kinds of weight scales (bath scale, kitchen scale, spring scale, package scale, and so on) for Lessons 10-3 and 10-4. For the optional Readiness activity in Lesson 10-3, you will need a liter bottle of water.

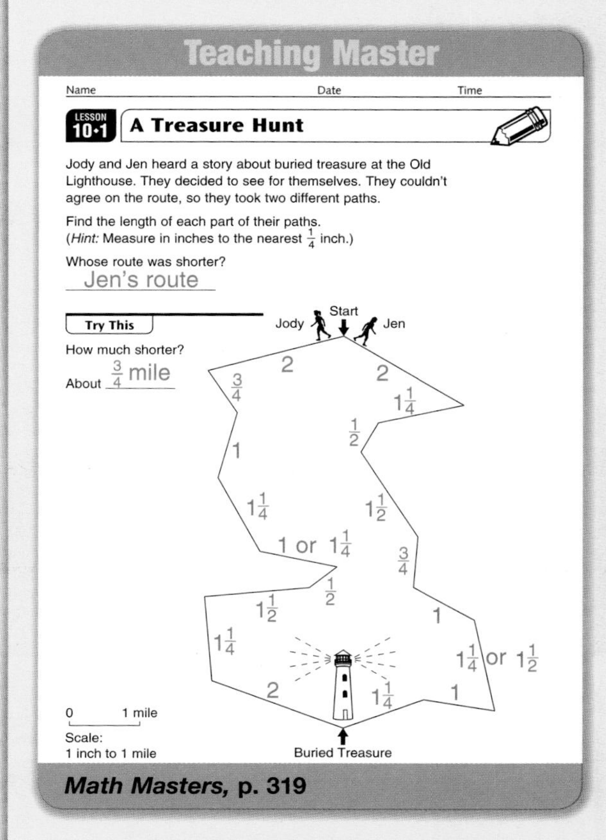
Teaching Master

Name Date Time

LESSON 10·1 A Treasure Hunt

Jody and Jen heard a story about buried treasure at the Old Lighthouse. They decided to see for themselves. They couldn't agree on the route, so they took two different paths.

Find the length of each part of their paths.
(*Hint:* Measure in inches to the nearest $\frac{1}{4}$ inch.)

Whose route was shorter? Jen's route

Try This

How much shorter?

About $\frac{3}{4}$ mile

Math Masters, p. 319

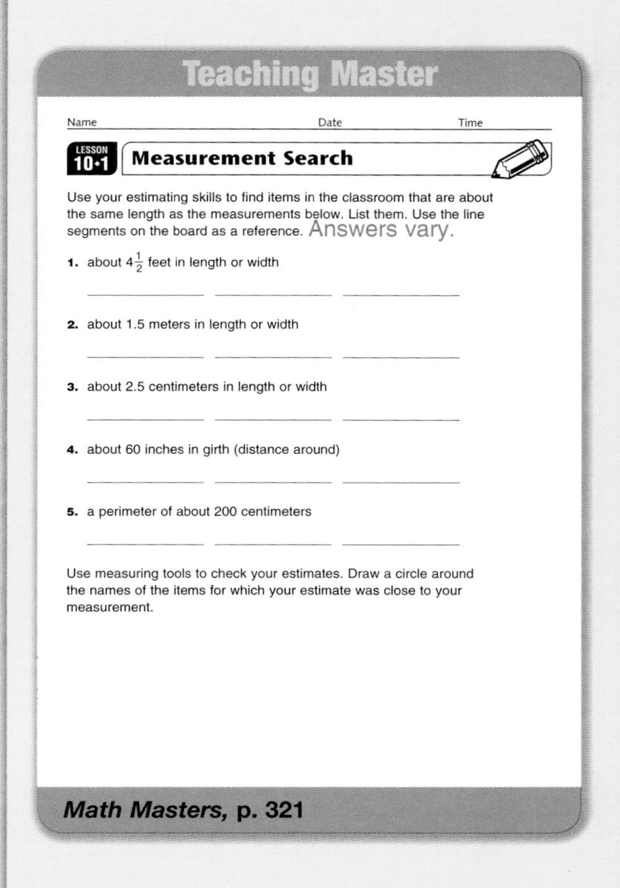
Teaching Master

Name Date Time

LESSON 10·1 Measurement Search

Use your estimating skills to find items in the classroom that are about the same length as the measurements below. List them. Use the line segments on the board as a reference. Answers vary.

1. about $4\frac{1}{2}$ feet in length or width
2. about 1.5 meters in length or width
3. about 2.5 centimeters in length or width
4. about 60 inches in girth (distance around)
5. a perimeter of about 200 centimeters

Use measuring tools to check your estimates. Draw a circle around the names of the items for which your estimate was close to your measurement.

Math Masters, p. 321

10•2 Volume

Objective To guide children as they explore the volume of rectangular prisms.

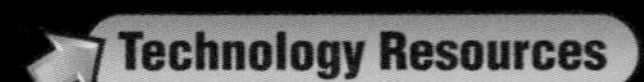

www.everydaymathonline.com

ePresentations

eToolkit

Algorithms Practice

EM Facts Workshop Game™

Family Letters

Assessment Management

Common Core State Standards

Curriculum Focal Points

Interactive Teacher's Lesson Guide

1 Teaching the Lesson

Key Concepts and Skills

- Measure length to the nearest centimeter. [Measurement and Reference Frames Goal 1]
- Measure area as square units. [Measurement and Reference Frames Goal 2]
- Identify parallel sides of a rectangular prism. [Geometry Goal 1]
- Identify bases of a rectangular prism. [Geometry Goal 2]

Key Activities

Children make boxes from centimeter-grid patterns. They estimate the volume of the boxes and then find the volumes by filling the boxes with centimeter cubes.

Ongoing Assessment: Recognizing Student Achievement Use Mental Math and Reflexes. [Number and Numeration Goal 1]

Ongoing Assessment: Informing Instruction See pages 816 and 817.

Key Vocabulary

height of a prism ◆ volume ◆ square inches ◆ square centimeters ◆ cubic centimeters

Materials

Math Journal 2, p. 244
Student Reference Book, pp. 154 and 155
Home Link 10•1
Math Masters, p. 323 (1 per 4 children); p. 416 (optional)
model of a rectangular prism ◆ cm cubes (10 per child) ◆ tape ◆ scissors ◆ half-sheet of paper ◆ 4 objects from Lesson 10•1

2 Ongoing Learning & Practice

Playing *Fraction Top-It*

Student Reference Book, p. 287
per partnership: 1 deck of Fraction Cards, paper
Children practice comparing fractions.

Math Boxes 10•2

Math Journal 2, p. 245
Children practice and maintain skills through Math Box problems.

Home Link 10•2

Math Masters, pp. 324 and 325
Children practice and maintain skills through Home Link activities.

3 Differentiation Options

READINESS

Identifying Bases of Rectangular Prisms

Math Masters, p. 326
various rectangular prisms (see Planning Ahead, Lesson 9•13) ◆ blank paper
Children identify the bases and faces of rectangular prisms.

ENRICHMENT

Exploring the Volumes of Cubes

Math Masters, p. 327
per partnership: at least 125 cm cubes
Children find the volumes of cubes and extend the pattern to find the volume of the next larger cube.

ELL SUPPORT

Building a Math Word Bank

Differentiation Handbook, p. 133
Children add the terms *centimeter, square centimeter,* and *cubic centimeter* to their Math Word Banks.

Advance Preparation

Place a box of cm cubes near the Math Message.

***Teacher's Reference Manual,* Grades 1–3** pp. 159–161

Mathematical Practices
SMP2, **SMP3,** SMP4, **SMP5,** SMP6, SMP7, SMP8
Content Standards
3.NF.3, 3.NF.3d

Getting Started

Mental Math and Reflexes 

On a half-sheet of paper, children write decimal numbers from dictation and identify the place value of digits. *Suggestions:*

●○○ Three and nineteen-hundredths 3.19 Circle the digit in the ones place. 3
Twenty-four and thirty hundredths 24.30 Put an X through the hundredths digit. 0

●●○ Six and seven-hundredths 6.07 Circle the digit in the tenths place. 0
Forty and eighty-hundredths 40.80 Put an X over the tenths digit. 8

●●● Seventy and twenty-one thousandths 70.021 Circle the digit in the thousandths place. 1
Eighty-three and one hundred fifty thousandths 83.150 Put an X through the tenths digit. 1

Math Message

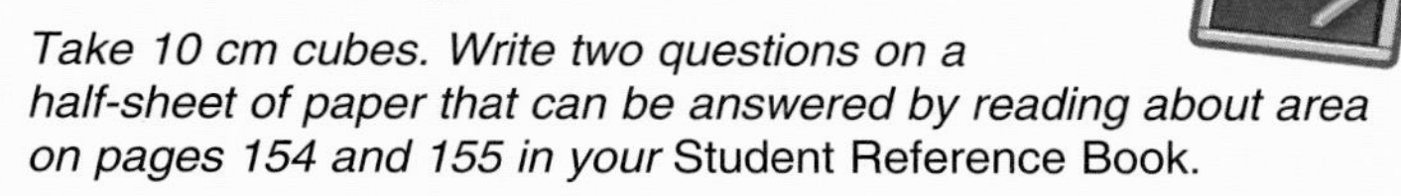

Take 10 cm cubes. Write two questions on a half-sheet of paper that can be answered by reading about area on pages 154 and 155 in your Student Reference Book.

Home Link 10·1 Follow-Up

Briefly discuss the differences between math book pages in 1897 and today. Have children share solution strategies with the class.

Ongoing Assessment: Recognizing Student Achievement

Mental Math and Reflexes 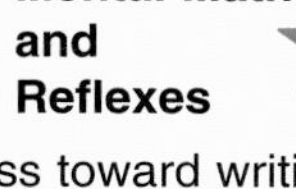

Use **Mental Math and Reflexes** to assess children's progress toward writing decimal numbers and identifying the value of the digits. Children are making adequate progress if they successfully complete the ●○○ and ●●○ problems. Some children may be able to complete the ●●● problems successfully.

[Number and Numeration Goal 1]

NOTE Have children continue to order the four objects from Lesson 10-1 (journal page 241) by weight.

1 Teaching the Lesson

▶ Math Message Follow-Up

WHOLE-CLASS DISCUSSION

(*Student Reference Book,* pp. 154 and 155)

Check that children have picked up their cm cubes. Explain that in the next activity, children will find the amount of space a 3-dimensional shape occupies. To review the concept of area have children share the questions they wrote and have volunteers answer the questions. Emphasize that area is the amount of surface inside a 2-dimensional shape.

▶ Introducing the Volume of a Rectangular Prism

WHOLE-CLASS ACTIVITY

(*Math Journal 2,* p. 244; *Math Masters,* p. 323)

Use a model of a rectangular prism to review the meaning of *bases of a rectangular prism.* The bases of a rectangular prism are any pair of opposite faces you designate as bases. The bases are rectangular, parallel, have the same area, and are connected by rectangular faces. Place the prism on one of its bases and define the **height of a prism** as the distance between the two opposite bases.

Student Page

Measurement

Area

Sometimes we want to know the amount of **surface inside** a shape. The amount of surface inside a shape is called the **area** of the shape.

One way to find the area of a shape is to count the number of squares of a certain size that cover the inside of the shape.

The rectangle below is covered by squares that are 1 centimeter on each side. Each square is called a **square centimeter.**

4 cm
2 cm
1 cm
1 cm
1 square centimeter (actual size)

Eight of the squares cover the rectangle. The area of the rectangle is 8 square centimeters.

A square with sides 1 inch long is a **square inch.**

1 in.
1 in.
1 square inch (actual size)

A square with 1-foot sides is a **square foot.**

The **square yard** and **square meter** are larger units of area. They are used to measure large areas such as the area of a floor.

Student Reference Book, **p. 154**

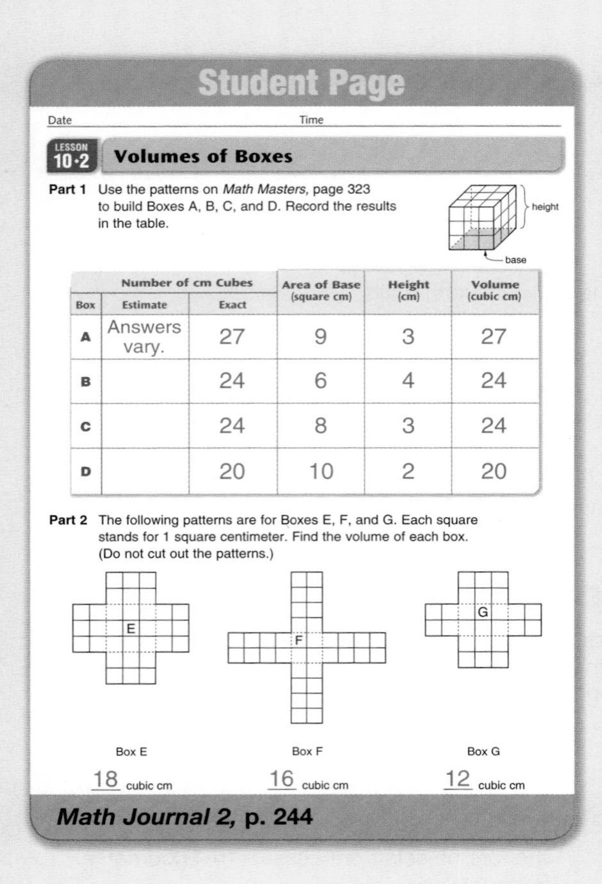

Student Page

Date _______ Time _______

LESSON 10·2 **Volumes of Boxes**

Part 1 Use the patterns on *Math Masters,* page 323 to build Boxes A, B, C, and D. Record the results in the table.

Box	Number of cm Cubes: Estimate	Number of cm Cubes: Exact	Area of Base (square cm)	Height (cm)	Volume (cubic cm)
A	Answers vary.	27	9	3	27
B		24	6	4	24
C		24	8	3	24
D		20	10	2	20

Part 2 The following patterns are for Boxes E, F, and G. Each square stands for 1 square centimeter. Find the volume of each box. (Do not cut out the patterns.)

Box E 18 cubic cm

Box F 16 cubic cm

Box G 12 cubic cm

Math Journal 2, p. 244

Remind children that they may choose any pair of opposite faces of a rectangular prism as bases. The height of the prism depends on which faces are chosen as bases.

Divide the class into groups of four. Each group should have 1 copy of *Math Masters,* page 323 and a total of 40 cubes that group members picked up in the Math Message. Guide the class in the following activity:

1. One member of the group cuts the masters into four pieces by cutting along the horizontal and vertical dashed lines.
2. Each group member takes one of the pieces, cuts out the pattern along the outside dashed lines, folds it along the dotted lines, and tapes it together to form an open box labeled *A, B, C,* or *D.*

It helps to score the dotted lines before folding. Run the point of a pencil along the fold line while applying pressure. The more accurate the folds are, the more successful this activity will be.

3. Point out that each box is made of centimeter grid paper. Each child estimates how many cm cubes are needed to fill each of the four boxes and records all four estimates in the Estimate column of the table in Part 1 on journal page 244.
4. Bring the class together to share estimates and strategies for obtaining estimates.
5. Within their groups, each child fills one box with cm cubes. Group members record the number of cubes needed to fill each of the four boxes in the Exact column and compare these results to their original estimates.

Ongoing Assessment: Informing Instruction

Watch for children who are having trouble counting the cubes that fill the box. Have them count the cubes one layer at a time.

6. Bring the class back together and ask children to describe how they counted the number of cubes needed to fill each box. Some children may have noticed that each layer has the same number of cubes, counted the number of cubes in one layer, and then multiplied that number by the number of layers.
7. Have children find the area of the base of each box and the height of the box. They should record the results in the Area of Base and Height columns.
8. The number of cm cubes needed to fill a box is called the **volume** of the box. Have children record the volume of each box in the Volume column.

To support English language learners, discuss the meanings of the word *volume.* Have children look up the word in the dictionary. Children may have heard the word used in contexts involving a radio or a book. Emphasize that *volume* is also used in a mathematical context.

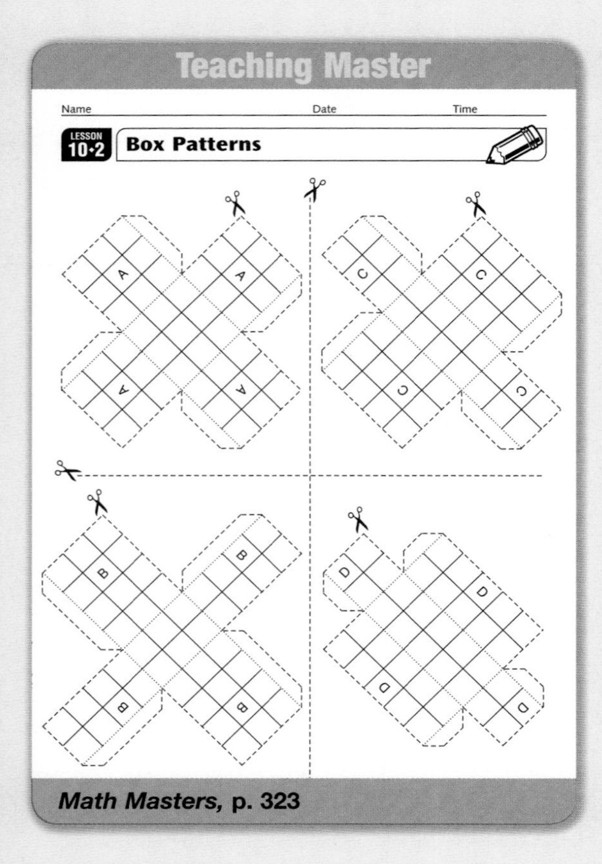

Teaching Master

Name _______ Date _______ Time _______

LESSON 10·2 **Box Patterns**

Math Masters, p. 323

NOTE: Both volume and capacity are measures of the amount of space something occupies. Common measures of volume and capacity are cubic units such as centimeter cubes, cubic inches, cubic feet, quarts, cups, gallons, or liters.

Remind children that in a mathematical context, volume is a measure of the amount of space taken up by a 3-dimensional object. Volume measurements are expressed in cubic units. For example, the volume of Box A on journal page 244 is 27 **cubic centimeters.** Write 27 cubic cm and 27 cm^3 on the board to illustrate two ways of writing cubic units. Also remind children that area measurements are expressed in square units, such as **square centimeters** (sq cm or cm^2) or **square inches** (sq in. or $in.^2$). Length, height, perimeter, and circumference are expressed in units of length, such as centimeters and feet. Ask: *Is it possible for two boxes to have different shapes but the same volume?* Yes. For example, Box B and Box C have different shapes but the same volume, 24 cm^3.

Children complete Part 2 on their own. They find the volume of each box from the pattern shown (without building the boxes).

Ongoing Assessment: Informing Instruction

Watch for children who need support for finding the volumes in Part 2 (*Math Journal 2,* page 244). Have them copy the patterns onto centimeter grid paper (*Math Masters,* page 416) and build the boxes. Some children may want to build the boxes to check their answers.

2 Ongoing Learning & Practice

▶ Playing *Fraction Top-It*

(*Student Reference Book,* p. 287)

Children practice comparing fractions using the shaded parts of cards in *Fraction Top-It.* For instructions, see Lesson 8-6 or page 287 in the *Student Reference Book.* Have children play at least five rounds, recording their comparisons of fraction pairs on paper using the symbols >, <, and =.

▶ Math Boxes 10•2

(*Math Journal 2,* p. 245)

Mixed Practice Math Boxes in this lesson are paired with Math Boxes in Lesson 10-4. The skill in Problem 6 previews Unit 11 content.

Student Page

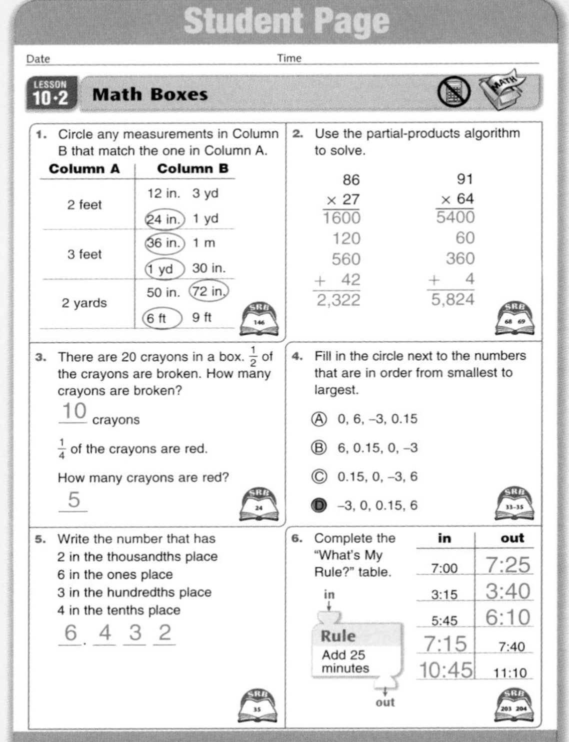

Date Time

LESSON 10•2 **Math Boxes**

1. Circle any measurements in Column B that match the one in Column A.

Column A	Column B	
2 feet	12 in.	3 yd
	(24 in.)	1 yd
3 feet	(36 in.)	1 m
	(1 yd)	30 in.
2 yards	50 in.	(72 in.)
	(6 ft)	9 ft

2. Use the partial-products algorithm to solve.

86 × 27: 1600 + 120 + 560 + 42 = 2,322

91 × 64: 5400 + 60 + 360 + 4 = 5,824

3. There are 20 crayons in a box. $\frac{1}{2}$ of the crayons are broken. How many crayons are broken?
10 crayons
$\frac{1}{4}$ of the crayons are red.
How many crayons are red?
5

4. Fill in the circle next to the numbers that are in order from smallest to largest.
Ⓐ 0, 6, –3, 0.15
Ⓑ 6, 0.15, 0, –3
Ⓒ 0.15, 0, –3, 6
● –3, 0, 0.15, 6

5. Write the number that has
2 in the thousandths place
6 in the ones place
3 in the hundredths place
4 in the tenths place
6 . 4 3 2

6. Complete the "What's My Rule?" table.
Rule: Add 25 minutes

in	out
7:00	7:25
3:15	3:40
5:45	6:10
7:15	7:40
10:45	11:10

Math Journal 2, p. 245

Links to the Future

It may take time for children to understand that area is measured in square units and volume is measured in cubic units. Although some children will recognize the pattern, do not expect all children to understand the relationship between the area of the base and the volume of a box. Finding the volume of a rectangular prism is a Grade 4 Goal.

Home Link Master

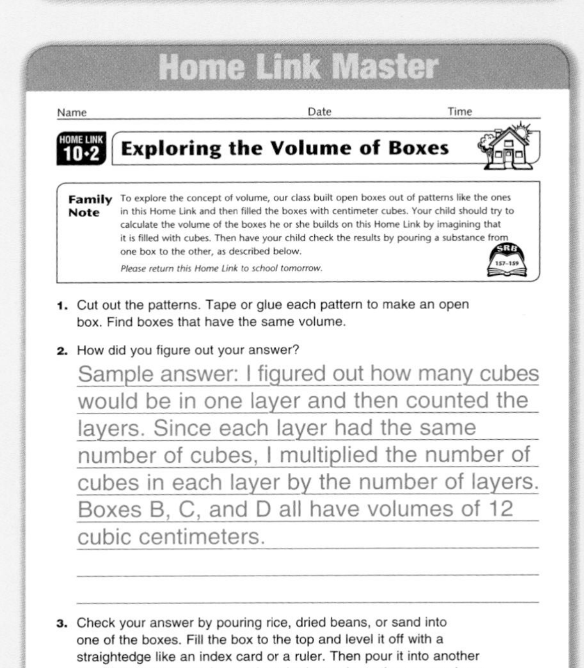

Name Date Time

HOME LINK 10•2 **Exploring the Volume of Boxes**

Family Note To explore the concept of volume, our class built open boxes out of patterns like the ones in this Home Link and then filled the boxes with centimeter cubes. Your child should try to calculate the volume of the boxes he or she builds on this Home Link by imagining that it is filled with cubes. Then have your child check the results by pouring a substance from one box to the other, as described below.

Please return this Home Link to school tomorrow.

1. Cut out the patterns. Tape or glue each pattern to make an open box. Find boxes that have the same volume.
2. How did you figure out your answer?
Sample answer: I figured out how many cubes would be in one layer and then counted the layers. Since each layer had the same number of cubes, I multiplied the number of cubes in each layer by the number of layers. Boxes B, C, and D all have volumes of 12 cubic centimeters.
3. Check your answer by pouring rice, dried beans, or sand into one of the boxes. Fill the box to the top and level it off with a straightedge like an index card or a ruler. Then pour it into another box. Explain how you know when the boxes have the same volume.
Sample answer: Boxes with the same volume hold the same amount.

Math Masters, p. 324

Teaching Master

Name Date Time

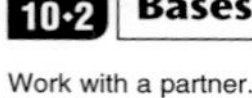

Bases of Rectangular Prisms

Work with a partner.

Get a rectangular prism from your teacher.

Count the number of faces. It has 6 faces.

What shape is each face? rectangle

Place the rectangular prism on a sheet of paper.

1. Trace the face that the prism sits on.
2. Turn the prism so that the opposite face is on the paper. Trace that face. You have traced one pair of bases.
3. Find and trace all the pairs of bases.

How many pairs of bases did you find? 3

What shape is each base? rectangle

Write what you notice about the relationships between the faces and the bases for rectangular prisms.

Sample answers: The faces are perpendicular to the bases; the faces and bases are all rectangles; opposite faces are parallel and congruent; each pair of opposite faces can be bases.

Math Masters, **p. 326**

Teaching Master

Name Date Time

LESSON 10•2 **Exploring the Volume of Cubes**

Do the following activities. Remember that all faces of a cube are the same size.

1. Use centimeter cubes to build a cube whose faces each have an area of 4 square centimeters.
   How many layers does the cube have? 2 layers
   What is the volume of the cube? 8 cubic centimeters
2. Build a cube whose faces each have an area of 9 square centimeters.
   How many layers does the cube have? 3 layers
   What is the volume of the cube? 27 cubic centimeters
3. Build a cube whose faces each have an area of 16 square centimeters.
   How many layers does the cube have? 4 layers
   What is the volume of the cube? 64 cubic centimeters
4. What do you think is the area of one face of the next larger cube? 25 square centimeters
   What is the volume of the cube? 125 cubic centimeters
   Explain how you found the volume.
   Sample answer: I knew that the next-larger cube would have 5 cm × 5 cm square faces, so there would be 5 layers of 25 cubes. I multiplied 5 × 25.
5. Check the volume by building such a cube.

Math Masters, **p. 327**

Home Link 10•2

(*Math Masters,* pp. 324 and 325)

Home Connection Children match boxes having different dimensions but equal volumes.

3 Differentiation Options

READINESS

Identifying Bases of Rectangular Prisms

(*Math Masters,* p. 326)

To provide experience identifying the bases of rectangular prisms, have children trace opposite faces of a rectangular prism. They write what they notice about the relationship between the bases and the faces and record their work on *Math Masters,* page 326.

ENRICHMENT

PARTNER ACTIVITY

15–30 Min

Exploring the Volumes of Cubes

(*Math Masters,* p. 327)

To apply children's understanding of volume, have them find the volumes of progressively larger cubes. They extend the pattern to find the volume of the next larger cube.

ELL SUPPORT

Building a Math Word Bank

(*Differentiation Handbook,* p. 133)

To provide language support for volume, have children use the Math Word Bank template found on *Differentiation Handbook,* page 133. Ask children to write the terms *centimeter, square centimeter,* and *cubic centimeter;* draw a picture representing each term; and write other related words. See the *Differentiation Handbook* for more information.

Planning Ahead

Refer to the materials lists for Lessons 10-3, 10-4, and 10-5. Gather the necessary items for those lessons.

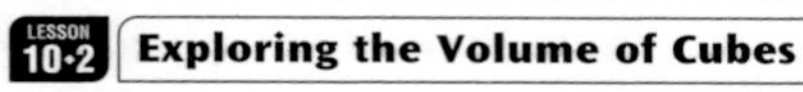

10•3 Weight

Objectives To provide a review of metric and U.S. customary units of weight; and to guide children as they examine different kinds of scales and read weights on scales.

Technology Resources www.everydaymathonline.com

ePresentations

eToolkit

Algorithms Practice

EM Facts Workshop Game™

Family Letters

Assessment Management

Common Core State Standards

Curriculum Focal Points

Interactive Teacher's Lesson Guide

1 Teaching the Lesson

Key Concepts and Skills

- Compare numbers to interpret intervals.
  [Number and Numeration Goal 6]
- Order objects by weight.
  [Number and Numeration Goal 6]
- Check predictions of weights of objects to the actual weights of objects.
  [Data and Chance Goal 4]

Key Activities

Children discuss the meaning of *weight*. They weigh the four objects from Lesson 10•1 and compare the weights to their predictions. They examine various kinds of scales, discuss objects that might be weighed with each kind of scale, and read weights on scales.

Ongoing Assessment: Informing Instruction See page 822.

Key Vocabulary

weight ◆ capacity of a scale ◆ precision

Materials

Math Journal 2, pp. 241, 246, and 247
Student Reference Book, pp. 165 and 166
Home Link 10•2
Class Data Pad pages with equivalencies from Lesson 10•1 ◆ 4 objects from Lesson 10•1 ◆ a variety of scales ◆ slate ◆ counters ◆ half-sheet of paper

2 Ongoing Learning & Practice

Playing *Factor Bingo*

Math Masters, p. 448
Student Reference Book, pp. 285 and 286
per group: 4 each of number cards 2–9 (from the Everything Math Deck, if available), half-sheets of paper ◆ 12 counters per player
Children practice identifying factors.

Ongoing Assessment: Recognizing Student Achievement
Use the *Factor Bingo* record sheet.
[Operations and Computation Goal 3]

Math Boxes 10•3

Math Journal 2, p. 248
Children practice and maintain skills through Math Box problems.

Home Link 10•3

Math Masters, p. 329
Children practice and maintain skills through Home Link activities.

3 Differentiation Options

READINESS

Comparing Weights

Math Masters, p. 328
per partnership: liter bottle of water, scale
Children find objects that weigh about 1 kilogram.

ENRICHMENT

Comparing Units of Measure

Math Masters, p. 330
Children find relationships between units in the metric system and U.S. customary system.

ELL SUPPORT

Predicting and Weighing Objects

per partnership: 5 objects of varying weights, 5 index cards labeled with weights of the objects, scale
Children predict and then check the weights of objects.

Advance Preparation

Make the open boxes from the patterns shown on Home Link 10•2 for the Home Link Follow-Up. Provide scales with the capacity to weigh the 4 objects from Lesson 10•1.

Children should complete Part 1 on journal page 241 before the start of this lesson.

***Teacher's Reference Manual,* Grades 1–3** pp. 161–168

Mathematical Practices
SMP1, SMP2, **SMP4,** SMP5, **SMP6**
Content Standards
3.MD.2

Getting Started

Mental Math and Reflexes

Tell fraction stories. Children may use counters or draw pictures to help them. Children record their answers on slates and share solution strategies.

●○○ Rick's dad made 2 apple pies. 6 people shared the pies equally and finished them. What fraction of a pie did each person eat? $\frac{1}{3}$ of a pie

●●○ Louise had 10 quarters. She gave $\frac{2}{5}$ of her quarters to her brother. How much money did she give to her brother? $1

●●● Mark has 24 baseball cards. $\frac{3}{8}$ of his cards are rookie cards. How many rookie cards does he have? 9 rookie cards

Math Message

What does weight *mean? Think about it and be ready to discuss it. The pound is a unit of weight. On a half-sheet of paper, list as many other units of weight as you can.*

Home Link 10·2 Follow-Up

Children describe how they determined which boxes have the same volume. For each box, discuss the dimensions of the base and the number of layers.

1 Teaching the Lesson

▶ Math Message Follow-Up

Children may describe weight as *how heavy a thing is* or *how hard it is to lift something.* Technically, **weight** is the force of gravity pulling an object toward Earth.

Discuss units of weight. First, list units named by children in three columns on the board—one for metric units, one for U.S. customary units, and one for other units (for example, the stone, a British unit equal to 14 pounds). Then review equivalencies between units and add them to the Class Data Pad pages started in Lesson 10-1. (*See margin.*) Be sure to call attention to the abbreviations for the units.

NOTE For more information, see "Weight and Mass" in the *Teacher's Reference Manual.*

Metric Units
1 metric ton (T) = 1,000 kilograms (kg)
1 kilogram = 1,000 grams (g)
1 gram = 1,000 milligrams (mg)

U.S. Customary Units
1 ton (T) = 2,000 pounds (lb)
1 lb = 16 ounces (oz)

Class Data Pad

▶ Examining Various Kinds of Scales

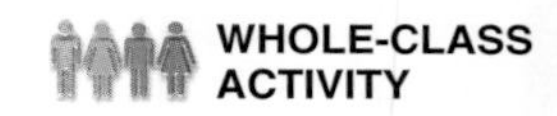

(*Student Reference Book,* pp. 165 and 166)

Ask children to look at the pictures of scales on pages 165 and 166 in the *Student Reference Book.* Discuss each kind of scale, paying special attention to the following topics. Demonstrate with available scales.

The **capacity of a scale** is the maximum weight a scale can measure. Most infant scales have a capacity of about 25 pounds. Therefore, an infant scale would not be used to weigh a third grader. Discuss meanings of the word *capacity.* Encourage children to look up the word in the *Student Reference Book.* The amount a container can hold or the heaviest weight a scale can measure In this lesson, *capacity* refers to the heaviest weight a scale can measure.

NOTE The concept of capacity as the greatest amount a container can hold will be investigated in Lesson 10-5.

Precision depends on the size of the unit displayed by the scale. The smaller the unit or fraction of a unit, the more precise the scale. For example, a scale that measures to the nearest 20 pounds may show that a baby weighs 0 pounds. A scale that measures to the nearest pound may show that the same baby weighs 9 pounds. A scale that measures to the nearest ounce may show that the same baby weighs 9 pounds, 3 ounces. Which scale is the most precise? The one that measures to the smallest unit, in this case ounces A scale that measures weight to the nearest 10 grams, such as some balance scales, is more precise than one that measures weight to the nearest 500 grams, such as most bath scales. For example, a bath scale would not be used to weigh a letter. Ask children if they have seen a postage scale at the local post office. Ask: *Why do post office employees weigh letters?* The amount of postage is determined by the weight of the letter and how quickly you want the letter to arrive.

You might want to discuss features of scales:

- ▷ Most scales display weights in metric and U.S. customary units.
- ▷ Most scales have a mechanism to adjust the scale to show a weight of 0 units when nothing is being weighed. For example, the pointer on a produce scale should point to 0 when nothing is in the pan.
- ▷ Some scales are electronic. They display weights with digits, using decimals to show fractions of a unit.
- ▷ Some scales are extremely precise and can weigh things that cannot be seen with the naked eye. Some scales are very large and are used for objects that weigh as much as 100 tons (200,000 pounds).

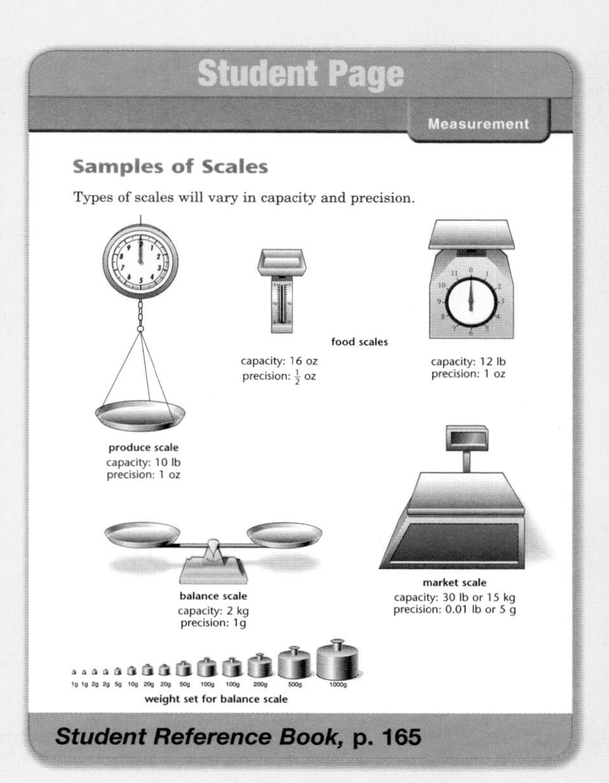

▶ Naming Objects to Weigh with Scales

SMALL-GROUP ACTIVITY

(*Math Journal 2,* p. 246; *Student Reference Book,* pp. 165 and 166)

Have children work in groups to name things they might weigh using the scales shown on pages 165 and 166 of the *Student Reference Book*. Each child should record three things for each scale in his or her journal. Bring children together to share their lists.

Adjusting the Activity

ELL

Make a bulletin-board display about scales. Children may use illustrations from magazines or other sources, drawings of their own, or any relevant information they find.

AUDITORY ◆ KINESTHETIC ◆ TACTILE ◆ VISUAL

Student Page

Date _______ Time _______

LESSON 10·3 **Various Scales**

Refer to pages 165 and 166 in your *Student Reference Book*. For each scale shown, list three things you could weigh on the scale.

Answers vary.

balance scale	produce scale
market scale	letter scale
package scale	platform scale
bath scale	infant scale
spring scale	diet/food scale

***Math Journal 2,* p. 246**

Student Page

Date ____ Time ____

LESSON 10·3 Reading Scales

Read each scale and record the weight.

1. 200 g
2. 2 oz
3. 15 lb
4. 35 kg
5. 3 g

Math Journal 2, p. 247

Factor	Product
6	30
4	36

Record Sheet for *Factor Bingo*

Student Page

Date ____ Time ____

LESSON 10·1 Weight and Volume

Complete Part 1 before the start of Lesson 10-3. Answers vary.

Part 1 Order the objects on display from heaviest (1) to lightest (4). Lift them to help you guess. Record your guesses below.

1. ____ 2. ____
3. ____ 4. ____

Complete Part 2 as part of Lesson 10-3.

Part 2 Record the actual order of the objects from heaviest (1) to lightest (4). How close were your guesses?

1. ____ 2. ____
3. ____ 4. ____

Complete Parts 3 and 4 and Problems 1–3 as part of Lesson 10-4.

Part 3 Order the objects on display from largest (1) to smallest (4) volume. Record your guesses below.

1. ____ 2. ____
3. ____ 4. ____

Part 4 Record the actual order of the objects from largest (1) to smallest (4) volume. How close were your guesses?

1. ____ 2. ____
3. ____ 4. ____

1. Make a dot on the produce scale to show 1 kg. Label it *A*.
2. Make a dot on the produce scale to show $3\frac{1}{2}$ kg. Label it *B*.
3. Make a dot on the produce scale to show 2 kg, 500 g. Label it *C*.

Math Journal 2, p. 241

▶ Reading Scales

INDEPENDENT ACTIVITY

(*Math Journal 2,* p. 247)

Children read a variety of scales on journal page 247.

Ongoing Assessment: Informing Instruction

Watch for children who need support for reading scales when the weight falls between whole numbers. Have them count the smaller marks between the whole numbers to determine their values.

▶ Ordering Four Objects by Weight

(*Math Journal 2,* p. 241)

Weigh to the nearest gram each of the four objects on display from Lesson 10-1. Children record the order of the objects by weight in Part 2 on journal page 241. They compare these results to their estimates in Part 1.

2 Ongoing Learning & Practice

▶ Playing *Factor Bingo*

(*Math Masters,* p. 448; *Student Reference Book,* pp. 285 and 286)

This game was introduced in Lesson 9-6. If necessary, review the rules for the game on page 285 in the *Student Reference Book.* As they play, have children record several of their turns on a half-sheet of paper with 2 columns labeled Factor and Product. (*See margin.*)

Ongoing Assessment: Recognizing Student Achievement

Record Sheet 

Use the **Record Sheet** from *Factor Bingo* to assess children's progress toward automaticity with multiplication facts through 10 × 10. Children are making adequate progress if they are able to record five factors and one product for each factor. Some children may realize that certain products have more factors than others.

[Operations and Computation Goal 3]

▶ Math Boxes 10•3

INDEPENDENT ACTIVITY

(*Math Journal 2,* p. 248)

Mixed Practice Math Boxes in this lesson are paired with Math Boxes in Lesson 10-1. The skill in Problem 6 previews Unit 11 content.

Writing and Reasoning Have children write an answer to the following: *Write 3 more questions about the shape in Problem 3. Then write the answers to your questions.* Sample answer: How many faces does it have? Six; What shape are the bases? Rectangles; How many pairs of parallel faces does it have? Three

▶ Home Link 10•3

(*Math Masters,* p. 329)

Home Connection Children explain which weighs more: a pound of feathers or a pound of books.

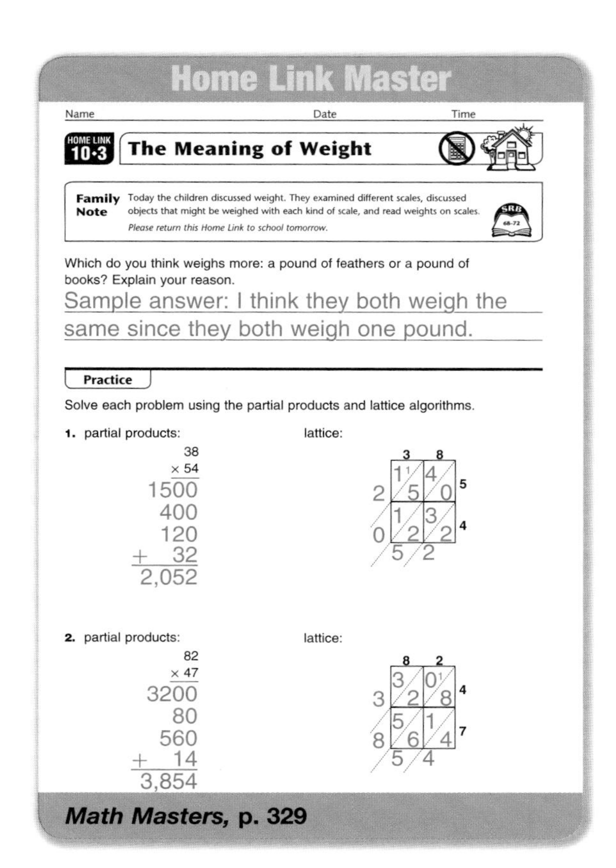

Home Link Master

Name Date Time

HOME LINK 10•3 **The Meaning of Weight**

Family Note Today the children discussed weight. They examined different scales, discussed objects that might be weighed with each kind of scale, and read weights on scales. *Please return this Home Link to school tomorrow.*

Which do you think weighs more: a pound of feathers or a pound of books? Explain your reason.

Sample answer: I think they both weigh the same since they both weigh one pound.

Practice

Solve each problem using the partial products and lattice algorithms.

1. partial products:

```
   38
 × 54
 1500
  400
  120
+  32
2,052
```

lattice: 38 × 54 = 2,052

2. partial products:

```
   82
 × 47
 3200
   80
  560
+  14
3,854
```

lattice: 82 × 47 = 3,854

Math Masters, p. 329

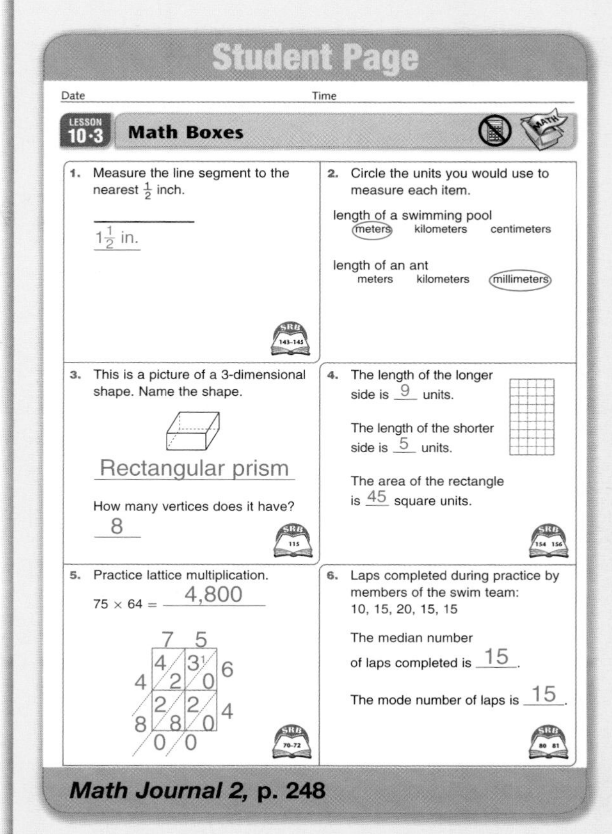

Student Page

Date Time

LESSON 10•3 **Math Boxes**

1. Measure the line segment to the nearest $\frac{1}{2}$ inch. $1\frac{1}{2}$ in.

2. Circle the units you would use to measure each item.
length of a swimming pool: (meters) kilometers centimeters
length of an ant: meters kilometers (millimeters)

3. This is a picture of a 3-dimensional shape. Name the shape. Rectangular prism
How many vertices does it have? 8

4. The length of the longer side is 9 units.
The length of the shorter side is 5 units.
The area of the rectangle is 45 square units.

5. Practice lattice multiplication.
75 × 64 = 4,800

6. Laps completed during practice by members of the swim team: 10, 15, 20, 15, 15
The median number of laps completed is 15.
The mode number of laps is 15.

Math Journal 2, p. 248

3 Differentiation Options

READINESS

PARTNER ACTIVITY

5–15 Min

▶ Comparing Weights

(*Math Masters,* p. 328)

To provide experience with predicting and measuring the weights of objects, have children identify objects that weigh about as much as a liter bottle of water, which weighs about 1 kilogram. Children record their work on *Math Masters,* page 328.

ENRICHMENT

PARTNER ACTIVITY

5–15 Min

▶ Comparing Units of Measure

(*Math Masters,* p. 330)

To explore the relationship between weighing objects in pounds and kilograms, have children study the chart on *Math Masters,* page 330. They describe the patterns and use them to figure the number of pounds equal to 60 kilograms.

ELL SUPPORT

PARTNER ACTIVITY

5–15 Min

▶ Predicting and Weighing Objects

To provide language support for weight, provide children with opportunities to hold objects as well as weigh them to determine their weights in kilograms or grams. Give them five objects of varying weights and five index cards with the respective weights listed in kilograms or grams. Ask children to predict which card matches each object. Then ask the children to weigh the objects to determine their weights, and report their findings.

Teaching Master

Name Date Time

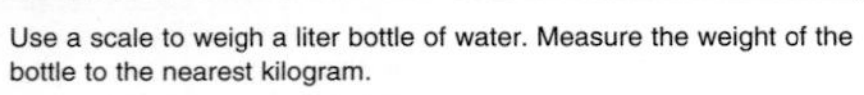

LESSON 10·3 **Comparing Weights**

Use a scale to weigh a liter bottle of water. Measure the weight of the bottle to the nearest kilogram.

The bottle weighs about 1 kilogram.

Find other objects that feel like they have about the same weight. Compare each one to the bottle of water by holding the object in one hand and the bottle in the other.

In the first column of the table below, list the objects that have about the same weight as the bottle of water. Answers vary.

Name of Object	Actual Weight of Object
	about ____ kg ____ g
	about ____ kg ____ g
	about ____ kg ____ g
	about ____ kg ____ g
	about ____ kg ____ g
	about ____ kg ____ g

After you have listed at least four objects, measure and record the actual weight of each one to the nearest kilogram and gram. How close were your estimates?

***Math Masters,* p. 328**

Teaching Master

Name Date Time

LESSON 10·3 **Comparing Units of Measure**

Units of Measure	
Kilograms (kg)	Pounds (lb)
5	11
10	22
15	33
20	44
25	55
60	132

Describe the patterns you see in the table.

Sample answers: A pound is a little more than twice the measure of a kilogram. To change 5 kilograms to pounds, double the kilograms and add 1; to change 10 kilograms to pounds, double the kilograms and add 2; to change 15 kilograms to pounds, double the kilograms and add 3; and so on.

Try This

Figure out how many pounds are equal to 60 kg. Enter the number of pounds in the table. Explain how you figured it out.

Sample answer: I continued the pattern to find out that 30 kilograms is equal to 66 pounds. Then I doubled 66 pounds to find out that 60 kilograms equals 132 pounds.

***Math Masters,* p. 330**

10•4 Exploring Weight and Volume

Explorations

Objectives To provide experiences ordering objects by volume, using a pan balance to measure mass, and measuring weight using various kinds of scales.

www.everydaymathonline.com

ePresentations

eToolkit

Algorithms Practice

EM Facts Workshop Game™

Family Letters

Assessment Management

Common Core State Standards

Curriculum Focal Points

Interactive Teacher's Lesson Guide

1 Teaching the Lesson

Key Concepts and Skills

- Collect and organize data in a table. [Data and Chance Goal 1]
- Predict the volumes of objects and test the predictions. [Data and Chance Goal 4]
- Predict the weights of objects and test the predictions. [Data and Chance Goal 4]

Key Activities

Exploration A: Children guess the relative volumes of objects and check their guesses by measuring displaced water to the nearest 50 mL. They discuss the relationships between the volumes and weights of the objects.

Exploration B: Children measure the mass of a variety of objects.

Exploration C: Children weigh a variety of objects, recording the measurements in either U.S. customary units, metric units, or both.

Materials

Home Link 10•3
counters (optional) ◆ slate ◆ *Student Reference Book,* pp. 162 and 163

Exploration A:
Math Journal 2, p. 241
Per group: *Math Masters,* p. 331
4 objects from Lesson 10•1 ◆ empty 2- or 3-lb coffee can ◆ water ◆ large bucket or tub ◆ liter pitcher ◆ paper towels or tray

Exploration B: Per partnership:
Math Masters, p. 333
pan balance ◆ plastic base-10 cubes and longs ◆ liter bottle of water ◆ objects to weigh

Exploration C: Per group:
Math Masters, p. 335
objects to weigh ◆ bath scale ◆ other various scales ◆ 30 small, plastic base-10 cubes ◆ 3 long, plastic base-10 blocks ◆ chalkboard eraser ◆ 5-pound bag of sugar or flour ◆ paper clip ◆ nickel ◆ 1 long, plastic base-10 block ◆ liter bottle of water ◆ 1-pound box of pasta

2 Ongoing Learning & Practice

Playing *Beat the Calculator* (Multiplication)
Math Journal 2, p. 282
Student Reference Book, p. 279
per group: calculator
Children practice multiplication facts.

Ongoing Assessment: Recognizing Student Achievement
Use an Exit Slip (*Math Masters,* page 398).
[Operations and Computation Goal 3]

Math Boxes 10•4
Math Journal 2, p. 249

Home Link 10•4
Math Masters, p. 332

3 Differentiation Options

EXTRA PRACTICE
Investigating Liters and Milliliters
Math Masters, p. 334

EXTRA PRACTICE
Minute Math+
Minute Math®+, pp. 74, 75, and 121

Advance Preparation

For Exploration A, use a permanent marker to label the 50 mL increments on the liter pitcher. For Exploration C, provide a variety of scales such as a food scale, letter scale, spring scale, and so on.

***Teacher's Reference Manual,* Grades 1–3** p. 160

Mathematical Practices
SMP2, SMP3, SMP4, **SMP5,** SMP6
Content Standards
3.OA.3, 3.OA.7, **3.MD.2**

Getting Started

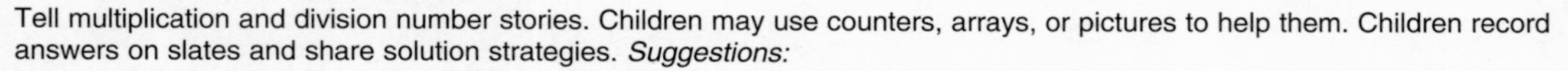

Mental Math and Reflexes

Tell multiplication and division number stories. Children may use counters, arrays, or pictures to help them. Children record answers on slates and share solution strategies. *Suggestions:*

●○○ There are 6 boxes of crayons with 8 crayons in a box. How many crayons in all? 48 crayons
There are 9 tables with 4 children at each table. How many children in all? 36 children

●●○ 49 candies are shared by 5 friends. How many candies does each friend receive? 9 candies with 4 left over
300 pennies are shared by 10 children. How many pennies are there for each child? 30 pennies

●●● 365 days are in a year. 7 days are in a week. How many weeks are in a year? 52 weeks with 1 day left over
How many inches are in 5 yards? 180 inches

Math Message

Read pages 162 and 163 in your Student Reference Book. *Work with a partner to solve the Check Your Understanding problem on page 163.*

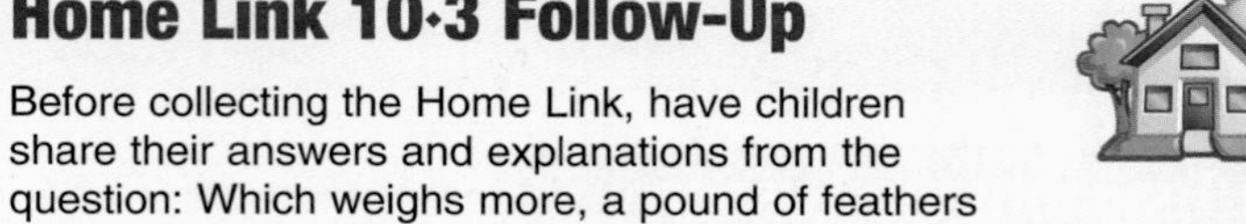

Home Link 10·3 Follow-Up

Before collecting the Home Link, have children share their answers and explanations from the question: Which weighs more, a pound of feathers or a pound of books?

NOTE To provide experience with measuring liquids in ounces, have children repeat Exploration A and use a measuring cup marked with ounces. They can record their measures on a half-sheet.

1 Teaching the Lesson

▶ Math Message Follow-Up

WHOLE-CLASS DISCUSSION

(*Student Reference Book,* pp. 162 and 163)

Have children briefly share their solution strategies for the Check Your Understanding problem. A possible strategy is to use the information from the pictures on *Student Reference Book,* page 163. Since 1 ounce equals about 30 grams, then 1 pound equals about 16×30 grams, or 480 grams. 600 grams is heavier than 1 pound.

Explain that the exploration activities in this lesson provide experience with volume and weight. Plan to spend more of your time assisting children with Exploration A.

▶ Exploration A: Ordering Four Objects by Volume

SMALL-GROUP ACTIVITY

(*Math Masters,* p. 331; *Math Journal 2,* p. 241)

Children guess the relative volumes of the four objects on display from Lesson 10-1 and record their guesses in Part 3 on journal page 241. Then they follow the directions on *Math Masters,* page 331 to find the amount of water displaced by each of the four objects. They record the order of the objects' volumes from largest to smallest in Part 4 on journal page 241 and compare these results to their estimates.

To prepare children for the activity, demonstrate how to read the scale on the liter pitcher to the nearest 50 mL. When children have completed the Exploration, have them discuss the relationships between the volume and weight of each of the four objects.

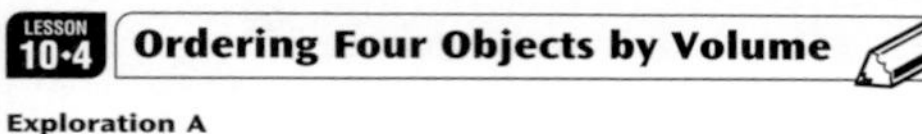

Teaching Master

Name Date Time

LESSON 10·4 **Ordering Four Objects by Volume**

Exploration A

Find the *actual* order of the 4 objects on display from largest to smallest volume. Work with a partner. You will need the following materials:

- 4 objects from Lesson 10-1
- coffee can filled with water
- paper towels, large tub
- liter pitcher

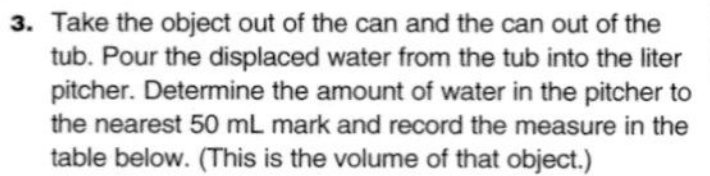

1. Place the coffee can inside the tub. Make sure the can is filled to the rim with water.
2. Slowly place one of the four objects into the can. If the object floats, push it down gently until it is completely, but just barely, underwater. The tub will catch the displaced water.
3. Take the object out of the can and the can out of the tub. Pour the displaced water from the tub into the liter pitcher. Determine the amount of water in the pitcher to the nearest 50 mL mark and record the measure in the table below. (This is the volume of that object.)
4. Place the can back inside the tub and pour the water from the pitcher back into the can. If necessary, add more water to the can to fill it to the rim.

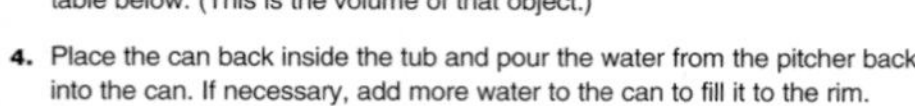

Repeat Steps 2–4 for each of the other objects.

Record the order of the objects from largest to smallest volume in Part 4 on journal page 241.

When you have finished, wipe up spilled water and dry off the wet objects. Leave the area ready for the next group.

Name of Object	Volume to Nearest 50 mL

Math Masters, p. 331

- Name two objects for which the heavier of the two also has the greater volume. Answers vary.
- Name two objects for which the heavier of the two also has the smaller volume. Answers vary.

Have children complete Problems 1–3 on journal page 241.

Exploration B: Measuring Mass of Objects

PARTNER ACTIVITY

(*Math Masters,* p. 333)

Working with a partner, children use a pan balance to measure the mass of a variety of objects. They record their work on *Math Masters,* page 333. Explain that mass is a measure of the amount of matter in an object, while weight is the force of gravity on the object. In everyday life, mass and weight are hard to distinguish. It may help children understand the difference between mass and weight by thinking about outer space. For example, on the moon an object's mass is the same as it is on Earth—the object has the same amount of matter whether it is on Earth or on the moon—but because there is less gravity on the moon, it weighs less than on Earth. Similarly, astronauts in orbit are "weightless"—their weight is 0—but they still have the same mass they have on Earth. Scientists use kilograms and grams to measure mass.

NOTE Tools and units for measuring mass and weight can be confusing; see Section 14.6 in the *Teacher's Reference Manual* for a discussion. For example, many bathroom scales include both pounds (usually considered a unit of weight) and kilograms (usually considered a unit of mass). In *Everyday Mathematics*, the distinction is not made between mass and weight since it is believed that it is better to address the topic when students study physical science in middle or high school.

In general, however, mass can be measured by using a balance to compare a known amount of material with an unknown amount of material, and weight can be measured using a scale. So, in the optional Part 3 Readiness activity in Lesson 10-3, when children use a scale, they find that a liter bottle of water has a *weight* of about 1 kilogram. In this Exploration, however, children use a pan balance and a liter bottle of water with a mass of about 1 kilogram to measure the mass of various objects.

Demonstrate how to zero the pan balance by moving the white rider clips left or right. It may be necessary to add a few base-10 block cubes to one pan to zero the balance. Then place a small object in one pan and to the other pan add plastic base-10 cubes, which have a mass of approximately 1 gram each, or longs, which have a mass of approximately 10 grams each. The mass of the object is approximately the same as the number of base-10 cubes in the pan.

For objects with greater masses, use a liter bottle of water, which has a mass of about 1,000 grams or 1 kilogram, and base-10 cubes to balance the pans.

Suggested items for measurement include large paper clips, bulldog clips, coins, a whiteboard eraser, a pencil eraser, large metal washers, several pencils or pens taped together, batteries, cans of pop (try regular vs. diet), a roll of tape, and resealable plastic bags of sand, gravel, or grain.

Teaching Master

Name Date Time

LESSON 10•4 **Using a Pan Balance to Measure Mass**

Exploration B

Work with a partner.

Materials ☐ pan balance with 2 pans ☐ liter bottle of water ☐ plastic base-10 cubes and longs ☐ objects

1 base-10 cube has a mass of about 1 gram.
1 base-10 long has a mass of about 10 grams.
1 liter bottle of water has a mass of about 1,000 grams or 1 kilogram.

1. Make sure that the empty pans on the pan balance are balanced.
2. Place an object in one pan. Then place base-10 cubes and longs in the other pan until the two pans are balanced. The number of cubes in the pan is about the mass of the object in grams.
3. For objects with greater mass, use a liter bottle of water and base-10 cubes and longs to balance the two pans.
4. Record your findings in the table below.

Object	Mass

Math Masters, p. 333

Teaching Master

Name Date Time

LESSON 10•4 **Weighing Objects on Scales**

Exploration C

Work with a partner. Weigh items in the classroom using the different scales your teacher has provided.

For each item:

1. Decide which scale you and your partner will use to weigh each item. Discuss why that scale is the best one to use for that item.
2. Weigh the item in both U.S. customary and metric units.
3. Record your results in the chart below. Answers vary.

Object	Scale	U.S. Customary Units (ounces, pounds)	Metric Units (grams, kilograms)

Try This

4. Talk to your partner and figure out a strategy to weigh an object that will not easily fit on a bath scale. On the back of this paper, describe how you weighed the object.

Math Masters, p. 335

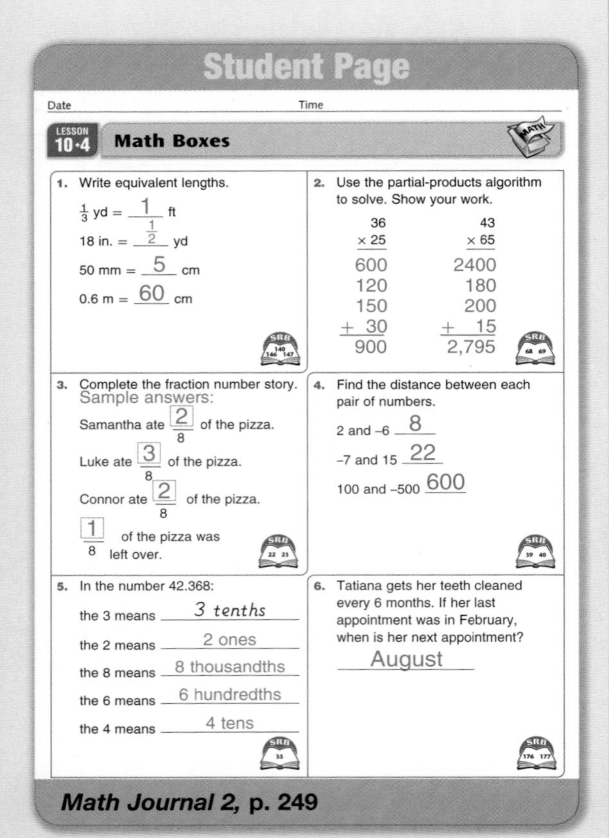
Student Page

Date Time

LESSON 10·4 **Math Boxes**

1. Write equivalent lengths.
$\frac{1}{3}$ yd = 1 ft
18 in. = $\frac{1}{2}$ yd
50 mm = 5 cm
0.6 m = 60 cm

2. Use the partial-products algorithm to solve. Show your work.

36	43
× 25	× 65
600	2400
120	180
150	200
+ 30	+ 15
900	2,795

3. Complete the fraction number story.
Sample answers:
Samantha ate $\frac{2}{8}$ of the pizza.
Luke ate $\frac{3}{8}$ of the pizza.
Connor ate $\frac{2}{8}$ of the pizza.
$\frac{1}{8}$ of the pizza was left over.

4. Find the distance between each pair of numbers.
2 and –6 8
–7 and 15 22
100 and –500 600

5. In the number 42.368:
the 3 means 3 tenths
the 2 means 2 ones
the 8 means 8 thousandths
the 6 means 6 hundredths
the 4 means 4 tens

6. Tatiana gets her teeth cleaned every 6 months. If her last appointment was in February, when is her next appointment?
August

Math Journal 2, p. 249

Ongoing Assessment: Recognizing Student Achievement — Exit Slip

Use an **Exit Slip** (*Math Masters,* page 398) to assess children's progress toward automaticity with multiplication facts through 10 × 10. Children record facts from the Multiplication Fact Power Table for which they earned a check mark. Children are making adequate progress if they record most facts from the shaded portion of the record sheet. Some children may record all of the facts.

[Operations and Computation Goal 3]

▶ Exploration C: Weighing Objects on Scales

PARTNER ACTIVITY

(*Math Masters,* p. 335)

Working with a partner, have children select several small classroom objects and record the names of the objects and their estimated weights on a sheet of paper. To assist children with the estimates, you may wish to provide some items for use as benchmarks. Children compare weights by holding the benchmark item in one hand and the classroom object in the other.

- ▷ about 1 ounce — 30 small, plastic base-10 cubes; 3 long, plastic base-10 blocks; chalkboard eraser
- ▷ about 1 pound — box of pasta
- ▷ about 5 pounds — bag of sugar or flour
- ▷ about 1 gram — paper clip
- ▷ about 5 grams — nickel
- ▷ about 10 grams — 1 long, plastic base-10 block
- ▷ about 1 kilogram — liter bottle of water

Consider adding these measurement benchmarks to the Class Data Pad for future reference.

Next, have partners weigh their objects. For each object, they select the appropriate scale, weigh the object, and record its weight on *Math Masters,* page 335 in U.S. customary and metric units. They compare their estimated weights to the actual weights.

Then, have children find larger objects in the classroom, weigh them, and record the results on page 335. Have them figure out how to weigh objects that do not easily fit on a bath scale (for example, a backpack or a sack of sport balls). One strategy is for children to weigh themselves holding the object. Then they weigh themselves *not* holding the object and find the difference.

2 Ongoing Learning & Practice

▶ Playing *Beat the Calculator* (Multiplication)

SMALL-GROUP ACTIVITY

(*Math Journal 2,* p. 282; *Student Reference Book,* p. 279)

Children develop automaticity with multiplication facts by playing *Beat the Calculator*. Have children use the Multiplication Fact Power Table, journal page 282, to record the facts for which they get the correct answer first when playing the role of the Brain. Have the Caller select facts from the shaded portion of the table. For Fact Power Table directions, see Lesson 4-5. For game directions, see page 279 in the *Student Reference Book*. Remind children to write the product in the table when they have earned 3 check marks for a fact.

▶ Math Boxes 10•4

INDEPENDENT ACTIVITY

(*Math Journal 2,* p. 249)

Mixed Practice Math Boxes in this lesson are paired with Math Boxes in Lesson 10-2. The skill in Problem 6 previews Unit 11 content.

Writing and Reasoning Have children draw and write an answer to the following: *Draw a picture of the pizza in Problem 3. Label the amount of pizza that each child ate. Show the amount left over. How much of the pizza did the three children eat altogether?* Sample answer: Together the children ate $\frac{7}{8}$ of the pizza.

▶ Home Link 10•4

(*Math Masters,* p. 332)

Home Connection Children bring labels from food packages and/or food containers (empty and clean) from home. Labels and containers will be used in Lesson 10-5. They also play *Multiplication Top-It* with someone at home.

3 Differentiation Options

EXTRA PRACTICE

▶ Investigating Liters and Milliliters

PARTNER ACTIVITY

(*Math Masters,* p. 334)

To provide additional practice with liters and milliliters, have children solve problems on *Math Masters,* page 334.

EXTRA PRACTICE

▶ *Minute Math+*

SMALL-GROUP ACTIVITY

To offer children more experience with volume and weight, see the following pages in *Minute Math+*:

Measurement: variation 3 on pp. 74 and 75

Number Stories: p. 121

Planning Ahead

For Lesson 10-5, bring food labels with content and nutrition information to supplement those brought by children. Gather half-pint, quart, half-gallon, gallon, and liter-size containers. Pop $\frac{1}{2}$ cup of popcorn kernels for the optional Enrichment activity in Part 3. For the optional Readiness activity, bring in rice, sand, or dried beans, and 5 containers in a variety of sizes and shapes. Label each container with a letter from *A* to *E*.

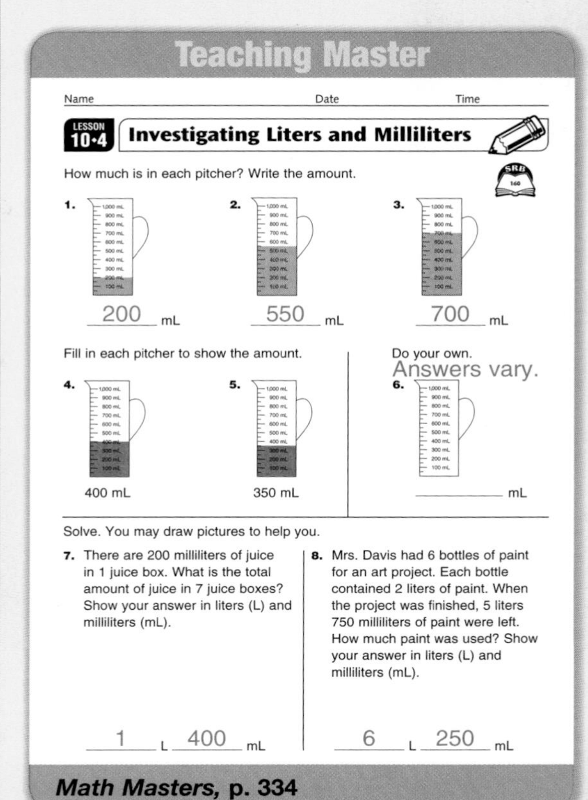

Teaching Master

Name Date Time

LESSON 10•4 **Investigating Liters and Milliliters**

How much is in each pitcher? Write the amount.

1. 200 mL
2. 550 mL
3. 700 mL

Fill in each pitcher to show the amount.

4. 400 mL
5. 350 mL

Do your own. Answers vary.

6. ______ mL

Solve. You may draw pictures to help you.

7. There are 200 milliliters of juice in 1 juice box. What is the total amount of juice in 7 juice boxes? Show your answer in liters (L) and milliliters (mL).

1 L 400 mL

8. Mrs. Davis had 6 bottles of paint for an art project. Each bottle contained 2 liters of paint. When the project was finished, 5 liters 750 milliliters of paint were left. How much paint was used? Show your answer in liters (L) and milliliters (mL).

6 L 250 mL

Math Masters, p. 334

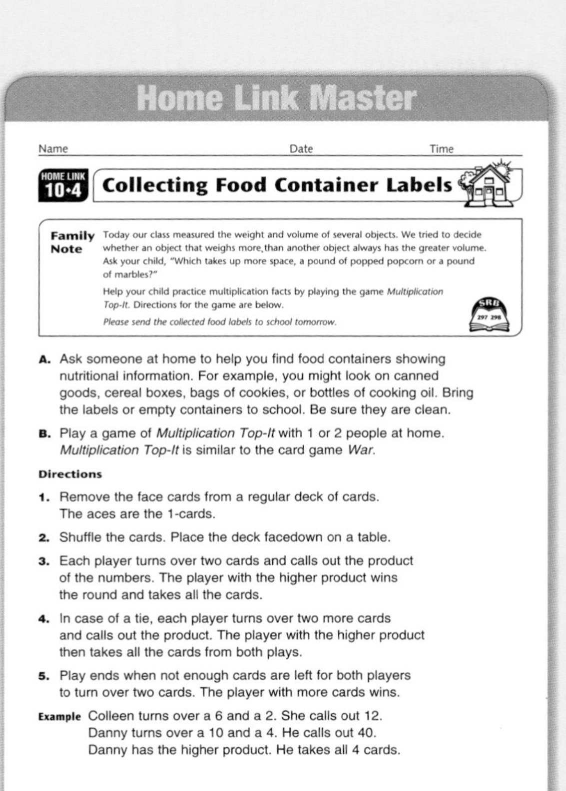

Home Link Master

Name Date Time

HOME LINK 10•4 **Collecting Food Container Labels**

Family Note Today our class measured the weight and volume of several objects. We tried to decide whether an object that weighs more than another object always has the greater volume. Ask your child, "Which takes up more space, a pound of popped popcorn or a pound of marbles?"

Help your child practice multiplication facts by playing the game *Multiplication Top-It.* Directions for the game are below.

Please send the collected food labels to school tomorrow.

A. Ask someone at home to help you find food containers showing nutritional information. For example, you might look on canned goods, cereal boxes, bags of cookies, or bottles of cooking oil. Bring the labels or empty containers to school. Be sure they are clean.

B. Play a game of *Multiplication Top-It* with 1 or 2 people at home. *Multiplication Top-It* is similar to the card game *War.*

Directions

1. Remove the face cards from a regular deck of cards. The aces are the 1-cards.
2. Shuffle the cards. Place the deck facedown on a table.
3. Each player turns over two cards and calls out the product of the numbers. The player with the higher product wins the round and takes all the cards.
4. In case of a tie, each player turns over two more cards and calls out the product. The player with the higher product then takes all the cards from both plays.
5. Play ends when not enough cards are left for both players to turn over two cards. The player with more cards wins.

Example Colleen turns over a 6 and a 2. She calls out 12. Danny turns over a 10 and a 4. He calls out 40. Danny has the higher product. He takes all 4 cards.

Math Masters, p. 332

10•5 Capacity

Objectives To explore the concept of capacity; and to demonstrate equivalencies between measures of capacity.

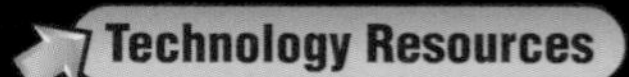

www.everydaymathonline.com

ePresentations

eToolkit

Algorithms Practice

EM Facts Workshop Game™

Family Letters

Assessment Management

Common Core State Standards

Curriculum Focal Points

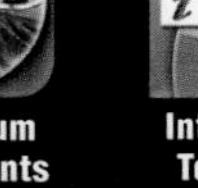

Interactive Teacher's Lesson Guide

1 Teaching the Lesson

Key Concepts and Skills

- Describe relationships among measures.
  [Measurement and Reference Frames Goal 3]
- Compare fractions.
  [Number and Numeration Goal 6]
- Use multiplication facts to find customary-unit equivalencies.
  [Operations and Computation Goal 3]

Key Activities

Demonstrate and discuss capacity equivalencies in the U.S. customary and metric systems. Children share the information they found on food labels. They choose appropriate units of measure for items.

Key Vocabulary

capacity of a container

Materials

Math Journal 2, p. 250
Student Reference Book, pp. 160 and 161
Home Link 10•4
containers (half-pint, pint, quart, half-gallon, gallon, liter, 100 mL) ◆ water ◆ paper towels ◆ tray ◆ Class Data Pad with equivalencies from Lessons 10•1 and 10•3 ◆ food labels ◆ half-sheet of paper

2 Ongoing Learning & Practice

Completing a Body-Measure Table
Math Journal 2, p. 251
per partnership: tape measure
Children take and record body measurements.

Math Boxes 10•5
Math Journal 2, p. 252
Children practice and maintain skills through Math Box problems.

Ongoing Assessment: Recognizing Student Achievement
Use an Exit Slip (*Math Masters,* page 398).
[Data and Chance Goal 2]

Home Link 10•5
Math Masters, p. 337
Children practice and maintain skills through Home Link activities.

3 Differentiation Options

READINESS

Comparing Capacities in Nonstandard Units
Math Masters, p. 336
per partnership: at least 5 containers of different sizes and shapes (labeled *A–E*); tub of rice, dried beans, or sand; small paper cups; funnel (optional)
Children compare capacities using a nonstandard unit of measure.

ENRICHMENT

Finding the Volume and Weight of Popcorn
Math Masters, p. 338
per partnership: scale, measuring cup, $\frac{1}{2}$ cup of unpopped popcorn kernels, popped popcorn from $\frac{1}{2}$ cup of kernels
Children compare the weight of popped and unpopped corn kernels.

EXTRA PRACTICE

Minute Math+
Minute Math®+, pp. 93, 99, 131, and 159
Children solve number stories involving measures of capacity.

Advance Preparation

For Part 1, set up the containers, supply of water, and paper towels for the capacity demonstration.

***Teacher's Reference Manual,* Grades 1–3** p. 158

Getting Started

Mathematical Practices
SMP2, SMP3, **SMP4,** SMP5, **SMP6**
Content Standards
3.MD.2

Mental Math and Reflexes

Children compare fractions to $\frac{1}{2}$. They show a thumbs up for fractions greater than $\frac{1}{2}$, a thumbs down for fractions less than $\frac{1}{2}$, and a fist for fractions equal to $\frac{1}{2}$. *Suggestions:*

●○○ $\frac{5}{10}$ equal to $\frac{1}{2}$; fist
$\frac{2}{6}$ less than $\frac{1}{2}$; thumbs down

●●○ $\frac{7}{8}$ greater than $\frac{1}{2}$; thumbs up
$\frac{3}{8}$ less than $\frac{1}{2}$; thumbs down

●●● $\frac{4}{12}$ less than $\frac{1}{2}$; thumbs down
$\frac{5}{6}$ greater than $\frac{1}{2}$; thumbs up

Math Message

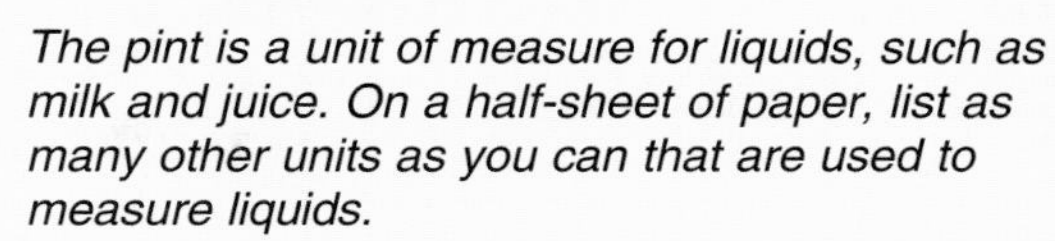

The pint is a unit of measure for liquids, such as milk and juice. On a half-sheet of paper, list as many other units as you can that are used to measure liquids.

Home Link 10·4 Follow-Up

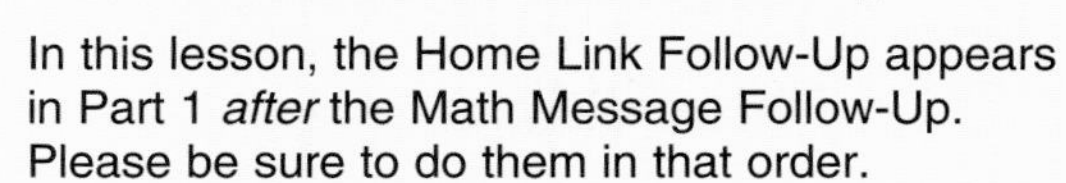

In this lesson, the Home Link Follow-Up appears in Part 1 *after* the Math Message Follow-Up. Please be sure to do them in that order.

1 Teaching the Lesson

▶ Math Message Follow-Up

WHOLE-CLASS ACTIVITY

(*Student Reference Book,* pp. 160 and 161)

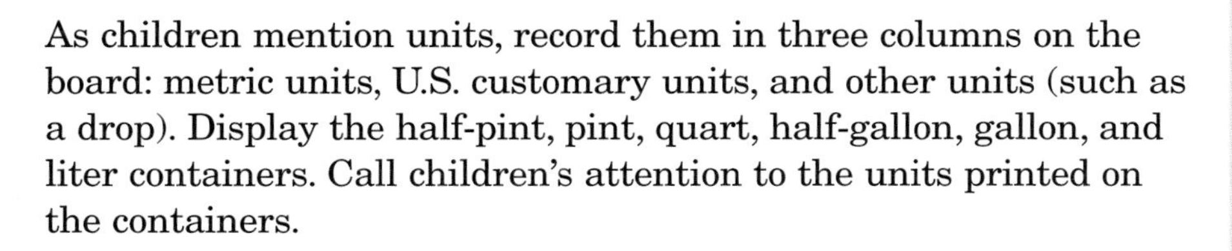

As children mention units, record them in three columns on the board: metric units, U.S. customary units, and other units (such as a drop). Display the half-pint, pint, quart, half-gallon, gallon, and liter containers. Call children's attention to the units printed on the containers.

NOTE The word *capacity* is used in two different ways in this unit. In Lesson 10-3, the capacity of a scale was defined as the greatest weight a scale can measure. In this lesson, *capacity* refers to the amount a container can hold. Call children's attention to the two meanings of the word.

After the list of units is complete, review equivalencies by pouring water from smaller containers into larger containers. For example, you can fill a 100 mL container with water and pour it into a liter container and then repeat the process 9 times to demonstrate that 1 liter is equivalent to 1,000 mL. Add these equivalencies to those previously recorded on the Class Data Pad. (*See margin.*)
Call children's attention to the abbreviations for the units.

Use the term *capacity.* Explain that the **capacity of a container** is the amount a container can hold. Point out that the half-pint (or cup), pint, quart, half-gallon, gallon, and liter containers can serve as personal references for units of capacity. Measures of capacity are the same as measures of volume. Have children read pages 160 and 161 in their *Student Reference Books.*

Metric Units
1 liter (l) = 1,000 milliliters (mL)

U.S. Customary Units
1 gallon (gal) = 2 half-gallons
1 gallon = 4 quarts (qt)
1 half-gallon = 2 quarts
1 quart = 2 pints (pt)
1 pint = 2 cups (c)
1 cup = 8 fluid ounces (fl oz)
1 pint = 16 fluid ounces
1 quart = 32 fluid ounces
1 half-gallon = 64 fluid ounces
1 gallon = 128 fluid ounces

Student Page

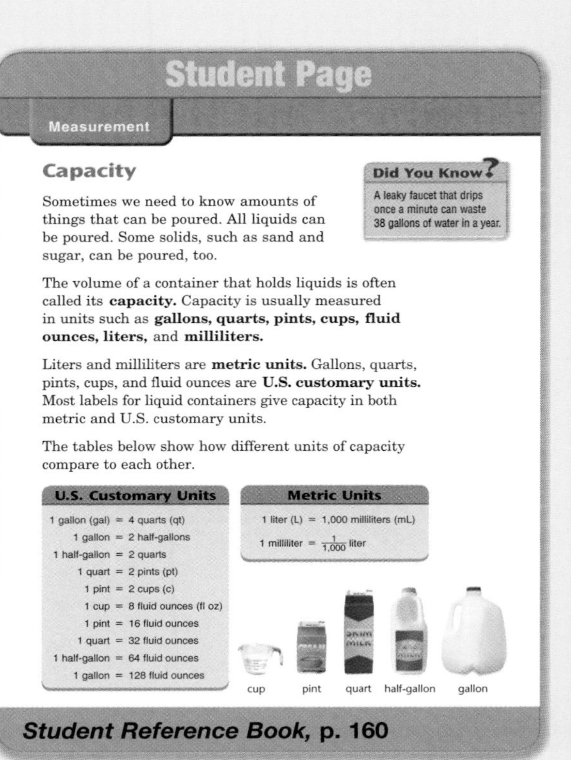

Measurement

Capacity

Sometimes we need to know amounts of things that can be poured. All liquids can be poured. Some solids, such as sand and sugar, can be poured, too.

Did You Know? A leaky faucet that drips once a minute can waste 38 gallons of water in a year.

The volume of a container that holds liquids is often called its **capacity.** Capacity is usually measured in units such as **gallons, quarts, pints, cups, fluid ounces, liters,** and **milliliters.**

Liters and milliliters are **metric units.** Gallons, quarts, pints, cups, and fluid ounces are **U.S. customary units.** Most labels for liquid containers give capacity in both metric and U.S. customary units.

The tables below show how different units of capacity compare to each other.

U.S. Customary Units
1 gallon (gal) = 4 quarts (qt)
1 gallon = 2 half-gallons
1 half-gallon = 2 quarts
1 quart = 2 pints (pt)
1 pint = 2 cups (c)
1 cup = 8 fluid ounces (fl oz)
1 pint = 16 fluid ounces
1 quart = 32 fluid ounces
1 half-gallon = 64 fluid ounces
1 gallon = 128 fluid ounces

Metric Units
1 liter (L) = 1,000 milliliters (mL)
1 milliliter = $\frac{1}{1,000}$ liter

Student Reference Book, p. 160

Student Page

Date ____ Time ____

LESSON 10·5 **Units of Measure**

Mark the unit you would use to measure each item.

1. thickness of a dime	● millimeter	○ gram	○ foot
2. flour used in cooking	○ gallon	● cup	○ liter
3. bottle of water	○ meter	○ ton	● liter
4. distance to the moon	○ foot	○ square mile	● kilometer
5. area of a floor	● square foot	○ cubic foot	○ foot
6. draperies	○ kilometer	○ millimeter	● yard
7. diameter of a basketball	○ mile	● inch	○ square inch
8. perimeter of a garden	● yard	○ square yard	○ centimeter
9. spices in a recipe	● teaspoon	○ pound	○ fluid ounce
10. weight of a nickel	○ pound	● gram	○ inch
11. volume of a suitcase	○ square inch	○ foot	● cubic inch
12. length of a cat's tail	● centimeter	○ meter	○ yard

Solve. You may draw pictures to help you.

13. When full, a juice carton holds 2 L 860 mL of juice. The carton is half full of juice. How much juice is in the carton?

Answer: 1 L 430 mL

14. Lindsay weighs 32 kg 550 g. Together she and her cat weigh 37 kg 250 g. How much does Lindsay's cat weigh?

Answer: 4 kg 700 g

Math Journal 2, p. 250

Equivalencies

1 oz is about 28.35 g

1 lb is about 453.59 g

1 L is about 1.06 qt

Class Data Pad

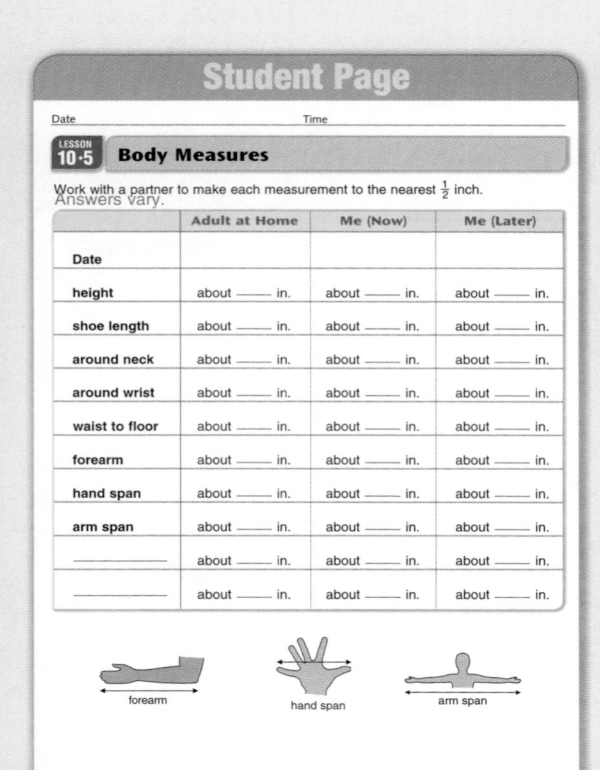

Student Page

Date ____ Time ____

LESSON 10·5 **Body Measures**

Work with a partner to make each measurement to the nearest $\frac{1}{2}$ inch.
Answers vary.

	Adult at Home	Me (Now)	Me (Later)
Date			
height	about ___ in.	about ___ in.	about ___ in.
shoe length	about ___ in.	about ___ in.	about ___ in.
around neck	about ___ in.	about ___ in.	about ___ in.
around wrist	about ___ in.	about ___ in.	about ___ in.
waist to floor	about ___ in.	about ___ in.	about ___ in.
forearm	about ___ in.	about ___ in.	about ___ in.
hand span	about ___ in.	about ___ in.	about ___ in.
arm span	about ___ in.	about ___ in.	about ___ in.
______	about ___ in.	about ___ in.	about ___ in.
______	about ___ in.	about ___ in.	about ___ in.

Math Journal 2, p. 251

▶ Discussing Information on Labels of Food Containers

Health Link Discuss the nutritional information on various labels, such as serving size, number of servings per container, nutritional values, and recommended daily allowances (RDAs). Talk about the differences between the nutritional information and the ingredients listed on the label.

Point out that the calorie is not a unit of weight but a unit that expresses the energy value of food. With respect to nutritional information, call attention to such entries as *cholesterol 15 mg/serving.* Remind children that the abbreviation *mg* stands for milligram, or $\frac{1}{1,000}$ of 1 gram. That is less than $\frac{1}{1,000}$ of the weight of a paper clip!

▶ Home Link 10·4 Follow-Up

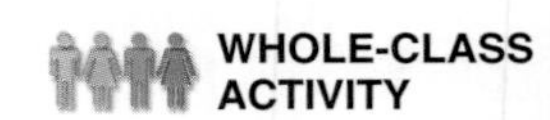

Children share the information on the labels they brought from home. Some possible observations:

▷ On most labels, the net weight or capacity is given in metric and U.S. customary units, such as grams and ounces or milliliters and fluid ounces. From this information, children can derive some rough equivalencies between metric and U.S. customary units: 500 grams is about 1 pound; 30 grams is a little more than 1 ounce; 1 liter is a little more than 1 quart. (*See margin.*) (You can demonstrate the quart/liter equivalence by pouring a liter of water into a quart bottle.)

▷ Weight and capacity may be expressed with fractions as well as with decimals.

▷ The amount of liquid in a container is often expressed in fluid ounces (fl oz). There are 8 fluid ounces in 1 cup. How many fluid ounces are in 1 pint? 16 In 1 quart? 32 In a half-gallon? 64 In 1 gallon? 128 Add these equivalencies to the list on the Class Data Pad.

▷ Recipes are often displayed on labels. Some of the quantities may be expressed as fractions of cups. How many fluid ounces are in $\frac{1}{2}$ cup? 4 $\frac{1}{4}$ cup? 2 Smaller quantities are expressed in tablespoons and teaspoons.

▷ Add the following equivalencies to the list on the Class Data Pad: 1 fluid ounce = 2 tablespoons (tbs); 1 tablespoon = 3 teaspoons (tsp).

Ask: *How many teaspoons are in 1 fluid ounce?* 6 teaspoons

Working with Units of Measure

INDEPENDENT ACTIVITY

(*Math Journal 2,* p. 250)

Children select the most appropriate units of measure to use in a variety of situations. They also solve number stories involving units of measure. Bring the class together to compare answers.

2 Ongoing Learning & Practice

Completing a Body-Measure Table

PARTNER ACTIVITY

(*Math Journal 2,* p. 251)

Recall that children copied the information onto this page from journal page 64 before *Math Journal 1* was sent home. Children work with a partner to measure parts of the body for the third column in the table. These measurements should be completed before the start of Lesson 10-7.

Math Boxes 10•5

INDEPENDENT ACTIVITY

(*Math Journal 2,* p. 252)

Mixed Practice Math Boxes in this lesson are paired with Math Boxes in Lesson 10-7. The skill in Problem 6 previews Unit 11 content.

Writing/Reasoning Have children write an answer to the following on an Exit Slip: *Use pictures or words or both to explain how you figured out which fractions were less than $\frac{2}{3}$ in Problem 4.* Sample answers: I knew that $\frac{1}{3}$ was less than $\frac{2}{3}$ because you need two $\frac{1}{3}$s to make $\frac{2}{3}$. I knew $\frac{2}{5}$ was less than $\frac{2}{3}$ because the numerator in $\frac{2}{5}$ is less than $\frac{1}{2}$ of the denominator. In $\frac{2}{3}$ the numerator is more than half of the denominator. So, $\frac{2}{5}$ is less than $\frac{2}{3}$.

Ongoing Assessment: Recognizing Student Achievement

Exit Slip

Use an **Exit Slip** (*Math Masters,* page 398) to assess children's progress toward drawing conclusions about data representations. Children are making adequate progress if they are able to use two data landmarks (maximum, minimum, range, median) to describe the graph in Problem 2. Some children may use more than two data landmarks.

[Data and Chance Goal 2]

Student Page

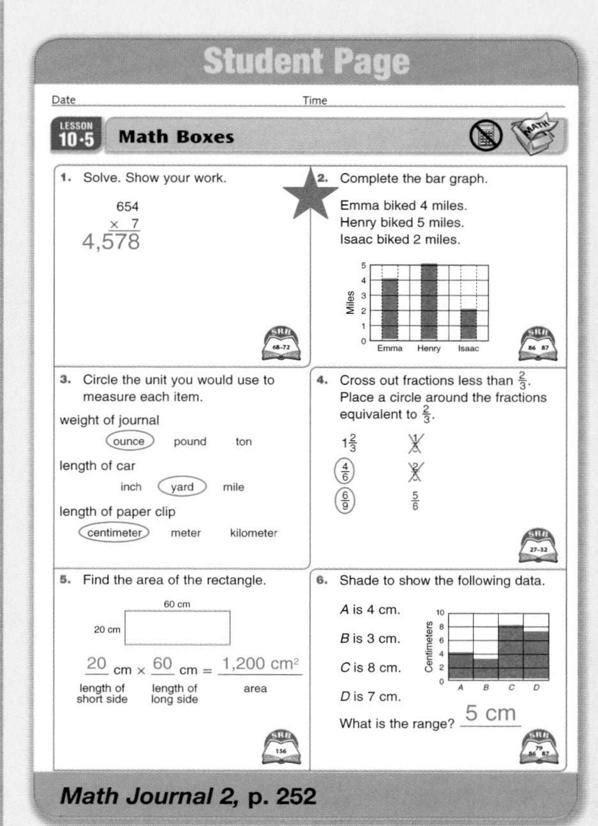

Date Time

LESSON 10•5 **Math Boxes**

1. Solve. Show your work.
654 × 7 = 4,578

2. Complete the bar graph.
Emma biked 4 miles.
Henry biked 5 miles.
Isaac biked 2 miles.

3. Circle the unit you would use to measure each item.
weight of journal: (ounce) pound ton
length of car: inch (yard) mile
length of paper clip: (centimeter) meter kilometer

4. Cross out fractions less than $\frac{2}{3}$. Place a circle around the fractions equivalent to $\frac{2}{3}$.
$1\frac{2}{3}$ ~~$\frac{1}{3}$~~ ($\frac{4}{6}$) ~~$\frac{2}{5}$~~ ($\frac{6}{9}$) $\frac{5}{6}$

5. Find the area of the rectangle.

20 cm × 60 cm = 1,200 cm²
length of short side; length of long side; area

6. Shade to show the following data.
A is 4 cm.
B is 3 cm.
C is 8 cm.
D is 7 cm.
What is the range? 5 cm

Math Journal 2, p. 252

Home Link Master

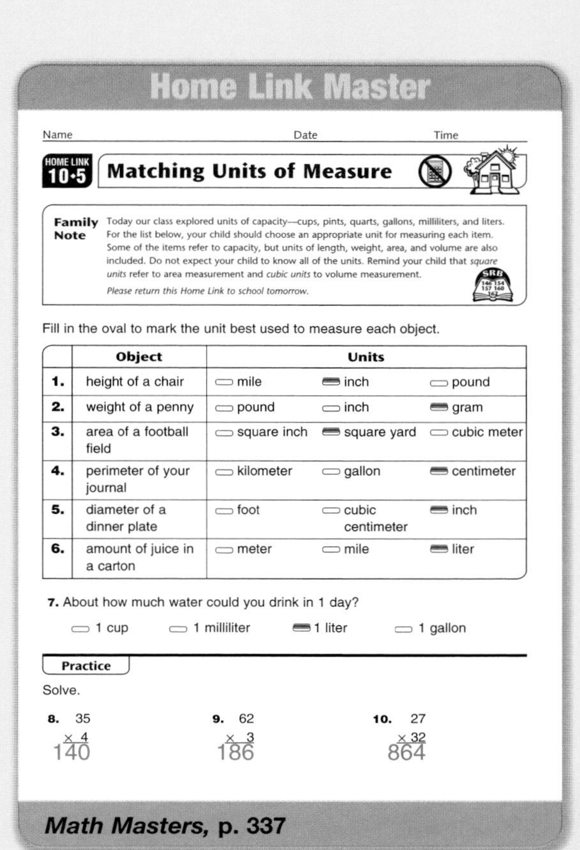

Name Date Time

HOME LINK 10•5 **Matching Units of Measure**

Family Note Today our class explored units of capacity—cups, pints, quarts, gallons, milliliters, and liters. For the list below, your child should choose an appropriate unit for measuring each item. Some of the items refer to capacity, but units of length, weight, area, and volume are also included. Do not expect your child to know all of the units. Remind your child that *square units* refer to area measurement and *cubic units* to volume measurement.

Please return this Home Link to school tomorrow.

Fill in the oval to mark the unit best used to measure each object.

	Object	Units		
1.	height of a chair	mile	inch (filled)	pound
2.	weight of a penny	pound	inch	gram (filled)
3.	area of a football field	square inch	square yard (filled)	cubic meter
4.	perimeter of your journal	kilometer	gallon	centimeter (filled)
5.	diameter of a dinner plate	foot	cubic centimeter	inch (filled)
6.	amount of juice in a carton	meter	mile	liter (filled)

7. About how much water could you drink in 1 day?
1 cup; 1 milliliter; 1 liter (filled); 1 gallon

Practice

Solve.

8. 35 × 4 = 140
9. 62 × 3 = 186
10. 27 × 32 = 864

Math Masters, p. 337

Teaching Master

Name Date Time

LESSON 10·5 **Capacity in Nonstandard Units** 

Work with a partner. Follow these steps.

1. Choose a container.
2. Predict the number of paper cups full of rice, beans, or sand that will fill the container. Find the row in the table below that matches the letter on your container. Record your prediction.
3. Check your prediction. Fill a paper cup with rice, sand, or beans. Pour it into the container, counting each paper cup as you go. Record your results in the table.
4. Repeat the steps for each of the containers. Answers vary.

Letter on Container	Prediction of Capacity (full paper cups)	Measured Capacity (full paper cups)
A		
B		
C		
D		
E		

5. Compare the capacities of the containers. Write at least 2 things you notice about the capacities.
Sample answers: Container E holds 3 paper cups full of sand and Container A holds 6 paper cups. That is twice as much. Container B holds 1 paper cup. Container E is 3 times larger than B.

Math Masters, **p. 336**

Teaching Master

Name Date Time

 **Finding the Volume & Weight of Popcorn**

Part 1

Make predictions. Answers vary.

- Does popcorn weigh about the same before and after it is popped? ______
- Does it have the same volume? ______

Part 2

1. Measure the volume and weight of the unpopped corn kernels. Record your data in the data chart below.
2. Measure the volume and weight of the popped popcorn. Record your data in the data chart.

	Unpopped Kernels	Popped Kernels
Weight		
Volume		

3. Were your predictions correct? Explain.
Sample answer: My predictions were correct. The weight stays the same since I'm not adding or taking any popcorn away, but the volume changes because popped kernels take up more space.

Math Masters, **p. 338**

▶ Home Link 10·5

INDEPENDENT ACTIVITY

(*Math Masters,* p. 337)

Home Connection Children choose appropriate units for measurement of given items.

3 Differentiation Options

READINESS

▶ Comparing Capacities in Nonstandard Units

15–30 Min

(*Math Masters,* p. 336)

To provide experience with comparing capacities, have children predict and then check the amount of material that will fill a variety of containers. Provide at least five containers in a variety of sizes and shapes each labeled with a letter. Place the containers and a few small paper cups near a tub of rice, sand, or dried beans. Provide a funnel (you can make one out of sturdy paper) for filling small-mouthed containers. Children record their work on *Math Masters,* page 336. Discuss the relationships between the sizes and capacities of the containers.

ENRICHMENT

▶ Finding the Volume and Weight of Popcorn

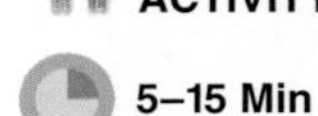

(*Math Masters,* p. 338)

To further explore volume and weight, have children estimate and measure the volume and weight of $\frac{1}{2}$ cup of unpopped popcorn kernels, and then repeat with popped popcorn from the $\frac{1}{2}$ cup of kernels. Children record their work on *Math Masters,* page 338.

NOTE If children note some weight loss from the popped corn, it is likely due to gases escaping during the popping.

EXTRA PRACTICE

SMALL-GROUP ACTIVITY

▶ *Minute Math+*

To offer children more experience with measures of capacity, see the following pages in *Minute Math+*:

Number Stories: pp. 93, 99, 131, and 159

10•6 The Mean and the Median

Objectives To introduce the mean of a set of data; and to review the median of a set of data.

www.everydaymathonline.com

ePresentations

eToolkit

Algorithms Practice

EM Facts Workshop Game™

Family Letters

Assessment Management

Common Core State Standards

Curriculum Focal Points

Interactive Teacher's Lesson Guide

1 Teaching the Lesson

Key Concepts and Skills

- Order whole numbers.
  [Number and Numeration Goal 6]
- Use data to complete a bar graph.
  [Data and Chance Goal 1]
- Find the median and mean of data sets.
  [Data and Chance Goal 2]
- Use graphs to ask and answer questions.
  [Data and Chance Goal 2]

Key Activities

Children make bar graphs for given sets of data. They model the bar graphs with pennies and then rearrange the pennies to determine the mean (average) for each data set. They compare the mean and median of data sets.

Ongoing Assessment: Recognizing Student Achievement Use journal page 254.
[Data and Chance Goal 1]

Ongoing Assessment: Informing Instruction See page 838.

Key Vocabulary

mean ◆ average ◆ median

Materials

Math Journal 2, pp. 253 and 254
Student Reference Book, pp. 80 and 83–85
Home Link 10•5
ruler or straightedge ◆ tool-kit pennies or counters (30 per child) ◆ stick-on notes (optional) ◆ slate

2 Ongoing Learning & Practice

Interpreting a Pictograph and Creating a Bar Graph

Math Journal 2, pp. 255A and 255B
Student Reference Book, pp. 86–89
Children use data from a pictograph to answer questions. Then they create a bar graph to show the same data.

Math Boxes 10•6

Math Journal 2, p. 255
Children practice and maintain skills through Math Box problems.

Home Link 10•6

Math Masters, p. 340
Children practice and maintain skills through Home Link activities.

3 Differentiation Options

READINESS

Graphing Dice Rolls

Math Masters, p. 339
per partnership: 2 dice
Children make a bar graph to record dice-roll results.

ENRICHMENT

Making a Data Set

Math Masters, pp. 341 and 342
per partnership: counters
Children determine a set of data based on given landmarks and graph the data.

ELL SUPPORT

Building a Math Word Bank

Differentiation Handbook, p. 132
Children add the term *mean* to their Math Word Banks.

Advance Preparation

***Teacher's Reference Manual,* Grades 1–3** pp. 124–126

Mathematical Practices
SMP1, **SMP2, SMP4,** SMP5, SMP6
Content Standards
3.OA.7, 3.NF.3b, **3.MD.3**

Getting Started

Mental Math and Reflexes

Pose fact and fact extension problems like the following. Have children record the facts on slates and share their strategies for solving the fact extensions.

●○○ 6 × __9__ = 54
__7__ × 8 = 56
9 × 4 = __36__

●●○ __3__ × 90 = 270
__70__ × 7 = 490
80 × 6 = __480__

●●● 60 × 70 = __4,200__
80 × __80__ = 6,400
__40__ × 90 = 3,600

Math Message

Make a bar graph of the data in the table on journal page 253.

Home Link 10•5 Follow-Up

Have partners share answers.

NOTE *Everyday Mathematics* does not draw a distinction between bar graphs and histograms. For a discussion on how some people contrast them, see section 12.2.3, Organizing and Displaying Data in the *Teacher's Reference Manual.*

Student Page

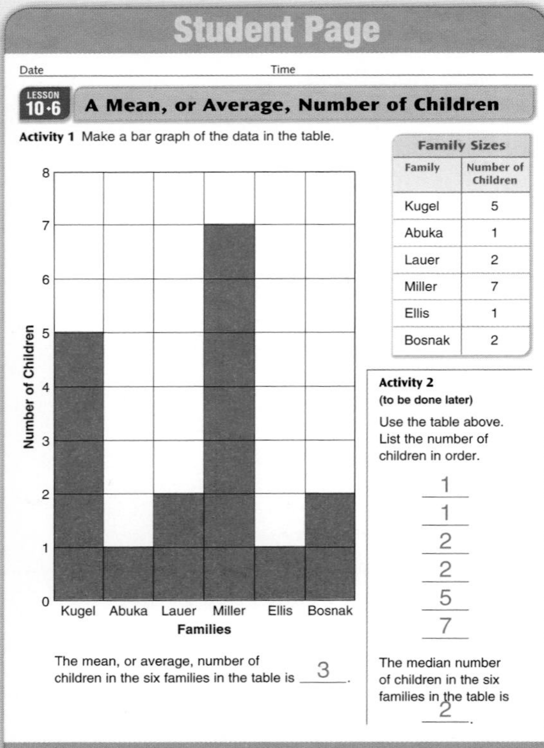

Date Time

LESSON 10•6 **A Mean, or Average, Number of Children**

Activity 1 Make a bar graph of the data in the table.

Family Sizes

Family	Number of Children
Kugel	5
Abuka	1
Lauer	2
Miller	7
Ellis	1
Bosnak	2

Activity 2
(to be done later)
Use the table above. List the number of children in order.

1
1
2
2
5
7

The mean, or average, number of children in the six families in the table is __3__.

The median number of children in the six families in the table is __2__.

Math Journal 2, **p. 253**

1 Teaching the Lesson

▶ Math Message Follow-Up

(*Math Journal 2,* p. 253)

Check that children have completed the bar graph. Ask: *What does the height of each bar represent?* The number of children in that family

▶ Finding the Mean Number of Children

(*Math Journal 2,* p. 253; *Student Reference Book,* pp. 83–85)

Ask whether anyone can remember how the class found an average class shoe length in an earlier unit. (In Lesson 3-1, 16 children lined up along a paper tape, each placing one foot heel-to-toe on the tape. After cutting off the leftover piece of tape, children folded the tape into 16 equal parts. Each part represented an average class shoe length.) Explain to the class that they are going to find the average number of children per family shown in the table using another method. Lead them in the following routine:

1. Cover each shaded cell in the bar graph with a penny (or other counter). What does each penny represent? A child
2. Level off the pennies; that is, rearrange the pennies so each column in the graph has the same number of pennies.
3. With a straightedge, draw a horizontal line just above the top row of pennies.
4. Remove the pennies.

The horizontal line represents the **mean,** or **average,** of this set of data. In this example, the mean number of children per family is 3. To support English language learners, discuss the social and mathematical meanings of the words *mean* and *average.* Emphasize that in this mathematical context, *mean* and *average* describe the same thing.

Ask children to count the number of shaded cells above the line and the number of unshaded cells below the line.

- Are the number of cells the same? Yes. Each time a penny was moved, a shaded cell was matched with an unshaded cell.
- How could you find the place to draw the horizontal line without using pennies? By trial and error, draw a horizontal line so that the number of shaded squares above the line is the same as the number of unshaded squares below the line.

Another method of finding the mean is to model each family by drawing a medium-size circle for each family and putting in the required number of pennies or counters to represent the number of children. The counters are then redistributed among the families (without adding or subtracting any) so each family has the same number.

Have children read the essay on The Mean (Average) on pages 83–85 in the *Student Reference Book.*

▶ Finding the Mean of Ostrich Egg Clutches

(*Math Journal 2,* p. 254)

Children make bar graphs of the data set about ostrich egg clutches. They use one of the methods from the previous activity to find the mean number of eggs.

Ongoing Assessment: Recognizing Student Achievement

Journal Page 254 ★

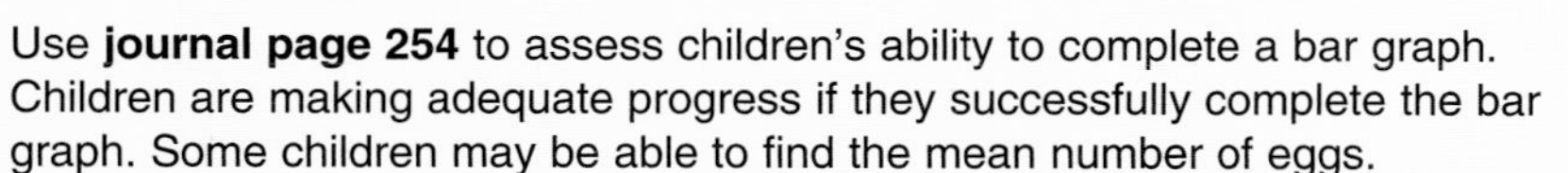

Use **journal page 254** to assess children's ability to complete a bar graph. Children are making adequate progress if they successfully complete the bar graph. Some children may be able to find the mean number of eggs.

[Data and Chance Goal 1]

Links to the Future

The activities in this lesson are an early exposure to finding the mean of a set of data. Finding the mean of a data set is a Grade 5 Goal.

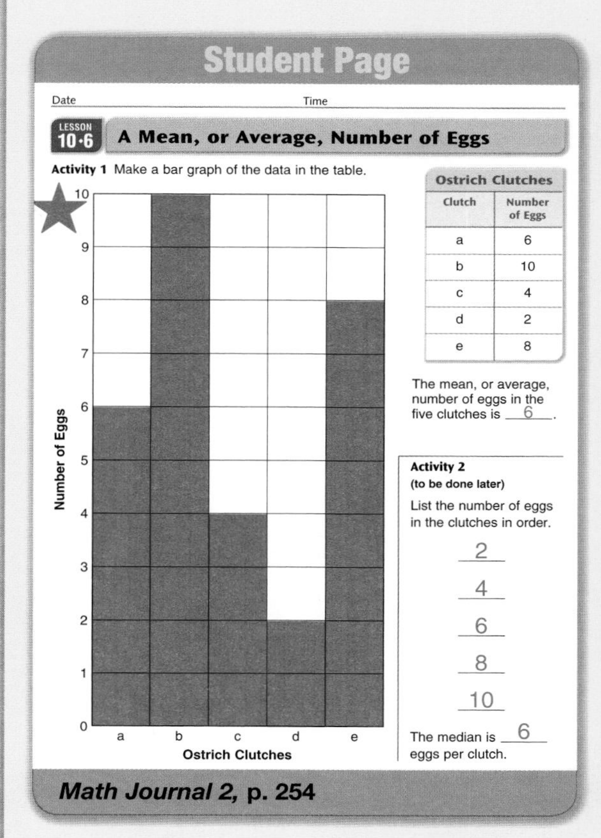

Student Page

Date ______ Time ______

LESSON 10·6 **A Mean, or Average, Number of Eggs**

Activity 1 Make a bar graph of the data in the table.

Ostrich Clutches

Clutch	Number of Eggs
a	6
b	10
c	4
d	2
e	8

The mean, or average, number of eggs in the five clutches is 6.

Activity 2
(to be done later)

List the number of eggs in the clutches in order.

2
4
6
8
10

The median is 6 eggs per clutch.

Math Journal 2, **p. 254**

NOTE Although the mean for this set of data is a whole number, the mean for other data sets will likely be *between* two whole numbers. A more efficient way to find the mean will be introduced in Lesson 10-7.

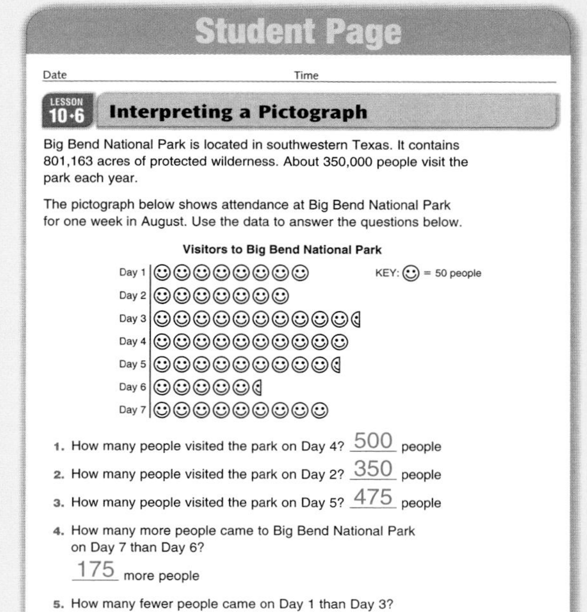

Student Page

Date ______ Time ______

LESSON 10·6 **Interpreting a Pictograph**

Big Bend National Park is located in southwestern Texas. It contains 801,163 acres of protected wilderness. About 350,000 people visit the park each year.

The pictograph below shows attendance at Big Bend National Park for one week in August. Use the data to answer the questions below.

1. How many people visited the park on Day 4? 500 people
2. How many people visited the park on Day 2? 350 people
3. How many people visited the park on Day 5? 475 people
4. How many more people came to Big Bend National Park on Day 7 than Day 6?
   175 more people
5. How many fewer people came on Day 1 than Day 3?
   125 fewer people

Math Journal 2, **p. 255A**

Student Page

Date Time

LESSON 10·6 **Making a Bar Graph from a Pictograph**

Use the information shown in the pictograph to make a bar graph. Remember to add labels and a title to your graph.

Visitors to Big Bend National Park

KEY: ☺ = 50 people

Day 1, Day 2, Day 3, Day 4, Day 5, Day 6, Day 7

Visitors to Big Bend National Park

Sample answer: Number of Visitors: 0, 50, 100, 150, 200, 250, 300, 350, 400, 450, 500, 550

Sample answer: Days of Visits: 1, 2, 3, 4, 5, 6, 7

Math Journal 2, p. 255B

▶ Finding the Median of Sets of Data

INDEPENDENT ACTIVITY

(*Math Journal 2,* pp. 253 and 254; *Student Reference Book,* p. 80)

Have children complete Activity 2 on journal pages 253 and 254. Children find the median number of children per family and the median number of eggs per clutch. If necessary, have them read page 80 in the *Student Reference Book* to review how to find the **median,** or middle value, of a set of data.

Ongoing Assessment: Informing Instruction

Watch for children who have difficulty finding the median. They can write the number of eggs in each nest on a small slip of paper or a stick-on note. Have them put the numbers in order and then find the middle number(s).

2 Ongoing Learning & Practice

▶ Interpreting a Pictograph and Creating a Bar Graph

(*Math Journal 2,* pp. 255A and 255B; *Student Reference Book,* pp. 86–89)

Have children examine the pictograph on journal page 255A. Ask them to explain what each smiley face means. 50 people Next ask them to explain what one-half of a smiley face means. 25 people Have children work independently or with a partner to complete journal page 255A. When they have finished, children create a bar graph on journal page 255B to show the same data. Discuss the scale for the bar graph. Since the pictograph key shows that each smiley face represents 50 people, the scale for the bar graph could be in increments of 50.

Student Page

Date Time

LESSON 10·6 **Math Boxes**

1. Measure each side of the triangle to the nearest centimeter.

   4 cm, 4 cm, 4 cm

   Perimeter = 12 cm

2. There are 5 blocks in a bag. 2 blocks are red, 2 blocks are blue, and 1 block is green. What are the chances of pulling out a red block?

   2 out of 5 chances

3. James built a rectangular prism out of base-10 blocks. He used 30 cm cubes to make the base. He put 4 more layers of cubes on top of that. What is the volume of the prism he built?

   150 cubic centimeters

4. Complete.

   1 gallon = 4 quarts
   3 gallons = 12 quarts
   1 pint = 2 cups
   7 pints = 14 cups
   1 liter = 1,000 milliliters
   5 liters = 5,000 milliliters

5. Molly is playing with 5 toy cars. This is only $\frac{1}{3}$ of her set of cars. How many cars are in her complete set? Fill in the circle next to the best answer.

   Ⓐ $\frac{5}{3}$ cars Ⓒ 10 cars
   Ⓑ 5 cars ● 15 cars

6. Color the circle so that it matches the description.

   $\frac{1}{2}$ blue
   $\frac{1}{3}$ green
   $\frac{1}{6}$ yellow

   Which color would you expect the spinner to land on most often? blue

Math Journal 2, p. 255

▶ Math Boxes 10·6

INDEPENDENT ACTIVITY

(*Math Journal 2,* p. 255)

Mixed Practice Math Boxes in this lesson are paired with Math Boxes in Lesson 10-8. The skill in Problem 6 previews Unit 11 content.

Writing/Reasoning Have children write an answer to the following: *Choose one of the units of capacity in Problem 4. Describe the unit of capacity by using one of the personal references for units of capacity from Lesson 10-5. For example, describe an object that has about the same measure as a liter (or the unit of capacity you chose).* Sample answer: I have a water bottle that holds 1 liter of water.

▶ Home Link 10·6

INDEPENDENT ACTIVITY

(*Math Masters,* p. 340)

Home Connection Children find the mean of a data set.

Home Link Master

Name Date Time

HOME LINK 10·6 Mean, or Average, Number of Fish

Family Note Many of us learned that to find the mean (average) of a set of numbers, we add all the numbers and then divide the total by how many numbers we added. In today's lesson, the class tried a different method of finding the mean. After your child has completed the page, ask him or her to explain how this method works. In the next lesson, we will introduce finding the mean by adding the numbers and dividing to find the answer.

Please return this Home Link to school tomorrow.

The table below lists how many goldfish each child won at the school fun fair.

Name	Number of Goldfish
Reba	3
Bill	1
Lucy	7
Meg	0
Nate	5
Pat	2

1. Put a penny over each shaded square in the bar graph.
2. Move the pennies so that each column has the same number of pennies.
3. Draw a horizontal line across your graph to show the height of the pennies when all of the columns are the same height.
4. The mean (average) number of goldfish won by children at the fun fair is 3.

Number of Goldfish: 0, 1, 2, 3, 4, 5, 6, 7

Names: Reba, Bill, Lucy, Meg, Nate, Pat

Math Masters, p. 340

3 Differentiation Options

READINESS

PARTNER ACTIVITY

▶ Graphing Dice Rolls

5–15 Min

(*Math Masters,* p. 339)

Portfolio Ideas

To provide experience with making a bar graph, have children predict how many times they think they will roll a 1 and then make a graph to record their results. When children have completed their graphs, have them discuss their predictions and results.

ENRICHMENT

PARTNER ACTIVITY

▶ Making a Data Set

15–30 Min

(*Math Masters,* pp. 341 and 342)

To apply children's understanding of landmarks (maximum, minimum, range, mode, and median), have them use the given median, range, and mode to display a possible data set when 5 children share 15 cookies. Children record their work on *Math Masters,* page 342 and make a bar graph of their data set on *Math Masters,* page 341.

ELL SUPPORT

SMALL-GROUP ACTIVITY

▶ Building a Math Word Bank

5–15 Min

(*Differentiation Handbook,* p. 132)

To provide language support for landmarks, have children use the Math Word Bank template found on *Differentiation Handbook,* page 132. Ask children to write the term *mean,* draw a picture representing the term, and write other related words. See the *Differentiation Handbook* for more information.

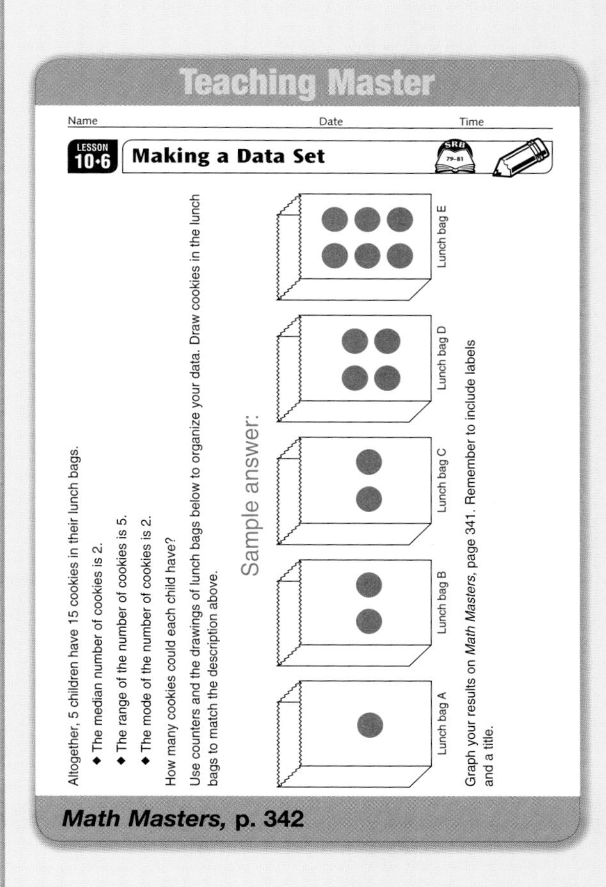

Teaching Master

Name Date Time

LESSON 10·6 Making a Data Set

Altogether, 5 children have 15 cookies in their lunch bags.

- The median number of cookies is 2.
- The range of the number of cookies is 5.
- The mode of the number of cookies is 2.

How many cookies could each child have?

Use counters and the drawings of lunch bags below to organize your data. Draw cookies in the lunch bags to match the description above.

Sample answer:

Lunch bag A, Lunch bag B, Lunch bag C, Lunch bag D, Lunch bag E

Graph your results on *Math Masters,* page 341. Remember to include labels and a title.

Math Masters, p. 342

10•7 Calculating the Mean

Objectives To guide children as they calculate the mean of a set of data; and to review the median of a set of data.

www.everydaymathonline.com

ePresentations

eToolkit

Algorithms Practice

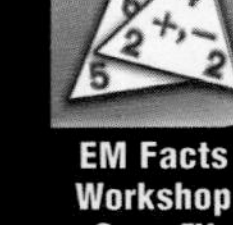
EM Facts Workshop Game™

Family Letters

Assessment Management

Common Core State Standards

Curriculum Focal Points

Interactive Teacher's Lesson Guide

1 Teaching the Lesson

Key Concepts and Skills

- Add 2- and 3-digit numbers with a calculator. [Operations and Computation Goal 2]
- Collect and organize data. [Data and Chance Goal 1]
- Find the median and mean of a data set. [Data and Chance Goal 2]
- Use graphs to answer questions and draw conclusions. [Data and Chance Goal 2]

Key Activities

Children find the median and mean arm spans and heights of adults and children. They practice finding the mean.

Ongoing Assessment: Recognizing Student Achievement
Use an Exit Slip (*Math Masters,* p. 398). [Data and Chance Goal 2]

Key Vocabulary

median ◆ mean ◆ average

Materials

Math Journal 2, pp. 251 and 256
Student Reference Book, pp. 80 and 83–85
Home Link 10•6
Math Masters, p. 398
stick-on notes ◆ small box ◆ calculator ◆ slate ◆ counters (optional)

2 Ongoing Learning & Practice

Playing *Multiplication Top-It*
Student Reference Book, pp. 297 and 298
per partnership: 4 each of number cards 0–10 (from the Everything Math Deck, if available)
Children practice multiplication facts.

Math Boxes 10•7
Math Journal 2, p. 257
Children practice and maintain skills through Math Box problems.

Home Link 10•7
Math Masters, p. 343
Children practice and maintain skills through Home Link activities.

3 Differentiation Options

READINESS

Matching Tally Charts to Bar Graphs
Math Masters, p. 345
Children match tally marks with bar graphs.

ENRICHMENT

Comparing Height and Arm Span Geometrically
Math Journal 2, p. 256
Math Masters, pp. 344 and 437
transparency of *Math Masters,* p. 437
crayons
Children make comparisons by representing data with rectangles.

EXTRA PRACTICE

Making a Line Plot
Student Reference Book, pp. 89A and 89B
paper
Children show data on a line plot.

Advance Preparation

Before beginning this lesson, children should have made and recorded the Me (Later) second measurements on journal page 251. Place a pad of stick-on notes, a small box, and copies of the Exit Slip (*Math Masters,* page 398) near the Math Message.

Getting Started

Mathematical Practices
SMP1, SMP2, SMP3, **SMP4,** SMP5, **SMP6**
Content Standards
3.OA.8, **3.MD.3, 3.MD.4**

Mental Math and Reflexes

Pose *Who Am I?* riddles like the following. Children may use counters or drawings and write their answers on slates. To support English language learners, explain that the use of *me* and *I* refers to a number. *Suggestions:*

●○○ $\frac{1}{3}$ of me is equal to $\frac{1}{2}$ of 16. Who am I? 24

●●○ If you take $\frac{1}{2}$ of me, I will be an odd number. I am less than 20. One of my factors is 5. Who am I? 10

●●● I am a 2-digit number. If you double me, I will be a 3-digit number. The sum of my digits is 6. 2, 3, 4, 5, and 6 are some of my factors. Who am I? 60

Math Message

Look up your last arm span measurement in the Me (Later) column on journal page 251. Copy it on a stick-on note and put the note in the box. Write large! Do not put your name on the note. Explain what median *means on an Exit Slip.*

Home Link 10·6 Follow-Up

Briefly go over the answers to the problem. Ask children to describe how they found the mean number of goldfish. Then have them find the *median* number of goldfish. The median value is halfway between 2 and 3, or $2\frac{1}{2}$.

1 Teaching the Lesson

▶ Math Message Follow-Up

WHOLE-CLASS DISCUSSION

(*Math Journal 2,* p. 251)

Check that children have found the right measurement and that they have written it on a stick-on note.

Ongoing Assessment: Recognizing Student Achievement

Exit Slip

Use an **Exit Slip** (*Math Masters,* page 398) to assess children's progress toward explaining what *median* means. Children are making adequate progress if they include *typical, middle,* or *middle value* in their explanation. Some children may be able to give an example of median in a set of data.

[Data and Chance Goal 2]

NOTE If you decide to have children complete the optional Part 3 Extra Practice line plot activity, save the stick-on notes from the Math Message.

▶ Finding the Median Arm Span of the Class

WHOLE-CLASS ACTIVITY

(*Math Journal 2,* p. 256)

Ask children to describe how they might go about finding the **median,** or typical, arm span from the data on the stick-on notes. Line up the stick-on notes on the board from the least to the greatest length. Count to the middle. Have a few children line up the stick-on notes in order on the board and count to the middle. If the number of notes is odd, there will be one note in the middle. If the number of notes is even, there will be two in the middle. In that case, if the two are the same, use that value; if they are not, use the value halfway between. Children record the median arm span for the class in Problem 1 on journal page 256.

Student Page

Date Time

LESSON 10·5 **Body Measures**

Work with a partner to make each measurement to the nearest $\frac{1}{2}$ inch.
Answers vary.

	Adult at Home	Me (Now)	Me (Later)
Date			
height	about ___ in.	about ___ in.	about ___ in.
shoe length	about ___ in.	about ___ in.	about ___ in.
around neck	about ___ in.	about ___ in.	about ___ in.
around wrist	about ___ in.	about ___ in.	about ___ in.
waist to floor	about ___ in.	about ___ in.	about ___ in.
forearm	about ___ in.	about ___ in.	about ___ in.
hand span	about ___ in.	about ___ in.	about ___ in.
arm span	about ___ in.	about ___ in.	about ___ in.
______	about ___ in.	about ___ in.	about ___ in.
______	about ___ in.	about ___ in.	about ___ in.

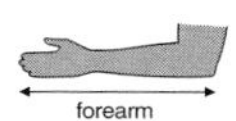

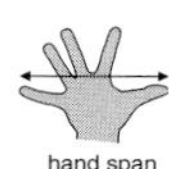

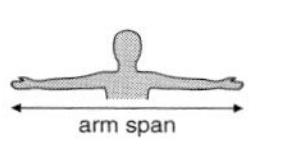

Math Journal 2, p. 251

▶ Finding the Mean Arm Span of the Class

(*Math Journal 2,* p. 256; *Student Reference Book,* pp. 80, and 83–85)

Explain that children are now going to calculate another typical arm span, the **mean** arm span. Remind them that they found the mean family size in Lesson 10-6 and that **average** is another word for *mean.*

Divide the class into groups of four or five and guide children through the three steps listed below. Each child should do the computations with a calculator, compare his or her results to those of other members of the group after each step, and resolve discrepancies before going on to the next step.

1. Add all the arm-span lengths to find the class total (sum).
2. Count the stick-on notes (number of measurements).
3. Divide the total (sum) by the number of stick-on notes (number of measurements).

The result is the *mean arm span* of children in the class. If the number has decimal places, tell children they can ignore any digits after tenths. Children record the average arm span in Problem 2 on journal page 256.

Student Page

Date ______ Time ______

LESSON 10·7 **Finding the Median and the Mean**

1. The median (middle) arm span in my class is about ____ inches. Answers vary.
2. The mean (average) arm span in my class is about ____ inches.
3. Look at page 251 in your journal. Use the measurements for an adult and the *second* measurements for yourself to find the median and mean arm spans and heights for your group. Record the results in the table below.
   a. Find the median and mean arm spans of the *adults* for your group.
   b. Find the median and mean arm spans of the *children* for your group.
   c. Find the median and mean heights of the *adults* for your group.
   d. Find the median and mean heights of the *children* for your group.

Summary of Measurements for Your Group

Measure	Adults	Children
Median arm span		
Mean arm span		
Median height		
Mean height		

Find the mean of each set of data. Use your calculator.

4. High temperatures: 56°F, 62°F, 74°F, 68°F 65 °F
5. Low temperatures: 32°F, 42°F, 58°F, 60°F 48 °F
6. Ticket sales: $710, $650, $905 $ 755
7. Throws: 40 ft, 32 ft, 55 ft, 37 ft, 43 ft, 48 ft 42.5 ft

Math Journal 2, p. 256

Ask:

- Are the median and mean arm spans fairly close to each other? Answers vary. As indicators of typical values, the median and mean of a data set are often close but may be skewed differently by outliers (extreme pieces of data).
- Which was easier to find—the median or the mean? Answers vary. In general, finding a median requires little or no computation but may involve counting many items; finding a mean involves computation but may be automated.

Have children read more about the median and mean on pages 80 and 83–85 in the *Student Reference Book.*

Finding Median and Mean Heights and Arm Spans

SMALL-GROUP ACTIVITY

(*Math Journal 2,* pp. 251 and 256)

Divide the class into groups of five to eight. Using data from journal page 251, children in each group find the median and mean heights and arm spans of the adults and children in their groups. They record the results in the table in Problem 3 on journal page 256.

After children have completed Problem 3, bring the class together to compare the medians and means they have found. Ask: *Are the average heights and arm spans about the same for the children in your group? Are they about the same for the adults in your group?*

NOTE Most people's arm span is almost the same as their height.

Summary: Both the median and the mean can identify a typical value for a data set. Sometimes they are close together, and sometimes they are quite different, depending on the information in the data set. Each is a useful estimate. Deciding which of them will provide the more useful information depends on the situation and how you want to use the results.

Finding the Mean

INDEPENDENT ACTIVITY

(*Math Journal 2,* p. 256)

Working alone or with a partner, children use their calculators to complete Problems 4–7 on journal page 256.

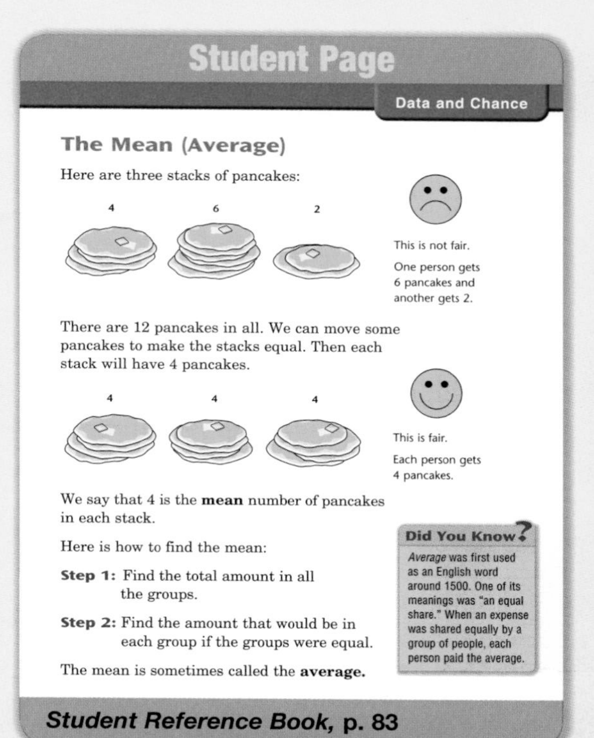

Student Page

Data and Chance

The Mean (Average)

Here are three stacks of pancakes:

There are 12 pancakes in all. We can move some pancakes to make the stacks equal. Then each stack will have 4 pancakes.

We say that 4 is the **mean** number of pancakes in each stack.

Here is how to find the mean:

Step 1: Find the total amount in all the groups.

Step 2: Find the amount that would be in each group if the groups were equal.

The mean is sometimes called the **average.**

Did You Know?

Average was first used as an English word around 1500. One of its meanings was "an equal share." When an expense was shared equally by a group of people, each person paid the average.

Student Reference Book, p. 83

NOTE *Everyday Mathematics* uses the median as a typical value far more often than the mean for two main reasons: The median reduces the effect of outliers, and, in most cases, it is easier to obtain.

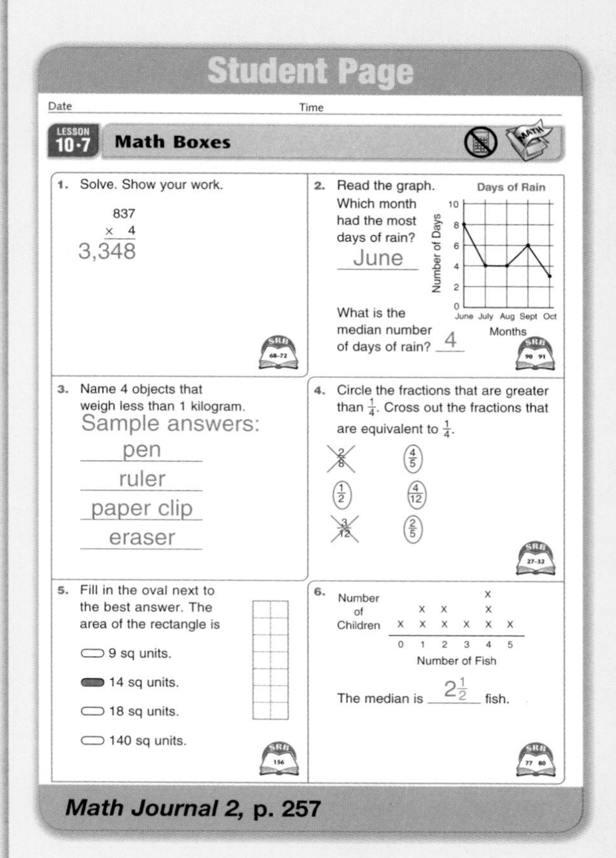

Student Page

Date Time

LESSON 10·7 **Math Boxes**

1. Solve. Show your work.

837
× 4
3,348

2. Read the graph. Which month had the most days of rain? June

What is the median number of days of rain? 4

3. Name 4 objects that weigh less than 1 kilogram.
Sample answers:
pen
ruler
paper clip
eraser

4. Circle the fractions that are greater than $\frac{1}{4}$. Cross out the fractions that are equivalent to $\frac{1}{4}$.

$\frac{2}{8}$ $\frac{4}{5}$ $\frac{1}{2}$ $\frac{4}{12}$ $\frac{3}{12}$ $\frac{2}{5}$

5. Fill in the oval next to the best answer. The area of the rectangle is

- 9 sq units.
- 14 sq units.
- 18 sq units.
- 140 sq units.

6.

The median is $2\frac{1}{2}$ fish.

Math Journal 2, p. 257

Home Link Master

Name Date Time

HOME LINK 10•7 **Finding the Mean**

Family Note The median and mean (average) indicate typical values in a set of data. The median is the middle value when the data numbers are listed in order. The mean (average) is found by the process described below. Your child may use a calculator to solve the problems. (In third grade, we ignore any digits to the right of the tenths place.)

SRB 80 83–85

Please return this Home Link to school tomorrow.

To find the mean (average):

1. Find the sum of the data numbers.
2. Count the data numbers.
3. Use a calculator to divide the sum by the number of data numbers.
4. Drop any digits after tenths.

Example:

Basketball Scores: 80, 85, 76

1. 80 + 85 + 76 = 241
2. There are 3 scores.
3. 241 ÷ 3 = 80.333333...
4. Mean: 80.3

Baseball Home Run Leaders		
1998	Mark McGwire	70
1999	Mark McGwire	65
2000	Sammy Sosa	50
2001	Barry Bonds	73
2002	Alex Rodriguez	57
2003	Jim Thome, Alex Rodriguez	47

1. Mean number of home runs: 60.3

Baseball Home Run Leaders		
1901	Sam Crawford	16
1902	Socks Seybold	16
1903	Buck Freeman	13
1904	Harry Davis	10
1905	Fred Odwell	9

2. Mean number of home runs: 12.8

Source: World Almanac, 2004

3. List some data for people in your home—for example, their ages, shoe sizes, or heights. Find the median and mean of the data.

Kind of data Answers vary.

Data ______

Median: ______ Mean: ______

***Math Masters*, p. 343**

Teaching Master

Name Date Time

LESSON 10•7 **Matching Tally Charts to Bar Graphs**

Work with a partner.

1. Match each tally chart with the bar graph that best describes the data. Write a title that tells about each graph. Fill in the missing labels.

Number of Books Read	Number of Children
0	
1	///
2	卌 ///
3	卌 /
4	卌

Number of Pockets	Number of Children
0	卌 /
1	
2	卌 /
3	//
4	卌
5	///

Title: Sample answer: Books Read

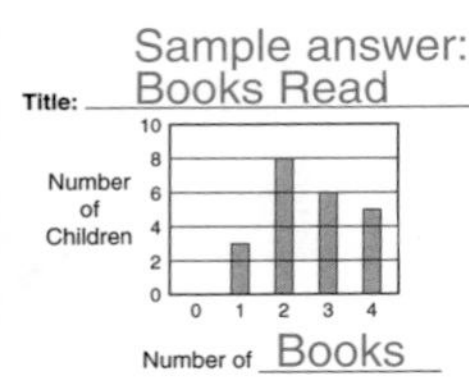

Number of Books

Title: Sample answer: Children's Pockets

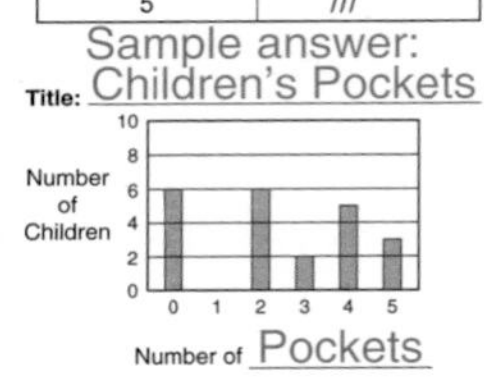

Number of Pockets

2. How many children in all read books?

22 children

3. How many more children have 2 or fewer pockets than have 3 or more pockets?

2 children

***Math Masters*, p. 345**

2 Ongoing Learning & Practice

▶ Playing *Multiplication Top-It*

(*Student Reference Book*, pp. 297 and 298)

Children practice multiplication facts by playing *Multiplication Top-It.* For game instructions, see pages 297 and 298 in the *Student Reference Book.*

▶ Math Boxes 10•7

(*Math Journal 2*, p. 257)

Mixed Practice Math Boxes in this lesson are paired with Math Boxes in Lesson 10-5. The skill in Problem 6 previews Unit 11 content.

Writing/Reasoning Have children write an answer to the following: *Choose one of the objects you listed in Problem 3. Describe how you can use a benchmark weight or personal reference to help you estimate the weight of the object in ounces.* Sample answer: I chose the plastic ruler. I know our chalkboard eraser weighs about 1 ounce. I held the plastic ruler in one hand and the chalkboard eraser in the other. The plastic ruler weighs more than the chalkboard eraser, so it weighs more than 1 ounce.

▶ Home Link 10•7

(*Math Masters*, p. 343)

Home Connection Children use baseball data to calculate averages. Then they list data about people in their homes and find the median and mean of the data.

3 Differentiation Options

READINESS

▶ Matching Tally Charts to Bar Graphs

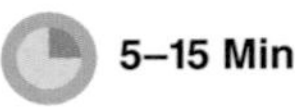

(*Math Masters*, p. 345)

To provide experience drawing conclusions from representations of data, have children match tally charts with graphs. Then they solve one- and two-step problems using information from the tally charts and bar graphs. They record their work on *Math Masters,* page 345.

ENRICHMENT

SMALL-GROUP ACTIVITY

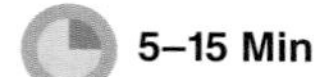

5–15 Min

▶ Comparing Height and Arm Span Geometrically

(*Math Journal 2,* p. 256; *Math Masters,* pp. 344 and 437)

To apply children's understanding of data sets, have them compare and contrast arm span and height data. Children use $\frac{1}{4}$-inch grid paper (*Math Masters,* page 437) to make rectangles that represent a scale drawing of the relationship between height and arm span for the adults and children in their group. Provide an example such as the following: Imagine the median height of an adult group is 64 inches and the median arm span is 64 inches. Ask: *What kind of rectangle would this be?* square

Point out that a scale drawing of a rectangle can be drawn to represent the relationship between arm span and height instead of drawing the actual rectangle size that is 64 inches by 64 inches. Show a transparency of *Math Masters,* page 437. Ask: *If the length of each square or unit on this grid represents 4 inches, what is the length of a line that represents 64 inches?* 16 squares or units Draw a vertical line to represent the median height of the group. Label this side of the rectangle *median height.* Then draw a horizontal line to represent the median arm span of the group. Label this side of the rectangle *median arm span.* Draw the remaining sides to complete the rectangle (square).

Have children follow directions on *Math Masters,* page 344 to draw rectangles to compare the median heights and arm spans of the adults with the median heights and arm spans of the children.

EXTRA PRACTICE

INDEPENDENT ACTIVITY

5–15 Min

▶ Making a Line Plot

(*Student Reference Book,* pp. 89A and 89B)

To provide additional practice with representing data, have children show the class arm-span data on a line plot. On the board, display the stick-on notes from the Math Message in order from least to greatest measure. Ask children to suggest a scale for their line plots. Sample answer: Since the arm-span measures are to the nearest $\frac{1}{2}$ inch, the scale should begin with the shortest arm-span measure, increase in $\frac{1}{2}$-inch increments, and end with the longest arm-span measure in the class. Have children make their line plots on paper. Remind them to include labels.

Planning Ahead

Prior to Lesson 10-8, you should become familiar with the memory keys of the calculators that your children use in the classroom. Refer to Lesson 10-8 ahead of time for instructions on calculator usage.

Teaching Aid Master

Name Date Time

$\frac{1}{4}$-inch Grid Paper

Math Masters, p. 437

Teaching Master

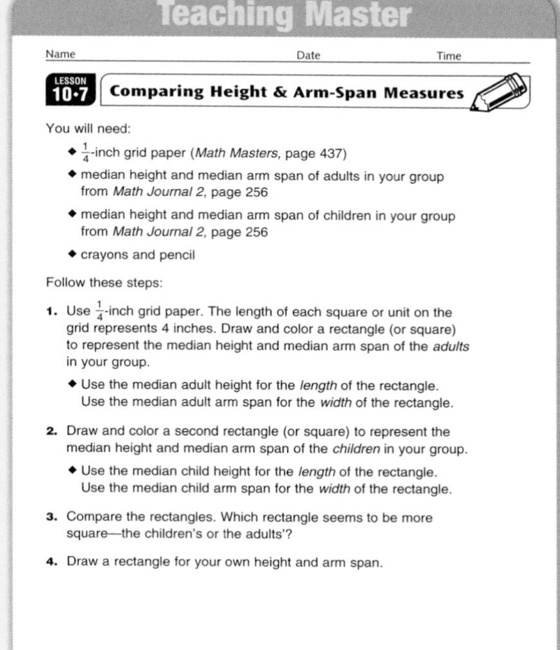

Name Date Time

LESSON 10•7 **Comparing Height & Arm-Span Measures**

You will need:

- $\frac{1}{4}$-inch grid paper (*Math Masters,* page 437)
- median height and median arm span of adults in your group from *Math Journal 2,* page 256
- median height and median arm span of children in your group from *Math Journal 2,* page 256
- crayons and pencil

Follow these steps:

1. Use $\frac{1}{4}$-inch grid paper. The length of each square or unit on the grid represents 4 inches. Draw and color a rectangle (or square) to represent the median height and median arm span of the *adults* in your group.
   - Use the median adult height for the *length* of the rectangle. Use the median adult arm span for the *width* of the rectangle.
2. Draw and color a second rectangle (or square) to represent the median height and median arm span of the *children* in your group.
   - Use the median child height for the *length* of the rectangle. Use the median child arm span for the *width* of the rectangle.
3. Compare the rectangles. Which rectangle seems to be more square—the children's or the adults'?
4. Draw a rectangle for your own height and arm span.

Math Masters, p. 344

10•8 Calculator Memory

Objective To introduce the memory keys on a calculator.

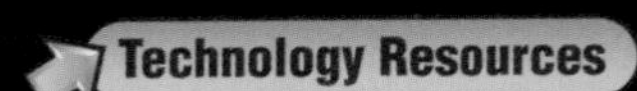

www.everydaymathonline.com

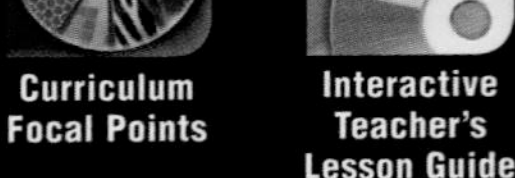

1 Teaching the Lesson

Key Concepts and Skills

- Use addition and subtraction facts to solve problems. [Operations and Computation Goal 1]
- Use mental arithmetic to add and subtract numbers. [Operations and Computation Goal 2]
- Use calculators to solve problems involving the addition and subtraction of whole numbers. [Operations and Computation Goal 2]

Key Activities

Children are introduced to and practice using the memory keys on their calculators.

Children play the game *Memory Addition/Subtraction* using their calculators.

Key Vocabulary

memory ◆ memory keys

Materials

Math Journal 2, p. 258
Student Reference Book, pp. 290 and 291
Home Link 10•7
Math Masters, p. 347
calculator ◆ slate ◆ index card or stick-on note (optional)

2 Ongoing Learning & Practice

Solving Measurement Number Stories
Math Journal 2, p. 259
Children solve number stories involving measurements.

Math Boxes 10•8
Math Journal 2, p. 260
Children practice and maintain skills through Math Box problems.

Ongoing Assessment: Recognizing Student Achievement
Use Math Boxes, Problem 2.
[Data and Chance Goal 4]

Home Link 10•8
Math Masters, p. 346
Children practice and maintain skills through Home Link activities.

3 Differentiation Options

READINESS

Practicing with Calculator Keys
Math Masters, p. 349
calculator
Children complete calculator problems.

ENRICHMENT

Solving Calculator Riddles
Math Masters, p. 348
calculator
Children solve calculator riddles.

Advance Preparation

Place copies of *Math Masters,* page 347 near the Math Message.

***Teacher's Reference Manual,* Grades 1–3** pp. 23–29

Getting Started

Mathematical Practices
SMP1, SMP3, SMP5, SMP6, SMP7
Content Standards
3.OA.3, 3.MD.2

Mental Math and Reflexes

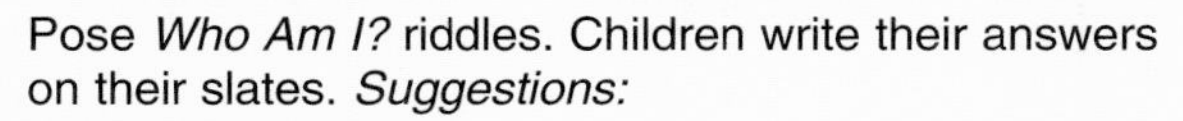

Pose *Who Am I?* riddles. Children write their answers on their slates. *Suggestions:*

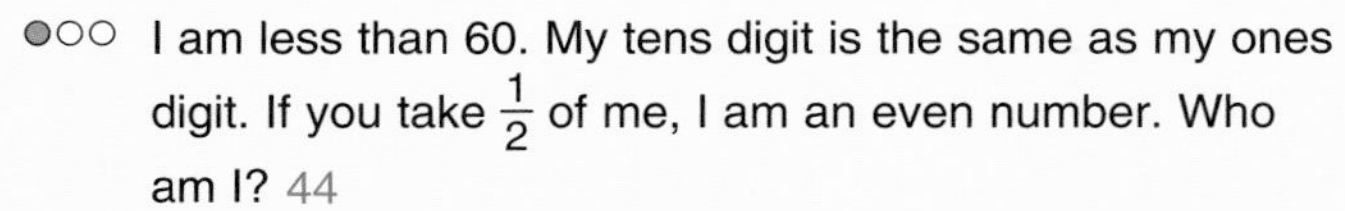

●○○ I am less than 60. My tens digit is the same as my ones digit. If you take $\frac{1}{2}$ of me, I am an even number. Who am I? 44

●●○ I am an odd number. If you double me, I will be between 40 and 50. My ones digit is half of my tens digit. Who am I? 21

●●● If you add 5 to me, I will be a multiple of 10. If you double me, I will be greater than 39 and less than 59. Who am I? 25

Math Message

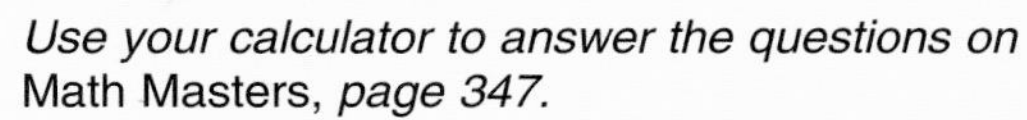

Use your calculator to answer the questions on Math Masters, *page 347.*

Home Link 10·7 Follow-Up

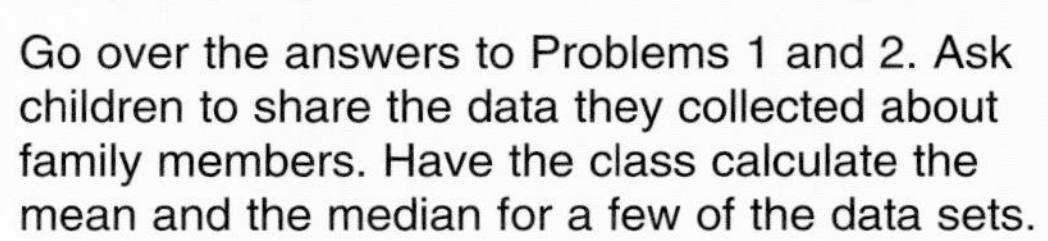

Go over the answers to Problems 1 and 2. Ask children to share the data they collected about family members. Have the class calculate the mean and the median for a few of the data sets.

1 Teaching the Lesson

Math Message Follow-Up

WHOLE-CLASS ACTIVITY

(*Math Masters,* p. 347)

Children share what they think the [M+] key on the calculator does. If no one suggests it, explain that this key can be used to make the calculator remember a number even after you have done other problems on the calculator.

After children turn on their calculators, remind them to clear the display so 0 is shown. Give the following directions to show how the [M+] key is used to put a number in the calculator's **memory.** Ask them to predict what will appear in the calculator display before entering the calculator key sequences.

NOTE Any calculators with [M+], [M−], and memory recall keys (for example, [MRC] or (MR)) can be used for this lesson. The keys noted in this lesson refer to the TI-108 and the Casio SL-450L calculators.

Teaching Master

Name Date Time

LESSON 10·8 **Math Message**

You will need your calculator. Refer to the table below.

- Begin with the first row. Press the keys on your calculator.
- Write what is in the display after each step.
- **Do not** clear your calculator between steps.

Press	Display
[MRC] [MRC] [ON/C] or (AC)	0.
5 (M+)	M 5.
7 (M+)	M 7.
[MRC]	M 12.
3 (M+)	M 3.
[MRC]	M 15.

What do you think (M+) does?

It adds a number to the previous number.

Math Masters, **p. 347**

Student Page

Games

Memory Addition/Subtraction

Materials ☐ 1 calculator

Players 2

Skill Mental addition and subtraction skills; using a calculator's memory keys

Object of the game To make the number in the memory of a calculator match a target number.

Directions

1. Players agree on a target number less than 50.
2. Either player clears the calculator's memory. (See **Using the Memory Keys** on the next page.) Both players must be able to see the calculator at all times.
3. Players take turns adding 1, 2, 3, 4, or 5 to the calculator's memory using the [M+] key, or subtracting 1, 2, 3, 4, or 5 from the memory using the [M-] key. They keep track of the results in their heads. A player cannot use the number that was just used by the other player.
4. The goal is to make the number in memory match the target number. When it is a player's turn and he or she thinks the number in memory is the same as the target number, the player says "same." Then he or she presses [MR] or [MRC] to display the number in memory.

   A player can say "same" and press [MR] or [MRC] before or after adding or subtracting a number.
5. If the number in the display matches the target number, the player who said "same" wins. If the number does not match the target number, the other player wins.

Student Reference Book, p. 290

Student Page

Games

Using the Memory Keys

- Press [AC] or [MRC] [MRC] to clear the memory.
- Press [M+] to add the number in the display to memory.
- Press [M-] to subtract the number in the display from memory.
- Press [MR] or [MRC] once to display the number in memory.
- Change the directions if your calculator works differently.

Example Target number: 19

Winnie presses	Display shows	Maria presses	Display shows
4 [M+]	M 4	5 [M+]	M 5
3 [M+]	M 3	1 [M+]	M 1
2 [M-]	M 2	3 [M+]	M 3
5 [M+] [MR] or 5 [M+] [MRC]	M 19		

Winnie says "same" after pressing 5 [M+]. Then she presses [MR] or [MRC] and the display shows the target number 19. Winnie wins. Either player presses [AC] or [MRC] [MRC] to clear the memory before starting a new game. Then, if the display shows a number that is different from 0, press [ON/C] to clear the display.

Student Reference Book, p. 291

Follow these steps to store a number in a calculator's memory:

1. Press 5. The display should read 5.

NOTE If children report that they are getting something other than 5 in their display, remind them to clear the calculator memory by pressing keys such as [MRC] [MRC] [ON/C] or [AC].

2. Press [M+]. The display should read M 5.

Mention that the M in the display indicates that the calculator is remembering a number. It has placed 5 in its memory.

3. Clear the calculator. For example, press the [ON/C] or [C] key. The calculator should read M 0.

   Ask: *Do you think the calculator still remembers the 5?* Yes, because the display still shows the letter M.

4. Use the calculator's memory recall. For example, press the [MRC] or [MR] key. The calculator should read M 5. Ask: *What does the memory recall key do?* It displays the number in memory.

5. Clear the calculator memory. For example, press [MRC] or [MR] (again), then [ON/C] or press [AC]. The calculator should read 0.

   Ask: *Is the number 5 still in memory?* No *How can you tell?* The display no longer shows M.

After you have repeated these steps a few times with different numbers, ask children to put a number you give them in memory. Then have them clear the display and recall the number.

Adjusting the Activity

ELL

To provide a visual representation of the calculator's memory, label a drawer in the classroom with a sign that says "Calculator's Memory." As you ask children to store numbers in the calculator's memory, write the numbers on an index card or stick-on note. Then throw the card in the drawer to demonstrate what the calculator does. When you recall a number from the calculator's memory, pull the card out of the drawer.

AUDITORY ◆ KINESTHETIC ◆ TACTILE ◆ VISUAL

Using Numbers Stored in Memory

WHOLE-CLASS ACTIVITY

Follow the steps below to show how to add 4 to a 7 stored in memory. Ask children to describe the display after each step and to discuss what took place.

1. Clear the calculator's memory.
2. Store the number 7 in memory. Press 7 [M+].
3. Press 4 [M+]. The calculator should read M 4.
4. Press the memory recall key.

Ask: *What is displayed on the calculator now?* M 11

5. Without clearing the memory, press 8 [M−]. The calculator should read M 8.

   Ask: *What number do you think is in the memory now?* 3 *Why?* 8 was subtracted from the number in memory. *How can you check to see if 3 is in the calculator's memory?* Press the memory recall key.

Adjusting the Activity

Ask children to predict what would happen if 7 [M+] [M+] [M+] [MRC] or [MR] is pressed. Have them enter the key sequence to check their predictions and explain what happened. Since [M+] adds a number to the calculator's memory, 7 was added 3 times. When the memory recall button was pressed, 21 appeared in the display.

AUDITORY ◆ KINESTHETIC ◆ TACTILE ◆ VISUAL

Continue with such routines until children have developed facility with the **memory keys.** Remind children to clear the calculator display before beginning a new problem.

Playing *Memory Addition/Subtraction*

PARTNER ACTIVITY

(*Student Reference Book,* pp. 290 and 291)

To provide practice with mental arithmetic using the calculator memory keys, play *Memory Addition / Subtraction.* Read the rules of the game on pages 290 and 291 in the *Student Reference Book* with the class. Divide the class into pairs and lead children through a few practice rounds. Partners share a calculator.

Using Memory Keys on the Calculator

INDEPENDENT ACTIVITY

(*Math Journal 2,* p. 258)

Children use calculators to solve Problems 1 through 8 on journal page 258.

Student Page

Date ________ Time ________

LESSON 10·8 **Calculator Memory**

For each problem:

- Clear the display and memory: Press [MRC] [MRC] [ON/C] or [AC].
- Enter the problem key sequence.
- Guess what number is in memory.
- Record your guess.
- Check your guess. Press [MRC] or [MR].
- Record the answer.

Your display should look like this [0.] before you start a new problem.

Problem Key Sequence	Your Guess	Number in Memory
1. 7 [M+] 9 [M+]	Answers vary.	16
2. 2 0 [M+] 1 6 [M−]		4
3. 5 [M+] 1 0 [M+] 2 0 [M+]		35
4. 1 2 [+] 8 [M+] 6 [M−]		14
5. 1 5 [−] 9 [M+] 2 [M−]		4
6. 2 5 [M+] 7 [+] 8 [M−]		10
7. 3 0 [M+] 1 5 [−] 5 [M+]		40
8. 2 [+] 2 [M+] 2 [−] 2 [M+] 2 [+] 2 [M+]		8

9. Make up your own key sequences with memory keys. Ask a partner to enter the key sequence, guess what number is in memory, and then check the answer.

Problem Key Sequence	Your Guess	Number in Memory
Answers vary.		

Math Journal 2, p. 258

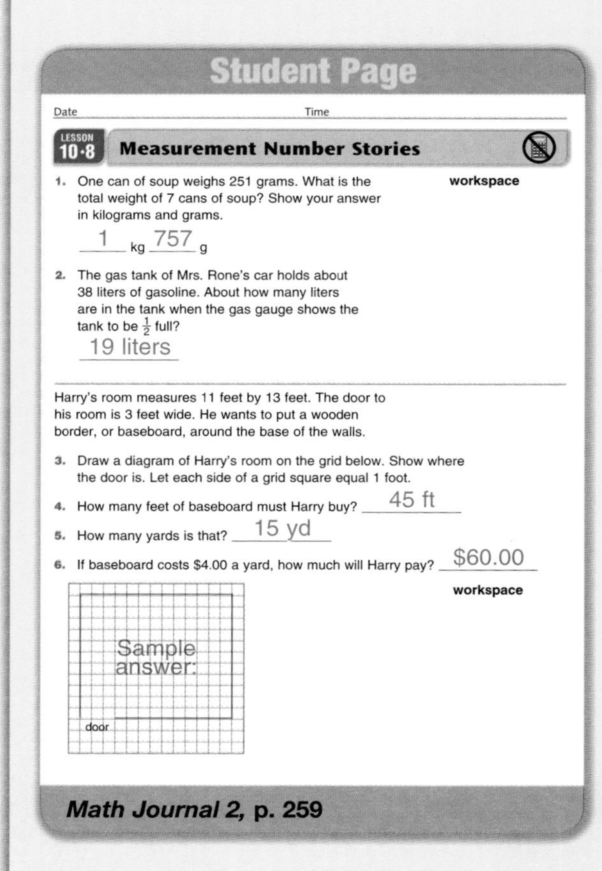

Student Page

Date ________ Time ________

LESSON 10·8 **Measurement Number Stories**

1. One can of soup weighs 251 grams. What is the total weight of 7 cans of soup? Show your answer in kilograms and grams.

   1 kg 757 g

   workspace

2. The gas tank of Mrs. Rone's car holds about 38 liters of gasoline. About how many liters are in the tank when the gas gauge shows the tank to be $\frac{1}{2}$ full?

   19 liters

Harry's room measures 11 feet by 13 feet. The door to his room is 3 feet wide. He wants to put a wooden border, or baseboard, around the base of the walls.

3. Draw a diagram of Harry's room on the grid below. Show where the door is. Let each side of a grid square equal 1 foot.
4. How many feet of baseboard must Harry buy? 45 ft
5. How many yards is that? 15 yd
6. If baseboard costs $4.00 a yard, how much will Harry pay? $60.00

workspace

Math Journal 2, p. 259

Student Page

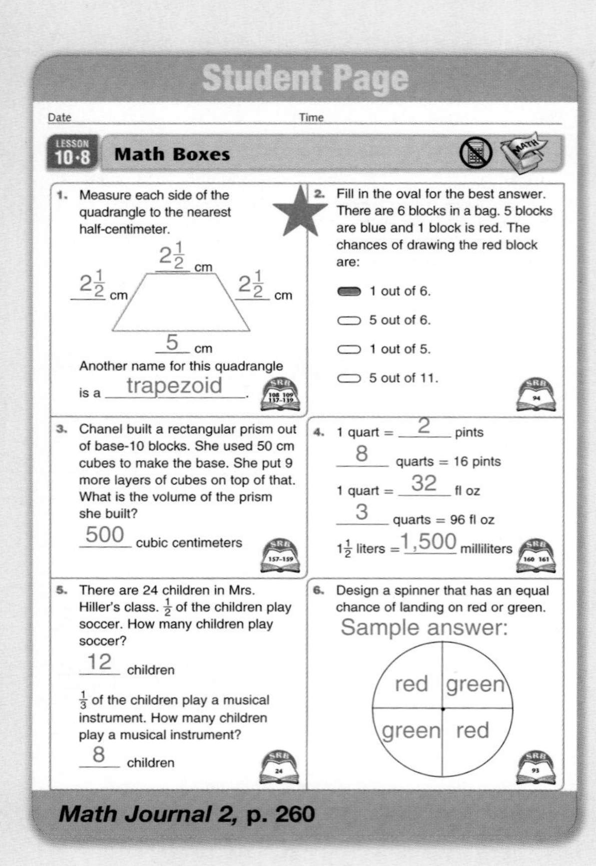
Date Time

LESSON 10·8 **Math Boxes**

1. Measure each side of the quadrangle to the nearest half-centimeter.
   $2\frac{1}{2}$ cm, $2\frac{1}{2}$ cm, $2\frac{1}{2}$ cm, 5 cm
   Another name for this quadrangle is a trapezoid.
2. Fill in the oval for the best answer. There are 6 blocks in a bag. 5 blocks are blue and 1 block is red. The chances of drawing the red block are:
   - (filled) 1 out of 6.
   - 5 out of 6.
   - 1 out of 5.
   - 5 out of 11.
3. Chanel built a rectangular prism out of base-10 blocks. She used 50 cm cubes to make the base. She put 9 more layers of cubes on top of that. What is the volume of the prism she built?
   500 cubic centimeters
4. 1 quart = 2 pints
   8 quarts = 16 pints
   1 quart = 32 fl oz
   3 quarts = 96 fl oz
   $1\frac{1}{2}$ liters = 1,500 milliliters
5. There are 24 children in Mrs. Hiller's class. $\frac{1}{2}$ of the children play soccer. How many children play soccer?
   12 children
   $\frac{1}{3}$ of the children play a musical instrument. How many children play a musical instrument?
   8 children
6. Design a spinner that has an equal chance of landing on red or green.
   Sample answer:

Math Journal 2, p. 260

Home Link Master

Name Date Time

HOME LINK 10·8 **Fact Triangles**

Family Note In today's lesson, we learned about the memory keys on our calculators. If you have a calculator, ask your child to show you how to store a number in the calculator's memory. If your calculator is different from the ones we use in class, you might need to help your child figure out how to use it.

In this Home Link, your child is reviewing fact extensions.

Please return this Home Link to school tomorrow.

Fill in the missing number in each Fact Triangle. Then write the number families for the three numbers in the Fact Triangle.

1. 600; ×, ÷; 20, 30
   $20 \times 30 = 600$
   $30 \times 20 = 600$
   $600 \div 30 = 20$
   $600 \div 20 = 30$
2. 800; ×, ÷; 20, 40
   $20 \times 40 = 800$
   $40 \times 20 = 800$
   $800 \div 40 = 20$
   $800 \div 20 = 40$
3. 500; ×, ÷; 5, 100
   $5 \times 100 = 500$
   $100 \times 5 = 500$
   $500 \div 100 = 5$
   $500 \div 5 = 100$
4. 4,200; ×, ÷; 600, 7
   $7 \times 600 = 4{,}200$
   $600 \times 7 = 4{,}200$
   $4{,}200 \div 600 = 7$
   $4{,}200 \div 7 = 600$

Math Masters, p. 346

2 Ongoing Learning & Practice

Solving Measurement Number Stories

(*Math Journal 2,* p. 259)

Briefly review the relationship between grams and kilograms and between feet and yards. Then have children solve measurement number stories.

Math Boxes 10·8

INDEPENDENT ACTIVITY

(*Math Journal 2,* p. 260)

Mixed Practice Math Boxes in this lesson are paired with Math Boxes in Lesson 10-6. The skill in Problem 6 previews Unit 11 content.

Writing/Reasoning Have children write an answer to the following: *Find the perimeter of the shape in Problem 1. Show your work and explain what you did.* Sample answer: I added the length of all sides to find the perimeter, $2\frac{1}{2} + 2\frac{1}{2} + 2\frac{1}{2} + 5 = 12\frac{1}{2}$ cm.

Ongoing Assessment: Recognizing Student Achievement

Math Boxes Problem 2 

Use **Math Boxes, Problem 2** to assess children's progress toward predicting the outcome of an experiment. Children are making adequate progress if they are able to complete Problem 2 successfully. Some children may be able to describe the chances of pulling a blue block.

[Data and Chance Goal 4]

Home Link 10·8

INDEPENDENT ACTIVITY

(*Math Masters,* p. 346)

Home Connection Children fill in missing numbers in Fact Triangles for extended facts and write each corresponding fact family.

3 Differentiation Options

READINESS

▶ Practicing with Calculator Keys

5–15 Min

(*Math Masters*, p. 349)

To explore using calculator keys to solve addition and subtraction problems, children perform calculator keystrokes to check answers to problems on *Math Masters*, page 349. If children are using a TI calculator, the ON/C clears the calculator. If children are using a Casio calculator, the AC key clears the calculator.

ENRICHMENT

PARTNER ACTIVITY

▶ Solving Calculator Riddles

5–15 Min

(*Math Masters*, p. 348)

To further explore using the calculator to solve problems, children solve calculator riddles where the final rotated display is read as a word. Encourage children who enjoy solving these riddles to make up their own for others to solve.

Planning Ahead

In Lesson 10-10, a large map, such as a road map of a county or state, is needed for the Math Message. The map should include an index of locations, with entries in letter-number form, such as B-3.

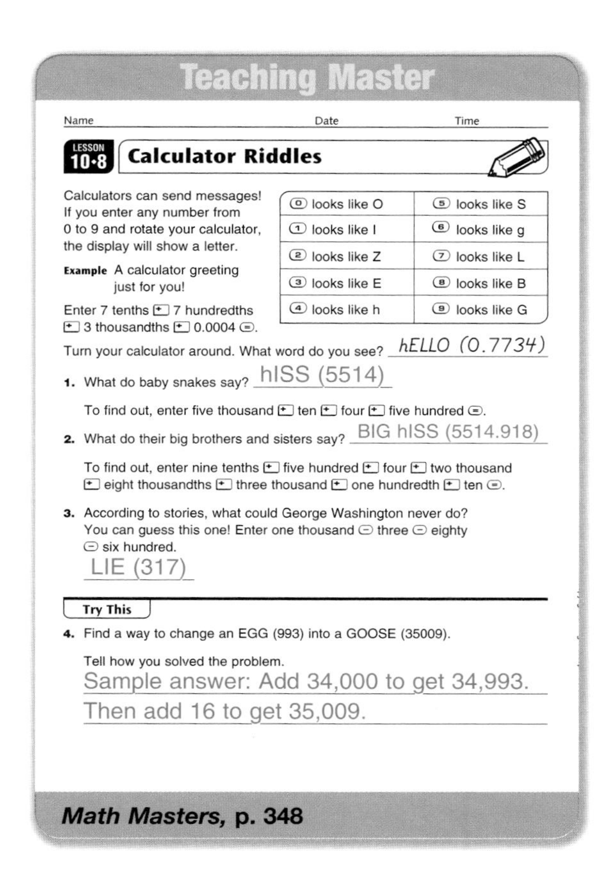

Teaching Master

Name Date Time

LESSON 10•8 **Calculator Riddles**

Calculators can send messages! If you enter any number from 0 to 9 and rotate your calculator, the display will show a letter.

0 looks like O	5 looks like S
1 looks like I	6 looks like g
2 looks like Z	7 looks like L
3 looks like E	8 looks like B
4 looks like h	9 looks like G

Example A calculator greeting just for you!

Enter 7 tenths + 7 hundredths + 3 thousandths + 0.0004 =.

Turn your calculator around. What word do you see? hELLO (0.7734)

1. What do baby snakes say? hISS (5514)

   To find out, enter five thousand + ten + four + five hundred =.

2. What do their big brothers and sisters say? BIG hISS (5514.918)

   To find out, enter nine tenths + five hundred + four + two thousand + eight thousandths + three thousand + one hundredth + ten =.

3. According to stories, what could George Washington never do? You can guess this one! Enter one thousand − three − eighty − six hundred.

   LIE (317)

Try This

4. Find a way to change an EGG (993) into a GOOSE (35009).

   Tell how you solved the problem.

   Sample answer: Add 34,000 to get 34,993. Then add 16 to get 35,009.

Math Masters, **p. 348**

Teaching Master

Name Date Time

LESSON 10•8 **Computing with Calculators**

For each problem, predict whether the number sentence is true or false. Then use your calculator to check your predictions. Remember to use ON/C or AC to clear the calculator before you begin each problem.

Number Sentence	Prediction (True/False)	Actual (True/False)
1. $5 + 9 + 8 + 6 = 28$		True
2. $10 - 2 - 1 = 7$		True
3. $12 + 5 + 50 + 3 = 53$		False
4. $100 - 40 - 9 = 51$		True
5. $98 + 3 + 128 + 3 = 198$		False

Try This

6. Explain how you made your guess for Problem 5.

   Sample answer: I knew it was false because the problem involved only addition and 128 + 98 is greater than 198.

Math Masters, **p. 349**

10•9 Frequency Distributions

Objectives To guide children as they make frequency tables, and as they find the median, mean, and mode of data sets.

www.everydaymathonline.com

ePresentations

eToolkit

Algorithms Practice

EM Facts Workshop Game™

Family Letters

Assessment Management

Common Core State Standards

Curriculum Focal Points

Interactive Teacher's Lesson Guide

1 Teaching the Lesson

Key Concepts and Skills

- Order whole numbers.
  [Number and Numeration Goal 6]
- Collect and organize data to create a frequency table.
  [Data and Chance Goal 1]
- Find the median and mode of a data set.
  [Data and Chance Goal 2]

Key Activities

Children record their waist-to-floor measurements on the Class Data Pad. They make a frequency table and use it to find the median, mean, and mode of the data set.

Ongoing Assessment: Informing Instruction See page 855.

Key Vocabulary

frequency table ◆ mode

Materials

Math Journal 2, pp. 251 and 261
Student Reference Book, p. 81 (optional)
Home Link 10•8
Class Data Pad ◆ calculator ◆ slate (optional) ◆ counters (optional)

2 Ongoing Learning & Practice

Making a Bar Graph of Measurements

Math Journal 2, p. 262
graphing software (optional)
Children make a bar graph of data from a frequency table.

Ongoing Assessment: Informing Instruction See page 856.

Math Boxes 10•9

Math Journal 2, p. 263
Children practice and maintain skills through Math Box problems.

Ongoing Assessment: Recognizing Student Achievement
Use Math Boxes, Problem 3.
[Number and Numeration Goal 2]

Home Link 10•9

Math Masters, p. 351
Children practice and maintain skills through Home Link activities.

3 Differentiation Options

READINESS

Organizing Data

per group: calculator, numbered index cards, two $8\frac{1}{2}$" by 11" sheets of paper
Children create a physical display of data.

ENRICHMENT

Comparing Waist-to-Floor Measurements

per partnership: 2 copies of *Math Masters,* pp. 350 and 352 ◆ Math Message data ◆ calculator
Children make two frequency tables and bar graphs. They compare the landmarks for two sets of data.

EXTRA PRACTICE

Minute Math+

Minute Math®+, pp. 3–7 and 27–29
Children practice ordering numbers.

Advance Preparation

For Part 1, divide a page of the Class Data Pad into three columns. Write the heading Waist-to-Floor Measurement (in.) above the first column. Write the heading Frequency above the second and third columns. (See *Math Journal 2,* page 261.)

For the optional Readiness activity in Part 3, write a 2-digit number on an index card for each child. There should be some duplicates. Label two $8\frac{1}{2}$" by 11" sheets of paper with *smallest* and *largest.*

Getting Started

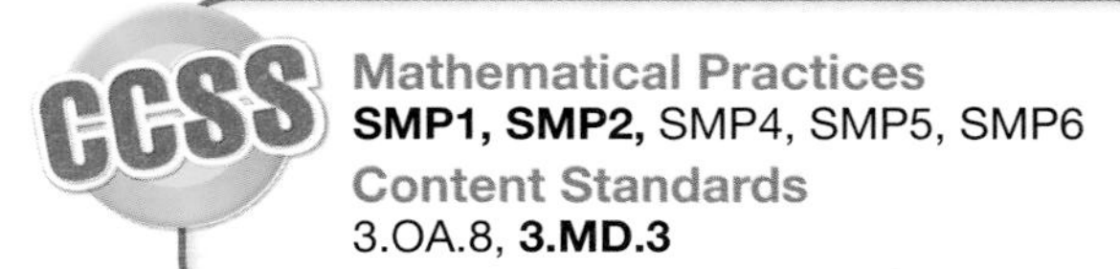

Mathematical Practices
SMP1, SMP2, SMP4, SMP5, SMP6
Content Standards
3.OA.8, **3.MD.3**

Mental Math and Reflexes

Children find the ordinal number for the middle value in a set of data. They may make a list on slates or use counters to help them solve each problem. Have them share solution strategies.

●○○ Which measurement would be the middle in a list of 5 measurements? The third measurement

●●○ Which measurement would be the middle in a list of 15 measurements? The eighth measurement

●●● Which measurements would be the middle in a list of 16 measurements? The eighth and ninth measurements

Math Message

Look up your last waist-to-floor measurement on journal page 251. Write it on the Class Data Pad. Do not write your name.

Home Link 10·8 Follow-Up

Have partners read to each other the basic facts that are suggested by the Fact Triangles in the Home Link problems.

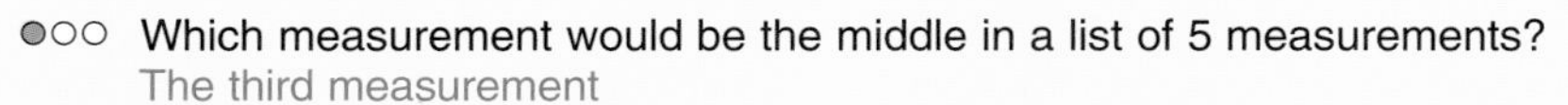

1 Teaching the Lesson

▶ Math Message Follow-Up

WHOLE-CLASS DISCUSSION

Count the number of entries on the Class Data Pad to check that all children have entered their measurements.

NOTE If you plan on having children do the optional Part 3 Enrichment activity, have all the boys write a *B* next to their waist-to-floor measurements and have all the girls write a *G* next to theirs.

▶ Making a Frequency Table of Waist-to-Floor Measurements

SMALL-GROUP ACTIVITY

ELL

(*Math Journal 2,* p. 261)

Divide the class into groups of three or four. In the second column of the Class Data Pad, draw a **frequency table,** a chart on which data are tallied to find the frequency of given events or values. To support English language learners, explain that the word *frequency* is used in different contexts to mean different things. A frequency table can be used to determine how often (or the number of times) an event or value occurs. Children complete the frequency table on page 261 in their journals for the measurements listed on the Class Data Pad. Guide them as follows:

1. Fill in the first column of the table. The first entry should be the smallest measurement on the Class Data Pad, followed by all other possible measurements in ascending order (to the nearest inch), up to the largest measurement.
2. Make a tally mark in the second column next to the appropriate measurement for each time it is listed on the Class Data Pad.
3. After all measurements have been tallied, write a number in the third column that represents each set of tallies.
4. To check that no measurements have been omitted, add the numbers in the third column and compare the sum to the number of measurements listed on the Class Data Pad.

Waist-to-Floor Measurement (in.)	Frequency	
	Tallies	Number
27	//	2
28		0
29	~~////~~	5
30	~~////~~ ///	8
31	~~////~~ //	7
32	////	4

Student Page

Date ______ Time ______

LESSON 10·9 **Frequency Table**

1. Fill in the table of waist-to-floor measurements for the class. This kind of table is called a frequency table. Answers vary.

Waist-to-Floor Measurement (inches)	Frequency	
	Tallies	Number
Total =		

2. What is the median (middle value) of the measurements? ______ in.
3. What is the mean (average) of the measurements? ______ in.
4. The *mode* is the measurement, or measurements, that occur most often. What is the mode of the waist-to-floor measurements for the class? ______ in.

Math Journal 2, **p. 261**

▶ Finding the Median and Mean of the Data Set

(*Math Journal 2,* p. 261)

Each member of each group finds the median and the mean of the set of data. Children should use a calculator to find the mean. Group members compare answers, resolve discrepancies, and record the group's answers on the journal page.

Bring the class together to share results and strategies.

- Did anyone find the median by listing the data on the Class Data Pad from smallest to largest?
- How could you find the median using only the frequency table? One way is to cross off one tally from the high end and then cross off one from the low end, repeating until only one or two tallies remain. Another way is to find the ordinal number for the middle measurement. For example, if there are 25 measurements, the middle measurement is the 13th measurement. If there are 26 measurements, there are two measurements in the middle—the 13th and 14th measurements. Starting at the top of the table, add the numbers in the third column until the sum is equal to or greater than the ordinal number for the middle measurement. The measurement in that row is the median.
- Which is more efficient—finding the median from the unordered data on the Class Data Pad or from the frequency table? Using the frequency table; if you use the data on the Class Data Pad, you must first order the data from smallest to largest.
- Did anyone use the memory keys on the calculator to find the mean?

If no one has done so, describe how to use the memory keys to find the sum of all the measurements. For example, if there are three measurements, each of 26 inches, press 3 [×] 26 [M+]. This adds the product, 78, to the number in the calculator's memory.

Ask children to enter the total for each measurement into the calculator's memory. When all data have been entered, press the memory recall key to display the number in memory. This is the sum of all measurements. Then divide the sum by the total number of tallies. The result is the mean height for the class. Remind children to clear the calculator's memory.

Ask: *Which is easier, finding the mean on the calculator with or without the help of the memory keys?* If you don't use the memory keys, the number displayed after entering and adding is the total to that point, not the value just added. This increases the likelihood of losing track of data and having to start over, or losing the total if an error is made pressing the keys. Also, with a large set of data containing many repeated values, using the memory keys reduces the number of keystrokes needed.

Compare the median and mean of the data set. Often, the median and the mean of a set of data are the same or almost the same.

Reviewing the Mode of the Set of Data

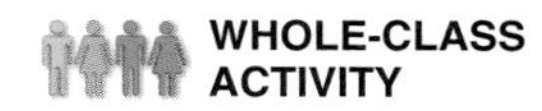

(*Math Journal 2,* p. 261; *Student Reference Book,* p. 81)

Ask children to explain the **mode** of a set of data. The mode is the value(s) that occurs most often. Have children find and record the mode of the set of waist-to-floor measurements in their journals.

Ongoing Assessment: Informing Instruction

Watch for children who have difficulty finding the mode of the data set. Have them review page 81 in the *Student Reference Book.*

Ask: *When might it be useful to know the mode of a set of data?* Sample answer: To determine which brands of a product are most popular in a store

When children have finished, bring the class together to discuss where the mode falls in relation to the data set.

Adjusting the Activity

If your school has more than one third-grade class, you might pool the data of all of the classes in a table.

AUDITORY • KINESTHETIC • TACTILE • VISUAL

2 Ongoing Learning & Practice

Making a Bar Graph of Measurements

(*Math Journal 2,* p. 262)

Make sure children copy the measurements onto the graph (journal page 262) correctly. Have them record the scale in increments of 2 and complete the graph. Help children verify that the number of data entries on their bar graphs matches the number of data in the frequency table.

Adjusting the Activity

If you pooled data for more than one third-grade class, make a bar graph.

AUDITORY • KINESTHETIC • TACTILE • VISUAL

NOTE If available, have children create bar graphs using graphing software.

Student Page

Date ______ Time ______

LESSON 10·9 **Bar Graph**

Make a bar graph of the data in the frequency table on journal page 261.

Class Waist-to-Floor Measurements

Waist-to-Floor Measurements (in.)

Number of Children

Math Journal 2, p. 262

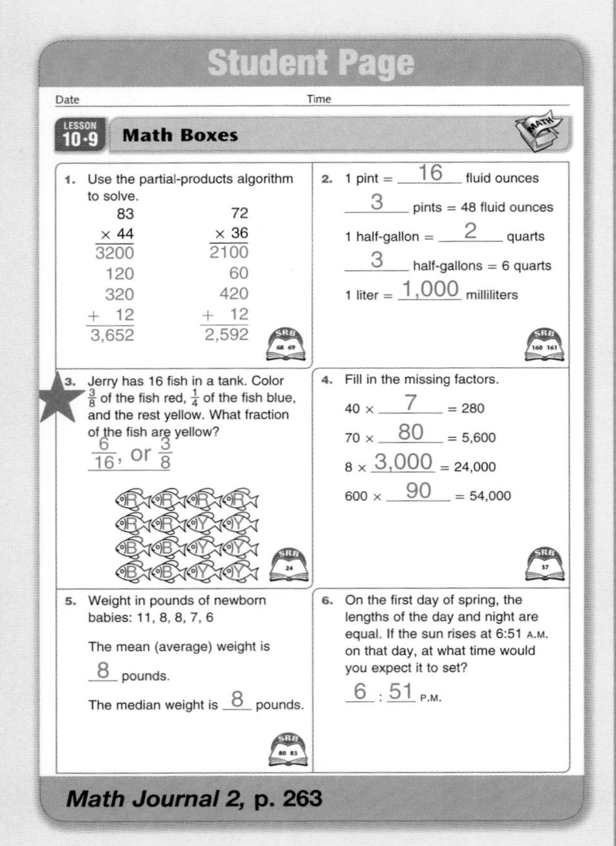

Student Page

Date Time

LESSON 10·9 **Math Boxes**

1. Use the partial-products algorithm to solve.

83	72
× 44	× 36
3200	2100
120	60
320	420
+ 12	+ 12
3,652	2,592

2. 1 pint = 16 fluid ounces
3 pints = 48 fluid ounces
1 half-gallon = 2 quarts
3 half-gallons = 6 quarts
1 liter = 1,000 milliliters

3. Jerry has 16 fish in a tank. Color $\frac{3}{8}$ of the fish red, $\frac{1}{4}$ of the fish blue, and the rest yellow. What fraction of the fish are yellow?
$\frac{6}{16}$, or $\frac{3}{8}$

4. Fill in the missing factors.
40 × 7 = 280
70 × 80 = 5,600
8 × 3,000 = 24,000
600 × 90 = 54,000

5. Weight in pounds of newborn babies: 11, 8, 8, 7, 6
The mean (average) weight is 8 pounds.
The median weight is 8 pounds.

6. On the first day of spring, the lengths of the day and night are equal. If the sun rises at 6:51 A.M. on that day, at what time would you expect it to set?
6 : 51 P.M.

Math Journal 2, p. 263

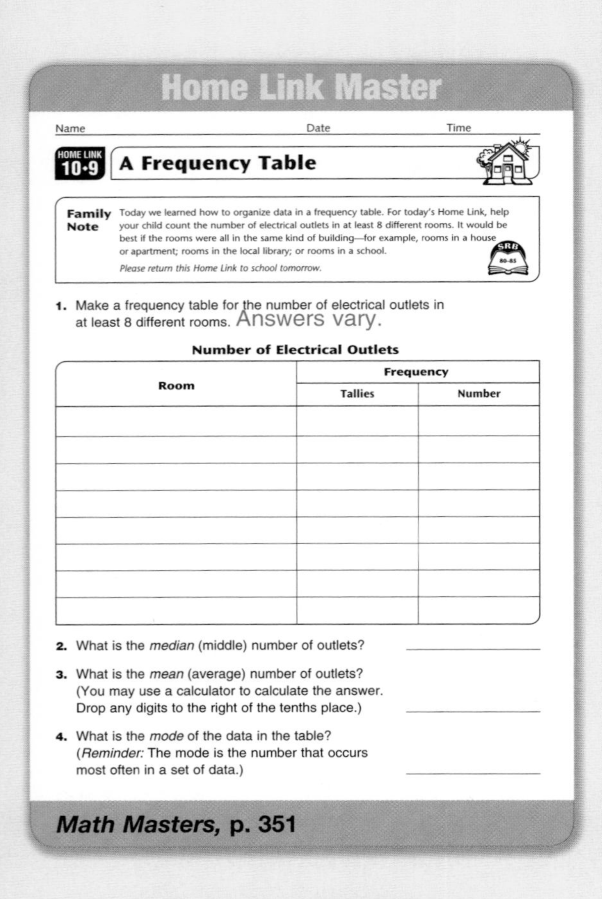

Home Link Master

Name Date Time

HOME LINK 10·9 **A Frequency Table**

Family Note Today we learned how to organize data in a frequency table. For today's Home Link, help your child count the number of electrical outlets in at least 8 different rooms. It would be best if the rooms were all in the same kind of building—for example, rooms in a house or apartment; rooms in the local library; or rooms in a school.

Please return this Home Link to school tomorrow.

1. Make a frequency table for the number of electrical outlets in at least 8 different rooms. Answers vary.

Number of Electrical Outlets

Room	Frequency	
	Tallies	Number

2. What is the *median* (middle) number of outlets? ______
3. What is the *mean* (average) number of outlets? (You may use a calculator to calculate the answer. Drop any digits to the right of the tenths place.) ______
4. What is the *mode* of the data in the table? (*Reminder:* The mode is the number that occurs most often in a set of data.) ______

Math Masters, p. 351

Ongoing Assessment: Informing Instruction

Watch for children who have difficulty comparing the total number of entries on their graphs to the total number of data on the table. Have them perform a one-to-one correspondence check to find out if measurements are missing.

Ask: *How does a bar graph make it easier to find the mode of a set of data?* You only need to look for the highest bar or bars.

You and the children pose *how many more* and *how many less* questions about the bar graph data.

▶ Math Boxes 10·9

INDEPENDENT ACTIVITY

(*Math Journal 2,* p. 263)

Mixed Practice Math Boxes in this lesson are paired with Math Boxes in Lesson 10-10. The skill in Problem 6 previews Unit 11 content.

Writing and Reasoning Have children write an answer to the following: *Explain how you found the mean weight of newborn babies in Problem 5.* Sample answer: I used my calculator and found the sum of the babies' weights and divided by the total number of babies, 40 ÷ 5 = 8.

Ongoing Assessment: Recognizing Student Achievement

Math Boxes Problem 3

Use **Math Boxes, Problem 3** to assess children's ability to solve problems involving fractional parts of sets. Children are making adequate progress if they are able to color the fish as directed. Some children may be able to write the fraction that represents the number of yellow fish.

[Number and Numeration Goal 2]

▶ Home Link 10·9

INDEPENDENT ACTIVITY

ELL

(*Math Masters,* p. 351)

Home Connection Children count the number of electrical outlets in at least eight different rooms. They record the data in a frequency table and find the median, mean, and mode for the data. To support English language learners, show them an electrical outlet.

3 Differentiation Options

READINESS

 SMALL-GROUP ACTIVITY

 5–15 Min

Organizing Data

To explore organizing data, have children create a physical display of data. Distribute the numbered index cards to children. (*See* Advance Preparation.) Have volunteers suggest what the numbers might represent. Sample answer: Pieces of candy each child has; number of marbles each child has, and so on. Ask children to stand in line holding their cards facing you. Display the *smallest* sign on the left end of the line (as you face the children), and the *largest* sign on the right end of the line.

Explain to children that they are going to put themselves in order from smallest to largest based on their number cards following these rules:

- ▷ Children can only move based on comparisons with the child next to them. (No one should be moving about the room comparing numbers randomly.)
- ▷ Children will stack up if they have the same number. They will be forming a human bar graph.

When they have finished putting themselves in order, discuss which numbers are the most frequent, least frequent, and not represented at all. Ask children to figure out the median and ask them how they would calculate the mean.

ENRICHMENT

 PARTNER ACTIVITY

15–30 Min

Comparing Waist-to-Floor Measurements

(*Math Masters,* pp. 350 and 352)

To apply their understanding of frequency tables and bar graphs, have children use the coded data from the Math Message (*G* for girls' data and *B* for boys' data) and make two frequency tables and two bar graphs: one each for boys and one each for girls. They determine landmarks (median, mean, and mode) and compare the two sets of data. Directions for the activity are on *Math Masters,* page 350. Children record their work on *Math Masters,* page 352.

EXTRA PRACTICE

 SMALL-GROUP ACTIVITY

 5–15 Min

Minute Math+

To offer children more experience with ordering whole numbers see the following pages in *Minute Math+*:

Basic Routines: pp. 3–7

Counting: pp. 27–29

Teaching Master

Name Date Time

LESSON 10•9 **Comparing Waist-to-Floor Measurements**

1. Use the floor-to-waist data from the Math Message. Divide the data into two groups, one for boys' data and one for girls' data.
2. Make two frequency tables (one for each set of data) on the back of this page.
3. Make a graph for each data set on copies of *Math Masters,* page 352.
4. Find and record the landmarks (median, mean, and mode) for each data set. Use your calculator to help you. Answers vary.

Median:

Girls ________ Boys ________

Mean:

Girls ________ Boys ________

Mode:

Girls ________ Boys ________

5. Compare the two graphs and the landmarks. What do you know from these results?

Sample answers: The longest girls' measurements are longer than the longest boys' measurements. More boys than girls are in the 32–34 inch range. Boys have a larger range of measures than girls.

Math Masters, p. 350

Teaching Master

Name Date Time

LESSON 10•9 **Bar Graph**

Title:

Math Masters, p. 352

10•10 Coordinate Grids

Objective To introduce plotting coordinates on coordinate grids.

www.everydaymathonline.com

ePresentations | eToolkit | Algorithms Practice | EM Facts Workshop Game™ | Family Letters | Assessment Management | Common Core State Standards | Curriculum Focal Points | Interactive Teacher's Lesson Guide

1 Teaching the Lesson

Key Concepts and Skills

- Order numbers on a number line. [Number and Numeration Goal 6]
- Draw line segments to connect plotted points on a coordinate grid. [Geometry Goal 1]

Key Activities

Children find locations on a map. They are introduced to coordinate grids and ordered pairs as a way of naming and locating points on a plane. Children plot points on a coordinate grid.

Key Vocabulary

coordinate grid ◆ coordinate ◆ plotting the point ◆ ordered pair

Materials

Math Journal 2, p. 264
Student Reference Book, pp. 180 and 181
Home Link 10•9
transparency of *Math Masters,* p. 438 (optional) ◆ map with index ◆ slate

2 Ongoing Learning & Practice

Playing *Memory Addition/Subtraction*
Student Reference Book, pp. 290 and 291
per partnership: calculator
Children practice mental computation.

Math Boxes 10•10
Math Journal 2, p. 265
Children practice and maintain skills through Math Box problems.

Ongoing Assessment: Recognizing Student Achievement
Use Math Boxes, Problem 5.
[Data and Chance Goal 2]

Home Link 10•10
Math Masters, p. 353
Children practice and maintain skills through Home Link activities.

3 Differentiation Options

ENRICHMENT

Plotting Geoboard Coordinates
Math Masters, pp. 355 and 438
geoboard ◆ rubber bands ◆ dry-erase marker (fine point) ◆ straightedge
Children make polygons and plot ordered pairs on coordinate grids.

EXTRA PRACTICE

Connecting the Dots on a Coordinate Grid
Math Masters, p. 354
straightedge
Children plot ordered pairs on a coordinate grid and connect the points to make a picture.

Advance Preparation

For Part 1, post a large map (see Planning Ahead in Lesson 10•8) near the Math Message. Make a transparency of *Math Masters,* page 438 or draw the grid on the board.

***Teacher's Reference Manual,* Grades 1–3** p. 182

Getting Started

Mathematical Practices
SMP1, SMP2, **SMP3,** SMP4, SMP5, SMP6, **SMP8**

Mental Math and Reflexes

Have children write answers on slates as you pose problems like the following:

●○○	●●○	●●●
8 [50s] 400	90 [60s] 5,400	2 [53s] 106
80 [50s] 4,000	90 [600s] 54,000	3 [52s] 156
800 [50s] 40,000	900 [600s] 540,000	5 [32s] 160

Math Message

Select a town on the map that will be fairly difficult for children to find unless they use the index. Find (name of town) *on the map.*

Home Link 10·9 Follow-Up

Children share the results of their surveys. If children counted outlets in different buildings, have them look for differences in the median, mean, and mode. Compare results as a class.

1 Teaching the Lesson

▶ Math Message Follow-Up

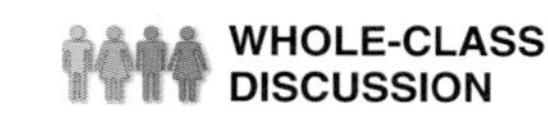

Social Studies Link Have children explain how they found the town on the map. If no one mentions it, show them how to use the index of locations. Point out that the letter-number entry identifies a region on the map in which the town is located. That entry limits the search to a small part of the map and makes the town easier to find. Call on children to find other locations on the map.

▶ Using Ordered Pairs to Locate Points

(*Math Journal 2,* p. 264; *Math Masters,* p. 438; *Student Reference Book,* pp. 180 and 181)

Ask children to look at the number line on journal page 264. Then ask them to locate and mark the point for the number 5 on the number line. Repeat with other numbers, such as 8, $3\frac{1}{2}$, $6\frac{1}{4}$, and -5.

Ask: *Is there a point on the number line for any number you can name?* Yes, because the line goes on forever.

Explain that there is a way to locate points that are not on the number line (that is, points that are above or below it) by drawing two number lines at right angles to each other to form a grid. This kind of grid is called a **coordinate grid.** Points are located on a coordinate grid by pairs of numbers written inside parentheses, such as (3,4) and (0,6). The numbers inside the parentheses are called the **coordinates** of the point. Marking a point on a coordinate grid is called **plotting the point.**

To support English language learners, explain that *coordinate* has different pronunciations resulting in different meanings: She will *coordinate* the party. She will use the *coordinate* grid.

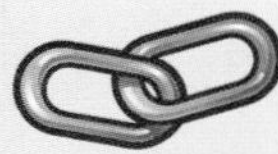

Links to the Future

The activities in this lesson are a beginning exposure to locating and plotting points on a coordinate grid. Locating positions on a coordinate grid is a Grade 4 Goal. Using ordered pairs to locate and plot points on a coordinate grid is a Grade 5 Goal.

Student Page

Date Time

LESSON 10·10 **Plotting Points on a Coordinate Grid**

1. Draw a dot on the number line for each number your teacher dictates. Then write the number under the dot.

−10 −5 0 $3\frac{1}{2}$ 5 $6\frac{1}{4}$ 8 10

2. Draw a dot on the grid for each ordered pair. Write the letter for the ordered pair next to the dot.

Sample *A*: (3,6)
B: (3,4) *C*: (4,3) *D*: (1,2)
E: (2,3) *F*: (5,2) *G*: (4,4)
H: (4,0) *I*: (6,4) *J*: (0,5)
K: (3,2) *L*: (5,4) *M*: (1,4)

3. Do you know the answer to this riddle? Which two letters contain nothing? To find out, draw the following line segments on the grid: $\overline{MD}$, $\overline{ME}$, $\overline{EB}$, $\overline{BK}$, $\overline{GI}$, and $\overline{LF}$.

MT (empty)

Draw the following line segments on the coordinate grid.

4. From (0,6) to (2,7); from (2,7) to (3,5); from (3,5) to (1,4); from (1,4) to (0,6)
What kind of quadrangle is this? square

5. From (7,0) to (7,4); from (7,4) to (5,3); from (5,3) to (5,1); from (5,1) to (7,0)
What kind of quadrangle is this? trapezoid

Math Journal 2, p. 264

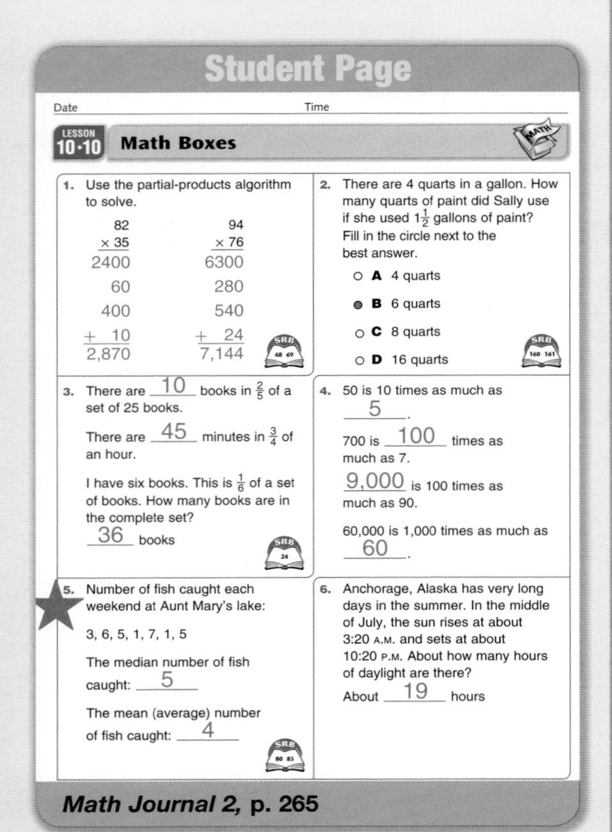

Student Page

Date Time

LESSON 10·10 **Math Boxes**

1. Use the partial-products algorithm to solve.

82	94
× 35	× 76
2400	6300
60	280
400	540
+ 10	+ 24
2,870	7,144

2. There are 4 quarts in a gallon. How many quarts of paint did Sally use if she used $1\frac{1}{2}$ gallons of paint? Fill in the circle next to the best answer.
   - ○ A 4 quarts
   - ● B 6 quarts
   - ○ C 8 quarts
   - ○ D 16 quarts

3. There are 10 books in $\frac{2}{5}$ of a set of 25 books.
   There are 45 minutes in $\frac{3}{4}$ of an hour.
   I have six books. This is $\frac{1}{6}$ of a set of books. How many books are in the complete set? 36 books

4. 50 is 10 times as much as 5.
   700 is 100 times as much as 7.
   9,000 is 100 times as much as 90.
   60,000 is 1,000 times as much as 60.

5. Number of fish caught each weekend at Aunt Mary's lake:
   3, 6, 5, 1, 7, 1, 5
   The median number of fish caught: 5
   The mean (average) number of fish caught: 4

6. Anchorage, Alaska has very long days in the summer. In the middle of July, the sun rises at about 3:20 A.M. and sets at about 10:20 P.M. About how many hours of daylight are there?
   About 19 hours

Math Journal 2, p. 265

Adjusting the Activity

A ladder or elevator metaphor may help some children plot ordered number pairs. The first number in the pair tells where to put the ladder or which elevator to go to. The second number in the pair tells how high to go.

AUDITORY ♦ KINESTHETIC ♦ TACTILE ♦ VISUAL

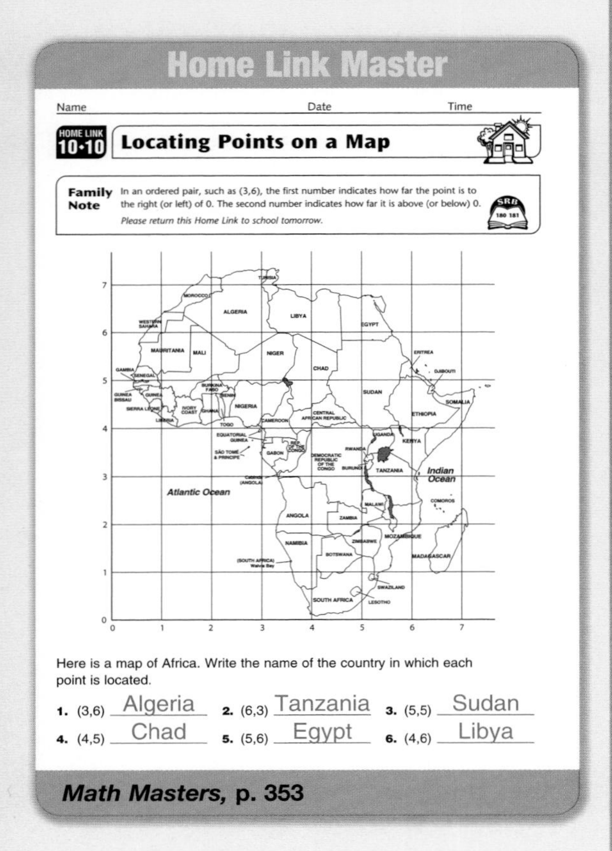

Home Link Master

Name Date Time

HOME LINK 10·10 **Locating Points on a Map**

Family Note In an ordered pair, such as (3,6), the first number indicates how far the point is to the right (or left) of 0. The second number indicates how far it is above (or below) 0.
Please return this Home Link to school tomorrow.

Here is a map of Africa. Write the name of the country in which each point is located.

1. (3,6) Algeria
2. (6,3) Tanzania
3. (5,5) Sudan
4. (4,5) Chad
5. (5,6) Egypt
6. (4,6) Libya

Math Masters, p. 353

Children work on the grid in Problem 2 on journal page 264, while you demonstrate on the board or on a transparency of *Math Masters,* page 438.

▷ Show children how to locate the point (3,4): Start at 0, go to the right 3 and then up 4. Draw a dot there and label it *B.*

▷ Next, name and locate the point (4,3) and label it *C.*

Ask: *Are the points* (3,4) *and* (4,3) *the same?* no *Does the order of the numbers in parentheses matter?* yes

Pairs of numbers used to locate points on a coordinate grid are called **ordered pairs.** The sequence of the numbers in an ordered pair is very important. Have children read more about coordinate grids on *Student Reference Book* pages 180 and 181.

▶ Plotting Points on a Coordinate Grid

(*Math Journal 2,* p. 264)

Partners complete Problems 2 and 3. Bring the class together to check answers. English language learners may experience difficulty understanding the riddle in Problem 3. Translating *MT* to *empty* may not be apparent to them.

For Problems 4 and 5, children continue to find points named by ordered pairs. Plot a couple of points with them and then have children complete the problems on their own or with partners. Bring the class together to check answers.

NOTE You might suggest a mnemonic device for remembering what the coordinates in an ordered pair mean. For example, *Over and Up/Down.* Since the letter *O* comes before *U* in the alphabet, the first number tells how far to go over; the second number tells how far to go up/down.

2 Ongoing Learning & Practice

▶ Playing *Memory Addition/Subtraction*

(*Student Reference Book,* pp. 290 and 291)

Children practice mental computation by playing *Memory Addition/Subtraction.* Game directions can be found in Lesson 10-8 or on pages 290 and 291 in the *Student Reference Book.*

Math Boxes 10•10

(*Math Journal 2,* p. 265)

Mixed Practice Math Boxes in this lesson are paired with Math Boxes in Lesson 10-9. The skill in Problem 6 previews Unit 11 content.

Ongoing Assessment: Recognizing Student Achievement

Math Boxes Problem 5

Use **Math Boxes, Problem 5** to assess children's ability to find the median of a data set. Children are making adequate progress if they find the median in Problem 5. Some children may be able to find the mean.

[Data and Chance Goal 2]

Home Link 10•10

(*Math Masters,* p. 353)

Home Connection Children locate points on a map of Africa, drawn on a coordinate grid. They write the name of the country in which each point is located.

3 Differentiation Options

ENRICHMENT

Plotting Geoboard Coordinates

(*Math Masters,* pp. 355 and 438)

To apply their knowledge of naming and plotting ordered pairs on coordinate grids, have children make polygons with rubber bands on coordinate grid geoboards. They use dry-erase markers to number the x-axis and y-axis on geoboards. The numbers can be easily wiped off at the end of the activity.

One partner creates polygons using a rubber band on the geoboard and names the coordinates of the vertices. The other partner plots the points on coordinate grid paper (*Math Masters,* page 438) and connects the points with line segments. They compare the picture to the polygon on the geoboard and discuss any differences.

EXTRA PRACTICE

Connecting the Dots on a Coordinate Grid

(*Math Masters,* p. 354)

Children plot ordered pairs on a coordinate grid and connect the points to form a picture.

Teaching Master

Name Date Time

LESSON 10•10 **Geoboard Polygons**

You need:

- one geoboard and several rubber bands per partnership
- straightedge
- dry-erase marker
- *Math Masters,* page 438 for each partner

1. Use a dry-erase marker to draw numbers on the horizontal and vertical lines of the geoboard. Use the picture to help you. Your geoboard can now be used as a coordinate grid.
2. Without letting your partner see, make a polygon on the geoboard coordinate grid with a rubber band.
3. Tell your partner the coordinate points of the vertices of the polygon. For example, the coordinate points of the triangle in this picture are (2,4), (4,4), and (4,2).
4. Your partner plots the points on one of the grids on *Math Masters,* page 438 and uses a straightedge to draw the line segments you name.
5. Compare the polygon made on the geoboard with the polygon drawn on the paper. Are they the same? If not, work together to find out why.
6. Continue until both partners have each taken 4 turns.

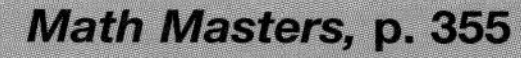

Math Masters, **p. 355**

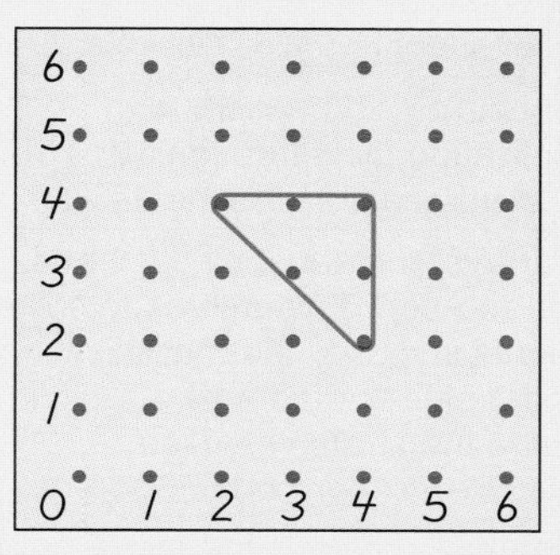

The coordinates for the triangle are (2,4), (4,2), and (4,4).

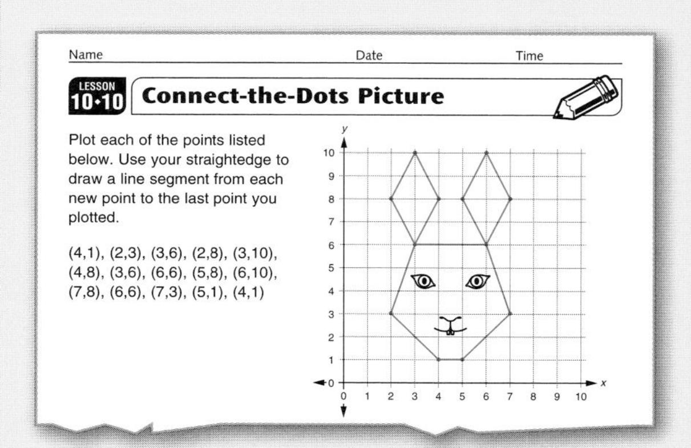

Name Date Time

LESSON 10•10 **Connect-the-Dots Picture**

Plot each of the points listed below. Use your straightedge to draw a line segment from each new point to the last point you plotted.

(4,1), (2,3), (3,6), (2,8), (3,10), (4,8), (3,6), (6,6), (5,8), (6,10), (7,8), (6,6), (7,3), (5,1), (4,1)

Math Masters, page 354

10•11 Progress Check 10

Objective To assess children's progress on mathematical content through the end of Unit 10.

1 Looking Back: Cumulative Assessment

Input children's data from Progress Check 10 into the **Assessment Management System**.

Materials
- Home Link 10•10
- *Assessment Handbook,* pp. 126–133, 192–196, 211, and 264–267
- ruler; slate; blue and green crayons; calculator; blank paper; counters

CONTENT ASSESSED	LESSON(S)	ASSESSMENT ITEMS				
		SELF	ORAL/SLATE	WRITTEN PART A	WRITTEN PART B	OPEN RESPONSE
Solve problems involving fractional parts of collections. [Number and Numeration Goal 2]	10•2, 10•4, 10•6, 10•8–10•10	5	3, 4	14		
Demonstrate automaticity with multiplication facts through 10 × 10. [Operations and Computation Goal 3]	10•1–10•10		1			
Use arrays, mental arithmetic, and paper-and-pencil algorithms to solve problems involving the multiplication of 2- and 3-digit numbers by a 1-digit number; describe the strategies used. [Operations and Computation Goal 4]	10•1–10•5, 10•7–10•10	6	2	6, 7	16, 17	✔
Use data to create a line plot. Complete a table with given data. [Data and Chance Goal 1]	10•1–10•5, 10•7–10•10	2, 3		9, 10		
Find the median, mode, and mean for a set of data. Answer simple questions and draw conclusions based on data landmarks. [Data and Chance Goal 2]	10•1, 10•3, 10•6, 10•7, 10•9, 10•10	4		11, 12	15	✔
Measure length to the nearest $\frac{1}{2}$ inch and $\frac{1}{2}$ centimeter. [Measurement and Reference Frames Goal 1]	10•1, 10•3, 10•5, 10•8	1		1, 3–5, 8		
Use strategies to measure the perimeter of a shape. [Measurement and Reference Frames Goal 2]	10•6, 10•8, 10•9			2		
Describe relationships among units of length. [Measurement and Reference Frames Goal 3]	10•1–10•5			13		

2 Looking Ahead: Preparing for Unit 11

Math Boxes 10•11

Home Link 10•11: Unit 11 Family Letter

Materials
- *Math Journal 2,* p. 266
- *Math Masters,* pp. 356–359

Getting Started

Math Message • Self Assessment

*Complete the Self Assessment (*Assessment Handbook*, p. 192).*

Home Link 10•10 Follow-Up

Briefly review answers. Have children explain how they located the points on the map.

1 Looking Back: Cumulative Assessment

▶ Math Message Follow-Up

INDEPENDENT ACTIVITY

(Self Assessment, *Assessment Handbook,* p. 192)

The Self Assessment offers children an opportunity to reflect upon their progress.

▶ Oral and Slate Assessments

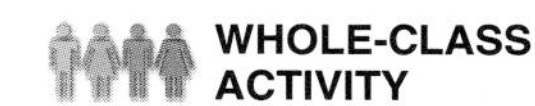

WHOLE-CLASS ACTIVITY

Problems 1, 2, and 3 provide summative information and can be used for grading purposes. Problem 4 provides formative information that can be useful in planning future instruction.

Oral Assessment

1. Pose multiplication facts. *Suggestions:*

   2×7 14 $\quad$ 6×3 18 $\quad$ 9×8 72

   5×9 45 $\quad$ 7×7 49 $\quad$ 10×8 80

2. Pose fact extensions. *Suggestions:*

   70×3 210 $\quad$ 300×6 1,800

   20×3 60 $\quad$ 800×4 3,200

Slate Assessment

3. Pose problems involving fractional parts of a collection. Children may use counters as needed. *Suggestions:*

   $\frac{1}{2}$ of 40 20 $\quad$ $\frac{3}{4}$ of 16 12 $\quad$ $\frac{2}{3}$ of 15 10

   $\frac{1}{4}$ of 16 4 $\quad$ $\frac{2}{3}$ of 12 8

4. Tell fraction stories. Children may use counters as needed. *Suggestions:*

   - Marcia had 36 dimes. She lost $\frac{2}{9}$ of them. How many did she lose? 8 How much money did she have left? \$2.80
   - Jeremy had 28 marbles. He gave $\frac{1}{2}$ of them to Marcy and $\frac{1}{4}$ of them to Rick. How many marbles did he have left? 7

Assessment Master

Name Date Time

LESSON 10•11 **Self Assessment** Progress Check 10

Check one box for each skill.

Skills	I can do this on my own and can explain how to do it.	I can do this on my own.	I can do this if I get help or look at an example.
1. Measure to the nearest $\frac{1}{2}$ inch and $\frac{1}{2}$ centimeter.			
2. Make a frequency table to show data.			
3. Make a line plot to show data.			
4. Find the median, mode, and mean for a set of data.			
5. Find fractional parts of collections.			
6. Multiply 3-digit numbers by 1-digit numbers.			

Assessment Handbook, **p. 192**

Assessment Master

Name Date Time

LESSON 10•11 **Written Assessment** Progress Check 10

Part A

1. Measure and label the sides of the polygon in centimeters.

   2 cm, 1 cm, 2 cm, 1 cm, 2 cm, 1 cm, 1 cm, 1 cm, 3 cm, 1 cm, 2 cm

2. The perimeter of the polygon is 16 cm.

A B C

0 1 2 3 4 5 6 inches

3. Make a dot at 2 inches. Label it with the letter *A*.
4. Make a dot at $4\frac{1}{2}$ inches. Label it with the letter *B*.
5. Make a dot at $5\frac{1}{2}$ inches. Label it with the letter *C*.

Solve. Show your work.

6. 286×4 = 1,144
7. 305×6 = 1,830

Assessment Handbook, **p. 193**

Assessment Master

Name Date Time

LESSON 10•11 **Written Assessment** *continued*

8. Measure the line segment to the nearest $\frac{1}{2}$ inch.

about 5 in.

9. The children in Mr. Barrie's class had the following scores on a spelling test. Show these scores in a frequency table.

Spelling Test Scores

85 95 90 100 70
95 100 75 85 85
90 75 95 100 90
85 95 85 90 100
95 75 85 95 95

Scores	Frequency	
	Tallies	Number
70	/	1
75	///	3
80		0
85	𝍸 /	6
90	////	4
95	𝍸 //	7
100	////	4
	Total	25

10. Make a line plot to show the spelling test data from the frequency table.

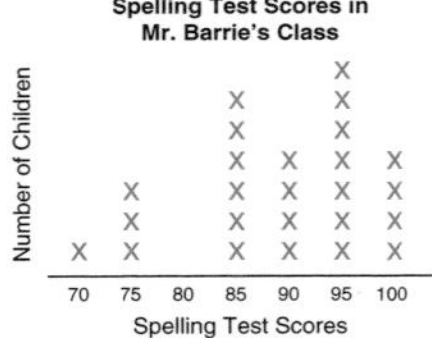

11. The median test score is 90.

12. The mode of the test scores is 95.

Assessment Handbook, **p. 194**

Assessment Master

Name Date Time

LESSON 10•11 **Written Assessment** *continued*

13. Fill in the blanks.

48 inches = 4 feet $1\frac{1}{2}$ feet = 18 inches

2 yards = 6 feet 72 inches = 2 yards

14. Color $\frac{1}{4}$ of the marbles blue. Color $\frac{2}{3}$ of the marbles green.

(B) (G) (G) (G)
(B) (G) (G) (G)
(B) (G) (G) ( )

Write a fraction that shows the number of marbles *not* colored. $\frac{1}{12}$

Part B

15. Look at the Litter Sizes table. Figure out the mean (average) number of puppies. Use your calculator to help you.

The mean number of puppies is 5.

Litter Sizes	
Dog's Name	Number of Puppies
Fifi	6
Spot	3
Duchess	5
Honey	5
Rover	7
Daisy	4

Solve. Show your work.

16. 29 × 34 = 986

17. 42 × 56 = 2,352

Assessment Handbook, **p. 195**

▶ Written Assessment

(*Assessment Handbook,* pp. 193–195)

Part A Recognizing Student Achievement

Problems 1 through 14 provide summative information and may be used for grading purposes.

Problem(s)	Description
1	Measure the sides of a rectangle in centimeters.
2	Calculate the perimeter of a shape.
3–5	Label points on a ruler.
6, 7	Use strategies to solve problems involving the multiplication of 3-digit numbers by 1-digit numbers.
8	Measure a line segment to the nearest $\frac{1}{2}$ inch.
9, 10	Use data to complete a frequency table and create a line plot.
11, 12	Find the median and mode of a data set.
13	Describe the relationships among units of length.
14	Solve problems involving fractional parts of a collection.

Part B Informing Instruction

Problems 15 through 17 provide formative information that can be useful in planning future instruction.

Problem(s)	Description
15	Find the mean of a data set.
16, 17	Use strategies to solve problems involving the multiplication of 2-digit numbers by 2-digit numbers.

Use the checklists on pages 265 and 267 of the *Assessment Handbook* to record results. Then input the data into the **Assessment Management System** to keep an ongoing record of children's progress toward Grade-Level Goals.

▶ Open Response

(*Assessment Handbook,* p. 196)

Writing About A Top Dog

The open-response item requires children to apply skills and concepts from Unit 10 to solve a multistep problem. See the *Assessment Handbook,* pages 130–133, for rubrics and children's work samples for this problem.

2 Looking Ahead: Preparing for Unit 11

▶ Math Boxes 10•11

INDEPENDENT ACTIVITY

(*Math Journal 2,* p. 266)

Mixed Practice This Math Boxes page previews Unit 11 content.

▶ Home Link 10•11: Unit 11 Family Letter

INDEPENDENT ACTIVITY

(*Math Masters,* pp. 356–359)

Home Connection The Unit 11 Family Letter provides parents and guardians with information and activities related to Unit 11 topics.

Assessment Master

Name Date Time

LESSON 10•11 **Open Response** Progress Check 10

Writing about a Top Dog

The Daily News has an article about "Top Dogs" in the same space each week. Last week's article is at the right.

Jenny wanted to write an article about her "Top Dog" Magic. Jenny needed to know how many words she should write.

She did not want to count all of the words. She used the *mean* number of words from the first 3 lines of the article to make her estimate.

Use Jenny's strategy to make an estimate for the total number of words in all 15 lines.

Show all of your work.
Describe each step.

This Week's Top Dog—Leif the Lab

Jim was hurt badly when his car crashed 4 years ago. He could not walk and he lost his ability to remember many things. He would not talk to anyone, even family and friends. He became sad and felt like he had no future. Soon, his wife and two children were angry with him. Then one day, he met Leif, a golden Labrador, who changed his life. Leif became a constant companion. He is able to help Jim with over one hundred tasks that Jim finds difficult. Leif can get laundry out of the washing machine, call the elevator, pick up items in the supermarket, and even hand over the payment at the supermarket checkout. Leif has saved Jim's life many times, because he always reminds Jim to look before crossing the street. Since Leif came along, Jim is a new man!

See the *Assessment Handbook* for sample answers and rubrics.

Do you think that Jenny's strategy is a good one? Explain.

***Assessment Handbook,* p. 196**

Home Link Masters

Name Date Time

HOME LINK 10•11 **Unit 11: Family Letter**

Probability; Year-Long Projects, Revisited

In this year's final unit, children will have the opportunity to bring closure to the yearlong data-collection projects about lengths of days and temperature changes. They will look at patterns in data and draw conclusions.

Unit 11 also contains informal spinner activities relating to chance and probability.

Some of these activities call for children to compare the likelihood of several possible outcomes of an event: why one thing is more likely to happen than another. For example, children will make predictions about where a paper clip on a spinner is more likely to land when the spinner is divided into unequal parts.

Other activities ask children to estimate the chance that something will happen. For example, children design a spinner so that a paper clip is twice as likely to land on one color as another.

Please keep this Family Letter for reference as your child works through Unit 11.

yellow green blue

***Math Masters,* pp. 356–359**

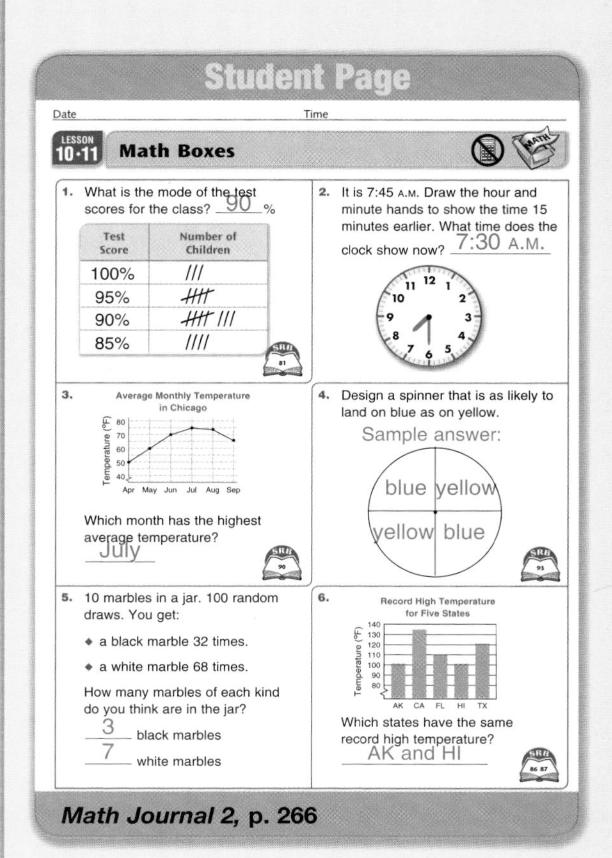

Student Page

Date Time

LESSON 10•11 **Math Boxes**

1. What is the mode of the test scores for the class? 90 %

Test Score	Number of Children
100%	///
95%	𝍸
90%	𝍸 ///
85%	////

2. It is 7:45 A.M. Draw the hour and minute hands to show the time 15 minutes earlier. What time does the clock show now? 7:30 A.M.

3. Average Monthly Temperature in Chicago

Which month has the highest average temperature? July

4. Design a spinner that is as likely to land on blue as on yellow.
Sample answer:
blue yellow yellow blue

5. 10 marbles in a jar. 100 random draws. You get:
- a black marble 32 times.
- a white marble 68 times.

How many marbles of each kind do you think are in the jar?
3 black marbles
7 white marbles

6. Record High Temperature for Five States

Which states have the same record high temperature? AK and HI

***Math Journal 2,* p. 266**

Unit 11 Organizer

Probability; Year-Long Projects, Revisited

Overview

Everyday Mathematics exposes children to concepts and skills many times and in many different ways. The chance and probability activities in *Everyday Mathematics* are a good example of this approach. The informal games and activities of first and second grade involve the idea of fairness and the use of random-number generators, such as cards and dice. The activities in this unit involve the exploration of chance and probability through the use of spinners, predictions based on samples, and random draw problems.

Unit 11 combines probability with year-end activities that include revisiting the Length-of-Day project and the National High-Low temperatures summaries. Unit 11 has three main areas of focus:

- To organize, graph, and interpret data,
- To represent the likelihood of outcomes with visual models, and
- To predict outcomes and estimate the makeup of a population using survey data and objects.

CCSS Linking to the Common Core State Standards

The content of Unit 11 addresses the Common Core State Standards for Mathematics in *Measurement and Data.* The correlation of the Common Core State Standards to the *Everyday Mathematics* Grade 3 lessons begins on page CS1.

Contents

*Visit **www.everydaymathonline.com** for Guiding Questions that support Standards for Mathematical Practice (SMPs).

Learning In Perspective

	Lesson Objectives	Links to the Past	Links to the Future
11•1	To guide children as they read and interpret line and bar graphs.	In second grade, children use graphs to answer simple questions and draw conclusions. They find the maximum, minimum, mode, and median of data sets.	In fourth grade, children use landmarks and graphs to ask and answer questions, draw conclusions, and make predictions.
11•2	To guide children as they organize, graph, and interpret data.	In earlier grades, children play the *Dice-Roll and Tally Game* and graph the outcomes of rolling two dice. In second grade, children collect and organize data to create graphs. They use graphs to answer simple questions and draw conclusions. They find the maximum, minimum, mode, and median of data sets.	In fourth grade, children continue to collect and organize data to create charts, tables, graphs, and line plots. They use landmarks and graphs to ask and answer questions, draw conclusions, and make predictions.
11•3	To guide children as they collect and interpret data from spinner experiments with outcomes that are equally likely and not equally likely.	In earlier grades, children are informally exposed to basic probability terms during games, through activities involving fairness, and in data-collection activities. Children are familiar with spinners, which have been used in a variety of games since Kindergarten.	In fourth grade, children continue to use basic probability terms to describe chance events. They perform further experiments with spinners. They also express the probability of an event as a fraction.
11•4	To guide children as they represent the likelihood of outcomes with visual models.	Children are familiar with spinners, which have been used in a variety of games since Kindergarten. In second grade, children use spinners divided into equal and unequal parts to predict the outcome of a game.	In fourth grade, children perform further experiments with spinners. They also express the probability of an event as a fraction.
11•5	To guide children as they organize and analyze survey data; to predict outcomes; and to estimate the makeup of populations of people and objects.	In second grade, children use graphs to answer simple questions and draw conclusions. They predict the outcomes of coin flips. They also use spinners divided into equal and unequal parts to predict the outcome of a game.	In fourth and fifth grades, children use real-life data from authentic problem situations to draw conclusions and predict outcomes.

	Key Concepts and Skills	Grade 3 Goals*
11•1	Use addition and subtraction to solve problems involving units of time.	Operations and Computation Goal 2
	Use graphs to ask and answer simple questions.	Data and Chance Goal 2
	Use graphs to draw conclusions.	Data and Chance Goal 2
	Use relationships between units of time to solve problems.	Measurement and Reference Frames Goal 3
11•2	Find the difference between high and low temperatures.	Operations and Computation Goal 2
	Use data to create a frequency table and bar graph.	Data and Chance Goal 1
	Find the maximum, minimum, and median of a data set.	Data and Chance Goal 2
	Answer questions and draw conclusions from a data set.	Data and Chance Goal 2
11•3	Shade fractional parts of a circle.	Number and Numeration Goal 2
	Apply equivalent fractions to shade fractional parts of a circle.	Number and Numeration Goal 5
	Organize the results of a probability experiment in a frequency table.	Data and Chance Goal 1
	Use basic probability terms to describe the outcomes of an experiment.	Data and Chance Goal 3
11•4	Share strategies for solving problems involving fractional parts of a circle.	Number and Numeration Goal 2
	Use basic probability terms to describe spinners.	Data and Chance Goal 3
	Express the probability of an event by using "______ out of ______" language.	Data and Chance Goal 4
	Use the number of degrees in a circle to construct a spinner.	Geometry Goal 2
11•5	Record survey results in a frequency table.	Data and Chance Goal 1
	Draw conclusions from survey data.	Data and Chance Goal 2
	Use basic probability terms to discuss the results of a survey.	Data and Chance Goal 3
	Use data to make predictions.	Data and Chance Goal 4

*See the Appendix for a complete list of Grade 3 Goals.

A Balanced Curriculum

Ongoing Practice

Everyday Mathematics provides numerous opportunities for ongoing practice. These activities are embedded throughout the lessons:

Mental Math and Reflexes activities promote speed and accuracy in mental computation.

Math Boxes offer mixed practice and are paired across lessons as shown in the brackets below. This makes them useful as assessment tools.

Mixed practice	[11•1, 11•3], [11•2, 11•4], [11•5, 11•6]
Mixed practice with multiple choice	11•1, 11•2, 11•3, 11•6
Mixed practice with writing/reasoning opportunity	11•1, 11•4, 11•5

Home Links are daily homework assignments that review the content of the lesson and often contain ongoing facts practice or computation practice.

Minute Math+ problems are offered for additional practice.

EM Facts Workshop Game provides online practice of basic facts and computation.

EXTRA PRACTICE **Extra Practice** activities are included in Lessons 11•3, 11•4, and 11•5.

Practice through Games

Games are an essential component of practice in the *Everyday Mathematics* program. Games offer skills practice and promote strategic thinking. See the *Differentiation Handbook* for ways to adapt games to meet children's needs.

Lesson	Game	Skill Practiced
11•1	*Beat the Calculator* (Multiplication)	Practicing multiplication facts [OC Goal 3]
11•2	*Memory Addition/Subtraction*	Practicing mental addition and subtraction skills; using memory keys on a calculator [OC Goal 2]
11•3	*Soccer Spin*	Making predictions [DC Goals 3 and 4]
11•4	*The Block-Drawing Game*	Making predictions [DC Goal 4]
11•4	*Spinning to Win*	Making predictions [DC Goal 4]

[NN] Number and Numeration
[MRF] Measurement and Reference Frames
[OC] Operations and Computation
[GEO] Geometry
[DC] Data and Chance
[PFA] Patterns, Functions, and Algebra

Problem Solving 

Good problem solvers use a variety of strategies, including the following:

- Draw a picture.
- Act out the problem.
- Make a table, chart, or list.
- Look for a pattern.
- Try a simpler version of the problem.
- Make a guess and try it out.

The table below lists some of the opportunities in this unit for children to practice these strategies.

Lesson	Activity
11•1	Interpret data to answer questions.
11•2	Interpret information from a data table.
11•3	Interpret data from spinner experiments.
11•4	Design spinners to match given descriptions.
11•5	Predict the number of left-handed teachers at school.

Lessons that teach *through* problem solving, not just *about* problem solving

See Chapter 18: Problem Solving in the *Teacher's Reference Manual* for more information.

The Language of Mathematics

Everyday Mathematics provides lesson-specific suggestions to help all children acquire, process, and express mathematical ideas. Throughout Unit 11, there are lesson-specific language development notes that address the needs of English language learners, indicated by .

ELL SUPPORT Activities to support English language learners are in Part 3 of Lessons 11•3 and 11•5.

The *English Learners Handbook* and the *Differentiation Handbook* have suggestions for promoting language development and acquisition of mathematics vocabulary. See Unit 11 in each handbook.

Unit 11 Vocabulary

autumnal equinox
summer solstice
vernal equinox
winter solstice

Cross-Curricular Links

Language Arts
Lesson 11•1 Children learn the etymology of *equinox*.

Balanced Assessment

Daily Assessments

- **Recognizing Student Achievement** – A daily assessment that is included in every lesson to evaluate children's progress toward the Grade 3 Grade-Level Goals.
- **Informing Instruction** – Notes that appear throughout the unit to help anticipate children's common errors and suggest appropriate problem-solving strategies.

Lesson	Recognizing Student Achievement	Informing Instruction
11•1	Demonstrate automaticity with multiplication facts through 10 × 10. [OC Goal 3]	
11•2	Tell and write time to the nearest minute on an analog clock. [MRF Goal 4]	
11•3	Collect and organize data. [DC Goal 1]	
11•4	Understand basic probability terms. [DC Goal 3]	Divide a circle into parts to make a spinner.
11•5	Draw conclusions based on data representations. [DC Goal 2]	Interpret descriptions of outcomes in random-draw problems.

[NN] Number and Numeration
[MRF] Measurement and Reference Frames
[OC] Operations and Computation
[GEO] Geometry
[DC] Data and Chance
[PFA] Patterns, Functions, and Algebra

Portfolio Opportunities

The following lessons provide opportunities to gather samples of children's mathematical writings, drawings, and creations to add balance to the assessment process: Lessons 11•1, 11•3, 11•4, 11•5, and 11•6.

See pages 16 and 17 in the *Assessment Handbook* for more information about portfolios and how to use them.

Unit Assessment

Progress Check 11 – A cumulative assessment of concepts and skills taught in Unit 11 and in previous units, providing information for evaluating children's progress and planning for future instruction. These assessments include oral/slate, written, and open-response activities, as shown below in the sample Progress Check lesson opener.

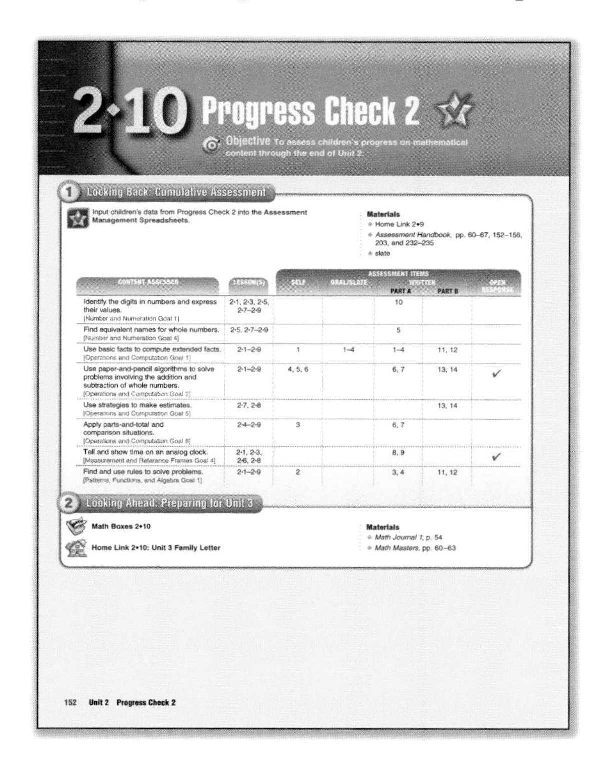

2·10 Progress Check 2

Objective To assess children's progress on mathematical content through the end of Unit 2.

1 Looking Back: Cumulative Assessment

Input children's data from Progress Check 2 into the Assessment Management Spreadsheets.

Materials
- Home Link 2•9
- *Assessment Handbook*, pp. 60–67, 152–156, 203, and 232–235
- slate

Content Assessed	Lesson(s)	Assessment Items: Self	Oral/Slate	Written: Part A	Written: Part B	Open Response
Identify the digits in numbers and express their values. [Number and Numeration Goal 1]	2·1, 2·3, 2·5, 2·7–2·9			10		
Find equivalent names for whole numbers. [Number and Numeration Goal 4]	2·5, 2·7–2·9			5		
Use basic facts to compute extended facts. [Operations and Computation Goal 1]	2·1–2·9	1	1–4	1–4	11, 12	
Use paper-and-pencil algorithms to solve problems involving the addition and subtraction of whole numbers. [Operations and Computation Goal 2]	2·1–2·9	4, 5, 6		6, 7	13, 14	✓
Use strategies to make estimates. [Operations and Computation Goal 5]	2·7, 2·8				13, 14	
Apply parts-and-total and comparison situations. [Operations and Computation Goal 6]	2·4–2·9	3		6, 7		
Tell and show time on an analog clock. [Measurement and Reference Frames Goal 4]	2·1, 2·3, 2·6, 2·8			8, 9		✓
Find and use rules to solve problems. [Patterns, Functions, and Algebra Goal 1]	2·1–2·9	2		3, 4	11, 12	

2 Looking Ahead: Preparing for Unit 3

Math Boxes 2•10

Home Link 2•10: Unit 3 Family Letter

Materials
- *Math Journal 1*, p. 54
- *Math Masters*, pp. 60–63

152 Unit 2 Progress Check 2

Core Assessment Resources

Assessment Handbook

- **Unit 11 Assessment Overview,** pages 134–141
- **Unit 11 Assessment Masters,** pages 197–201
- **Unit 11 Individual Profiles of Progress,** pages 268, 269, and 280
- **Unit 11 Class Checklists,** pages 270, 271, and 281
- **End-of-Year Assessment,** pages 217–225
- **Quarterly Checklist: Quarter 4,** pages 278 and 279
- **Math Logs,** pages 286–288
- **Exit Slip,** page 283
- **Other Student Assessment Forms,** pages 284, 285, 289, and 290

Assessment Management Spreadsheets

The Assessment Management Spreadsheets consist of the Digital Class Checklists and Individual Profile of Progress Checklists. Use them to monitor, record, and report children's progress.

Addressing All Needs

Differentiated Instruction

Adjusting the Activity – suggests adaptations that target advanced learners, English language learners, or learners who need additional instructional support.

ELL SUPPORT / ELL – provides lesson-specific suggestions to help English language learners understand and process the mathematical content.

READINESS – accesses children's prior knowledge or previews content that prepares children to engage in the lesson's Part 1 activities.

EXTRA PRACTICE – provides additional opportunities to apply the mathematical content of the lesson.

ENRICHMENT – enables children to apply or further explore the mathematical content of the lesson.

Lesson	Adjusting the Activity	ELL Support/ ELL	Readiness	Extra Practice	Enrichment
11•1	•	•	•		•
11•2	•	•	•		•
11•3		•	•	•	•
11•4	•		•	•	•
11•5	•	•	•	•	

Additional Resources

Differentiation Handbook
Provides ideas and strategies for differentiating instruction.
Pages 118–124

English Learners Handbook
Contains lesson-specific comprehension strategies.
Pages 106–110

Multilingual Handbook
Previews concepts and vocabulary. It is written in six languages.
Pages 211–221

Planning Tips

Multiage Classroom

Companion Lessons from Grades 2 and 4 can help you meet instructional needs of a multiage classroom. The full Scope and Sequence can be found in the Appendix.

Grade 2	12•6		3•5, 6•3, 7•6		
Grade 3	**11•1**	**11•2**	**11•3**	**11•4**	**11•5**
Grade 4			7•12	7•11	9•6, 9•7

Pacing for Success

Pacing depends on a number of factors, such as children's individual needs and how long your school has been using *Everyday Mathematics*. At the beginning of Unit 11, you may want to use tools available at www.everydaymathonline.com to help you set your pace.

Home Support

Unit 11 Family Letter (English/Spanish) provides families with an overview, Do-Anytime Activities, Building Skills through Games, a list of vocabulary, and answers to the daily homework (Home Links). Family Letters in English, Spanish, and seven other languages are also available online.

Home Links are the daily homework assignments. They consist of active projects and ongoing review problems.

Home Support Resources

Home Connection Handbook
Offers ideas and reproducible masters for communicating with families. See Table of Contents for unit information.

Student Reference Book
Provides a resource for children and parents.
Pages 90, 279–281, 290, 291, 309

Technology Resources

Materials

Technology Resources www.everydaymathonline.com

ePresentations

eToolkit

Algorithms Practice

EM Facts Workshop Game™

Family Letters

Assessment Management

Common Core State Standards

Curriculum Focal Points

Interactive Teacher's Lesson Guide

Lesson	Masters	Manipulative Kit	Other Items
11•1	Transparencies of *Math Masters,* pp. 159 and 160 Home Link Master, p. 360 Teaching Masters, pp. 361 and 362 Teaching Aid Master, p. 398	tool-kit clock; slate	classroom Sunrise/Sunset Chart; paper; 4 index cards*; string*; calculator
11•2	Teaching Masters, pp. 48, 352, 364, and 365 Home Link Master, p. 363		counters*; Class Data Pad*; 2 straightedges*; paper bag; half-sheet of paper; scissors; calculator
11•3	Teaching Masters, pp. 367 and 369–371 Transparency of *Math Masters,* p. 366* Home Link Master, p. 368 Game Masters, pp. 459–461 *Differentiation Handbook,* p. 132	slate	crayons (red, blue, yellow); tape or glue; permanent marker; large paper clips; Class Data Pad; erasable markers* (red, blue, yellow); scissors; counters; straightedge; calculator
11•4	Teaching Masters, pp. 371, 373, and 374 Home Link Master, p. 372 Game Master, p. 464		straightedge; crayons or coloring pencils (blue, red, yellow, and green); paper clips; blank transparency*; 50 pennies or other counters; paper; pencil; 1 paper bag and 7 blocks of the same size and shape, in 2 or 3 different colors
11•5	Teaching Aid Master, p. 398 Home Link Master, p. 375 Teaching Masters, pp. 360, 376, and 377 *Differentiation Handbook,* p. 132	slate	paper bag with survey results; Class Data Pad*
11•6	Assessment Masters, pp. 197–201 and 217–225 Home Link Masters, pp. 378–381	slate	counters*; paper clip; pencil

*Denotes optional materials

Mathematical Background

The discussion below highlights the major content ideas presented in Unit 11 and helps establish instructional priorities.

Summarizing the Yearlong Projects
(Lessons 11◆1 and 11◆2)

Since children have been collecting data throughout the school year, reviewing the results is a high priority. You will find suggestions for the year-end summary of the Length-of-Day Project. Additionally, activities are suggested to help children find patterns in the data collected for the National High/Low Temperatures Project.

For more information about data analysis, see Section 12.2.4 in the *Teacher's Reference Manual.*

Making Predictions (Lessons 11◆3–11◆5)

The probability activities in this unit follow a pattern: Children make a prediction about the likelihood of a particular outcome of an event; then they check their prediction by performing an experiment that involves collecting and interpreting data about the event.

In the spinner experiments of Lessons 11-3 and 11-4, most children will probably conclude very quickly that the spinner is more likely to land on the larger parts than on the smaller parts. They may remember activities in which they graphed outcomes of tossing a pair of dice—the numbers 2 and 12 come up much less often than the number 7. The reasons many events lend themselves to intuitive predictions is that their outcomes obey definite laws of chance. The outcome of spinner experiments (Lessons 11-3 and 11-4) are good examples of these events. Other events do not lend themselves to such intuitive notions. For example, how can one predict the number of teachers in the school who are left-handed? To answer this question, each child surveys 10 people outside of school. The class results are combined, and a prediction is made on the basis of this sample (Lesson 11-5).

For more information about making predictions, see Section 12.1.3 in the *Teacher's Reference Manual.*

Meteorologists study weather patterns to make predictions about the weather.

11•1 The Length-of-Day Project Revisited

Objective To guide children as they read and interpret line and bar graphs.

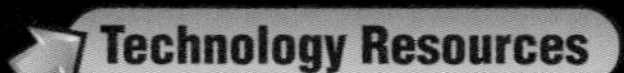
www.everydaymathonline.com

ePresentations

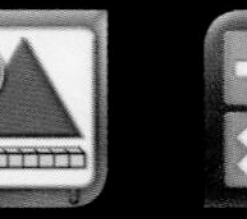
eToolkit

Algorithms Practice

EM Facts Workshop Game™

Family Letters

Assessment Management

Common Core State Standards

Curriculum Focal Points

Interactive Teacher's Lesson Guide

1 Teaching the Lesson

Key Concepts and Skills

- Use addition and subtraction to solve problems involving units of time.
  [Operations and Computation Goal 2]
- Use graphs to ask and answer simple questions.
  [Data and Chance Goal 2]
- Use graphs to draw conclusions.
  [Data and Chance Goal 2]
- Use relationships between units of time to solve problems.
  [Measurement and Reference Frames Goal 3]

Key Activities

Children discuss the Sunrise/Sunset Chart and the Length-of-Day Graph. Children investigate the relationship between hours of sunlight and seasons of the year.

Key Vocabulary

winter solstice ◆ summer solstice ◆ autumnal equinox ◆ vernal equinox

Materials

Math Journal 2, pp. 279–281
Student Reference Book, p. 90
transparencies of *Math Masters,* pp. 159 and 160 ◆ classroom Sunrise/Sunset Chart ◆ tool-kit clock (optional) ◆ slate ◆ 4 index cards and string (optional)

2 Ongoing Learning & Practice

Playing *Beat the Calculator* (Multiplication)

Math Journal 2, p. 282
Student Reference Book, p. 279
per group: calculator
Children practice multiplication facts.

Ongoing Assessment: Recognizing Student Achievement
Use an Exit Slip (*Math Masters,* page 398).
[Operations and Computation Goal 3]

Math Boxes 11•1

Math Journal 2, p. 267
Children practice and maintain skills through Math Box problems.

Home Link 11•1

Math Masters, p. 360
Children practice and maintain skills through Home Link activities.

3 Differentiation Options

READINESS

Determining Hours and Minutes

Math Masters, p. 361
tool-kit clock
Children use tool-kit clocks to solve problems involving hours and minutes.

ENRICHMENT

Planning a Field Trip

Math Masters, p. 362
paper
Children apply their understanding of elapsed time to plan a class field trip.

Advance Preparation

***Teacher's Reference Manual,* Grades 1–3** pp. 121–124

Getting Started

Mathematical Practices
SMP1, SMP2, SMP3, **SMP4,** SMP5, SMP6, SMP7
Content Standards
3.OA.7, **3.MD.1, 3.MD.3**

Mental Math and Reflexes

Pose problems like the following. Have children respond orally or on slates.

●○○	●●○	●●●
4 [70s] 280	6 [50s] 300	80 [80s] 6,400
40 [70s] 2,800	60 [50s] 3,000	80 [800s] 64,000
40 [700s] 28,000	600 [50s] 30,000	800 [800s] 640,000

Math Message

Find the shortest day (the day with the fewest hours and minutes of sunlight) on the Sunrise/Sunset Chart. Figure out how many more hours and minutes of darkness than sunlight there were on that day. Use your tool-kit clock to help you. Record your answer on your slate.

1 Teaching the Lesson

▶ Math Message Follow-Up

Point out that all days are the same length (24 hours), but people often refer to the *shortest day* as the day with the fewest hours and minutes of sunlight and the *longest day* as the day with the most hours and minutes of sunlight.

Children can find the shortest day on the Sunrise/Sunset Chart by examining the column labeled Hours of Sunlight. The shortest day shown on the sample Sunrise/Sunset Chart on pages 910 and 911 of this book is 9 hours 4 minutes.

Ask children to share strategies for finding the number of hours and minutes of darkness and for making the comparison with the number of hours and minutes of sunlight. The following examples of strategies use data from the sample Sunrise/Sunset Chart on pages 910 and 911.

- The shortest day (9 hours 4 minutes of sunlight) is 12/22. The Sunrise/Sunset Chart shows sunrise at 8:11 A.M., so there are 8 hours 11 minutes of darkness from midnight to sunrise. Sunset is at 5:15 P.M., so there are 6 hours 45 minutes of darkness from sunset to midnight. Add these two lengths of time: 8 hr 11 min + 6 hr 45 min = 14 hr 56 min of darkness on 12/22.
- A day has 24 hours. Subtract the hours and minutes of sunlight to find the number of hours and minutes of darkness: 24 hr 0 min − 9 hr 4 min. Trade 1 hour for 60 minutes and then subtract (an extension of the trade-first subtraction algorithm). (*See representation in margin.*)
- Represent the problem on an open number line and count up hours and minutes from 5:15 P.M. to 8:11 A.M.

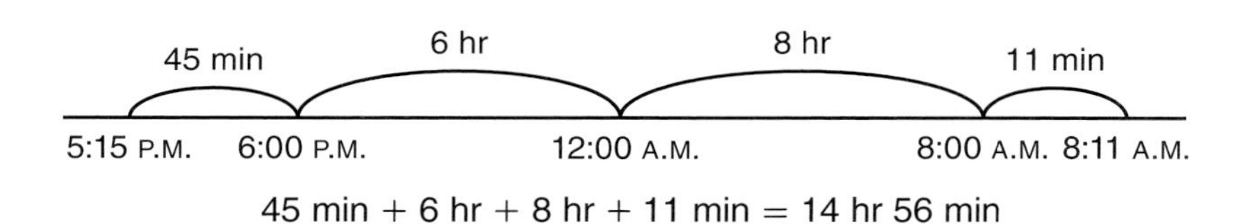

Interactive whiteboard-ready ePresentations are available at www.everydaymathonline.com to help you teach the lesson.

$$\begin{array}{r} 24 \text{ hr } 0 \text{ min} \\ -\ 9 \text{ hr } 4 \text{ min} \\ \hline \end{array} \qquad \begin{array}{r} 23 \text{ hr } 60 \text{ min} \\ -\ 9 \text{ hr } \ \ 4 \text{ min} \\ \hline 14 \text{ hr } 56 \text{ min} \end{array}$$

Student Page

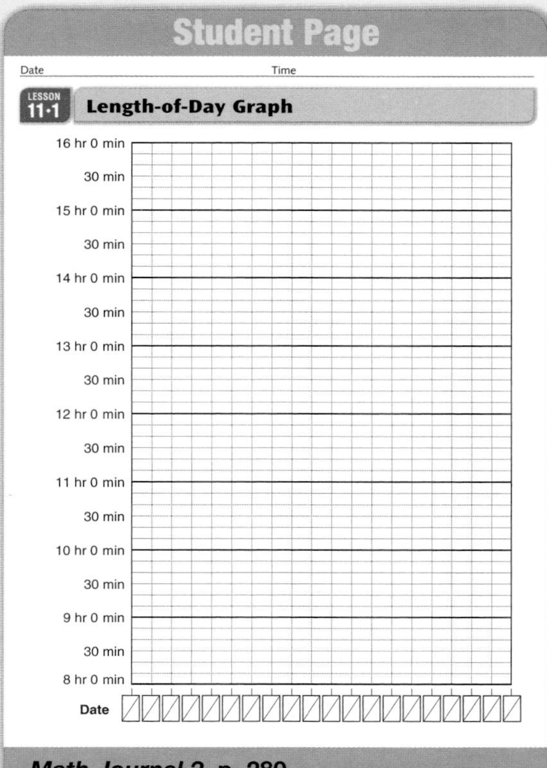

Math Journal 2, p. 280

Student Page

Date Time

LESSON 11·1 **Sunrise and Sunset Record**

Date	Time of Sunrise	Time of Sunset	Length of Day
			hr min
			hr min
			hr min
			hr min
			hr min
			hr min
			hr min
			hr min
			hr min
			hr min
			hr min
			hr min
			hr min
			hr min
			hr min
			hr min
			hr min
			hr min
			hr min
			hr min
			hr min

***Math Journal 2,* p. 279**

▶ Discussing the Length-of-Day Graph

ELL

(*Math Journal 2,* pp. 280 and 281; *Student Reference Book,* p. 90; *Math Masters,* pp. 159 and 160)

Discuss the Length-of-Day Graph by referring to the line graph on journal pages 280 and 281 and displaying transparencies of *Math Masters,* pages 159 and 160.

- On what date did the shortest day occur? Around December 21
- How is the shortest day shown on the line graph? It is the lowest point on the graph.
- On what date did the longest day occur? This date will vary, depending on how long you have continued the project (around June 21 if you have continued that long).
- How is the longest day shown on the line graph? It is the highest point on the graph.

Mention that the shortest day of the year, the **winter solstice,** is the first day of winter. The longest day, the **summer solstice,** is the first day of summer. To support English language learners, write these terms and their meanings on the board. In the Northern Hemisphere, the winter solstice occurs on or about December 21; the summer solstice occurs on or about June 21. (In some years, these dates may range from the 20th to the 23rd of the month.) Winter and summer are reversed in the Southern Hemisphere. *Suggestions for discussion:*

- On what dates does sunlight last about as long as darkness? Around September 21 and March 21
- Which seasons begin around those dates? Autumn and spring
- Locate these points on the line graph. They are the two points on the line graph at which the graph crosses the horizontal line for 12 hr 0 min.

Have children read more about line graphs on page 90 in their *Student Reference Books.*

Adjusting the Activity

ELL

Label four 3" x 5" index cards with winter solstice - shortest day, summer solstice - longest day, autumnal equinox - hours of day and night almost equal, and vernal equinox - hours of day and night almost equal. Attach a piece of string to each card, and hang the labels on the Class Sunrise/Sunset Chart in the appropriate places.

AUDITORY ◆ KINESTHETIC ◆ TACTILE ◆ VISUAL

Language Arts Link The dates on which the lengths of sunlight and darkness are about equal are called the **autumnal equinox** and the **vernal equinox.** The word *equinox* comes from the Latin prefix *aequi-,* meaning equal, and the word *nox,* meaning night.

▶ Discussing the Sunrise/Sunset Record

(*Math Journal 2,* p. 279; pp. 910 and 911 in this book)

Ask children to gather around the classroom Sunrise/Sunset Chart or to refer to the Sunrise and Sunset Record on page 279 in their journals. Relate the observations in the previous activity to this record. *Suggestions:*

- On what date did the sun rise the latest? Answers vary.
- On what date did it set the earliest? Answers vary.

- Are these dates the same as the date of the shortest recorded day? Probably not. For several weeks after December 21, the sun rises slightly later than it does on December 21. And for several weeks before December 21, the sun sets slightly earlier than it does on December 21.
- On what date did the sun rise the earliest? Answers vary.
- On what date did it set the latest? Answers vary.
- Are these dates the same as the date of the longest recorded day? They probably are for your chart, unless you have continued to record data for several weeks in June.

Have several children estimate the time they usually wake up, and then use the classroom Sunrise/Sunset Poster to help them find the part of the year when they will wake up in darkness. The example below is based on the sample Sunrise/Sunset Poster on pages 910 and 911 in this book.

For example, Brian says that he always wakes up at 7:30. Locate 7:30 A.M. along the top of the Sunrise/Sunset Chart. Look down along the dark vertical line through 7:30. The shaded bars for the dates 11/17 through 2/16 extend beyond and to the right of the vertical line through 7:30. So, from mid-November through mid-February, the sun rises after 7:30, and Brian wakes up in darkness.

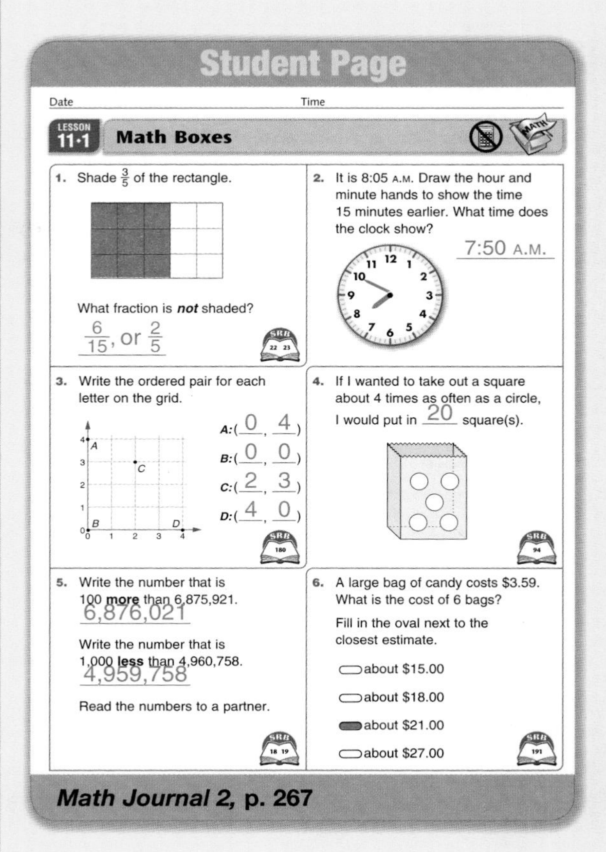
Student Page

Date Time

LESSON 11·1 **Math Boxes**

1. Shade $\frac{3}{5}$ of the rectangle.

What fraction is *not* shaded?

$\frac{6}{15}$, or $\frac{2}{5}$

2. It is 8:05 A.M. Draw the hour and minute hands to show the time 15 minutes earlier. What time does the clock show?

7:50 A.M.

3. Write the ordered pair for each letter on the grid.

A: (0, 4)
B: (0, 0)
C: (2, 3)
D: (4, 0)

4. If I wanted to take out a square about 4 times as often as a circle, I would put in 20 square(s).

5. Write the number that is 100 **more** than 6,875,921.

6,876,021

Write the number that is 1,000 **less** than 4,960,758.

4,959,758

Read the numbers to a partner.

6. A large bag of candy costs $3.59. What is the cost of 6 bags?

Fill in the oval next to the closest estimate.

- about $15.00
- about $18.00
- about $21.00 (filled)
- about $27.00

Math Journal 2, p. 267

2 Ongoing Learning & Practice

Playing *Beat the Calculator* (Multiplication)

PARTNER ACTIVITY

FACTS PRACTICE

(*Math Journal 2,* p. 282; *Student Reference Book,* p. 279)

Children develop automaticity with multiplication facts by playing *Beat the Calculator.* Have children use the Multiplication Fact Power Table, journal page 282, to record the facts for which they get the correct answer first when playing the role of the Brain. Have the Caller select facts from the shaded portion of the table. For Fact Power Table directions, see Lesson 4-5. For game directions, see page 279 in the *Student Reference Book.* Remind children to write the product in the table when they have earned 3 check marks for a fact.

Ongoing Assessment: Recognizing Student Achievement

Exit Slip

Use an **Exit Slip** (*Math Masters,* page 398) to assess children's progress toward demonstrating automaticity with multiplication facts through 10 × 10. Children record the facts from the Multiplication Fact Power Table for which they earned at least one check mark. Children are making adequate progress if they record all of the facts from the shaded portion of the record sheet.

[Operations and Computation Goal 3]

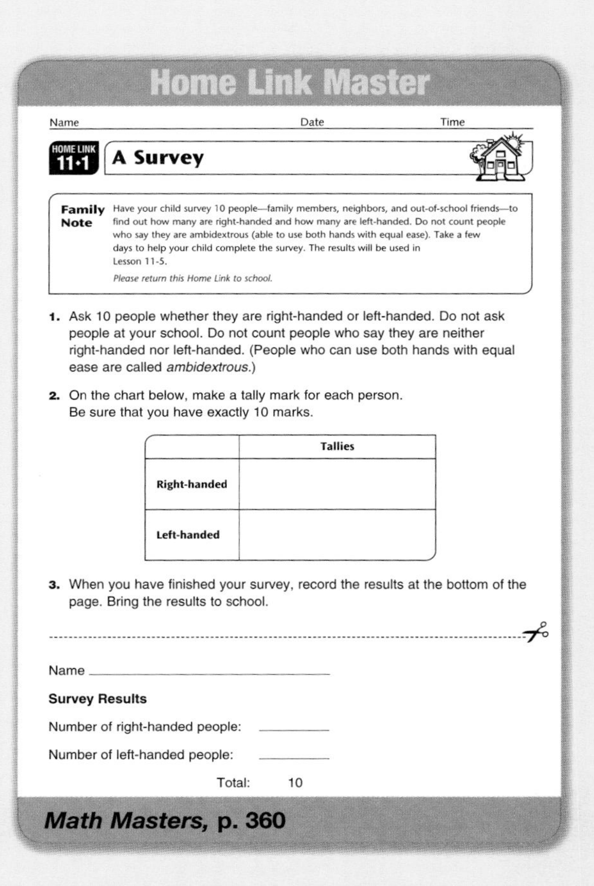
Home Link Master

Name Date Time

HOME LINK 11·1 **A Survey**

Family Note Have your child survey 10 people—family members, neighbors, and out-of-school friends—to find out how many are right-handed and how many are left-handed. Do not count people who say they are ambidextrous (able to use both hands with equal ease). Take a few days to help your child complete the survey. The results will be used in Lesson 11-5.

Please return this Home Link to school.

1. Ask 10 people whether they are right-handed or left-handed. Do not ask people at your school. Do not count people who say they are neither right-handed nor left-handed. (People who can use both hands with equal ease are called *ambidextrous.*)

2. On the chart below, make a tally mark for each person. Be sure that you have exactly 10 marks.

	Tallies
Right-handed	
Left-handed	

3. When you have finished your survey, record the results at the bottom of the page. Bring the results to school.

Name ____________

Survey Results

Number of right-handed people: ______

Number of left-handed people: ______

Total: 10

Math Masters, p. 360

Teaching Master

Name Date Time

LESSON 11•1 **How Many Hours and Minutes?** 

Solve each problem. Use your tool-kit clock to help you.

1. The basketball game lasted 100 minutes, including time-outs and halftime.

   How many whole hours are in 100 minutes?
   1 hour(s)

   How many minutes are left over?
   40 minute(s)

2. The bus trip to the basketball game took 45 minutes. The return trip took another 45 minutes. How many minutes were spent on the bus in all?
   90 minutes

   How many whole hours?
   1 hour(s)

   How many minutes are left over?
   30 minute(s)

3. How many minutes in all did the basketball team play in the game and ride on the bus?
   190 minutes

   How many whole hours?
   3 hour(s)

   How many minutes are left over?
   10 minute(s)

4. Describe how you figured out the answer to Problem 3.
   Sample answer: I added the number of minutes spent on the bus to the number of minutes it took to play the game. I figured that 3 [60s] are in 180. There are 3 hours in 190 minutes with 10 minutes left over.

***Math Masters,* p. 361**

Teaching Master

Name Date Time

LESSON 11•1 **Planning a Field Trip**

Use the schedule below to plan a field trip for Mr. Murer's third-grade class. The children will arrive at the City Zoo at 9:30 A.M. and must leave by 2:00 P.M.

Create a plan that includes

- the Predator or Prey? show,
- the Rainforest Animals show,
- the Endangered Reptiles exhibit,
- one or two other activities,
- and a 30-minute lunch break.

In your plan, show the times at which each activity will begin and end. Write your plan on another sheet of paper.

City Zoo Schedule

Title	Start time	Length*
Predator or Prey? show	9:25 A.M. 10:55 9:55 11:25 10:25	30 min
Rainforest Animals show	9:00 11:15 9:45 12:00 P.M. 10:30	45 min
African Journey (long tour)	Any time	90 min
African Journey (short tour)	Any time	25 min
Big Cats Habitat	Any time	45 min
Great Ape House	Any time	25 min
Sea Lion Pool	Any time	20 min
Endangered Reptiles exhibit	Any time	90 min

*The length of each activity includes travel time and bathroom breaks.

***Math Masters,* p. 362**

▶ Math Boxes 11•1

INDEPENDENT ACTIVITY

(*Math Journal 2,* p. 267)

Mixed Practice The Math Boxes in this lesson are paired with the Math Boxes from Lesson 11-3.

Writing/Reasoning Write an answer to the following: *Explain the estimation strategy you used in Problem 6. Then find the exact answer to the problem. Show your work.* Sample answer: I know that $3 × 6 is $18. I know that $0.59 is close to $0.60. $0.60 × 6 is $3.60. $18 + $3.60 is $21.60. $21 is the closest estimate. I used partial products to find the exact answer to $3.59 × 6. It is $21.54.

▶ Home Link 11•1

(*Math Masters,* p. 360)

Home Connection Children survey 10 people outside of school to find out whether they are right-handed or left-handed. The results will be used in Lesson 11-5, so children have a few days to collect the data. Children should count only people who express a definite preference for one hand over the other.

3 Differentiation Options

READINESS

INDEPENDENT ACTIVITY

▶ Determining Hours and Minutes

 5–15 Min

(*Math Masters,* p. 361)

To provide experience with relationships between units of time, have children use their tool-kit clocks to solve problems involving hours and minutes. Children record their work on *Math Masters,* page 361.

ENRICHMENT

PARTNER ACTIVITY

▶ Planning a Field Trip

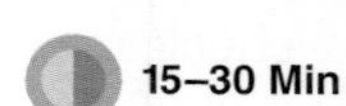

(*Math Masters,* p. 362)

To apply children's understanding of elapsed time, have them plan a schedule for a class field trip. Children use information about events at a zoo to plan their class schedule for the day. Have them share their schedules.

11·2 National High/Low Temperatures Summaries

Objective To guide children as they organize, graph, and interpret data.

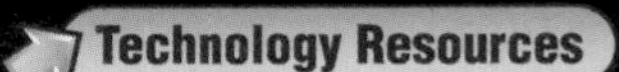

www.everydaymathonline.com

ePresentations

eToolkit

Algorithms Practice

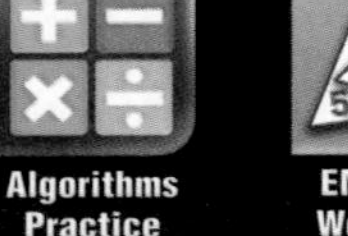
EM Facts Workshop Game™

Family Letters

Assessment Management

Common Core State Standards

Curriculum Focal Points

Interactive Teacher's Lesson Guide

1 Teaching the Lesson

Key Concepts and Skills

- Find the difference between high and low temperatures.
  [Operations and Computation Goal 2]
- Use data to create a frequency table and bar graph.
  [Data and Chance Goal 1]
- Find the maximum, minimum, and median of a data set.
  [Data and Chance Goal 2]
- Answer questions and draw conclusions from a data set.
  [Data and Chance Goal 2]

Key Activities

Children organize and display data from the National High/Low Temperatures Project and look for patterns in the data.

Materials

Math Journal 2, pp. 175–177
Home Link 11•1
Math Masters, pp. 48 and 352
paper bag ◆ half-sheet of paper ◆ scissors ◆ counters (optional) ◆ Class Data Pad (optional) ◆ 2 straightedges (optional)

2 Ongoing Learning & Practice

Playing *Memory Addition/Subtraction*
Student Reference Book, pp. 290 and 291
per partnership: calculator
Children practice mental addition and subtraction skills.

Math Boxes 11·2
Math Journal 2, p. 268
Children practice and maintain skills through Math Box problems.

Ongoing Assessment: Recognizing Student Achievement
Use Math Boxes, Problem 1.
[Measurement and Reference Frames Goal 4]

Home Link 11·2
Math Masters, p. 363
Children practice and maintain skills through Home Link activities.

3 Differentiation Options

READINESS

Finding Differences
Math Masters, p. 364
Children find the difference between pairs of numbers on a number grid.

ENRICHMENT

Comparing Seasonal Temperature Differences
Math Journal 2, p. 175
per partnership: 2 copies of *Math Masters,* p. 352; p. 365
calculator
Children graph and compare seasonal temperature differences.

Advance Preparation

Place one copy per partnership of the class National High/Low Temperatures Project data (*Math Masters,* page 48) next to the Math Message. Provide today's high and low temperatures for the Math Message. *Math Masters,* page 48, should be filled in with temperature data collected throughout the school year.

***Teacher's Reference Manual,* Grades 1–3** pp. 124–126

Getting Started

Mathematical Practices
SMP2, SMP4, **SMP5,** SMP6, SMP7

Mental Math and Reflexes

Children solve fraction-of number stories. Children may use counters. *Suggestions:*

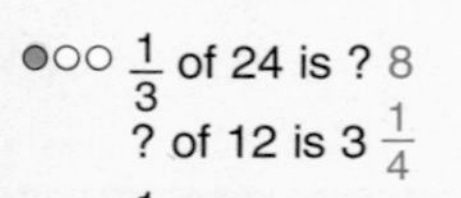

●○○ $\frac{1}{3}$ of 24 is ? 8
? of 12 is 3 $\frac{1}{4}$
$\frac{1}{2}$ of ? is 7 14

●●○ $\frac{2}{5}$ of 10 is ? 4
? of 16 is 12 $\frac{3}{4}$
$\frac{2}{3}$ of ? is 10 15

●●● $\frac{9}{10}$ of 100 is ? 90
? of 300 is 200 $\frac{2}{3}$
$\frac{3}{4}$ of ? is 36 48

Math Message

Turn to the National High/Low Temperatures Project on journal page 175. Record the high and low temperatures for today and the difference in the temperatures. Then, on a half-sheet of paper, write the names of the states that appear most often on journal page 175.

Home Link 11·1 Follow-Up

Ask children to cut off the bottom of their completed Home Link (survey of left- and right-handedness), fold the paper in half, and put the slips into a paper bag for the random draw activity in Lesson 11-5. Tell children who have not completed the survey to continue gathering responses and to bring in the final results as soon as possible.

1 Teaching the Lesson

▶ Math Message Follow-Up

WHOLE-CLASS DISCUSSION

(*Math Journal 2,* p. 175; *Math Masters,* p. 48)

Have children share the difference in today's high and low temperatures. Next, record the names of the states that appear most often on journal page 175 on the board or Class Data Pad. The list can be extended by using data from *Math Masters,* page 48, the National High/Low Temperatures Project record started in Lesson 2-6.

▶ Looking for Temperature Patterns

WHOLE-CLASS DISCUSSION

The data collected for the National High/Low Temperatures Project are considerably less predictable than the data from the Length-of-Day Project. The discovery of patterns, if any, requires some manipulation of the data. Activities suggested in this lesson may reveal patterns.

▶ Activity 1: Reporting Extreme Temperatures

SMALL-GROUP ACTIVITY

(*Math Journal 2,* p. 175; *Math Masters,* p. 48)

Use the Highest Temperature (maximum) column on the table. Make a list of states that appear more than once in the column. Tally how often these states appear in the column. Repeat this activity using the Lowest Temperature (minimum) column on the table. Ask: *Can you find any geographical patterns? Are any states on both lists?* Answers vary. To extend the activity, include data from earlier in the year recorded on *Math Masters,* page 48.

Student Page

Date Time

LESSON 7·8 **National High/Low Temperatures Project**

Date	Highest Temperature (maximum)		Lowest Temperature (minimum)		Difference (range)
	Place	Temperature	Place	Temperature	
		°F		°F	°F
		°F		°F	°F
		°F		°F	°F
		°F		°F	°F
		°F		°F	°F
		°F		°F	°F
		°F		°F	°F
		°F		°F	°F
		°F		°F	°F
		°F		°F	°F
		°F		°F	°F
		°F		°F	°F
		°F		°F	°F
		°F		°F	°F
		°F		°F	°F
		°F		°F	°F
		°F		°F	°F
		°F		°F	°F
		°F		°F	°F
		°F		°F	°F
		°F		°F	°F

Math Journal 2, p. 175

▶ Activity 2: Finding the Most Frequent Temperature Difference

(*Math Journal 2,* pp. 175–177, *Math Masters,* p. 352)

Find the greatest and least differences in daily temperatures. To support English language learners, discuss the meanings of greatest and least daily differences. Separate the temperature range between the greatest daily difference and the least daily difference into intervals: for example, 60° to 69°, 70° to 79°, and so on. Explain that organizing temperature differences into 10-degree intervals, or periods, helps keep the data manageable. Use these intervals to make a frequency chart (see below). Use the data from the National High/Low Temperatures Project and Temperature Ranges Graph to tally the number of days on which the difference falls within each interval. Ask: *Which interval has the greatest number of days?* Answers vary. Make a bar graph of the data on *Math Masters,* page 352.

Temperature Difference Lies Between...	Number of Days
60°–69°F	////
70°–79°F	~~////~~ //
80°–89°F	~~////~~ ~~////~~ //
90°–99°F	~~////~~ ~~////~~
100°–110°F	~~////~~ /

Adjusting the Activity

The number of days for each category can be found without sorting through the large quantity of data on the National High/Low Temperatures Project. Instead, use the Temperature Ranges graph. For example, to find the number of days tallied in the interval 80°–89°F, place a straightedge just beneath the horizontal line for 80°F and another just above the line for 89°F. Then count the number of dots between the two lines.

AUDITORY ◆ KINESTHETIC ◆ TACTILE ◆ VISUAL

▶ Activity 3: Finding the Median Temperature Difference

(*Math Journal 2,* pp. 175–177)

List the temperature differences from lowest to highest on a half-sheet of paper. Find the median value.

Teaching Master

Name   Date   Time

LESSON 2·6 **National High/Low Temperatures**

Date	Highest Temperature (maximum)		Lowest Temperature (minimum)		Difference (range)
	Place	Temperature	Place	Temperature	
		°F		°F	°F
		°F		°F	°F
		°F		°F	°F
		°F		°F	°F
		°F		°F	°F
		°F		°F	°F
		°F		°F	°F
		°F		°F	°F
		°F		°F	°F
		°F		°F	°F
		°F		°F	°F
		°F		°F	°F
		°F		°F	°F
		°F		°F	°F
		°F		°F	°F
		°F		°F	°F
		°F		°F	°F
		°F		°F	°F
		°F		°F	°F
		°F		°F	°F

Math Masters, p. 48

NOTE For practice with the Fahrenheit and Celsius thermometer scales, go to www.everydaymathonline.com.

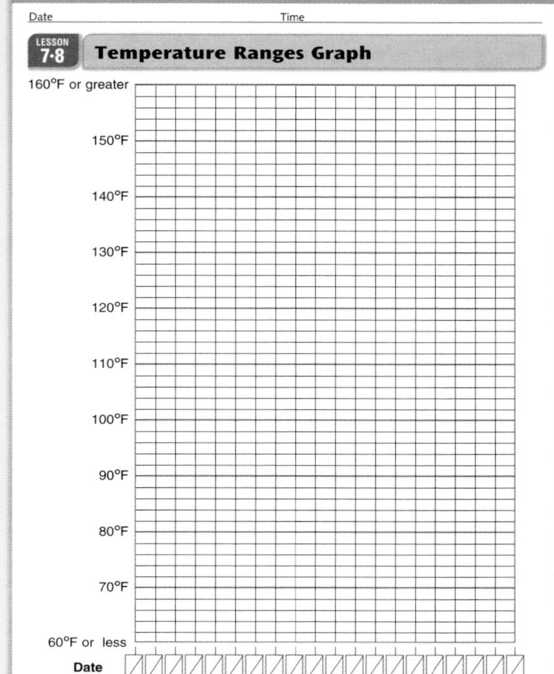

Math Journal 2, p. 176

Student Page

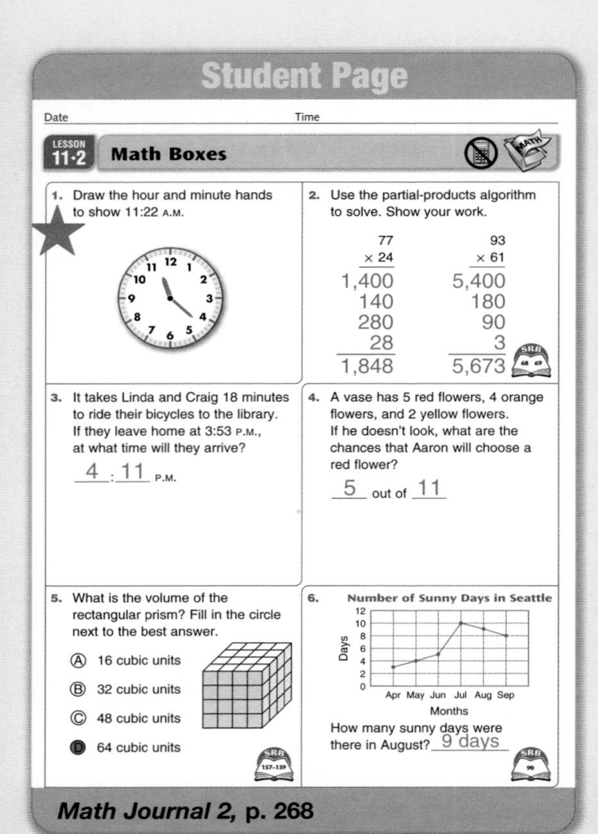
Date Time

LESSON 11·2 Math Boxes

1. Draw the hour and minute hands to show 11:22 A.M.

2. Use the partial-products algorithm to solve. Show your work.

77 × 24 = 1,400 + 140 + 280 + 28 = 1,848

93 × 61 = 5,400 + 180 + 90 + 3 = 5,673

3. It takes Linda and Craig 18 minutes to ride their bicycles to the library. If they leave home at 3:53 P.M., at what time will they arrive?

4 : 11 P.M.

4. A vase has 5 red flowers, 4 orange flowers, and 2 yellow flowers. If he doesn't look, what are the chances that Aaron will choose a red flower?

5 out of 11

5. What is the volume of the rectangular prism? Fill in the circle next to the best answer.

Ⓐ 16 cubic units
Ⓑ 32 cubic units
Ⓒ 48 cubic units
Ⓓ 64 cubic units

6. Number of Sunny Days in Seattle

How many sunny days were there in August? 9 days

Math Journal 2, p. 268

Home Link Master

Name Date Time

HOME LINK 11·2 Computation Round-Up

Family Note Please observe as your child adds, subtracts, multiplies, and divides pairs of whole numbers. Encourage your child to use and explain his or her favorite strategies.
Please return this Home Link to school.

For each of the number pairs below, use mental arithmetic or other strategies to perform the operations indicated in each column in the table. Show any work on the back of this page. Explain your favorite strategies to someone at home.

Numbers	Add	Subtract	Multiply	Divide
30 and 7	30 + 7 = 37	30 − 7 = 23	30 × 7 = 210	30 ÷ 7 → 4 R2
50 and 5	50 + 5 = 55	50 − 5 = 45	50 × 5 = 250	50 ÷ 5 = 10
40 and 6	40 + 6 = 46	40 − 6 = 34	40 × 6 = 240	40 ÷ 6 → 6 R4
150 and 3	150 + 3 = 153	150 − 3 = 147	150 × 3 = 450	150 ÷ 3 = 50
3,000 and 50	3,000 + 50 = 3,050	3,000 − 50 = 2,950	3,000 × 50 = 150,000	3,000 ÷ 50 = 60
12,000 and 60	12,000 + 60 = 12,060	12,000 − 60 = 11,940	12,000 × 60 = 720,000	12,000 ÷ 60 = 200

Math Masters, p. 363

2 Ongoing Learning & Practice

▶ Playing *Memory Addition/Subtraction*

PARTNER ACTIVITY

(*Student Reference Book,* pp. 290 and 291)

Children practice mental addition and subtraction skills in *Memory Addition / Subtraction.* Game directions are in Lesson 10-8 and in the *Student Reference Book*, pages 290 and 291.

▶ Math Boxes 11·2

INDEPENDENT ACTIVITY

(*Math Journal 2,* p. 268)

Mixed Practice The Math Boxes in this lesson are paired with the Math Boxes in Lesson 11-4.

Ongoing Assessment: Recognizing Student Achievement

Math Boxes Problem 1

Use **Math Boxes, Problem 1** to assess children's progress toward telling and writing time to the nearest minute on an analog clock. Children are making adequate progress if they draw clock hands to show 11:22 in Problem 1.

[Measurement and Reference Frames Goal 4]

▶ Home Link 11·2

INDEPENDENT ACTIVITY

(*Math Masters,* p. 363)

Home Connection Children use a variety of strategies to add, subtract, multiply, and divide pairs of numbers.

3 Differentiation Options

READINESS

INDEPENDENT ACTIVITY

▶ Finding Differences

5–15 Min

(*Math Masters,* p. 364)

To provide experience with subtraction of signed numbers using a visual model, have children use a number grid to find the difference between signed numbers. When children have completed *Math Masters,* page 364, have them describe how the number grid helped them solve the problems. Ask what was easy and what was difficult about using the number grid to find differences.

ENRICHMENT

PARTNER ACTIVITY

▶ Comparing Seasonal Temperature Differences

15–30 Min

(*Math Journal 2,* p. 175; *Math Masters,* pp. 352 and 365)

To apply children's ability to ask and answer questions and draw conclusions based on data representations, have them organize the National High/Low Temperatures by month and find the mean (average) temperature difference for each. Create two graphs (one for fall and winter; the other for spring and summer) and discuss the results. Children record their work on *Math Masters,* pages 352 and 365.

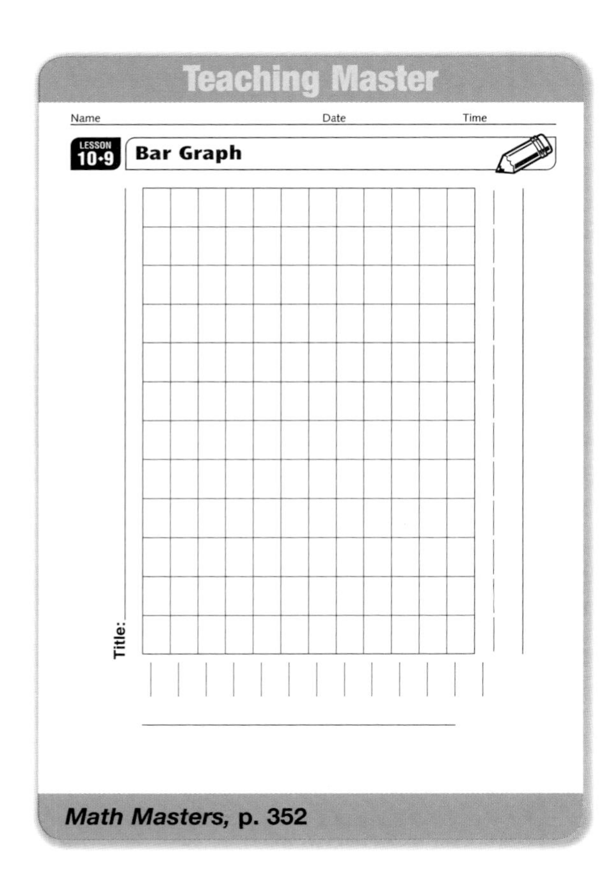

Teaching Master

Name Date Time

LESSON 10•9 **Bar Graph**

Title:

Math Masters, p. 352

Teaching Master

Name Date Time

LESSON 11•2 **Finding Differences**

−19	−18	−17	−16	−15	−14	−13	−12	−11	−10
−9	−8	−7	−6	−5	−4	−3	−2	−1	0
1	2	3	4	5	6	7	8	9	10
11	12	13	14	15	16	17	18	19	20
21	22	23	24	25	26	27	28	29	30
31	32	33	34	35	36	37	38	39	40
41	42	43	44	45	46	47	48	49	50
51	52	53	54	55	56	57	58	59	60
61	62	63	64	65	66	67	68	69	70
71	72	73	74	75	76	77	78	79	80
81	82	83	84	85	86	87	88	89	90
91	92	93	94	95	96	97	98	99	100
101	102	103	104	105	106	107	108	109	110

1. Describe how you can use the number grid to find the difference between −5 and 51.
   Sample answer: Count down rows from −5 to 55, which is 6 rows, or 60. Then count back as you move left 4 spaces to 51. 60, 59, 58, 57, 56.

Find the difference between each pair of numbers.

2. 22 and 46 24
3. 91 and 36 55
4. 104 and 17 87
5. −16 and 65 81
6. 83 and −9 92
7. 101 and −13 114

Math Masters, p. 364

Planning Ahead

For Lesson 11-5 you will need to know the number of teachers in your school and how many of them are left-handed.

Teaching Master

Name Date Time

LESSON 11•2 **Comparing Seasonal Temperature Differences**

1. Organize the temperature differences from the National High/Low Temperatures Project on journal page 175 by month. For example, group together all of the differences for the month of October. Then group the differences for November, and so on.
2. Use your calculator to find the mean (average) temperature difference for each month for which you have data. Record your results below. Answers vary.
3. Use copies of *Math Masters,* page 352 to create two graphs showing seasonal temperature differences. One graph should show data for fall and winter months (October through March). The other graph should show the data for spring and summer months (April through September).

   Reminder: Be sure to label your graphs clearly.
4. Compare the 2 bar graphs. Record at least 2 things you know from looking at your graphs.

Fall/Winter Months	Mean Temperature Difference
October	
November	
December	
January	
February	
March	

Spring/Summer Months	Mean Temperature Difference
April	
May	
June	
July	
August	
September	

Math Masters, p. 365

11•3 Spinner Experiments

Objective To guide children as they collect and interpret data from spinner experiments with outcomes that are equally likely and not equally likely.

www.everydaymathonline.com

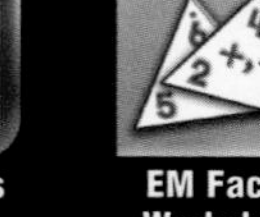

1 Teaching the Lesson

Key Concepts and Skills

- Shade fractional parts of a circle. [Number and Numeration Goal 2]
- Apply equivalent fractions to shade fractional parts of a circle. [Number and Numeration Goal 5]
- Organize the results of a probability experiment in a frequency table. [Data and Chance Goal 1]
- Use basic probability terms to describe the outcomes of an experiment. [Data and Chance Goal 3]

Key Activities

Children perform experiments with spinners that are divided equally and unequally.

Ongoing Assessment: Recognizing Student Achievement Use journal page 269. [Data and Chance Goal 1]

Materials

Math Journal 2, p. 269
Home Link 11•2
Math Masters, p. 367
transparency of *Math Masters,* p. 366 (optional) ◆ crayons (red, blue, yellow) ◆ tape ◆ permanent marker ◆ calculator ◆ large paper clips ◆ slate ◆ Class Data Pad ◆ erasable markers (red, blue, yellow) optional

2 Ongoing Learning & Practice

Estimating and Calculating
Math Journal 2, p. 270
Children make ballpark estimates and then solve multidigit addition and subtraction problems.

Math Boxes 11•3
Math Journal 2, p. 271
Children practice and maintain skills through Math Box problems.

Home Link 11•3
Math Masters, p. 368
Children practice and maintain skills through Home Link activities.

3 Differentiation Options

READINESS

Identifying Equivalent Fractions
Math Masters, pp. 369 and 370
scissors ◆ tape or glue
Children identify equivalent fractions by matching fractional parts of circles.

ENRICHMENT

Designing and Testing Spinners
Math Masters, p. 371
straightedge ◆ paper clip ◆ crayons
Children design spinners whose outcomes are not equally likely.

EXTRA PRACTICE

Playing *Soccer Spin*
Math Masters, pp. 459–461
per partnership: large paper clip, counter
Children practice making predictions.

ELL SUPPORT

Building a Math Word Bank
Differentiation Handbook, p. 132
Children add the term *equally likely* to their Math Word Banks.

Advance Preparation

Make a small mark with a permanent marker on the paper clips used as spinners to clarify where the spinner is pointing.

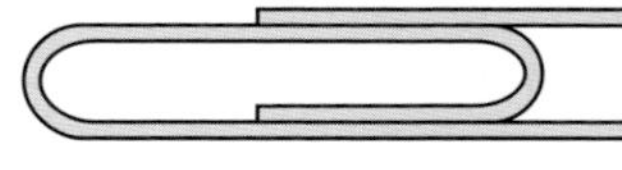

Make a mark at one end of the paper clip.

***Teacher's Reference Manual,* Grades 1–3** pp. 126–128

Getting Started

Mathematical Practices
SMP1, SMP2, SMP3, SMP4, **SMP5,** SMP6, **SMP8**
Content Standards
3.NF.1, 3.NF.3, 3.NF.3b

Mental Math and Reflexes

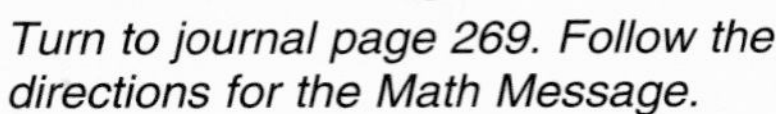

On their slates, children write at least one equivalent mixed number, whole number, or fraction for each number dictated.
Suggestions: Sample Answer:

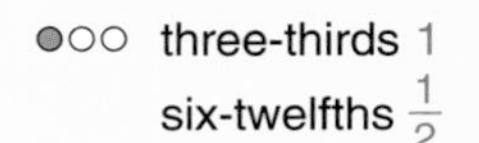

●○○ three-thirds 1
six-twelfths $\frac{1}{2}$

●●○ six-thirds 2
six-fourths
$1\frac{2}{4}$ or $1\frac{1}{2}$

●●● two and five-eighths
$\frac{21}{8}$
seventeen-eighths
$2\frac{1}{8}$

Math Message

Turn to journal page 269. Follow the directions for the Math Message.

Home Link 11·2 Follow-Up

Briefly review answers. Have a few children share solution strategies with the class.

1 Teaching the Lesson

▶ Math Message Follow-Up

WHOLE-CLASS DISCUSSION

(*Math Journal 2,* p. 269; *Math Masters,* p. 366)

Review and discuss the answers to the Math Message. If you made a transparency of *Math Masters,* page 366, have children show how they found their answers.

Ask: *Where have you seen spinners before?* Board games, carnivals, game shows *What are they used for?* Spinners are often used in games to select a color, number, word, and so on. Ask: *How are the circles you colored on the journal page like spinners?* The bases of spinners have circles like these, with areas that are colored or labeled in different ways.

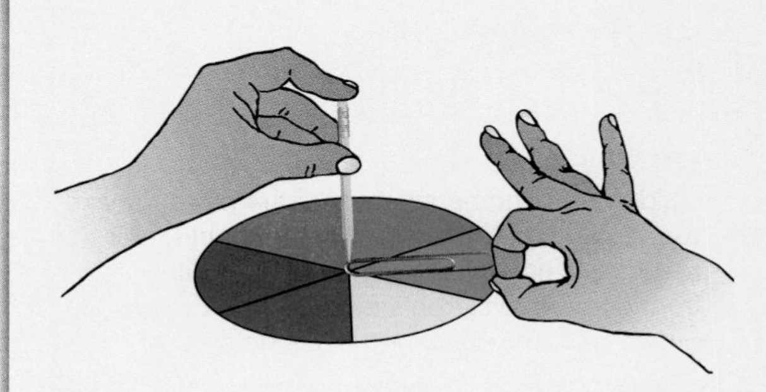

Flick the paper clip. Always spin on a level surface.

▶ Demonstrating Making and Using a Spinner

WHOLE-CLASS ACTIVITY

(*Math Masters,* p. 367)

Have children tape a copy of *Math Masters,* page 367 to their desks or tables. Show children how to make a spinner with a paper clip and pencil. (*See margin.*)

A large 2-inch paper clip is preferable because it spins more easily, but a standard 1-inch paper clip can be used. To spin the paper clip, place the point of the pencil on the center of a circle as shown in the margin. Flick the paper clip near its midpoint.

Have children practice spinning with the first circle on *Math Masters,* page 367. Discuss what constitutes a fair spin. Mention that the spinner might not spin fairly if it is not placed on a level surface.

Teaching Master

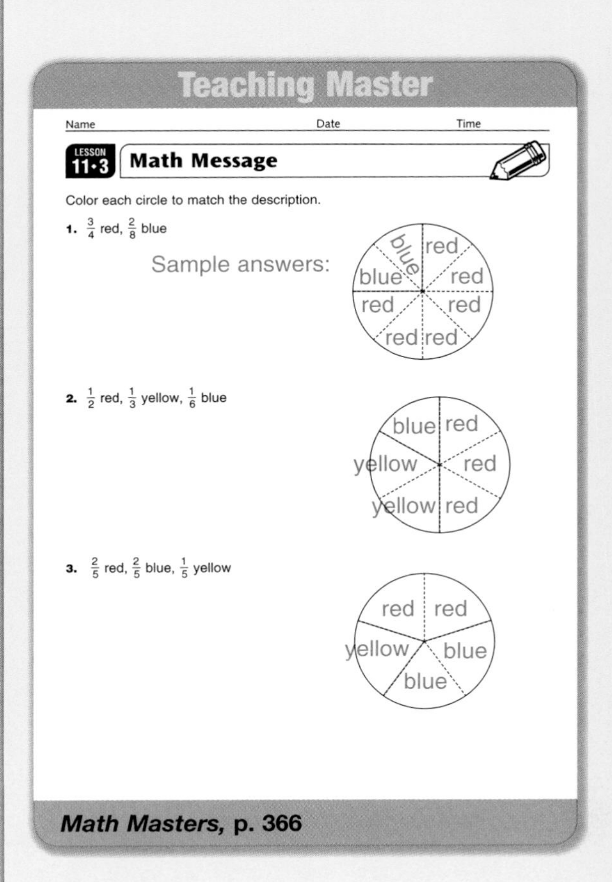

Name Date Time

LESSON 11·3 **Math Message**

Color each circle to match the description.

1. $\frac{3}{4}$ red, $\frac{2}{8}$ blue

Sample answers:

2. $\frac{1}{2}$ red, $\frac{1}{3}$ yellow, $\frac{1}{6}$ blue

3. $\frac{2}{5}$ red, $\frac{2}{5}$ blue, $\frac{1}{5}$ yellow

Math Masters, p. 366

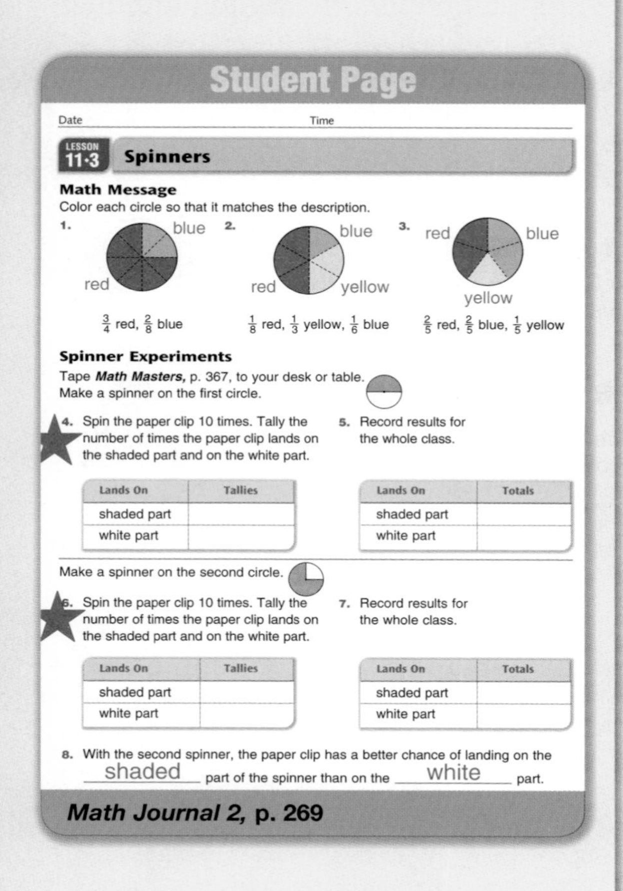

Student Page

Date Time

LESSON 11·3 **Spinners**

Math Message

Color each circle so that it matches the description.

1. blue, red — $\frac{3}{4}$ red, $\frac{2}{8}$ blue
2. blue, red, yellow — $\frac{1}{8}$ red, $\frac{1}{3}$ yellow, $\frac{1}{6}$ blue
3. red, blue, yellow — $\frac{2}{5}$ red, $\frac{2}{5}$ blue, $\frac{1}{5}$ yellow

Spinner Experiments

Tape *Math Masters,* p. 367, to your desk or table.
Make a spinner on the first circle.

4. Spin the paper clip 10 times. Tally the number of times the paper clip lands on the shaded part and on the white part.

Lands On	Tallies
shaded part	
white part	

5. Record results for the whole class.

Lands On	Totals
shaded part	
white part	

Make a spinner on the second circle.

6. Spin the paper clip 10 times. Tally the number of times the paper clip lands on the shaded part and on the white part.

Lands On	Tallies
shaded part	
white part	

7. Record results for the whole class.

Lands On	Totals
shaded part	
white part	

8. With the second spinner, the paper clip has a better chance of landing on the shaded part of the spinner than on the white part.

Math Journal 2, p. 269

NOTE *Everyday Mathematics* wants children to become aware that the more they repeat an experiment, the more reliable their results will be. Combining spinner results from different children's experiments creates a more reliable combined class data set.

Results for ◕ spinner

	Shaded	White
	8	2
	7	3
	5	5
	9	1
	7	3
	8	2
	•	•
	•	•
	•	•
Totals:	180	70

▶ Conducting Equally Likely and Not Equally Likely Experiments

(*Math Journal 2,* p. 269; *Math Masters,* p. 367)

When children become adept at fair spins, they each spin their paper clip 10 times and tally the results in Problem 4 on journal page 269. Ask children to report their results while you record them on the Class Data Pad.

Results for ◒ spinner

	Shaded	White
	4	6
	5	5
	7	3
	4	6
	5	5
	6	4
	•	•
	•	•
	•	•
Totals:	130	120

Sample totals for 25 children

You or the children can use a calculator to find the class totals. Children will record the totals in Problem 5 on the journal page.

Help children summarize the results. Look for responses like the following:

- There is just as good a chance of the paper clip landing on the shaded part as on the white part.
- If you spin many times, the paper clip will land on white about one out of two times.

Point out that if the shaded and white areas of the spinner were labeled Heads and Tails, spinning the spinner would have results equivalent to tossing a coin.

Next, children repeat the experiment using the second circle on *Math Masters,* page 367. Spin 10 times, and tally the results in Problem 6 on the journal page. As before, find the class totals and have children record them in Problem 7 on the journal page.

Ongoing Assessment: Recognizing Student Achievement

Journal page 269 Problems 4 and 6

Use **journal page 269, Problems 4 and 6** to assess children's ability to collect and organize data. Children are making adequate progress if they are able to complete Problems 4 and 6. Some children may be able to explain why individual results might be different from whole-class results.

[Data and Chance Goal 1]

Help children summarize the results. Did they get the results they expected? Look for responses like the following:

- The second circle has a bigger shaded part than the first circle, so the paper clip should land on the shaded part more often.
- With the first spinner, the paper clip has the same chance of landing on shaded or white. With the second spinner, the paper clip has a better chance of landing on shaded. That's what happened in our experiment.
- With the second spinner I expected the paper clip to land on the shaded part most of the time. I was surprised because 5 of my 10 spins landed on white. Most other kids got a lot more shaded than white. If I did 10 more spins, I would probably get more shaded than white, too.

The last response makes a good discussion topic. Help children understand that the results of an experiment might not always match the predicted outcomes, especially if the experiment is not repeated for reliability.

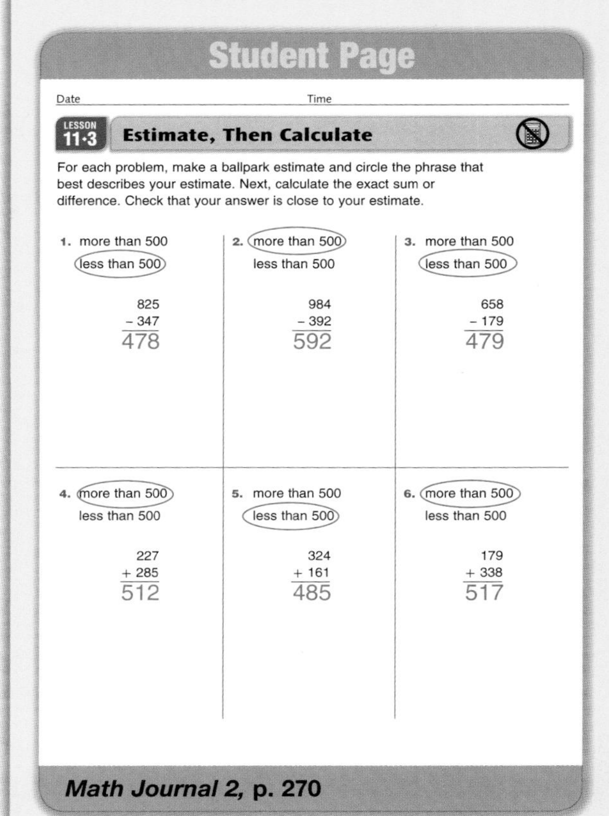

Student Page

Date Time

LESSON 11·3 **Estimate, Then Calculate**

For each problem, make a ballpark estimate and circle the phrase that best describes your estimate. Next, calculate the exact sum or difference. Check that your answer is close to your estimate.

1. more than 500 / (less than 500) — 825 − 347 = 478
2. (more than 500) / less than 500 — 984 − 392 = 592
3. more than 500 / (less than 500) — 658 − 179 = 479
4. (more than 500) / less than 500 — 227 + 285 = 512
5. more than 500 / (less than 500) — 324 + 161 = 485
6. (more than 500) / less than 500 — 179 + 338 = 517

Math Journal 2, p. 270

2 Ongoing Learning & Practice

Estimating and Calculating

INDEPENDENT ACTIVITY

(*Math Journal 2*, p. 270)

Children estimate and solve multidigit addition and subtraction problems.

Math Boxes 11·3

INDEPENDENT ACTIVITY

(*Math Journal 2*, p. 271)

Mixed Practice The Math Boxes in this lesson are paired with Math Boxes in Lesson 11-1.

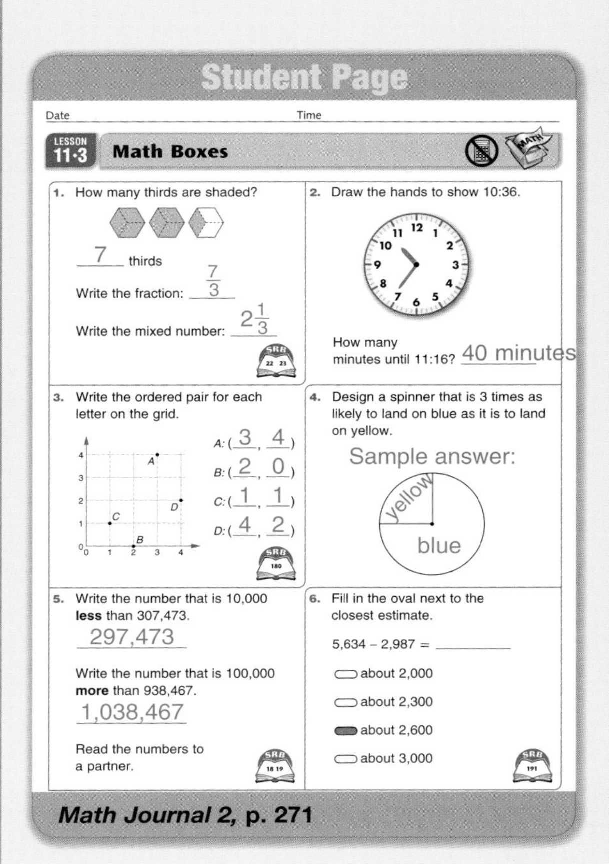

Student Page

Date Time

LESSON 11·3 **Math Boxes**

1. How many thirds are shaded?
7 thirds
Write the fraction: $\frac{7}{3}$
Write the mixed number: $2\frac{1}{3}$
SRB 22 23

2. Draw the hands to show 10:36.
How many minutes until 11:16? 40 minutes

3. Write the ordered pair for each letter on the grid.
A: (3, 4)
B: (2, 0)
C: (1, 1)
D: (4, 2)
SRB 180

4. Design a spinner that is 3 times as likely to land on blue as it is to land on yellow.
Sample answer: yellow, blue

5. Write the number that is 10,000 **less** than 307,473.
297,473
Write the number that is 100,000 **more** than 938,467.
1,038,467
Read the numbers to a partner.
SRB 18 19

6. Fill in the oval next to the closest estimate.
5,634 − 2,987 = ______
○ about 2,000
○ about 2,300
● about 2,600
○ about 3,000
SRB 191

Math Journal 2, p. 271

Home Link Master

Name Date Time

HOME LINK 11·3 **A Fair Game?**

Family Note To explore probability, play the game *Fingers* with your child. After 20 games, have your child decide if the game is fair and explain why or why not. (A game is fair if all players have an equal chance of winning or losing.)

Please return this Home Link to school tomorrow.

Play *Fingers* at least 20 times. Keep a tally of wins and losses in the table below.

Rules for *Fingers*

This is a game for 2 players. One player tries to guess the number of fingers the other player will throw (display).

You, the *Everyday Mathematics* student, can throw 1, 2, 3, or 4 fingers. The other player can throw only 1 or 2 fingers.

Players face each other. Each one puts a closed fist on his or her chest.

One player counts, "One, two, three." On "three," each player throws some number of fingers.

At the same time, both players call out what they think will be the total number of fingers thrown by both players.

- The player who calls out the correct total wins.
- If *neither* player calls out the correct total, no one wins.
- If *both* players call out the correct total, no one wins.

Tallies for Wins	Tallies for Losses

1. Is this game fair? (Fair means each player has the same chance of winning.) No
2. On the back of this page explain your answer.

Adaptation of rules for *Mora* in *Family Fun and Games*, The Diagram Group, Sterling Publishing, 1992, p. 365

***Math Masters*, p. 368**

▶ Home Link 11·3

INDEPENDENT ACTIVITY

(*Math Masters*, p. 368)

Home Connection Children play *Fingers* with someone at home. They tally wins and losses and tell whether they think the game is fair.

3 Differentiation Options

READINESS

INDEPENDENT ACTIVITY

▶ Identifying Equivalent Fractions

5–15 Min

(*Math Masters*, pp. 369 and 370)

To provide experience identifying equivalent fractions of a region, have children cover circles with fractional parts from *Math Masters*, page 370. They record their work on *Math Masters*, page 369.

Teaching Master

Name Date Time

LESSON 11·3 **Equivalent Fractions**

- Cut the Fraction Circles from *Math Masters*, page 370 into parts along the dotted lines.
- Tape or glue the cut-out pieces onto the circles on this page as directed.
- Write the missing numerators to complete the equivalent fractions.

1. Cover $\frac{3}{4}$ of the circle with **eighths.**
   $\frac{3}{4} = \frac{6}{8}$
2. Cover $\frac{1}{4}$ of the circle with **eighths.**
   $\frac{1}{4} = \frac{2}{8}$
3. Cover $\frac{1}{2}$ of the circle with **sixths.**
   $\frac{1}{2} = \frac{3}{6}$
4. Cover $\frac{1}{3}$ of the circle with **sixths.**
   $\frac{1}{3} = \frac{2}{6}$

***Math Masters*, p. 369**

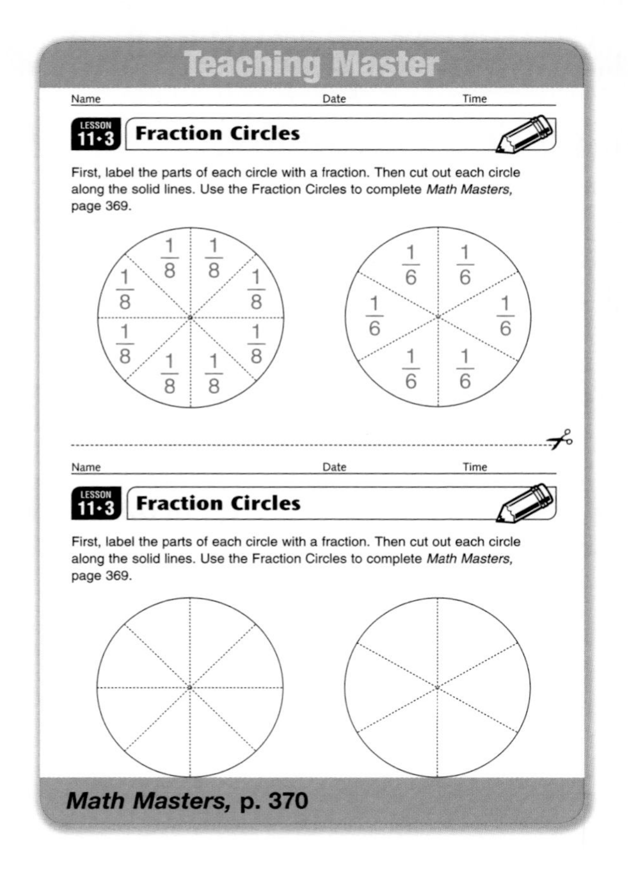
Teaching Master

Name Date Time

LESSON 11·3 **Fraction Circles**

First, label the parts of each circle with a fraction. Then cut out each circle along the solid lines. Use the Fraction Circles to complete *Math Masters*, page 369.

Name Date Time

LESSON 11·3 **Fraction Circles**

First, label the parts of each circle with a fraction. Then cut out each circle along the solid lines. Use the Fraction Circles to complete *Math Masters*, page 369.

***Math Masters*, p. 370**

ENRICHMENT

PARTNER ACTIVITY

5–15 Min

▶ Designing and Testing Spinners

(*Math Masters,* p. 371)

To apply their understanding of outcomes that are not equally likely, have children design spinners and conduct spinner experiments. Children use the circles on *Math Masters,* page 371 to make spinners. They test the spinners 20 times and record the results on the tally charts on *Math Masters,* page 371.

EXTRA PRACTICE

PARTNER ACTIVITY

15–30 Min

▶ Playing *Soccer Spin*

(*Math Masters,* pp. 459–461)

To provide practice with making predictions, have children play *Soccer Spin.* After choosing one of three spinners, players predict which team will get to its goal first. Children follow the directions on *Math Masters,* page 459. When children have played the game using all three spinners, ask and discuss the following:

Which spinners might you use if you were cheering for the checks team? Sample answer: I would choose the spinner with the largest area covered by checks. The paper clip is more likely to land there.

Which spinner might you use if you were cheering for the stripes team? Sample answer: The spinner that has $\frac{3}{4}$ of the area covered with stripes because the paper clip is more likely to land on stripes.

ELL SUPPORT

SMALL-GROUP ACTIVITY

5–15 Min

▶ Building a Math Word Bank

(*Differentiation Handbook,* p. 132)

To provide language support for chance events, have children use the Word Bank Template found on *Differentiation Handbook,* page 132. Ask children to write the term *equally likely,* draw a picture representing the term, and write other related words. See the *Differentiation Handbook* for more information.

Teaching Master

Name Date Time

LESSON 11•3 **Spinners and Tallies**

1. Use a straightedge and divide the spinner into two *unequal* parts. Shade one part so a paper clip is more likely to land on the unshaded part than on the shaded part.
2. Test your spinner at least 20 times and tally the results below.

Answers vary.

Lands On	Tallies
Shaded part	
Unshaded part	

3. Explain your results on the back of this page.
4. Design another spinner with *more than two unequal* parts. Color the parts different colors. Predict what the results might be for 20 or more spins. Check your prediction. Record your results below.

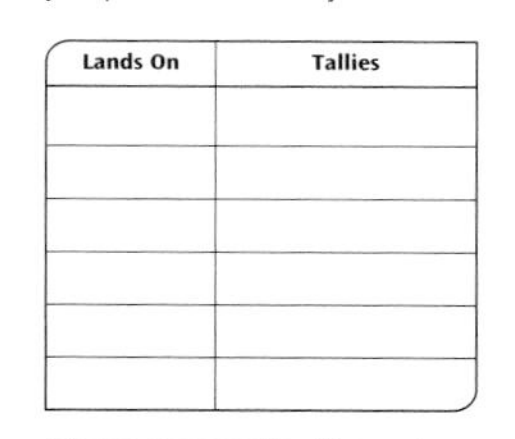
Lands On	Tallies

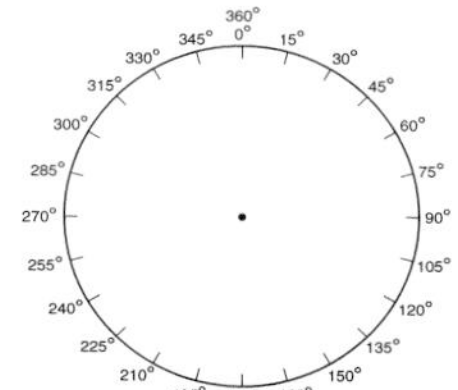

Discuss your results with a partner.

Math Masters, p. 371

Game Master

Name Date Time

Soccer Spin

Materials ☐ *Math Masters,* pp. 460 and 461 ☐ 1 large paper clip
☐ 1 counter per partnership ☐ 1 pencil

Players 2

Object of the game Test the prediction made at the beginning of the game.

Directions

1. Players choose a spinner on *Math Masters,* page 460 to use during the game.
2. Each player chooses a team to cheer for, **Checks** or **Stripes.** (Players can cheer for the same team.) They look at their spinner choice and predict which team will win the game.
3. The game begins with the counter (the ball) in the center of the *Soccer Spin* Game Mat (*Math Masters,* p. 461).
4. Players take turns spinning and moving the counter one space toward the team's goal that comes up on the spinner.
5. The game is over when the counter reaches a goal.
6. Players compare and discuss the results of their predictions.

Use a pencil and paper clip to make a spinner.

Play two more games using the other two spinners.

Math Masters, p. 459

11•4 Designing Spinners

Objective To guide children as they represent the likelihood of outcomes with visual models.

Technology Resources www.everydaymathonline.com

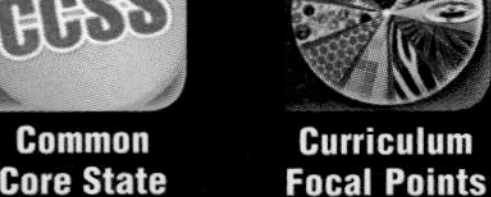

ePresentations | eToolkit | Algorithms Practice | EM Facts Workshop Game™ | Family Letters | Assessment Management | Common Core State Standards | Curriculum Focal Points | Interactive Teacher's Lesson Guide

1 Teaching the Lesson

Key Concepts and Skills

- Share strategies for solving problems involving fractional parts of a circle.
  [Number and Numeration Goal 2]
- Use basic probability terms to describe spinners.
  [Data and Chance Goal 3]
- Express the probability of an event by using "____ out of ____" language.
  [Data and Chance Goal 4]
- Use the number of degrees in a circle to construct a spinner.
  [Geometry Goal 2]

Key Activities

Children design spinners that represent the likelihood of various outcomes.

Ongoing Assessment: Informing Instruction See page 895.

Ongoing Assessment: Recognizing Student Achievement Use journal page 272.
[Data and Chance Goal 3]

Materials

Math Journal 2, pp. 272 and 273
Home Link 11•3
Math Masters, p. 371
blank transparency (optional) ◆ straightedge ◆ crayons ◆ paper clips (optional)

2 Ongoing Learning & Practice

Playing *The Block-Drawing Game*
Student Reference Book, pp. 280 and 281
per group: paper bag, 7 blocks of the same size and shape, in 2 or 3 different colors
Children practice making predictions using chance data.

Math Boxes 11•4
Math Journal 2, p. 274
Children practice and maintain skills through Math Box problems.

Home Link 11•4
Math Masters, p. 372
Children practice and maintain skills through Home Link activities.

3 Differentiation Options

READINESS

Shading Fractions on Spinners
Math Masters, p. 373
straightedge ◆ crayons or colored pencils (blue, red, and green) ◆ paper (optional) ◆ paper clip (optional)
Children shade fractions on a spinner.

ENRICHMENT

Creating a Spinner
Math Masters, p. 374
straightedge ◆ paper clip ◆ crayons or colored pencils (blue, red, yellow, and green)
Children create a spinner that matches given clues.

EXTRA PRACTICE

Playing *Spinning to Win*
Math Masters, p. 464
Student Reference Book, p. 309
per group: large paper clip, paper, 50 pennies or other counters
Children use chance data to develop a winning game strategy.

Advance Preparation

Make copies of *Math Masters,* page 371 for children who make mistakes while designing spinners on the journal pages.

***Teacher's Reference Manual,* Grades 1–3** pp. 118, 119

Getting Started

Mathematical Practices
SMP1, SMP2, SMP3, SMP5, SMP6
Content Standards
3.NF.1

Mental Math and Reflexes

Children stand and face the front of the room. They make turns with their bodies as directed. *Suggestions:*

●○○ Children return to the start position after each direction.
- Make one half-turn clockwise.
- Turn 90 degrees to the left.
- Make a one-fourth turn counter clockwise.

●●○ Children do NOT return to the start position after each direction.
- Turn 180 degrees clockwise.
- Make a one quarter-turn counter clockwise.
- Turn 90 degrees clockwise.

●●● Children do NOT return to the start position after each direction. Have them tell which number on a clock face they would be facing if they started at 12 for the first problem.
- Turn one-third turn clockwise. 4
- Turn 180 degrees counter clockwise. 10
- Turn two-thirds turn clockwise. 6

Math Message

Complete Problem 1 on journal page 272.

Home Link 11·3 Follow-Up

Collect the class data for wins and losses, which should confirm that the child has a 2-to-1 advantage. The child knows his or her number and must decide whether to add 1 or 2 to that. The opponent knows his or her number but must choose among 1, 2, 3, and 4 as the number the child may throw. Discuss whether the game is fair.

1 Teaching the Lesson

NOTE To review right, acute, and obtuse angles, go to www.everydaymathonline.com.

▶ Math Message Follow-Up

(*Math Journal 2,* pp. 272 and 273; *Math Masters,* p. 371)

The four circles on journal pages 272 and 273 used in this lesson are labeled with degree measures to help children design four different spinners. Have extra copies of blank spinners from *Math Masters,* page 371 available if children make mistakes while designing spinners.

Ongoing Assessment: Informing Instruction

Watch for children who may not understand how to divide the circle into parts to make a spinner. Help them see that each shaded part of the circle must resemble a wedge (or semicircle) whose angle is at the center of the circle—like a piece of pie.

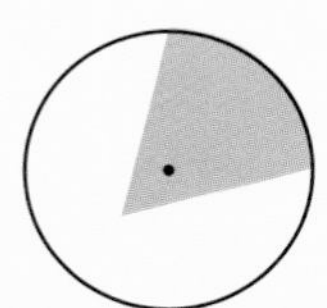
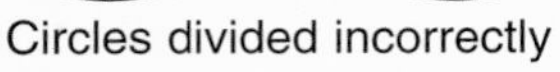

Circles divided incorrectly

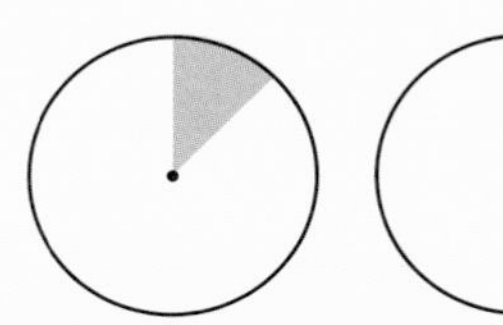

Circles divided correctly

Student Page

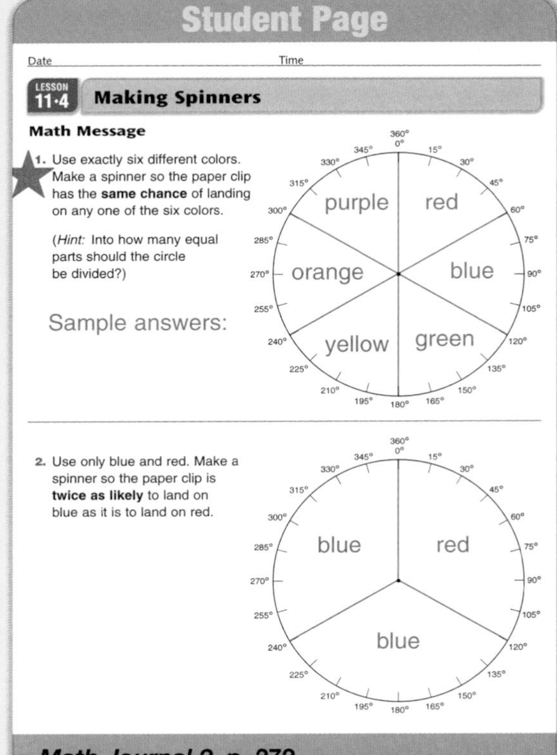

Date Time

LESSON 11·4 **Making Spinners**

Math Message

1. Use exactly six different colors. Make a spinner so the paper clip has the **same chance** of landing on any one of the six colors.

   (*Hint:* Into how many equal parts should the circle be divided?)

   Sample answers:

2. Use only blue and red. Make a spinner so the paper clip is **twice as likely** to land on blue as it is to land on red.

Math Journal 2, p. 272

Student Page

Date Time

LESSON 11·4 **Making Spinners** *continued*

3. Use only blue, red, and green. Make a spinner so the paper clip:

- has the **same chance** of landing on blue and on red

and

- is **less likely** to land on green than on blue.

Sample answers:

blue red green

4. Use only blue, red, and yellow. Make a spinner so that the paper clip:

- is **more likely** to land on blue than on red

and

- is **less likely** to land on yellow than on blue.

yellow blue red

***Math Journal 2,* p. 273**

Adjusting the Activity

As an alternate solution to Problem 2, have children divide a spinner into 24 equal parts. They color the spinner $\frac{1}{3}$ red and $\frac{2}{3}$ blue, alternating red and blue.

Collect class data with each child spinning 10 times. Although individual results are likely to vary, the data for the whole class should show blue about $\frac{2}{3}$ of the time.

AUDITORY ◆ KINESTHETIC ◆ TACTILE ◆ VISUAL

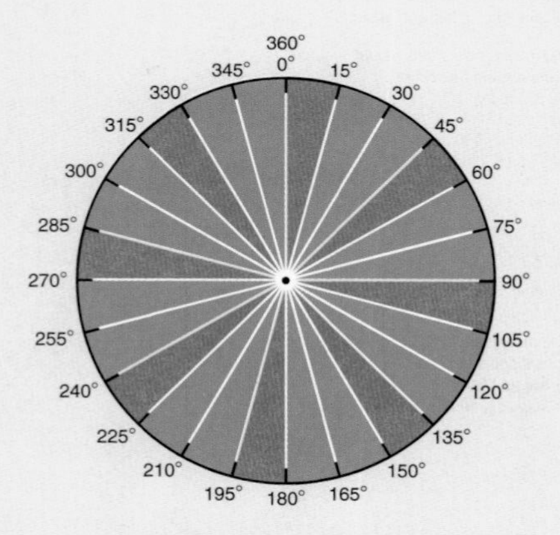

One solution to Problem 2

Ongoing Assessment: Recognizing Student Achievement

Journal Page 272 Problem 1

Use **journal page 272, Problem 1** to assess children's ability to understand basic probability terms. Children are making adequate progress if they divide the spinner into six nearly equal parts and color each part a different color. Some children may use the degree measures to divide the spinner into six equal parts.

[Data and Chance Goal 3]

For Problem 1, children should have divided the circle into six nearly equal or equal parts. Ask: *How did you decide what size to make each part?* Possible answers: $\frac{1}{6}$ of $360° = 60°$, so the circle can be divided into six equal parts by counting off 60° segments, starting at 0°; or the circle can be divided into two equal parts, and then each half can be divided into three equal parts. Encourage children to use phrases such as *equally likely, equal chance,* and *1 out of 6 chances of landing on red* when discussing their strategies.

▶ Designing Spinners to Match Given Descriptions

PARTNER ACTIVITY

(*Math Journal 2,* pp. 272 and 273)

For Problem 2 on journal page 272, children design a spinner so the paper clip is twice as likely to land on blue as on red. Children share designs. Use the board or transparency to illustrate different solutions. Children's circles should be divided into equivalent portions of one part red to two parts blue. Sample answers: Circle divided into 3 equal parts with one part red and two parts blue; circle divided into 6 equal parts with 2 parts red and 4 parts blue; circle divided into 9 equal parts with 3 parts red and 6 parts blue

Help children summarize possible outcomes. Encourage language such as:

- The paper clip is more likely to land on blue than red.
- Spin many times, and blue comes up twice as often as red.
- It's hard to predict, but if you spin a lot, blue will come up about 2 out of 3 spins, or $\frac{2}{3}$ of the time.
- There is a $\frac{1}{3}$ chance that red will come up.

Assign journal page 273. A description that compares the likelihood of the paper clip landing on various parts of a spinner is given for each of the two spinners. Partners design spinners to match the descriptions. For Problem 3, children's spinners should have three parts: blue and red parts that are the same size and a green part that is smaller. For example, if the smaller part is formed by a 60° angle, the two equal parts must each be formed by a 150° angle.

There are three solutions for Problem 4. In one, red and yellow are equal in size; in another, red is larger than yellow; and in another, yellow is larger than red. The blue part is always the largest.

2 Ongoing Learning & Practice

▶ Playing *The Block-Drawing Game*

(*Student Reference Book,* pp. 280 and 281)

Children make predictions in *The Block-Drawing Game* introduced in Lesson 8-2. Directions can be found on pages 280 and 281 in the *Student Reference Book*.

▶ Math Boxes 11•4

INDEPENDENT ACTIVITY

(*Math Journal 2,* p. 274)

Mixed Practice The Math Boxes in this lesson are paired with Math Boxes in Lesson 11-2.

Portfolio Ideas

Writing/Reasoning Have children answer the following: *Describe the steps you followed to find the median for Problem 6.* Sample answer: I put the number of miles run each day in order from smallest to largest: 0, 0, 2, 3, 5, 6, 12. Then I found the middle number, 3.

▶ Home Link 11•4

INDEPENDENT ACTIVITY

(*Math Masters,* p. 372)

Home Connection Children color a spinner to meet given conditions, as well as a spinner of their own design. Children design their own second spinner and tell how likely it is that the paper clip will land on each of the colors used.

3 Differentiation Options

READINESS

PROBLEM SOLVING

PARTNER ACTIVITY

15–30 Min

▶ Shading Fractions on Spinners

(*Math Masters,* p. 373)

To explore constructing spinners based on degrees of a circle, have children color spinners according to given instructions. Children represent fractions as specified on a circle divided into twenty-four 15° sections. When they have completed the page, have them make a list of how many degrees each fractional part represents.

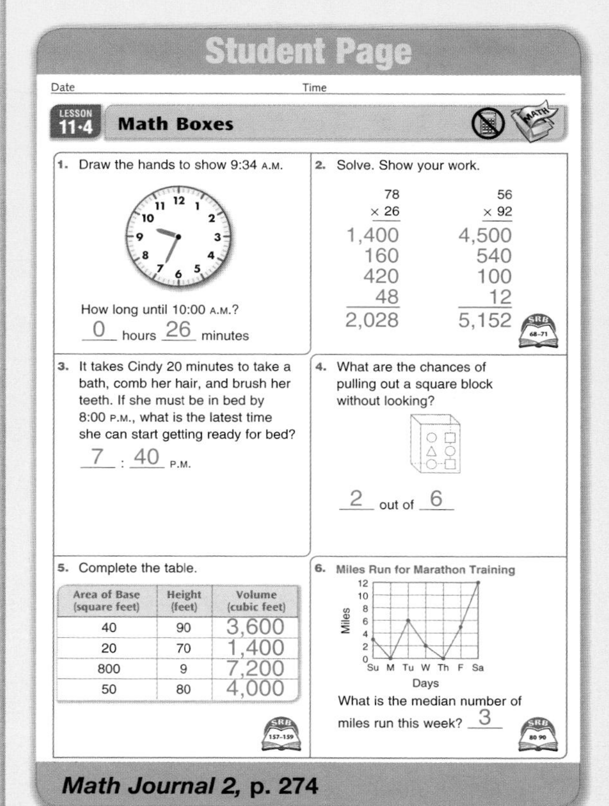

Student Page

Date Time

LESSON 11•4 **Math Boxes**

1. Draw the hands to show 9:34 A.M.

How long until 10:00 A.M.?
0 hours 26 minutes

2. Solve. Show your work.

78	56
× 26	× 92
1,400	4,500
160	540
420	100
48	12
2,028	5,152

3. It takes Cindy 20 minutes to take a bath, comb her hair, and brush her teeth. If she must be in bed by 8:00 P.M., what is the latest time she can start getting ready for bed?
7 : 40 P.M.

4. What are the chances of pulling out a square block without looking?
2 out of 6

5. Complete the table.

Area of Base (square feet)	Height (feet)	Volume (cubic feet)
40	90	3,600
20	70	1,400
800	9	7,200
50	80	4,000

6. Miles Run for Marathon Training

What is the median number of miles run this week? 3

Math Journal 2, p. 274

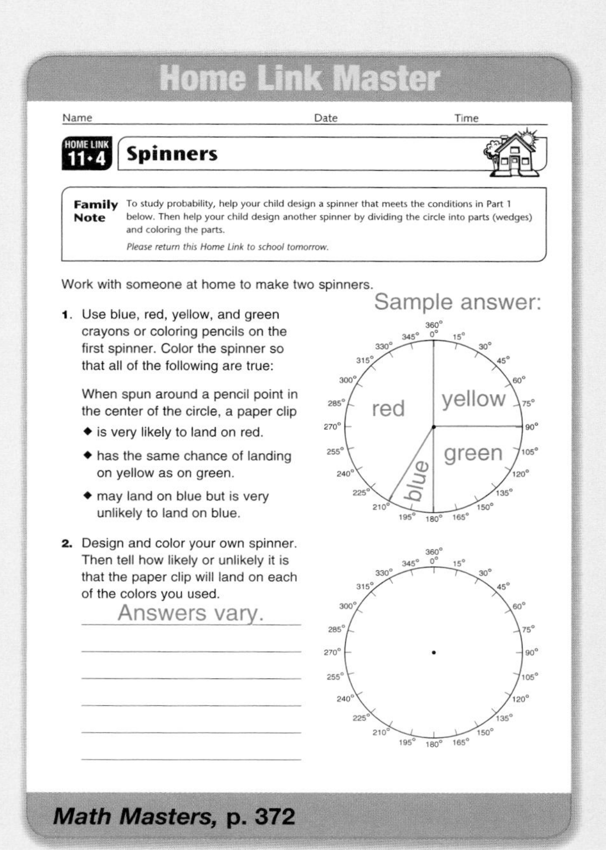

Home Link Master

Name Date Time

HOME LINK 11•4 **Spinners**

Family Note To study probability, help your child design a spinner that meets the conditions in Part 1 below. Then help your child design another spinner by dividing the circle into parts (wedges) and coloring the parts.

Please return this Home Link to school tomorrow.

Work with someone at home to make two spinners.

1. Use blue, red, yellow, and green crayons or coloring pencils on the first spinner. Color the spinner so that all of the following are true:

When spun around a pencil point in the center of the circle, a paper clip
- is very likely to land on red.
- has the same chance of landing on yellow as on green.
- may land on blue but is very unlikely to land on blue.

Sample answer:

2. Design and color your own spinner. Then tell how likely or unlikely it is that the paper clip will land on each of the colors you used.

Answers vary.

Math Masters, p. 372

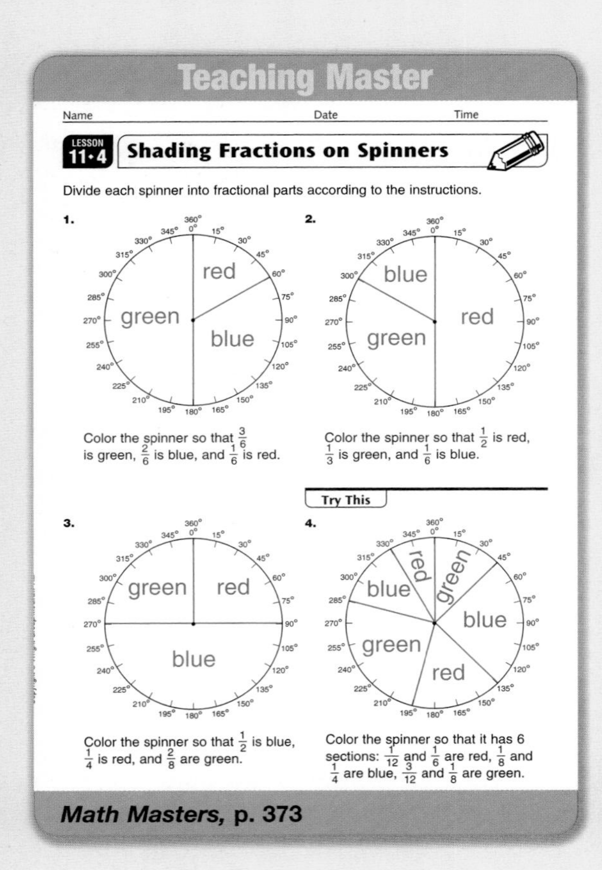
Teaching Master

Name Date Time

LESSON 11·4 **Shading Fractions on Spinners**

Divide each spinner into fractional parts according to the instructions.

1. Color the spinner so that $\frac{3}{6}$ is green, $\frac{2}{6}$ is blue, and $\frac{1}{6}$ is red.

2. Color the spinner so that $\frac{1}{2}$ is red, $\frac{1}{3}$ is green, and $\frac{1}{6}$ is blue.

Try This

3. Color the spinner so that $\frac{1}{2}$ is blue, $\frac{1}{4}$ is red, and $\frac{2}{8}$ are green.

4. Color the spinner so that it has 6 sections: $\frac{1}{12}$ and $\frac{1}{6}$ are red, $\frac{1}{8}$ and $\frac{1}{4}$ are blue, $\frac{3}{12}$ and $\frac{1}{8}$ are green.

Math Masters, p. 373

NOTE Several teachers have reported that they have children gather win/loss data every time *Spinning to Win* is played. This provides opportunities to draw conclusions about winning strategies from a larger pool of data.

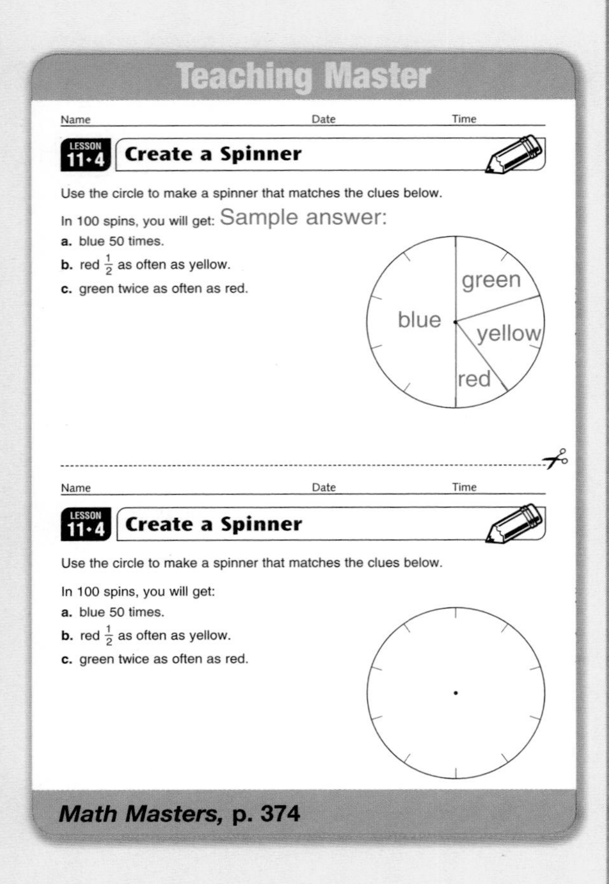
Teaching Master

Name Date Time

LESSON 11·4 **Create a Spinner**

Use the circle to make a spinner that matches the clues below.

In 100 spins, you will get: Sample answer:

a. blue 50 times.

b. red $\frac{1}{2}$ as often as yellow.

c. green twice as often as red.

Name Date Time

LESSON 11·4 **Create a Spinner**

Use the circle to make a spinner that matches the clues below.

In 100 spins, you will get:

a. blue 50 times.

b. red $\frac{1}{2}$ as often as yellow.

c. green twice as often as red.

Math Masters, p. 374

Have children predict which color each spinner will land on the most. Spinner 1 is most likely to land on green the most; Spinner 2 is most likely to land on red the most; Spinner 3 is likely to land on blue the most; Spinner 4 has an equal chance of landing on blue and green. They can test their predictions by collecting data for all four spinners.

ENRICHMENT

▶ Creating a Spinner

(*Math Masters,* p. 374)

To apply children's understanding of outcomes and the language of probability, have children make a spinner on *Math Masters,* page 374 that matches given clues.

EXTRA PRACTICE

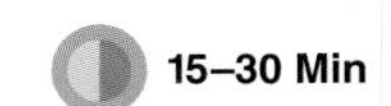

▶ Playing *Spinning to Win*

(*Math Masters,* p. 464; *Student Reference Book,* p. 309)

Children play *Spinning to Win* and determine winning strategies for a spinner game in which the spinner is not equally divided. Game directions are on *Math Masters,* page 464 and in the *Student Reference Book* on page 309. After children play several rounds, have them write about winning strategies—which section they think is best to choose and why.

The table below shows the *theoretical* probability of winning counters for each section. The probability activities in third grade involve children documenting *experimental* probabilities. Actual results will vary. The table below shows that for a large number of spins, the best sections to choose are Win 5 or Win 10.

Section	Win 1	Win 2	Win 5	Win 10
Chances of spinning	5 out of 12 or $\frac{5}{12}$	4 out of 12 or $\frac{4}{12}$	2 out of 12 or $\frac{2}{12}$	1 out of 12 or $\frac{1}{12}$
Total counters expected	$5 \times 1 =$ 5 counters	$4 \times 2 =$ 8 counters	$2 \times 5 =$ 10 counters	$1 \times 10 =$ 10 counters

11•5 Using Data to Predict Outcomes

Objectives To guide children as they organize and analyze survey data, predict outcomes, and estimate the make-up of populations of people and objects.

Technology Resources www.everydaymathonline.com

ePresentations

eToolkit

Algorithms Practice

EM Facts Workshop Game™

Family Letters

Assessment Management

Common Core State Standards

Curriculum Focal Points

Interactive Teacher's Lesson Guide

1 Teaching the Lesson

Key Concepts and Skills

- Record survey results in a frequency table. [Data and Chance Goal 1]
- Draw conclusions from survey data. [Data and Chance Goal 2]
- Use basic probability terms to discuss the results of a survey. [Data and Chance Goal 3]
- Use data to make predictions. [Data and Chance Goal 4]

Key Activities

Children pool data collected on right- and left-handedness and use it to predict the number of left-handed teachers at their school. Children predict the contents of a jar by using random-draw data.

Ongoing Assessment: Recognizing Student Achievement Use an Exit Slip (*Math Masters,* page 398). [Data and Chance Goal 2]

Ongoing Assessment: Informing Instruction See page 902.

Materials

Math Journal 2, p. 275
Home Links 11•1 and 11•4
Math Masters, pp. 360 and 398
paper bag with survey results from Home Link 11•1 ◆ slate ◆ Class Data Pad (optional)

2 Ongoing Learning & Practice

Reading and Writing Numbers in a Place-Value Chart
Math Journal 2, p. 276
Children write the values of digits in a place-value chart.

Math Boxes 11•5
Math Journal 2, p. 277
Children practice and maintain skills through Math Box problems.

Home Link 11•5
Math Masters, p. 375
Children practice and maintain skills through Home Link activities.

3 Differentiation Options

READINESS

Expressing the Likelihood of Events
Math Masters, p. 376
Children use basic probability terms to express the likelihood of events.

EXTRA PRACTICE

Matching Spinners with Outcomes
Math Masters, p. 377
Children match outcomes to spinners.

ELL SUPPORT

Building a Math Word Bank
Differentiation Handbook, p. 132
Children add the terms *outcome* and *random draw* to their Math Word Banks.

Advance Preparation

For Part 1, you need to know the total number of third graders, the total number of teachers, and the number of left-handed teachers at your school.

***Teacher's Reference Manual,* Grades 1–3** pp. 117, 118, 120, 121

Getting Started

Mathematical Practices
SMP1, SMP2, **SMP3,** SMP4, SMP6, **SMP7**

Mental Math and Reflexes

Children estimate amounts and share estimation strategies. They use slates to make notes or record steps. They show thumbs up or thumbs down to indicate whether the customer has enough money. *Suggestions:*

●○○ Rupert has $8.00. Does he have enough to buy 3 packs of pencils for $1.98 a pack? Yes; thumbs up

●●○ Luiz has $10.00. Does he have enough to buy 4 movie tickets for $2.79 each? No; thumbs down

●●● Frances earns $2.90 a week. After 3 weeks, does she have enough to buy 2 of her favorite beanbag animals for $4.75 each? No; thumbs down

Math Message

There are [fill in the total number] third graders at our school. Guess: About how many third graders know how to swim? Record your guess on your slate.

Home Link 11·4 Follow-Up

Have children share and discuss their spinners with partners.

NOTE The fraction of people who can swim varies widely from one area of the country to another. Overall, about $\frac{2}{3}$ of adults can swim. Coin tossing and spinner activities are chance situations for which children can make plausible predictions based on their intuitive understanding of the likelihood of possible outcomes. For many other situations, such as swimming ability and hand preference, children don't have such intuitive understandings and must either rely on information from their own experience or simply guess at the likelihood of outcomes. After data have been collected, children are in a much better position to make reliable predictions.

Home Link Master

Name ______ Date ______ Time ______

HOME LINK 11·1 A Survey

Family Note Have your child survey 10 people—family members, neighbors, and out-of-school friends—to find out how many are right-handed and how many are left-handed. Do not count people who say they are ambidextrous (able to use both hands with equal ease). Take a few days to help your child complete the survey. The results will be used in Lesson 11-5.

Please return this Home Link to school.

1. Ask 10 people whether they are right-handed or left-handed. Do not ask people at your school. Do not count people who say they are neither right-handed nor left-handed. (People who can use both hands with equal ease are called *ambidextrous.*)
2. On the chart below, make a tally mark for each person. Be sure that you have exactly 10 marks.

	Tallies
Right-handed	
Left-handed	

3. When you have finished your survey, record the results at the bottom of the page. Bring the results to school.

Name ______

Survey Results

Number of right-handed people: ______

Number of left-handed people: ______

Total: 10

Math Masters, p. 360

1 Teaching the Lesson

▶ Math Message Follow-Up

WHOLE-CLASS DISCUSSION

Record children's guesses on the board or Class Data Pad. Survey the class to find out how many children in the class know how to swim. Discuss how to use this information to check the guesses.

For example, ask: *If half of the class knows how to swim, how might this help us predict the number of third-grade swimmers in the whole school?* We might predict that about half of the third graders at the school can swim. *Would this information help us predict how many teachers can swim?* It might but not in the same way. Since many people learn to swim after third grade, we would expect that a larger fraction of the teachers can swim.

▶ Organizing and Analyzing Survey Data on Hand Preference

WHOLE-CLASS ACTIVITY

(*Math Masters,* p. 360)

Remind children that they collected survey results over the past few days for right-handedness and left-handedness for Home Link 11-1. Based on their individual survey results, ask children to predict whether there are more right-handed people or left-handed people.

Divide the board into two columns labeled Right-handed and Left-handed. Shake the paper bag containing the Survey Results slips from Home Link 11-1. Draw 10 slips from the bag. Each slip should include data for 10 people, so 10 slips will include data for 100 people surveyed.

For each slip, you or a child can record the numbers of right-handed and left-handed people in the appropriate columns. As a class, find the total number of right-handed people and the total number of left-handed people. (If the bag contains at least 20 slips to begin with, you can obtain a larger sample by drawing 20 slips instead of 10.)

Ask children to use these totals to make statements about chance. *For example:*

- Chances are that there are more right-handed than left-handed children in the class.
- People are more likely to be right-handed than left-handed.
- If I ask a new friend, there are *x chances out of 100* (or 200, if you compiled the results from 20 slips) that he or she will be left-handed. (For the sample data, this statement would read *11 chances out of 100.*)

Ask questions like the following:

- According to your survey results, if x out of 100 people are left-handed, about how many people out of 50 might be left-handed? half of x
- About how many people out of 25 might be left-handed? one-fourth of x

Ongoing Assessment: Recognizing Student Achievement

Exit Slip 

Use an **Exit Slip** (*Math Masters,* page 398) to assess children's progress toward drawing conclusions based on data representations. Have children record at least three statements about the survey data. Children are making adequate progress if they draw appropriate conclusions based on the data. Some children may find the median and mode of the data and use them to make predictions.

[Data and Chance Goal 2]

NOTE Estimates vary, but the percent of left-handers in the population might be as high as 10 percent. About 90 percent of adults use their right hand for writing. Two-thirds favor their right hand for most activities requiring coordination and skill. (Source: *The Handy Science Answer Book,* Science and Technology Department of the Carnegie Library of Pittsburgh. Detroit: Visible Ink, 1996.)

	Right-handed	Left-handed
	10	0
	9	1
	7	3
	10	0
	8	2
	9	1
	9	1
	9	1
	10	0
	8	2
Totals:	89	11

Sample data for 100 people

Student Page

Date ______ Time ______

LESSON 11·5 **Random-Draw Problems**

Each problem involves marbles in a jar. The marbles are blue, white, or striped. A marble is drawn at random (without looking) from the jar. The type of marble is tallied. Then the marble is returned to the jar.

- Read the description of the random draws in each problem.
- Circle the picture of the jar that best matches the description.

1. From 100 random draws, you get:
   a blue marble ● 62 times.
   a white marble ○ 38 times.

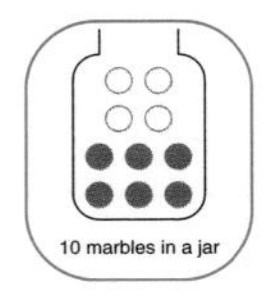

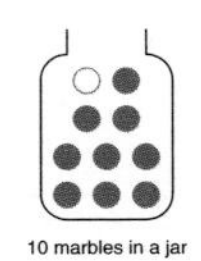

2. From 100 random draws, you get:
   a blue marble ● 23 times.
   a white marble ○ 53 times.
   a striped marble 24 times.

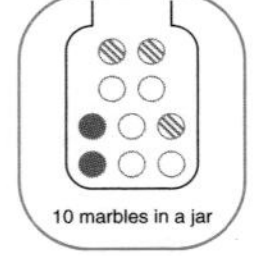

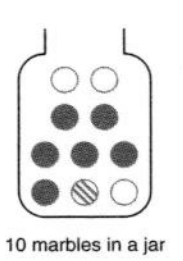

Try This

3. From 50 random draws, you get:
   a blue marble ● 30 times.
   a white marble ○ 16 times.
   a striped marble 4 times.

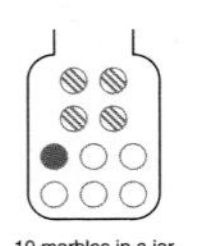

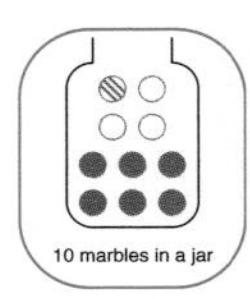

***Math Journal 2,* p. 275**

Student Page

Date ______ Time ______

LESSON 11·5 **Reading and Writing Numbers**

Write the value of 7 for each column below.

L	K	J	,	I	H	G	,	F	E	D	.	C	B	A
hundred millions	ten millions	millions	,	hundred thousands	ten thousands	thousands	,	hundreds	tens	ones	.	tenths	hundredths	thousandths
7	7	7	,	7	7	7	,	7	7	7	.	7	7	7

Example: Column K: *70,000,000 or 70 millions*

1. Column A: 0.007 or 7 thousandths
2. Column G: 7,000 or 7 thousands
3. Column F: 700 or 7 hundreds
4. Column I: 700,000 or 7 hundred thousands
5. Column C: 0.7 or 7 tenths
6. Column B: 0.07 or 7 hundredths
7. Column L: 700,000,000 or 7 hundred millions

Write the numbers that your teacher dictates.

8. Answers vary. 9. ______ 10. ______
11. ______ 12. ______ 13. ______

***Math Journal 2,* p. 276**

▶ Making Predictions

Tell children the number of teachers at school. Ask them to predict the number of left-handed teachers. Either share the number of left-handed teachers with the children, or have the class organize and conduct a survey of teachers to find out how many are left-handed.

Adjusting the Activity

Compile children's predictions. Then find the median and mode of these data.

AUDITORY ◆ KINESTHETIC ◆ TACTILE ◆ VISUAL

▶ Solving Random-Draw Problems

(*Math Journal 2,* p. 275)

Children are given the results of random draws of marbles from jars. They choose the picture that best represents the contents of the jar. Have children discuss their choices.

Ongoing Assessment: Informing Instruction

Watch for children who are having difficulty interpreting the descriptions of the random draws. For the problems that involve 100 draws, have them think of each marble in the jar as having been drawn about 10 times. For the problems that involve 50 draws, have them think of each marble in the jars as having been drawn about 5 times.

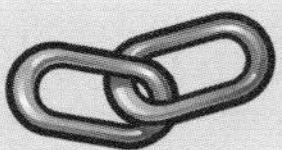

Links to the Future

Children may struggle with the idea that there can be a great deal of variance in actual outcomes because outcomes rely on chance. Comparing predictions based on theoretical probability to predictions based on experimental results is a Grade 6 Goal.

2 Ongoing Learning & Practice

▶ Reading and Writing Numbers in a Place-Value Chart

(*Math Journal 2,* p. 276)

Children complete journal page 276 alone or with a partner. Dictate numbers to be recorded for Problems 8–13. *Suggestions:* 638,570; 800,006; 3,001,020; 102.6; 40.008; 999,000,000.09

▶ Math Boxes 11•5

(*Math Journal 2,* p. 277)

Mixed Practice The Math Boxes in this lesson are paired with the Math Boxes in Lesson 11-6.

Writing/Reasoning Have children write an answer to the following: *Explain how you figured out how long Danielle skates in a week in Problem 6.* Sample answer: Danielle skates 45 minutes x 7 days or 315 minutes in the mornings and 50 minutes x 2 afternoons or 100 minutes in the afternoons. Together, she skates 415 minutes. There are 6 [60s], or 6 hours, in 415 minutes with 55 minutes left. She skates for 6 hours and 55 minutes each week.

▶ Home Link 11•5

INDEPENDENT ACTIVITY

(*Math Masters,* p. 375)

Home Connection Children solve random-draw problems similar to those on journal page 275.

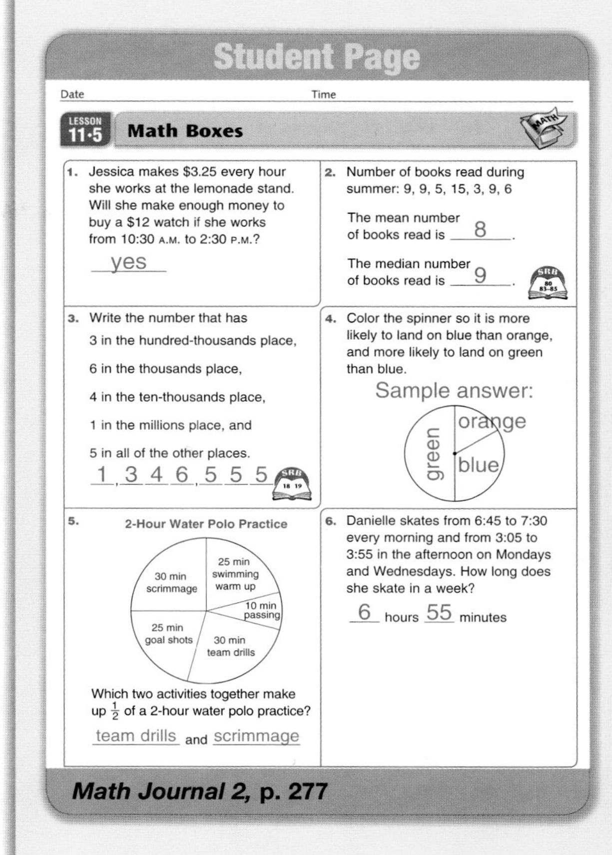

Student Page

Date Time

LESSON 11•5 **Math Boxes**

1. Jessica makes $3.25 every hour she works at the lemonade stand. Will she make enough money to buy a $12 watch if she works from 10:30 A.M. to 2:30 P.M.?
yes

2. Number of books read during summer: 9, 9, 5, 15, 3, 9, 6
The mean number of books read is 8.
The median number of books read is 9.

3. Write the number that has
3 in the hundred-thousands place,
6 in the thousands place,
4 in the ten-thousands place,
1 in the millions place, and
5 in all of the other places.
1, 3 4 6, 5 5 5

4. Color the spinner so it is more likely to land on blue than orange, and more likely to land on green than blue.
Sample answer: orange, blue, green

5. 2-Hour Water Polo Practice
30 min scrimmage; 25 min swimming warm up; 10 min passing; 30 min team drills; 25 min goal shots
Which two activities together make up $\frac{1}{2}$ of a 2-hour water polo practice?
team drills and scrimmage

6. Danielle skates from 6:45 to 7:30 every morning and from 3:05 to 3:55 in the afternoon on Mondays and Wednesdays. How long does she skate in a week?
6 hours 55 minutes

Math Journal 2, **p. 277**

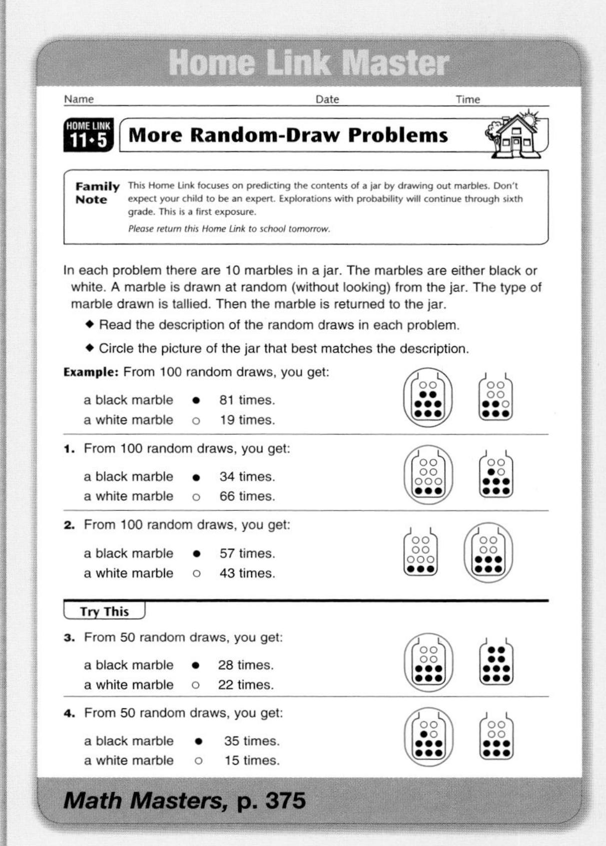

Home Link Master

Name Date Time

HOME LINK 11•5 **More Random-Draw Problems**

Family Note This Home Link focuses on predicting the contents of a jar by drawing out marbles. Don't expect your child to be an expert. Explorations with probability will continue through sixth grade. This is a first exposure.
Please return this Home Link to school tomorrow.

In each problem there are 10 marbles in a jar. The marbles are either black or white. A marble is drawn at random (without looking) from the jar. The type of marble drawn is tallied. Then the marble is returned to the jar.
- Read the description of the random draws in each problem.
- Circle the picture of the jar that best matches the description.

Example: From 100 random draws, you get:
a black marble ● 81 times.
a white marble ○ 19 times.

1. From 100 random draws, you get:
a black marble ● 34 times.
a white marble ○ 66 times.

2. From 100 random draws, you get:
a black marble ● 57 times.
a white marble ○ 43 times.

Try This

3. From 50 random draws, you get:
a black marble ● 28 times.
a white marble ○ 22 times.

4. From 50 random draws, you get:
a black marble ● 35 times.
a white marble ○ 15 times.

Math Masters, **p. 375**

3 Differentiation Options

READINESS

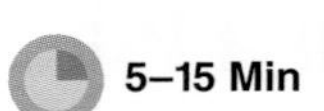
INDEPENDENT ACTIVITY

▶ Expressing the Likelihood of Events

5–15 Min

(*Math Masters,* p. 376)

To provide experience predicting outcomes, have children use basic probability terms to express the likelihood of events. They record their work on *Math Masters,* page 376.

EXTRA PRACTICE

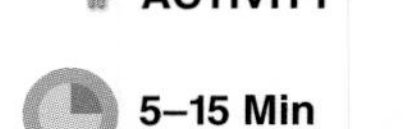
INDEPENDENT ACTIVITY

▶ Matching Spinners with Outcomes

5–15 Min

(*Math Masters,* p. 377)

Children match a set of outcomes with the correct spinner.

ELL SUPPORT

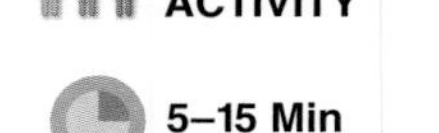
SMALL-GROUP ACTIVITY

▶ Building a Math Word Bank

5–15 Min

(*Differentiation Handbook,* p. 132)

To provide language support for probability, have children use the Word Bank template found on *Differentiation Handbook,* page 132. Ask children to write the terms *outcome* and *random draw,* draw a picture representing the terms, and write other related words. See the *Differentiation Handbook* for more information.

Teaching Master

Name Date Time

LESSON 11•5 **How Likely?**

Make an X on the line to show the likelihood of an event happening.

Example:

How likely is it that a glass falling off a table will hit the ceiling?

X (impossible)

impossible | less likely | 50/50 chance | more likely | certain

1. How likely is it that a cow will jump over the moon?

X (impossible)

impossible | less likely | 50/50 chance | more likely | certain

2. How likely is it that the paper clip will land on green?

blue, blue, blue, blue, green

X (less likely)

impossible | less likely | 50/50 chance | more likely | certain

3. How likely are you to see a friend today?

X (more likely)

impossible | less likely | 50/50 chance | more likely | certain

4. How likely is it that a tossed coin will land on heads 23 times out of 50?

X (50/50 chance)

impossible | less likely | 50/50 chance | more likely | certain

5. How likely is it that you will roll a sum greater than 3 with a pair of dice?

X (more likely)

impossible | less likely | 50/50 chance | more likely | certain

6. How did you decide where to put the mark in the box in Problem 5? Write your answer on the back of this page.

Math Masters, **p. 376**

Teaching Master

Name Date Time

LESSON 11•5 **Matching Spinners with Outcomes**

Spinner A: red, blue, yellow
Spinner B: red, blue, yellow
Spinner C: red, green, blue, yellow
Spinner D: white, red, green, blue, yellow

For each statement below, write the letter of the spinner that best matches the outcome.

1. You get yellow about half of the time. Spinner B
2. You get blue about twice as often as red. Spinner C
3. You are about 4 times as likely to get red as blue. Spinner D
4. You get either red or blue about half of the time. Spinner C
5. You don't get green, but *no* color is a favorite. Spinner A
6. The paper clip lands on yellow 23 times out of 100 spins. Spinner C
7. The paper clip lands on yellow 22 times out of 50 spins. Spinner B

Make up your own.

8. ______________________

Spinner ____

9. ______________________

Spinner ____

Math Masters, **p. 377**

11•6 Progress Check 11

Objective To assess children's progress on mathematical content through the end of Unit 11.

1 Looking Back: Cumulative Assessment

The **End-of-Year Assessment** in the *Assessment Handbook* is a written assessment that you may use to assess children's proficiency with Grade-Level Goals.

Input children's data from Progress Check 11 and the End-of-Year Assessment into the **Assessment Management System**.

Materials
- Home Link 11•5
- *Assessment Handbook,* pp. 134–141, 197–201, 212, and 268–271
- End-of-Year Assessment (*Assessment Handbook,* pp. 142, 143, 217–225, and 227–227B)
- slate; paper clip; pencil; counters (optional)

CONTENT ASSESSED	LESSON(S)	ASSESSMENT ITEMS: SELF	ORAL/SLATE	WRITTEN: PART A	WRITTEN: PART B	OPEN RESPONSE
Read and write whole numbers. Identify places and the value of digits in places in whole numbers up to 1,000,000. [Number and Numeration Goal 1]	11•1, 11•3, 11•5	1, 2	2, 3	1–3		
Model fractions; solve problems involving fractional parts of collections and regions, describe strategies used. [Number and Numeration Goal 2]	11•1–11•5	6	4	6, 7		✔
Make reasonable estimates. [Operations and Computation Goal 5]	11•1, 11•3, 11•5		1			
Describe events using basic probability terms. [Data and Chance Goal 3]	11•2–11•5	4		5		
Predict the outcome of a simple experiment and test the prediction. [Data and Chance Goal 4]	11•1–11•5	5		8	9–11	✔
Describe relationships among units of time. [Measurement and Reference Frames Goal 3]	11•1			4b		
Show time to the nearest minute on an analog clock. [Measurement and Reference Frames Goal 4]	11•1–11•4	3		4a, 4b		

2 Looking Ahead: Preparing for Grade 4

Math Boxes 11•6

Home Link 11•6: End-of-Year Family Letter

Materials
- *Math Journal 2,* p. 278
- *Math Masters,* pp. 378–381

Getting Started

Math Message • Self Assessment

Complete the Self Assessment (Assessment Handbook, *p. 197*).

Home Link 11·5 Follow-Up

Briefly review answers. Have children share solution strategies.

Assessment Master

Name Date Time

LESSON 11·6 **Self Assessment** Progress Check 11

Check one box for each skill.

Skills	I can do this on my own and explain how to do it.	I can do this on my own.	I can do this if I get help or look at an example.
1. Read and write numbers up to 1,000,000.			
2. Know the value of each digit in 6-digit numbers.			
3. Tell and show time to the nearest minute on an analog clock.			
4. Use basic probability terms to describe a spinner.			
5. Make predictions about the outcomes of a spinner experiment.			
6. Use fractions to describe parts of a spinner.			

Assessment Handbook, **p. 197**

Assessment Master

Name Date Time

LESSON 11·6 **Written Assessment** Progress Check 11

Part A

1. Write the number that has 9 in the ten-thousands place, 3 in the ones place, 7 in the hundred-thousands place, 0 in the tens place, 6 in the thousands place, and 1 in the hundreds place.
   7 9 6, 1 0 3

2. Write the number that is 10,000 more than the number in Problem 1.
   8 0 6, 1 0 3

3. Read the number below to yourself. Circle the digit that means forty thousand. Underline the digit that means four hundred.
   4 ④ 4, <u>4</u> 4 4

4. Last night, Corey started reading at 7:12 P.M. He stopped reading $\frac{1}{2}$ hour later. Draw hands on the clock face in Problem 4a to show the time he started reading. Draw hands on the clock face in Problem 4b to show the time he stopped reading.

   a. (clock) b. (clock)

Assessment Handbook, **p. 198**

1 Looking Back: Cumulative Assessment

▶ Math Message Follow-Up

INDEPENDENT ACTIVITY

(Self Assessment, *Assessment Handbook,* p. 197)

The Self Assessment offers children the opportunity to reflect upon their progress.

▶ Oral and Slate Assessment

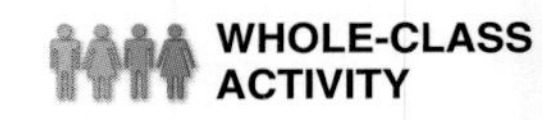

WHOLE-CLASS ACTIVITY

Problems 1–3 provide summative information and can be used for grading purposes. Problem 4 provides formative information that can be useful in planning future instruction.

Oral Assessment

1. Children estimate total costs. Children may make notes or record steps. They show thumbs up if the customer has enough money or thumbs down if the customer does not have enough. Have children share estimation strategies. *Suggestions:*
   - Julie has \$5. Does she have enough to buy 4 pairs of socks at \$1.10 a pair? Yes; thumbs up
   - Roger has \$14. Does he have enough to buy 6 toy cars that cost \$2.99 each? No; thumbs down
2. Write 6-digit numbers on the board. Children read them aloud. *Suggestions:*
   - 593,342
   - 904,006
   - 400,001

Slate Assessment

3. Dictate a number. Children write the number and identify digits in specified places. *Suggestion:*
   - Write *three hundred five thousand, eight hundred fourteen.* 305,814 Circle the digit in the tens place, 1 draw an X through the digit in the ten-thousands place, 0 and underline the digit in the hundred-thousands place. 3

4. Solve fraction-of problems. Children may use counters to help. *Suggestions:*

- $\frac{3}{4}$ of 32 24
- $\frac{5}{6}$ of 42 35
- $\frac{3}{8}$ of 56 21
- $\frac{4}{5}$ of 50 40

▶ Written Assessment

INDEPENDENT ACTIVITY

(*Assessment Handbook*, pp. 198–200)

Part A Recognizing Student Achievement

Problems 1–8 provide summative information and may be used for grading purposes.

Problem(s)	Description
1–3	Write whole numbers. Identify the value of digits in whole numbers.
4a, 4b	Show and tell time on an analog clock.
4b	Describe relationships between units of time.
5	Describe spinner outcomes using basic probability terms.
6, 7	Use fractions to describe parts of a spinner.
8	Predict and test the outcome of a spinner experiment.

Part B Informing Instruction

Problems 9–11 provide formative information that can be useful in planning future instruction.

Problem(s)	Description
9	Explain a prediction for the outcome of an experiment.
10, 11	Predict the outcomes of random-draw experiments.

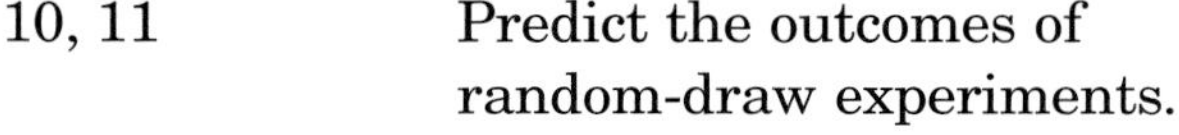

Use the checklists on pages 269 and 271 of the *Assessment Handbook* to record results. Then input the data into the **Assessment Management System** to keep an ongoing record of children's progress toward Grade-Level Goals.

Assessment Master

Name Date Time

LESSON 11•6 Written Assessment *continued*

5. Shade the oval next to each statement that is true for the spinner.

- (shaded) You are equally likely to get dots or black.
- You are less likely to get stripes than dots.
- (shaded) You are more likely to get stripes than white.
- You are certain to get stripes.

6. What fraction of the spinner in Problem 5 is covered with dots? $\frac{1}{4}$ or $\frac{3}{12}$

7. What fraction of the spinner in Problem 5 is covered with stripes? $\frac{1}{3}$ or $\frac{4}{12}$

8. Use the spinner from Problem 5. Predict the number of times a paper clip might land on each section of the spinner if you spin 12 times. Record your predictions in the second column of the table. Then take a paper clip and actually spin 12 times. Record your results in the third column of the table.

Section of the Spinner	Predicted Results for 12 Spins	Actual Results for 12 Spins
black	3	Answers vary.
white	2	Answers vary.
stripes	4	Answers vary.
dots	3	Answers vary.

Assessment Handbook, **p. 199**

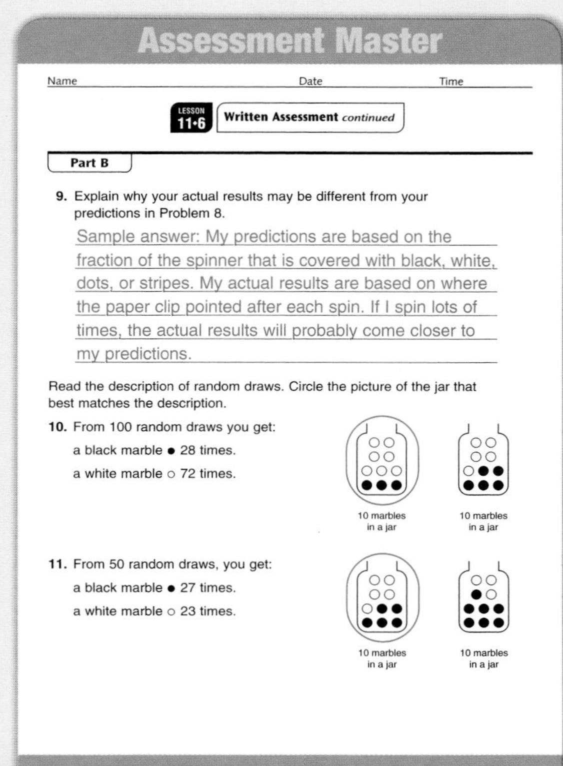

Assessment Master

Name Date Time

LESSON 11•6 Written Assessment *continued*

Part B

9. Explain why your actual results may be different from your predictions in Problem 8.
Sample answer: My predictions are based on the fraction of the spinner that is covered with black, white, dots, or stripes. My actual results are based on where the paper clip pointed after each spin. If I spin lots of times, the actual results will probably come closer to my predictions.

Read the description of random draws. Circle the picture of the jar that best matches the description.

10. From 100 random draws you get:
a black marble ● 28 times.
a white marble ○ 72 times.

10 marbles in a jar 10 marbles in a jar

11. From 50 random draws, you get:
a black marble ● 27 times.
a white marble ○ 23 times.

10 marbles in a jar 10 marbles in a jar

Assessment Handbook, **p. 200**

▶ Open Response

(*Assessment Handbook,* p. 201)

The Sandwich Spinner

The open-response item requires children to apply skills and concepts from Unit 11 to solve a multistep problem. See the *Assessment Handbook,* pages 137–141 for rubrics and children's work samples for this problem.

▶ End-of-Year Assessment

(*Assessment Handbook,* pp. 217–225)

The End-of-Year Assessment (*Assessment Handbook,* pages 217–225) provides an additional assessment opportunity that you may use as part of your balanced assessment plan. This assessment covers many of the important concepts and skills presented in *Third Grade Everyday Mathematics*. It should be used along with ongoing and periodic assessments. See the *Assessment Handbook* for more information.

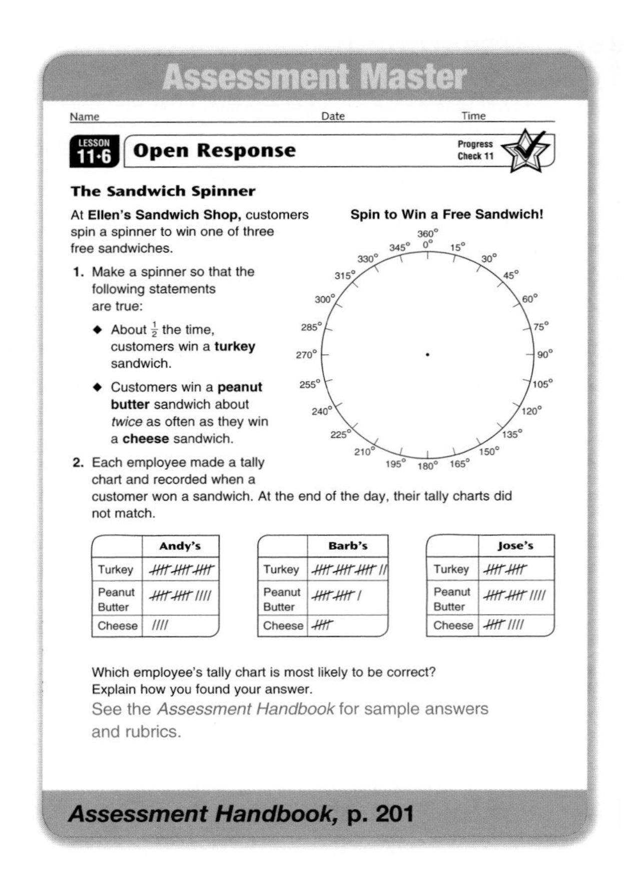

Assessment Master

Name Date Time

LESSON 11·6 **Open Response** Progress Check 11

The Sandwich Spinner

At **Ellen's Sandwich Shop,** customers spin a spinner to win one of three free sandwiches.

Spin to Win a Free Sandwich!

1. Make a spinner so that the following statements are true:
   - About $\frac{1}{2}$ the time, customers win a **turkey** sandwich.
   - Customers win a **peanut butter** sandwich about *twice* as often as they win a **cheese** sandwich.
2. Each employee made a tally chart and recorded when a customer won a sandwich. At the end of the day, their tally charts did not match.

	Andy's
Turkey	𝍸 𝍸 𝍸
Peanut Butter	𝍸 𝍸 ////
Cheese	////

	Barb's
Turkey	𝍸 𝍸 𝍸 //
Peanut Butter	𝍸 𝍸 /
Cheese	𝍸

	Jose's
Turkey	𝍸 𝍸
Peanut Butter	𝍸 𝍸 ////
Cheese	𝍸 ////

Which employee's tally chart is most likely to be correct? Explain how you found your answer.

See the *Assessment Handbook* for sample answers and rubrics.

Assessment Handbook, p. 201

2 Looking Ahead: Preparing for Grade 4

▶ Math Boxes 11•6

INDEPENDENT ACTIVITY

(*Math Journal 2,* p. 278)

Mixed Practice The Math Boxes in this lesson are paired with Math Boxes from Lesson 11-5.

▶ Home Link 11•6: Family Letter

INDEPENDENT ACTIVITY

(*Math Masters,* pp. 378–381)

Home Connection The Family Letter thanks parents for their participation in *Third Grade Everyday Mathematics,* suggests home-based activities for the summer, and provides a preview of *Fourth Grade Everyday Mathematics.*

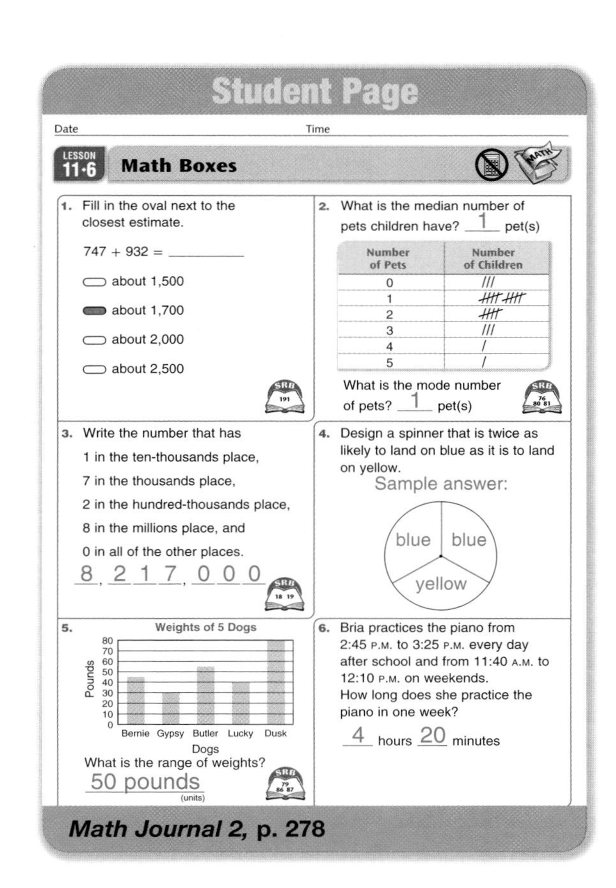

Student Page

Date Time

LESSON 11•6 **Math Boxes**

1. Fill in the oval next to the closest estimate.

747 + 932 = ______

- about 1,500
- about 1,700 (filled)
- about 2,000
- about 2,500

SRB 191

2. What is the median number of pets children have? 1 pet(s)

Number of Pets	Number of Children
0	///
1	~~////~~ ~~////~~
2	~~////~~
3	///
4	/
5	/

What is the mode number of pets? 1 pet(s)

SRB 76 80 81

3. Write the number that has
1 in the ten-thousands place,
7 in the thousands place,
2 in the hundred-thousands place,
8 in the millions place, and
0 in all of the other places.

8, 2 1 7, 0 0 0

SRB 18 19

4. Design a spinner that is twice as likely to land on blue as it is to land on yellow.

Sample answer:

5. Weights of 5 Dogs

What is the range of weights? 50 pounds (units)

SRB 79 86 87

6. Bria practices the piano from 2:45 P.M. to 3:25 P.M. every day after school and from 11:40 A.M. to 12:10 P.M. on weekends. How long does she practice the piano in one week?

4 hours 20 minutes

Math Journal 2, p. 278

Sample Sunrise/Sunset Chart

Sunrise A.M.

Date	Sun rises at	Hours of sunlight
9/8	6:16	12hr 51m
9/15	6:24	12hr 30m
9/22	6:31	12hr 11m
9/29	6:39	11hr 51m
10/6	6:47	11hr 31m
10/13	6:54	11hr 12m
10/20	7:03	10hr 52m
10/27	7:11	10hr 34m
11/3	7:20	10hr 15m
11/10	7:29	9hr 58m
11/17	7:37	9hr 44m
11/24	7:45	9hr 31m
12/1	7:55	9hr 18m
12/8	8:01	9hr 11m
12/15	8:07	9hr 5m
12/22	8:11	9hr 4m
12/29	8:13	9hr 7m
1/5	8:14	9hr 13m
1/12	8:12	9hr 22m
1/19	8:08	9hr 35m
1/26	8:03	9hr 49m
2/2	7:56	10hr 5m
2/9	7:48	10hr 22m
2/16	7:38	10hr 41m
2/23	7:28	11hr 0m
3/2	7:17	11hr 19m
3/9	7:05	11hr 40m
3/16	6:53	12hr 0m
3/23	6:41	12hr 20m
3/30	6:30	12hr 39m
4/6	6:17	13hr 0m
4/13	6:07	13hr 17m
4/20	5:54	13hr 38m
4/27	5:44	13hr 56m
5/4	5:35	14hr 13m
5/11	5:26	14hr 29m
5/18	5:19	14hr 44m
5/25	5:14	14hr 55m
6/1	5:10	15hr 5m
6/8	5:08	15hr 12m
6/15	5:07	15hr 16m
6/22	5:08	15hr 17m
6/29	5:10	15hr 15m

Chart time axis: 5:00, 5:30, 6:00, 6:30, 7:00, 7:30, 8:00, 8:30, 9:00

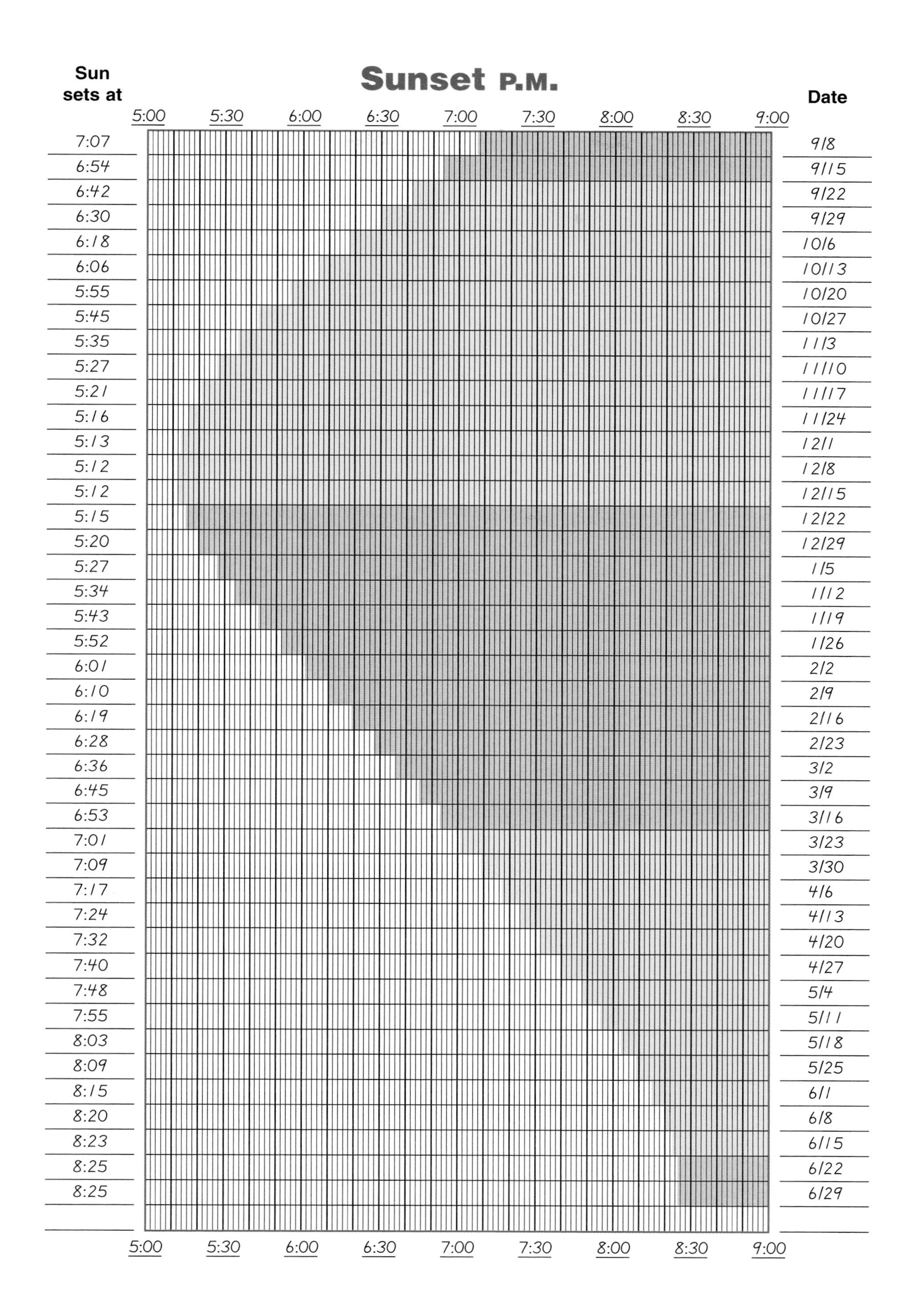
Sunset P.M.
Sun sets at
Date
5:00
5:30
6:00
6:30
7:00
7:30
8:00
8:30
9:00
7:07 9/8
6:54 9/15
6:42 9/22
6:30 9/29
6:18 10/6
6:06 10/13
5:55 10/20
5:45 10/27
5:35 11/3
5:27 11/10
5:21 11/17
5:16 11/24
5:13 12/1
5:12 12/8
5:12 12/15
5:15 12/22
5:20 12/29
5:27 1/5
5:34 1/12
5:43 1/19
5:52 1/26
6:01 2/2
6:10 2/9
6:19 2/16
6:28 2/23
6:36 3/2
6:45 3/9
6:53 3/16
7:01 3/23
7:09 3/30
7:17 4/6
7:24 4/13
7:32 4/20
7:40 4/27
7:48 5/4
7:55 5/11
8:03 5/18
8:09 5/25
8:15 6/1
8:20 6/8
8:23 6/15
8:25 6/22
8:25 6/29

Appendices

Contents

Project

1 Solid Waste

Objective To guide children as they estimate and measure the weight or volume of a week's accumulation of trash.

Technology Resources www.everydaymathonline.com

eToolkit

Algorithms Practice

EM Facts Workshop Game™

Family Letters

Assessment Management

Common Core State Standards

Curriculum Focal Points

Interactive Teacher's Lesson Guide

1 Doing the Project

CCSS Mathematical Practices
SMP1, SMP2, SMP4, SMP6

Recommended Use During or after Unit 10

Key Concepts and Skills

- Collect and organize data.
  [Data and Chance Goal 1]
- Predict the outcomes of simple experiments and test the predictions.
  [Data and Chance Goal 4]

Key Activities

Children explore the amount of trash that is thrown out during the course of a week and how they might find a more efficient use for part of this trash. Estimating, sorting, and measuring activities determine the weight or volume of the trash.

Materials

- Class Data Pad (optional)
- week's worth of classroom trash
- about 5 plastic trash bags (small and large)
- about 12 plastic grocery bags
- disposable plastic gloves, 1 pair per child
- scales
- calculator

2 Extending the Project

Children research trash and composting in books and on the Internet.

Children practice skills through Home Link activities.

Materials

- children's literature selections (optional)
- computer with Internet connection (optional)

Advance Preparation

Before the project begins, collect a week's worth of classroom trash. Since children may throw away less if they know that the amount of trash they are discarding is being monitored, try to collect the trash before you tell children about the project. Put any leftover food or messy garbage in a separate plastic bag. Assign two children to monitor this process and to help others remember, especially if lunches or snacks are eaten in the classroom. Before the bag of messy garbage is disposed of each day, children may weigh the bag and record its weight or keep a record of the number of bags. Make arrangements with the custodian to compact and keep all other trash in plastic bags during the week so it may be used for the project.

For Part 2, obtain the following books: ***Where Does the Garbage Go?*** by Paul Showers (HarperCollins, 1994); ***Understanding Garbage and Our Environment*** by Andrea J. Nolan (Terrific Science Press 1999); ***Worms Eat My Garbage: How to Set Up and Maintain a Worm Composting System*** by Mary Applehof (Flower Press, 1997).

1 Doing the Project

▶ Estimating Amounts of Classroom Solid Waste

WHOLE-CLASS ACTIVITY

Ask children to name examples of the types of trash they throw away at school each day. The list might include writing paper, art and construction paper, cardboard, cans, food waste, pencils, pencil shavings, and broken crayons.

Hold up a plastic grocery bag. Have children estimate, either by weight or by number of bags, about how much of each type of trash the class might throw away in a week. List a range of estimates on the board or on the Class Data Pad.

▶ Sorting a Week's Worth of Trash

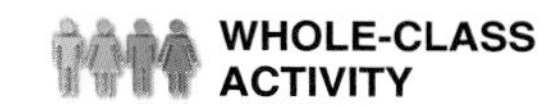
WHOLE-CLASS ACTIVITY

Bring out the bags of trash you collected and explain their source. Provide disposable gloves for the children to wear during the sorting activity. Divide the bags among small groups so children can sort the trash according to the types previously listed on the board. New categories might need to be added to the list.

Bring the class together. Combine the types of trash from each group. With classroom helpers, stuff each different type of trash into a separate plastic grocery bag. Weigh the bags or keep track of the number of bags for each type of trash.

With the children, create a report on the weight (or the number of bags) of the food and messy garbage thrown away. Then determine the totals for all categories of trash.

Compare the actual amounts of different types of waste to the estimates. Are there any surprises? Discuss.

▶ Estimating a Year's Worth of Trash

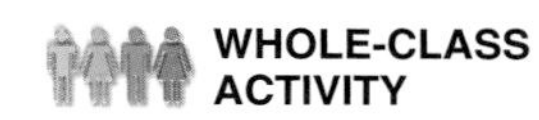
WHOLE-CLASS ACTIVITY

Using the week's trash sampling and calculators, project the volume or weight of classroom trash for the entire school year. Then extend the projection for the entire school.

- What is the total amount of classroom waste for the week? Tell the amount in weight or in number of filled bags.
- How many weeks are in a school year? Answers vary.
- About how much trash will our class throw away during the school year? Answers vary. Discuss the strategies children used to find the answer.

- How many classrooms are in the school? About how much trash will be thrown away by the whole school for a whole year? Answers vary.
- Much of the solid waste needs to be thrown away, but are there some things that could be better used or that could be reused instead of being thrown away? Yes. Paper, plastics, and glass could be recycled; organic waste could be composted. Does this mean that there would be less trash? Yes

Discuss ways that individuals and the class as a whole can carry through on ideas to use items more completely and on how everyone can recycle materials within the classroom. Discuss the possibility of connecting these ideas with your community's recycling program.

2 Extending the Project

Extension Suggestions

SMALL-GROUP ACTIVITY

- Read about waste disposal and recycling in the book ***Where Does the Garbage Go?*** by Paul Showers (HarperCollins, 1994). ***Understanding Garbage and Our Environment*** by Andrea J. Nolan (Terrific Science Press, 1999) contains information, lessons, and activities intended for middle school grades.
- Visit the U.S. Environmental Protection Agency Web site at www.epa.gov/kids. It includes a kids' section with news, games, and activities. A special section called Ask the EPA allows children to send questions for the EPA to answer.
- Ask whether any children's families compost garbage to use in their gardens. If so, ask how this is done. There are books for adults on the subject, such as ***Worms Eat My Garbage: How to Set Up and Maintain a Worm Composting System*** by Mary Applehof (Flower Press, 1997).

Home Link Suggestions

INDEPENDENT ACTIVITY

Children observe the amount of trash thrown away at home and suggest ways to reduce or recycle some of it. Children may report their findings in a paragraph, table, diagram, or other illustration.

Project 2

Watermelon Feast and Seed-Spitting Contest

Objective To guide children as they measure the distances they spit watermelon seeds and as they find data landmarks.

Technology Resources www.everydaymathonline.com

eToolkit

Algorithms Practice

EM Facts Workshop Game™

Family Letters

Assessment Management

Common Core State Standards

Curriculum Focal Points

Interactive Teacher's Lesson Guide

1 Doing the Project

Recommended Use During Unit 3, 4, 7, or 9

CCSS
Mathematical Practices
SMP2, SMP4, SMP6
Content Standards
3.MD.3, 3.MD.4

Key Concepts and Skills

- Collect and organize data to create a graph.
  [Data and Chance Goal 1]
- Find the maximum, minimum, range, and median of a data set.
  [Data and Chance Goal 2]
- Use graphs to answer questions and draw conclusions.
  [Data and Chance Goal 2]
- Measure length.
  [Measurement and Reference Frames Goal 1]

Key Activities

Children hold a contest to determine who can spit a watermelon seed the farthest. They list and order the individual distances for the class, find the median and range, and compare their findings to the world championship record. Partners graph the data to show the frequency and range of their distances.

Materials

- masking tape or chalk
- *Math Masters,* p. 416
- watermelon
- quarter-sheets of paper
- Class Data Pad (optional)
- yardstick or tape measure
- broom, paper towels, garbage bags

2 Extending the Project

Children read about the history of watermelons.

Children practice skills through Home Link activities.

Materials

- *Watermelon Day* (optional)
- computer with Internet connection (optional)

Advance Preparation

Prepare watermelon slices so each child has one. If watermelon is unavailable, you may substitute sunflower or pumpkin seeds. Use masking tape or chalk to mark a starting line. For Part 2, obtain the book ***Watermelon Day*** by Kathi Appelt (Henry Holt and Company, 1996).

Holding a Seed-Spitting Contest

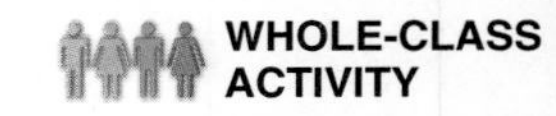

Pick a day when watermelons are available and the weather is nice. Hold the watermelon feast outdoors. During the feast, have children save their watermelon seeds. Children work in groups of two or three. After practicing a few seed-spits, each contestant makes 2 or 3 attempts for the contest.

Children measure the distances in feet and inches from the starting line, using their tape measures or yardsticks. Contestants keep track of their longest seed-spits on quarter-sheets of paper.

Collecting and Discussing Data

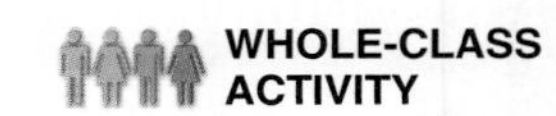

After cleanup, bring the class together and record individual distances on the board or Class Data Pad. With the children's help, arrange the data in ascending order and find the median.

Together, children share strategies for answering questions such as:

▷ What is the difference between the longest and shortest class seed-spits (the range)?

▷ What is the difference between the world champion's distance and the class champion's distance? (*See* NOTE *in margin.*)

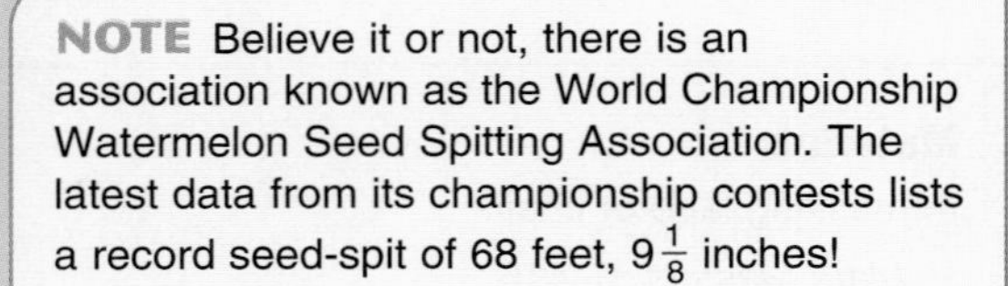

NOTE Believe it or not, there is an association known as the World Championship Watermelon Seed Spitting Association. The latest data from its championship contests lists a record seed-spit of 68 feet, $9\frac{1}{8}$ inches!

An interesting side note is that contestants wear special 12-inch, block-ended boots when they practice so seed-spits can be measured by walking heel-to-toe instead of having to use a tape measure.

Graphing Data

(*Math Masters,* p. 416)

Children can use the centimeter grid paper on *Math Masters,* page 416 to make their graphs. They decide how they want to label the variables (participants, distances). Ask questions about the class data as they decide on a graph format.

Suggestions:

▷ Will participants' names be listed?

▷ What are the longest and the shortest distances?

▷ How many distances will be shown?

▷ What type of graph should they make?

▷ Will the graph show intervals of 1 inch? 2 inches? 3 inches?

▷ Will the intervals start at zero?

Now or at a later time, partners can display their graphs and talk about how they set up their graphs and how the range and frequency of the data are displayed.

Teaching Aid Master

Name Date Time

Centimeter Grid Paper

Math Masters, p. 416

2 Extending the Project

▶ Extension Suggestions

SMALL-GROUP ACTIVITY

- ▷ Read stories with watermelons in them, such as ***Watermelon Day*** by Kathi Appelt (Harry Holt and Company, 1996).
- ▷ Find out about the history, production, and uses of watermelons at the National Watermelon Promotion Board's Web site at www.watermelon.org.

▶ Home Link Suggestions

INDEPENDENT ACTIVITY

Children describe the watermelon project to family members. With their approval and assistance, children hold a contest similar to the one in the Project (for example, a Penny-Tossing Contest). Children collect and discuss the data. Encourage children to graph the data from their family contest.

Project

3 Illusions

Objective To provide opportunities to experience geometric and other designs by exploring optical illusions.

Technology Resources www.everydaymathonline.com

eToolkit

Algorithms Practice

EM Facts Workshop Game™

Family Letters

Assessment Management

Common Core State Standards

Curriculum Focal Points

Interactive Teacher's Lesson Guide

1 Doing the Project

CCSS

Mathematical Practices
SMP4

Content Standards
3.OA.1

Recommended Use During or after Unit 3

Key Concepts and Skills

- Identify line segments.
  [Geometry Goal 1]
- Identify and describe plane figures.
  [Geometry Goal 2]

Key Activities
Students explore persistence of vision and other optical illusions.

Key Vocabulary
persistence of vision ◆ figure-and-ground illusion

Materials

- *Math Masters,* pp. 386 and 388
- transparency of *Math Masters,* p. 388 (optional)
- scissors
- 2 or more straws per child
- stapler
- ruler

2 Extending the Project

Children create optical illusions and explore optical illusions in contemporary art and illustrations.

Children practice skills through Home Link activities.

Materials

- *Math Masters,* p. 387
- children's literature selections (optional)
- computer with Internet connection (optional)

Additional Information

When complementary images are placed back-to-back and spun rapidly, the spinning gives the illusion that there is only one image. This phenomenon, called persistence of vision, occurs because the brain retains an image of what was seen for a short time after it was viewed. If a second image comes rapidly into view, the brain interprets this second image as part of the original image, and the viewer sees one combined image.

Advance Preparation

Project Masters for all projects are found on *Math Masters,* pages 386–394. For Part 2, obtain the following books: ***101 Amazing Optical Illusions: Fantastic Visual Tricks*** by Terry Jennings (Sterling, 1998); ***Can You Believe Your Eyes?: Over 250 Illusions and Other Visual Oddities*** by J. Richard Block and Harold E. Yuker (Brunner/Mazel, 1992); ***M. C. Escher: His Life and Complete Graphic Work*** by J. L. Locher, editor (Abrams, 1992); ***M. C. Escher: The Graphic Work*** by M. C. Escher (Barnes and Noble Books, 2001).

1 Doing the Project

Creating Simple Illusions

WHOLE-CLASS ACTIVITY

(*Math Masters,* p. 386)

Distribute copies of *Math Masters,* page 386. Children can create simple illusions by following these directions:

1. Have children cut out both circles for Set 1 or Set 2.
2. Children place the circles back-to-back, lining up the arrows at A and B. Help children staple the circles together at the left and right, near the edge.

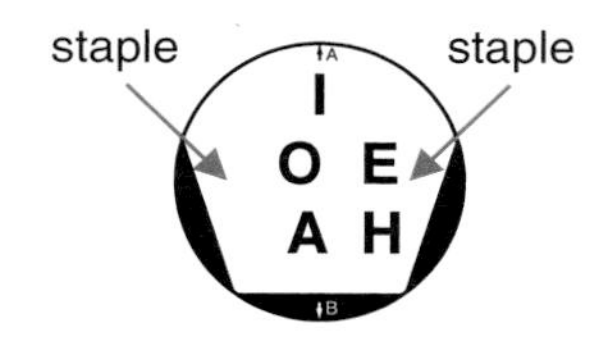

3. Tell children to slip a drinking straw between the circles so it lines up with the arrows at A and B. The arrows should be centered on the straw. Help children staple through the straw and circles near the arrows at A and B to make a lollipop shape.

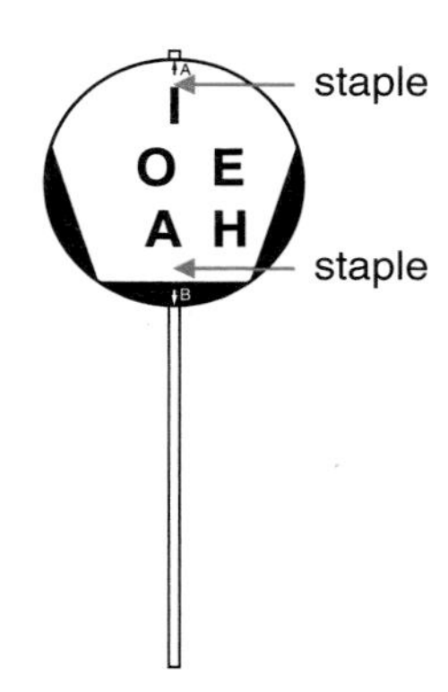

4. Children hold the straw in both hands at arm's length. They twirl the straw rapidly by moving their hands back and forth against each other.

Spin straw between hands.

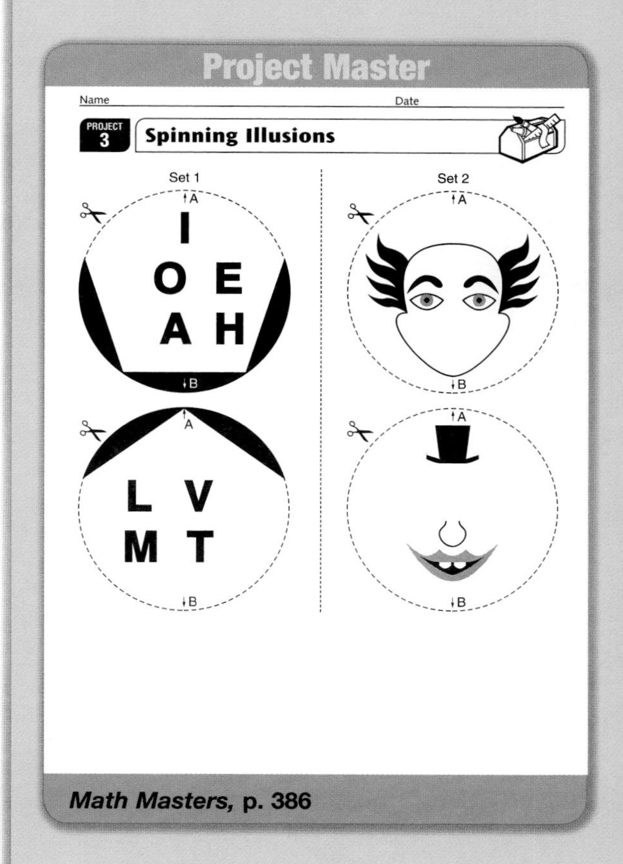

Math Masters, p. 386

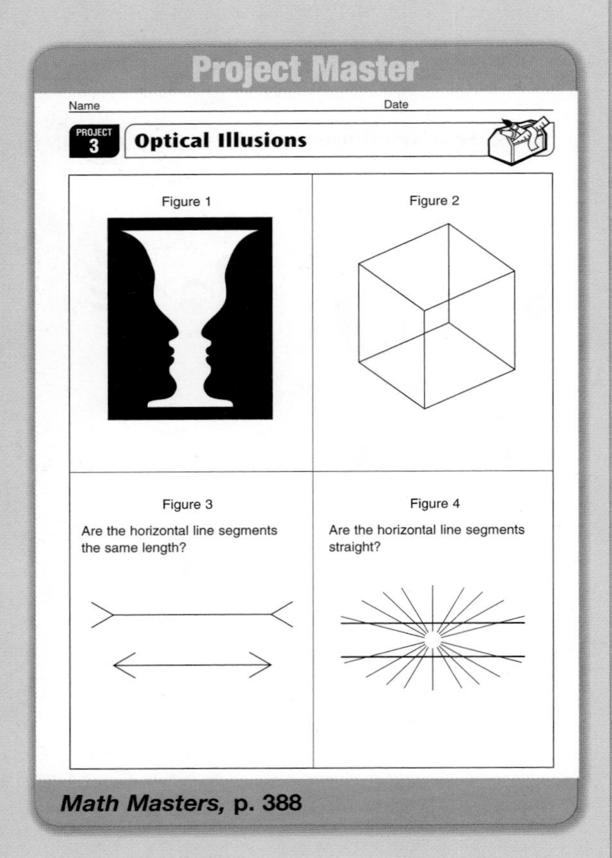

Project Master
Name
Date
PROJECT 3
Optical Illusions
Figure 1
Figure 2
Figure 3
Are the horizontal line segments the same length?
Figure 4
Are the horizontal line segments straight?

Math Masters, p. 388

Children watch the designs as they spin the circles. Invite volunteers to describe what they see. Because of **persistence of vision,** it is likely that a combination of the two sides will be seen, creating one complete image.

▶ Investigating Other Illusions

WHOLE-CLASS ACTIVITY

(*Math Masters,* p. 388)

Distribute copies of *Math Masters,* page 388, or display a transparency.

- Direct children's attention to Figure 1. Ask: *What do you see—two faces or a vase? Or, do you first see one and then the other?*

Figure 1

Tell children that this is a **figure-and-ground illusion,** in which the viewer sees one part as the figure and the other part as the ground. The figure and ground tend to reverse, often without conscious effort. Seeing one aspect excludes seeing the other.

- Explain that Figure 2 is a different kind of illusion in which the figure seems to reverse. Invite volunteers to describe any changes they see.

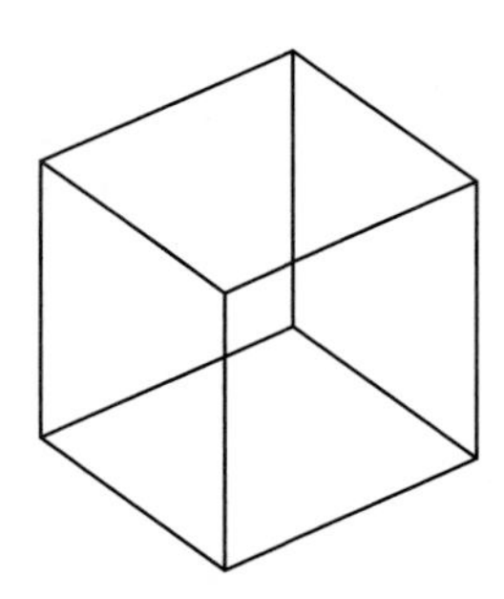

Figure 2

Help children observe how the diagram of the cube, seen as a 3-dimensional object, seems to change its orientation—it flip-flops. You might want to mention that children tend to see these reversals more readily than adults do.

Point out that the other figures are illusions in which lines or the arrangement of objects creates a false impression of length or distance.

Have children look at the line segments in Figure 3. Ask: *Are the horizontal line segments the same length?* yes Measure the lengths of each line segment to check.

Then have children look at Figure 4. Ask: *Are the horizontal line segments straight?* yes Measure the distance between the lines at one end and in the middle to check.

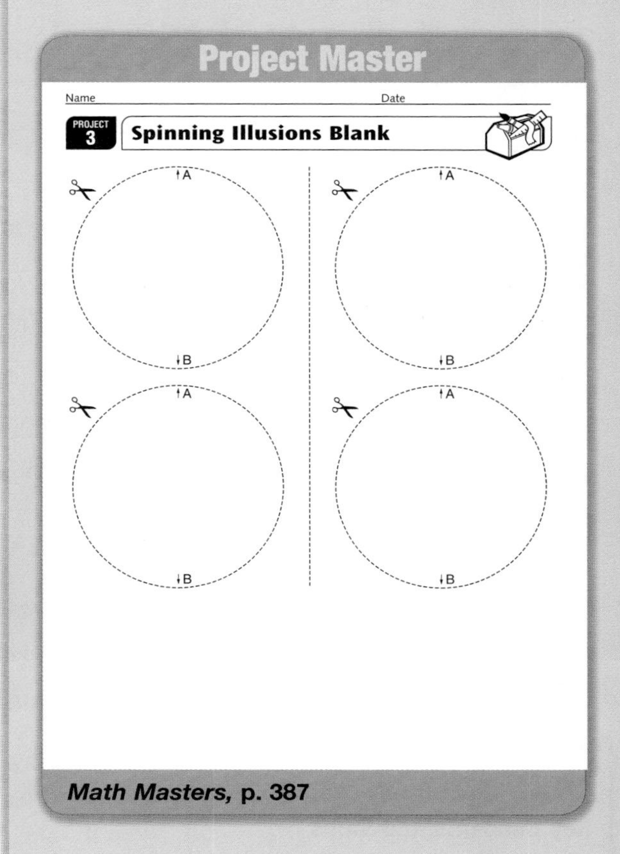

Math Masters, p. 387

2 Extending the Project

▶ Extension Suggestions

SMALL-GROUP ACTIVITY

(*Math Masters,* p. 387)

- ▷ Children can create simple illusions from their own designs by using the blank circles provided on *Math Masters,* page 387.
- ▷ Children can look at and read about optical illusions in a variety of books, including ***101 Amazing Optical Illusions: Fantastic Visual Tricks*** by Terry Jennings (Sterling, 1998) and ***Can You Believe Your Eyes?: Over 250 Illusions and Other Visual Oddities*** by J. Richard Block and Harold E. Yuker (Brunner/Mazel, 1992).
- ▷ Explore optical illusions on the Internet at sites such as www.sandlotscience.com.
- ▷ Children can try to create a figure-and-ground illusion or another type of illusion of their own.
- ▷ Obtain examples of illustrations by M. C. Escher, which include field-and-ground pictures of birds in flight, stairs that seem to go both up and down, and so on. Books include ***M. C. Escher: His Life and Complete Graphic Work,*** J. L. Locher, editor (Abrams, 1992) and ***M. C. Escher: The Graphic Work*** by M. C. Escher (Barnes and Noble Books, 2001). To investigate the works of Escher on the Internet, see sites such as www.etropolis.com/escher/index.html.

▶ Home Link Suggestions

INDEPENDENT ACTIVITY

Children investigate optical illusions on the Internet or write a brief paragraph describing one of the project activities they enjoyed. Children may wish to draw their own version of the optical illusions involving the line segments.

Project

Dodecahedron Calendar

Objective To guide children as they construct dodecahedron calendars.

Technology Resources www.everydaymathonline.com

eToolkit

Algorithms Practice

EM Facts Workshop Game™

Family Letters

Assessment Management

Common Core State Standards

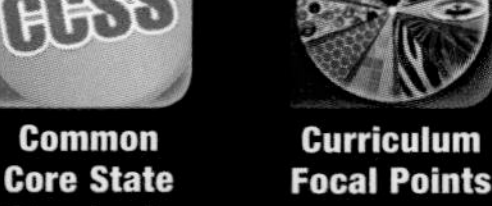
Curriculum Focal Points

Interactive Teacher's Lesson Guide

1 Doing the Project

Recommended Use During or after Unit 5

CCSS Mathematical Practices
SMP2, SMP4, SMP7

Key Concepts and Skills

- Describe relationships between days, weeks, months, and years.
  [Measurement and Reference Frames Goal 3]
- Identify polygons and solid figures.
  [Geometry Goal 2]
- Model a solid figure.
  [Geometry Goal 2]

Key Activities
Children examine the structure and organization of a 12-month calendar and create a 12-month calendar on a dodecahedron.

Key Vocabulary
dodecahedron

Materials

- *Math Masters,* pp. 389–391
- 12-month calendar
- lightweight cardstock (optional)
- laminating supplies (optional)
- Class Data Pad
- pencil
- scissors
- black crayon
- straightedge
- clear tape or glue
- calculator (optional)

2 Extending the Project

Children explore regular polyhedrons.

Children practice skills through Home Link activities.

Materials

- *Student Reference Book,* p. 115 (optional)

Additional Information

Math Masters, page 389 shows 21 months arranged in 7 rows. Each row shows three 31-day months beginning on one of the seven days of the week. The months in the first row begin on Sunday, the months in the second row begin on Monday, and so on. Any year can be generated from these 21 months. Each month features a space for the name of the month and the year to be filled in by the children. Children can alter the length of any month by crossing out any extra date or dates.

Advance Preparation

Display a 12-month calendar that matches the one the children will be making. The calendar may begin with any month you choose.

Make copies of *Math Masters,* pages 390 and 391 on lightweight cardstock so the calendar will be more durable. Or, copy the masters on regular copy paper and laminate the patterns after children have cut them out. (*See Step 6 on page 926.*)

It might be a good idea to enlist the help of 2 or 3 parents or a group of older children for the construction of the dodecahedrons.

1 Doing the Project

▶ Discussing the 12-Month Calendar

WHOLE-CLASS DISCUSSION

Have children look at a 12-month calendar. On the board or Class Data Pad, list the names of the months. Next to each month, write the day of the week it begins on and the number of days in that month.

Month	Day It Begins	Number of Days
January	Monday	31
February	Thursday	28
March	Thursday	31

Discuss the lengths of the months. All the months have 30 or 31 days except February, which has 28 or 29 days. Explain that leap years have an additional day, February 29, to make up for time lost when the $365\frac{1}{4}$-day cycle is rounded to 365 days. Leap years have 366 days and occur in years that are divisible by 4. Century years (such as 1800 or 1900), however, are leap years only if they are divisible by 400. So 1600 and 2000 were leap years, whereas 1800 and 1900 were not.

Adjusting the Activity

Beginning with the present year, write 12 to 16 consecutive years on the board. Have the class (in partnerships, small groups, or as a whole) use calculators to figure out which of the years are leap years. Ask: *Does anyone see a pattern?* Every fourth year is a leap year.

AUDITORY ◆ KINESTHETIC ◆ TACTILE ◆ VISUAL

▶ Preparing the Calendar Months and Names

WHOLE-CLASS ACTIVITY

(*Math Masters,* p. 389)

After children have had a few minutes to study *Math Masters,* page 389, ask what they notice. There are 21 unnamed months; each month has 31 days; each row has 3 months beginning on one of the 7 days of the week. Months in the top row start on Sunday, months in the second row on Monday, and so on.

Point out that a 31-day month can be made into a 28-, 29-, or 30-day month by marking out extra dates.

Project Master

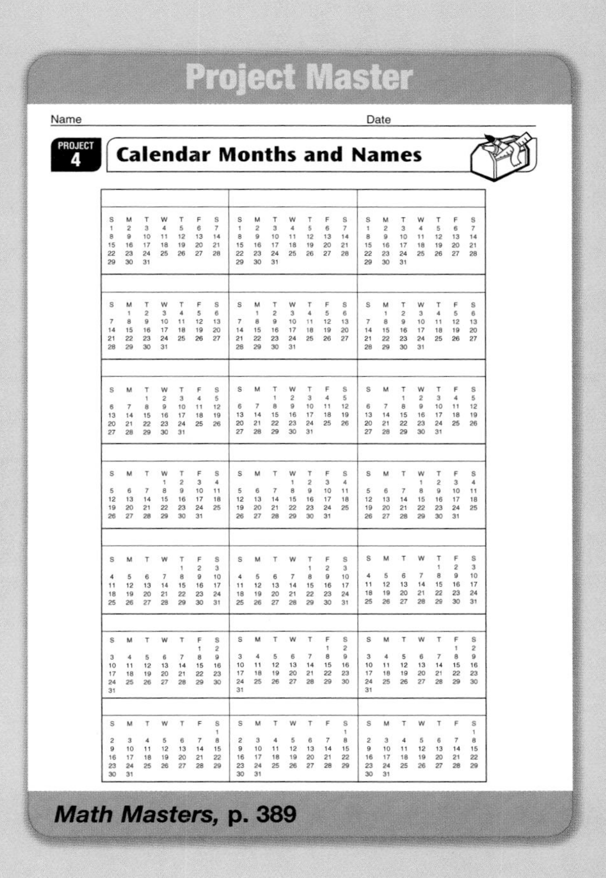

***Math Masters,* p. 389**

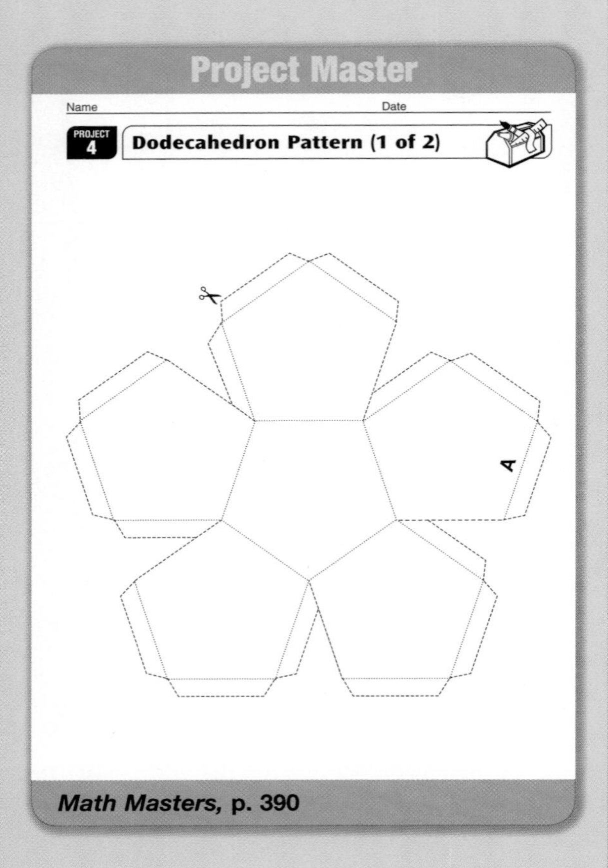

Math Masters, **p. 390**

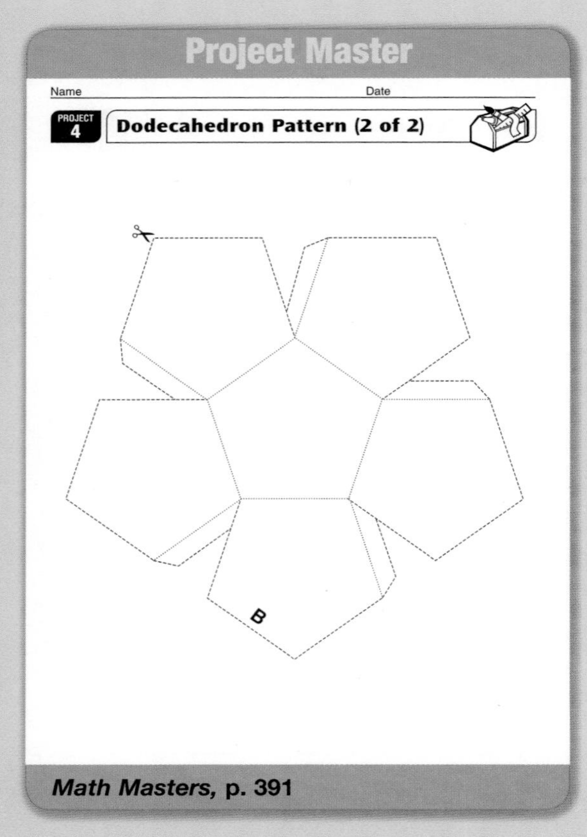

Math Masters, **p. 391**

Children find a month on the master that begins on the same day as one of the months on the board or Class Data Pad. They write the name of that month in the space above the days of the week. They may write the year next to the name of the month. Then they neatly mark out extra dates, if any, using pencils or crayons.

Continue as above until all 12 months from the Class Data Pad are found on the master.

NOTE You might want to pause this Project after preparing the calendar months and names. Resume construction of the dodecahedrons on the following day.

▶ Assembling the Dodecahedron Calendar

(*Math Masters,* pp. 390 and 391)

Distribute copies of *Math Masters,* pages 390 and 391. Have children follow the directions below to assemble their dodecahedron calendars. Partners can help each other as needed.

1. Using a straightedge, score the dotted lines by running a sharp pencil along them. Some children may need assistance.
2. Cut out the **dodecahedron** patterns on all of the dashed lines, including those next to the tabs, all the way up to the corners of the center pentagons. Explain that a dodecahedron is a 12-sided regular polyhedron (all of the faces are the same).
3. Carefully cut out the 12 completed months from *Math Masters,* page 389.
4. Tape or glue a completed month onto each face of the dodecahedron. Encourage children to do this in a systematic way. For example, put January in the center pentagon on the side marked A and the next five months in order around it lining up the tops of the months with the dashed sides of the center pentagon. Then put December in the center pentagon on the side marked B and continue as before.
5. Children write their initials in small letters above one of the months (perhaps the month of their birthday) to identify their dodecahedron.
6. *Optional:* You might want to laminate the dodecahedron patterns at this stage. Teachers report that this results in a sturdy calendar.
7. To begin assembly, tape or glue the tabs to the sides of adjacent pentagons. Taping the tabs to the outside of the adjacent pentagons might be the easiest method of construction. The tabs can also be put behind adjacent edges so they are inside the calendar; this makes a neater calendar, but construction is more difficult.
8. Construct the dodecahedron by taping or gluing the tab under the A to the edge under the B.
9. Rotate the desired month into view.

2 Extending the Project

Extension Suggestions

▷ Tell children that the dodecahedron in this project is a regular polyhedron. In a regular polyhedron, the faces are congruent (same size and shape), the edges are all the same length, and the angles are equal. The dodecahedron is one of the five regular polyhedrons (or polyhedra), which are shown below.

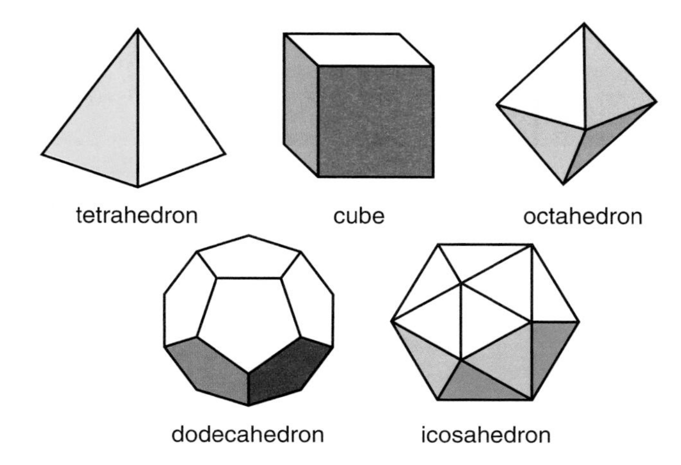

▷ For more information on regular polyhedrons, see *Student Reference Book,* page 115.

Home Link Suggestions

Children use a calendar to find the day of the week of their birthday for the current year and the next two years. They then find the day of the week of a family member's birthday for the current year and the next two years. Encourage children to look for a pattern for each person's birthday.

Project

5 Attributes

Objective To provide experience with classification and opportunities to solve problems and play games with a set of picture cards containing four attributes, each with two values.

Technology Resources www.everydaymathonline.com

eToolkit

Algorithms Practice

EM Facts Workshop Game™

Family Letters

Assessment Management

Common Core State Standards

Curriculum Focal Points

Interactive Teacher's Lesson Guide

1 Doing the Project

Mathematical Practices
SMP1, SMP2, SMP8

Recommended Use During or after Unit 6

Key Concepts and Skills

- Describe rules for patterns and use them to solve problems.
  [Patterns, Functions, and Algebra Goal 1]

Key Activities

Children use attribute labels to create Venn diagrams. They place game pieces in the appropriate section of the Venn diagrams.

Key Vocabulary

attribute

Materials

Per partnership:
- *Math Masters,* pp. 392 and 393
- 2 pieces of string or yarn (each about 1 yard long)
- scissors per child

2 Extending the Project

Children create Venn diagrams with 3 loops.

Children practice skills through Home Link activities.

Materials

- string or yarn loops (3 per partnership)
- attribute label and picture cards

Additional Information

These activities can be done in partnerships or small groups. The suggestions given are for partnerships. Children can work through the Two-Loop Guessing Game as part of the project, but make the materials available so partners can replay the game over the next several weeks. The four attributes are: *kind of dog:* Labrador/poodle, *size:* large/small, *position:* sitting/standing, *color:* light/dark.

Advance Preparation

Tie the 1 yard pieces of string or yarn into large loops. (*See the margin on page 929.*)

1 Doing the Project

▶ Using Label and Picture Cards

PARTNER ACTIVITY

(*Math Masters,* pp. 392 and 393)

Before partners cut out the label and picture cards, discuss the four **attributes** and the two values of each attribute. Encourage children to use the labels shown on the cards for the values of each attribute for this discussion.

After children cut out the label and picture cards, give them enough time to explore and arrange them. Suggest that they take turns picking a label card and then lining up all the picture cards that fit that label. Then have them match picture cards with two label cards (pictures that fit both labels at once, such as poodle and small); then repeat the activity with three label cards.

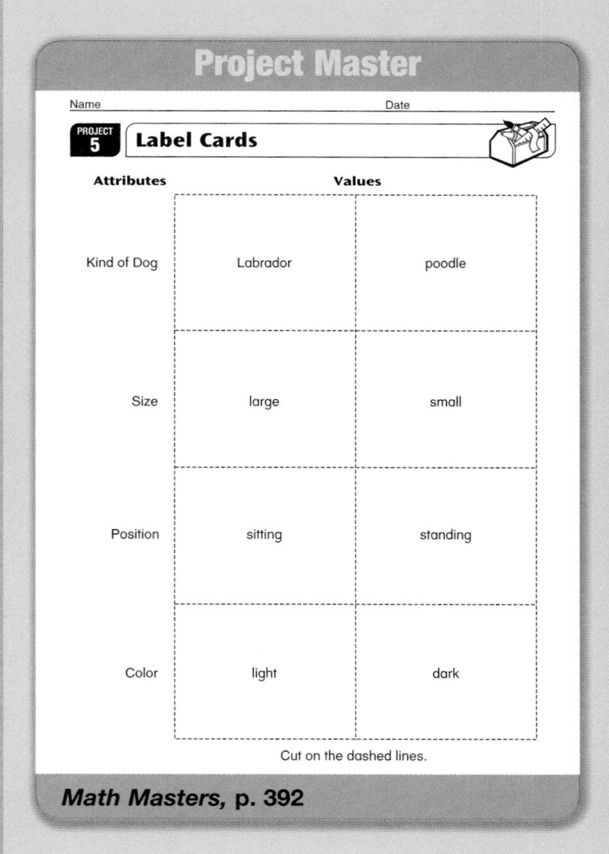
Project Master

Name Date

PROJECT 5 **Label Cards**

Attributes	Values	
Kind of Dog	Labrador	poodle
Size	large	small
Position	sitting	standing
Color	light	dark

Cut on the dashed lines.

Math Masters, p. 392

▶ Solving a Two-Loop Problem

PARTNER ACTIVITY

Draw two overlapping circles on the board. Label the left circle poodle and the right circle small. Partners lay out two overlapping string or yarn loops and put label cards by them (as shown in the margin). This provides three spaces in which to put picture cards.

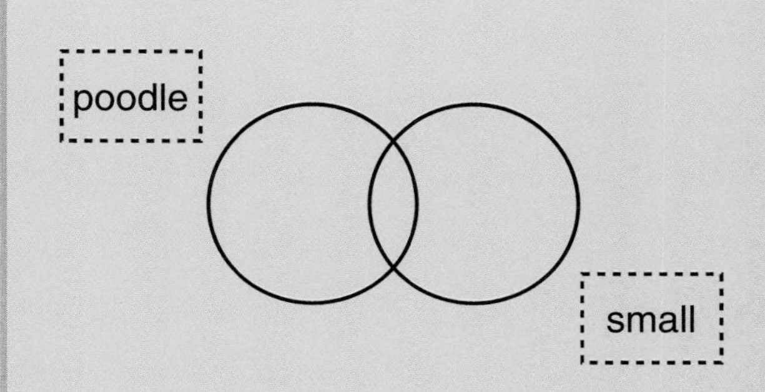

- Which picture cards go in the space where the loops overlap? Cards that show a small poodle The rule is that shapes with both attributes go in the overlap space.
- Which picture cards go in the other parts of the loops? Cards that show poodles that are not small go in the remainder of the loop labeled poodle; cards that show small dogs that are not poodles go in the remainder of the loop labeled small.
- Which picture cards are not included in any part of the loops? Cards that show dogs that are neither poodles nor small

Pose a slightly different problem. Label the overlapping loops with two values for the same attribute, such as sitting and standing. Ask: *What difference does this make in placing the picture cards?* All of the picture cards are used and there are no shapes in the overlapping part of the loops. Discuss.

Partners try a two-loop problem with two different attributes of their own choice and record the results.

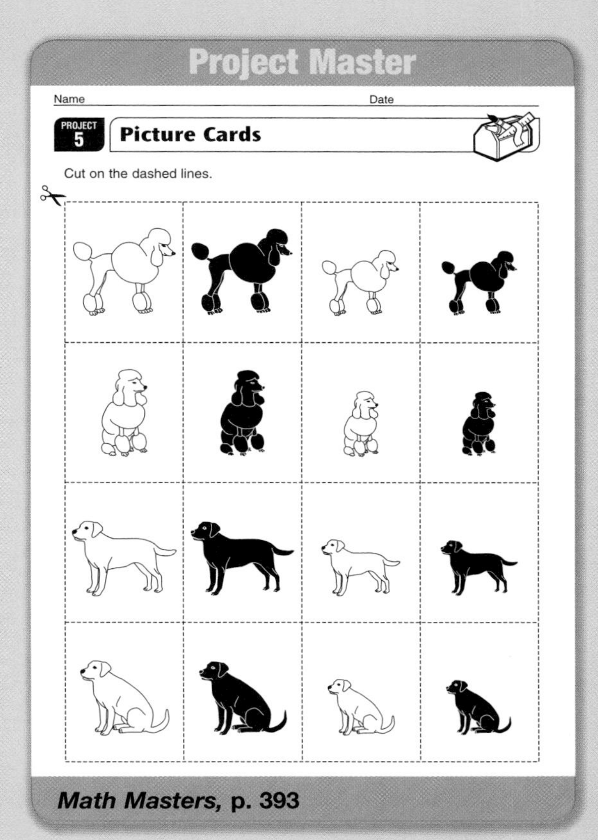
Project Master

Name Date

PROJECT 5 **Picture Cards**

Cut on the dashed lines.

Math Masters, p. 393

Playing a Two-Loop Guessing Game

Model the game and then have partners play to make sure they understand the rules. In the days and weeks to come, children can play the game on their own.

Directions

1. Lay out two overlapping loops.
2. Player 1 chooses two label cards and places them facedown, one next to each loop.
3. Player 2 tries to discover what the labels are by placing picture cards one by one in any of the loop spaces and asking, "Does this belong?" Player 1 can answer only *yes* or *no*.

2 Extending the Project

Extension Suggestions

This activity is a follow-up to the two-loop problem.

Have each partnership lay out three overlapping loops and put label cards by the loops. Three loops provide 7 spaces within the loops to classify the picture cards. Pictures with attributes of two overlapping loops go in the overlapping space of those two loops. Pictures with all three attributes go in the space where all three loops overlap. *See margin.*

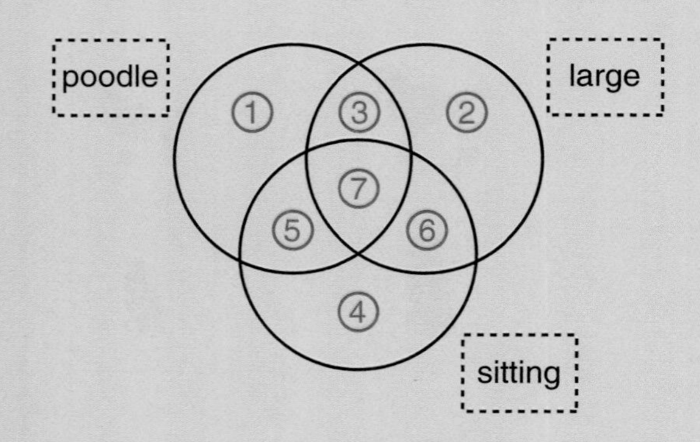

For the initial problem, label the loops with values for 3 of the 4 different attributes. For example, use *poodle, large,* and *sitting.* Subsequent problems may use values of the same attribute.

Have partners put picture cards into each space. Space 1: small, standing, dark, poodle; small, standing, light, poodle; Space 2: large, standing, dark, Labrador; large, standing, light, Labrador; Space 3: large, standing, dark, poodle; large, standing, light, poodle; Space 4: small, sitting, dark, Labrador; small, sitting, light, Labrador; Space 5: small, sitting, dark, poodle; small, sitting, light poodle; Space 6: large, sitting, dark, Labrador; large, sitting, light, Labrador; Space 7: large, sitting, dark, poodle; large, sitting, light, poodle

After a few minutes, bring the class together to share results and discuss.

NOTE Reinforce the principle that shapes in any overlapping spaces must have all the attributes of the loops that overlap.

Home Link Suggestions

Children write individual attributes on slips of paper. They invite family members to choose two (or three) slips of paper and play a version of *I Spy*. For example, after drawing three attribute slips, a player would say, "I spy with my little eye something narrow, brown, and leather" (a belt). Suggest that children make a simple diagram of overlapping circles to illustrate some of the choices.

Project 6

How Far Can You Go in a Million Steps?

Objectives To provide opportunities to measure and estimate distances; and to guide children as they work with powers of 10 and large numbers.

Technology Resources www.everydaymathonline.com

eToolkit

Algorithms Practice

EM Facts Workshop Game™

Family Letters

Assessment Management

Common Core State Standards

Curriculum Focal Points

Interactive Teacher's Lesson Guide

1 Doing the Project

CCSS

Mathematical Practices
SMP1, SMP4, SMP5, SMP6

Content Standards
3.OA.8

Recommended Use During or after Unit 10

Key Concepts and Skills

- Estimate length without measuring tools.
  [Measurement and Reference Frames Goal 1]
- Measure length.
  [Measurement and Reference Frames Goal 1]
- Find multiples of 10.
  [Number and Numeration Goal 3]
- Find landmarks of a data set using calculators.
  [Data and Chance Goal 2]

Key Activities

Powers of 10 and the magnitude of large numbers are reinforced as children estimate how far they can travel in a million steps. Children then relate the distance to U.S. and world maps.

Materials

- *Math Journal 1* or *2*, inside back cover (Tables of Measures)
- *Math Masters,* p. 394
- Class Data Pad (optional)
- tape measures, yardsticks, or metersticks
- U.S. map
- world map or globe
- calculator

2 Extending the Project

Children explore the distance covered in a billion steps and the time required to walk a million and a billion steps.

Children practice skills through Home Links activities.

Materials

- *Math Masters,* p. 394
- calculator

Additional Information

Depending on the children in your class, this project may be done as a guided whole-class activity or in independent small groups after a class discussion. A few children can measure the distance covered by 10 steps using feet or meters. Use the same system of measurement as appears on your world map or globe. The group finds the average of these distances rounded to a whole number. That average 10-step distance is then used to find successive estimations for 1 million steps and the follow-up questions on *Math Masters,* page 394.

1 Doing the Project

Making Estimates

WHOLE-CLASS DISCUSSION

Ask the class to estimate about how far they would travel if they walked 1 million steps. Record some of the estimates on the board or Class Data Pad for later use.

Ask if anyone can think of ways to check these estimates by making closer approximations. Discuss any suggestions, refining them to approximate the procedures recommended in the following activities.

Measuring the Distance of 10 Normal Steps

PARTNER ACTIVITY

Using units in the same system of measurement as that used on your maps (feet if the map scale is in miles, meters if the map scale is in kilometers), partners measure how far they can walk in 10 normal steps. Discuss what constitutes a normal step so everyone agrees. The measurements should be rounded to the nearest whole unit. Record these distances on the board or on the Class Data Pad.

Finding an Average Distance of 10 Normal Steps

WHOLE-CLASS ACTIVITY

Using calculators, children find an average distance (mean) of 10 normal steps. Briefly discuss that the extra decimal places that might appear in the average can be disregarded since the calculations are only estimates.

Adjusting the Activity

Have the children measure how far you, as an adult, walk in 10 normal steps so they can compare how longer legs affect the solution.

AUDITORY ◆ KINESTHETIC ◆ TACTILE ◆ VISUAL

▶ Determining the Distance Traveled in 1 Million Steps

(*Math Masters,* p. 394; *Math Journal 1* or *2,* inside back cover)

Children use the Powers of Ten chart on *Math Masters,* p. 394, to

- ▷ multiply the average distance of 10 steps by 10 to find the distance in 100 steps;
- ▷ multiply by 10 again to find the distance in 1,000 steps;
- ▷ multiply by 10 again to find the distance in 10,000 steps.

Children continue multiplying by 10 a total of five times to find how far they would walk in 1 million steps. Using the Tables of Measures on the inside back cover of their journals, children convert the number of yards or meters they would walk in 1 million steps to a number of miles (divide by 5,280 feet) or kilometers (divide by 1,000 meters). For example, at $1\frac{1}{2}$ feet, or 0.46 meters, per step, they would walk about 284 miles, or 460 kilometers, in 1 million steps.

Compare the estimates made at the beginning of the Project to these closer estimates.

If you have the information about your own adult steps, ask: *How far would I go? How much farther can I travel than one of you?*

▶ Relating the Distance to a Map

Use the map scale on a U.S. and a world map. Locate where a person could go by traveling 1 million steps.

Project Master

Name ______ Date ______

PROJECT 6 How Far Can You Go in a Million Steps?

Powers of Ten

10 × 10 = 100 (one hundred)
10 × 100 = 1,000 (one thousand)
10 × 1,000 = 10,000 (ten thousand)
10 × 10,000 = 100,000 (one hundred thousand)
10 × 100,000 = 1,000,000 (one million)
10 × 1,000,000 = 10,000,000 (ten million)
10 × 10,000,000 = 100,000,000 (one hundred million)
10 × 100,000,000 = 1,000,000,000 (one billion)

1. We walk an average of 15 feet (unit) in 10 steps. or 4.6 meters
2. This means we can walk about: Sample answers:
   a. 150 feet (unit) in 100 steps. or 46 meters
   b. 1,500 feet (unit) in 1,000 steps. or 460 meters
   c. 15,000 feet (unit) in 10,000 steps. or 4,600 meters
   d. 150,000 feet (unit) in 100,000 steps. or 46,000 meters
   e. 1,500,000 feet (unit) in 1,000,000 steps. or 460,000 meters
3. About how many miles or kilometers can we walk in 1,000,000 steps?
   About 284 miles (unit) or 460 kilometers

Try This

4. About how many miles or kilometers can we travel in 1,000,000,000 steps? About 284,000 miles or 460,000 kilometers (unit)
5. Earth is about 25,000 miles, or 40,000 kilometers, around its circumference. About how many times could we travel around Earth in 1,000,000,000 steps?
   About $11\frac{1}{2}$ times (unit)

***Math Masters,* p. 394**

Student Page

Tables of Measures

Metric System

Units of Length
1 kilometer (km) = 1,000 meters (m)
1 meter (m) = 10 decimeters (dm)
= 100 centimeters (cm)
= 1,000 millimeters (mm)
1 decimeter (dm) = 10 centimeters (cm)
1 centimeter (cm) = 10 millimeters (mm)

Units of Area
1 square meter (sq m) = 10,000 square centimeters (sq cm)
1 square centimeter (sq cm) = 100 square millimeters (sq mm)

Units of Volume
1 cubic meter (cu m) = 1,000,000 cubic centimeters (cu cm)
1 cubic centimeter (cu cm) = 1,000 cubic millimeters (cu mm)

Units of Capacity
1 kiloliter (kL) = 1,000 liters (L)
1 liter (L) = 1,000 milliliters (mL)

Units of Weight
1 metric ton (t) = 1,000 kilograms (kg)
1 kilogram (kg) = 1,000 grams (g)
1 gram (g) = 1,000 milligrams (mg)

U.S. Customary System

Units of Length
1 mile (mi) = 1,760 yards (yd)
= 5,280 feet (ft)
1 yard (yd) = 3 feet (ft)
= 36 inches (in.)
1 foot (ft) = 12 inches (in.)

Units of Area
1 square yard (sq yd) = 9 square feet (sq ft)
= 1,296 square inches (sq in.)
1 square foot (sq ft) = 144 square inches (sq in.)

Units of Volume
1 cubic yard (cu yd) = 27 cubic feet (cu ft)
1 cubic foot (cu ft) = 1,728 cubic inches (cu in.)

Units of Capacity
1 gallon (gal) = 4 quarts (qt)
1 quart (qt) = 2 pints (pt)
1 pint (pt) = 2 cups (c)
1 cup (c) = 8 fluid ounces (fl oz)
1 fluid ounce (fl oz) = 2 tablespoons (tbs)
1 tablespoon (tbs) = 3 teaspoons (tsp)

Units of Weight
1 pound (lb) = 16 ounces (oz)
1 ton (T) = 2,000 pounds (lb)

Units of Time
1 millennium = 10 centuries
= 100 decades
= 1,000 years (yr)
1 century = 10 decades
= 100 years (yr)
1 year (yr) = 12 months (mo)
= 52 weeks (wk) plus 1 or 2 days
= 365 or 366 days
1 month (mo) = 28, 29, 30, or 31 days
1 week (wk) = 7 days
1 day = 24 hours (hr)
1 hour (hr) = 60 minutes (min)
1 minute (min) = 60 seconds (sec)

Units of Body Measure
1 **digit** is about the width of a finger.
1 **hand** is about the width of the palm.
1 **span** is the distance from the tip of the thumb to the tip of the first (index) finger. Both fingers must be stretched as far apart as possible.
1 **cubit** is the length from the elbow to the tip of the extended middle finger.
1 **yard** is the distance from the middle of the chest to the tip of the middle finger. The arm must be stretched out at the side of the body, and at a right angle with the body. 1 yard = $\frac{1}{2}$ fathom
1 **fathom** is the length of outstretched arms measured across the chest from the tip of one middle finger to the tip of the other. 1 fathom = 2 yards

System Equivalents

1 inch is about 2.5 centimeters	1 meter is about 39 inches
1 centimeter is about 0.4 inch	1 liter is about 1.1 quarts
1 kilometer is about 0.6 mile	1 ounce is about 28 grams
1 mile is about 1.6 kilometers	1 kilogram is about 2.2 pounds

***Math Journal 1 or 2,* Inside Back Cover**

2 Extending the Project

Extension Suggestions

WHOLE-CLASS ACTIVITY

(*Math Masters,* p. 394)

If children are comfortable with billions, ask: *How far would you travel in 1 billion steps?* Using the previous examples, about 284,000 miles, or 460,000 kilometers

To find out, have children multiply the number of miles or kilometers in 1 million steps by 10 three more times. Some children may figure out that this is the same as multiplying by 1,000.

- *Earth is about 25,000 miles, or 40,000 kilometers, in circumference at the equator. About how many times around Earth could a person travel in 1 billion steps?* Using the previous examples, about $11\frac{1}{2}$ times
- *About how long would it take to walk 1 million steps?* At 1 step per second, it would take about $11\frac{1}{2}$ days without stopping.
- *About how long would it take to walk 1 billion steps?* At 1 step per second, it would take almost 32 years without stopping.

Home Link Suggestions

Children discuss the Project with family members. They investigate the difference between how far they can walk in 10 normal steps and how far another family member can walk in 10 normal steps. Encourage children to choose much younger family members (or neighbors) as well as adults.

Project 7

Order of Operations

Objective To introduce the rules for order of operations.

Technology Resources www.everydaymathonline.com

eToolkit

Algorithms Practice

EM Facts Workshop Game™

Family Letters

Assessment Management

Common Core State Standards

Curriculum Focal Points

Interactive Teacher's Lesson Guide

1 Doing the Project

Recommended Use During or after Unit 7

CCSS

Mathematical Practices
SMP1, SMP5, SMP6, SMP8

Content Standards
3.OA.5, 3.OA.8

Key Concepts and Skills

- Use basic facts to solve numeric expressions.
  [Operations and Computation Goals 1 and 3]
- Recognize that numeric expressions can have different values depending on the order in which the operations are carried out.
  [Patterns, Functions, and Algebra Goal 3]

Key Activities

To explore order of operations, children use two calculators, one that follows the conventional, algebraic order of operations and one that follows a simple left-to-right order of operations.

Key Vocabulary

order of operations

Materials

- *Student Reference Book,* p. 74H
- *Math Masters,* p. 394A
- Class Data Pad
- slate
- Per group: 2 calculators—one that follows the conventional order of operations (such as a scientific calculator) and one that follows a left-to-right order of operations (such as most four-function calculators, including the TI-108 and Casio SL-450). *See* Advance Preparation.

2 Extending the Project

Using a calculator that follows a left-to-right order of operations to solve number sentences, children record the key sequences that should be used to follow the conventional, algebraic order of operations.

Children practice skills through Home Link activities.

Materials

- *Math Masters,* p. 394A
- Per group: 2 calculators. *See* Materials list in Part 1.
- *Student Reference Book,* p. 74H

Additional Information

Once children begin to encounter expressions such as $5 + 3 \times 2$, they have to decide the order in which the indicated operations should be carried out. The simplest order is to begin at the left and carry out the operations in the order in which they appear. This simple left-to-right order of operations is built into many four-function calculators. But it is neither the order of operations commonly used in higher mathematics nor the one built into more advanced calculators.

When people refer to "Order of Operations," by convention they mean the "algebraic" order of operations in which multiplication and division take precedence over addition and subtraction and operations of equal precedence are performed from left to right. There are other, more specialized orders of operation that are used in technical fields but are not pertinent to school mathematics.

In *Everyday Mathematics,* we follow common usage and refer to the conventional order of operations as the "Order of Operations." See Section 10.1.2 of the *Teacher's Reference Manual* for further discussion.

Advance Preparation

For Part 1, gather enough calculators to provide two for each small group of 3 or 4 children. You might consider using calculators on cell phones and on the Internet. For each group, one calculator should follow the conventional order of operations (such as a scientific calculator); the other should follow a simple left-to-right order of operations (such as most four-function calculators including the TI-108 and Casio SL-450). To check whether a calculator follows the conventional order of operations, enter 6 [+] 5 [×] 3 [=]. Calculators that follow the conventional order of operations will show 21 in the display. Calculators that follow the left-to-right order will show 33 in the display. Copy the list of rules for order of operations from *Teacher's Lesson Guide,* page 502B onto the Class Data Pad.

1 Doing the Project

Exploring Order of Operations

SMALL-GROUP ACTIVITY

Tell the class that you have a mystery for them. Explain that you wanted to solve $6 + 5 \times 3$. But when you used two different calculators, you got two different answers. One calculator gave the result as 21; the other gave 33. Write the following number sentences on the board:

$$6 + 5 \times 3 = 21$$

$$6 + 5 \times 3 = 33$$

Ask children to figure out how each calculator solved the problem. To get 21, one calculator multiplied 5×3 first and then added the result to 6; $5 \times 3 = 15$; $6 + 15 = 21$. To get 33, the other calculator added $6 + 5$ first and then multiplied the result by 3; $6 + 5 = 11$; $11 \times 3 = 33$.

Distribute two calculators to each small group—one that follows the conventional order of operations (such as a scientific calculator) and one that follows a left-to-right order of operations (such as most four-function calculators, including the TI-108 and Casio SL-450).

Have each group use each calculator to solve $15 - 7 \times 2 = ?$ Have them share their answers. 16 (left-to-right) and 1 (scientific)

Ask children to explain how each of their calculators solved the problem. Sample answers: One calculator (scientific) multiplied first and then subtracted. The other calculator (left-to-right) subtracted first and then multiplied.

Explain that some calculators carry out operations in the order they are entered, or left-to-right, in the number sentence. Other calculators follow a special set of rules that tell which operation to do first and which operation to do next.

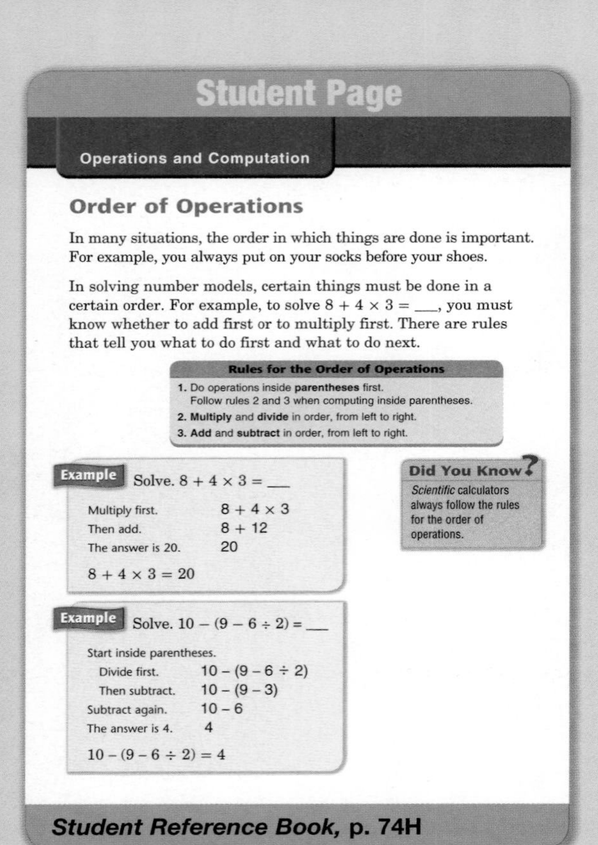
Student Page

Operations and Computation

Order of Operations

In many situations, the order in which things are done is important. For example, you always put on your socks before your shoes.

In solving number models, certain things must be done in a certain order. For example, to solve $8 + 4 \times 3 =$ ___, you must know whether to add first or to multiply first. There are rules that tell you what to do first and what to do next.

Rules for the Order of Operations

1. Do operations inside **parentheses** first. Follow rules 2 and 3 when computing inside parentheses.
2. **Multiply** and **divide** in order, from left to right.
3. **Add** and **subtract** in order, from left to right.

Example Solve. $8 + 4 \times 3 =$ ___

Multiply first.	$8 + 4 \times 3$
Then add.	$8 + 12$
The answer is 20.	20

$8 + 4 \times 3 = 20$

Did You Know? *Scientific* calculators always follow the rules for the order of operations.

Example Solve. $10 - (9 - 6 \div 2) =$ ___

Start inside parentheses.	
Divide first.	$10 - (9 - 6 \div 2)$
Then subtract.	$10 - (9 - 3)$
Subtract again.	$10 - 6$
The answer is 4.	4

$10 - (9 - 6 \div 2) = 4$

Student Reference Book, p. 74H

Introducing Order of Operations

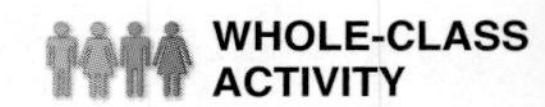

(*Student Reference Book,* p. 74H)

Tell children that to avoid confusion when solving number sentences, mathematicians have agreed to a set of rules, called the **order of operations.** These rules tell you what to do first and what to do next. Refer children to the list of rules you prepared on the Class Data Pad.

Rules for the Order of Operations

1. If there are parentheses, do the operations inside the parentheses first. Follow rules 2 and 3 when computing inside parentheses.
2. Then multiply or divide, in order, from left to right.
3. Finally, add or subtract, in order, from left to right.

NOTE It is important to emphasize that multiplication and division are of equal priority. This means that you perform whichever of these two operations comes first, from left to right. Likewise, addition and subtraction are of equal priority.

As a class, read about the order of operations on *Student Reference Book,* page 74H.

Practicing Order of Operations

(*Math Masters,* p. 394A, *Student Reference Book,* p. 74H)

Write number sentences on the board and have children copy them onto their slates. Referring to the Rules for the Order of Operations on the Class Data Pad or on *Student Reference Book,* page 74H, children underline the operation that should be performed first and then solve. Have volunteers share their solution strategies. *Suggestions:*

- $8 - \underline{2 \times 3} = \underline{\ 2\ }$
- $\underline{\ 20\ } = \underline{0 \times 20} + 20$
- $12 + \underline{6 \div 2} = \underline{\ 15\ }$
- $\underline{\ 13\ } = \underline{15 - 8} + 6$
- $10 \div 5 \times (\underline{2 + 5}) = \underline{\ 14\ }$
- $\underline{\ 6\ } = (\underline{15 - 6}) \div 9 + 5$

When children are ready, have them work in small groups, following the rules for the order of operations to solve the number sentences on *Math Masters,* page 394A. They use scientific calculators (those that follow the conventional order of operations) to check their work. Bring the class together to share answers.

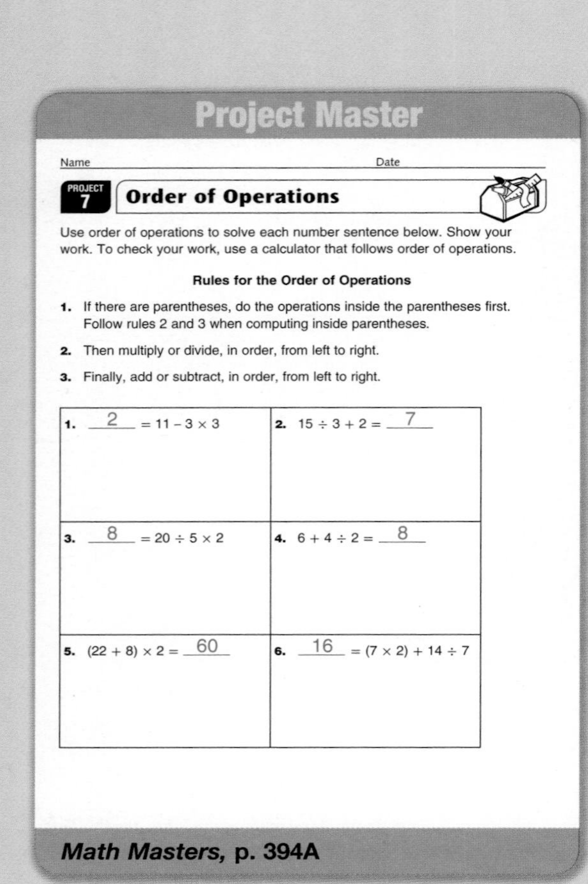
Project Master

Name Date

PROJECT 7 **Order of Operations**

Use order of operations to solve each number sentence below. Show your work. To check your work, use a calculator that follows order of operations.

Rules for the Order of Operations

1. If there are parentheses, do the operations inside the parentheses first. Follow rules 2 and 3 when computing inside parentheses.
2. Then multiply or divide, in order, from left to right.
3. Finally, add or subtract, in order, from left to right.

1. $\underline{\ 2\ } = 11 - 3 \times 3$	2. $15 \div 3 + 2 = \underline{\ 7\ }$
3. $\underline{\ 8\ } = 20 \div 5 \times 2$	4. $6 + 4 \div 2 = \underline{\ 8\ }$
5. $(22 + 8) \times 2 = \underline{\ 60\ }$	6. $\underline{\ 16\ } = (7 \times 2) + 14 \div 7$

Math Masters, p. 394A

2 Extending the Project

Extension Suggestions

PARTNER ACTIVITY

(*Math Masters,* p. 394A)

For each problem on *Math Masters*, page 394A, have children record the key sequence that should be used to correctly follow the conventional order of operations with a calculator that follows a left-to-right order. Children use a left-to-right calculator to check their work. For example, the key sequence to solve $11 - 3 \times 3$ is: 3 [×] 3 [=] 9 [AC] 11 [−] 9 [=] 2.

Home Link Suggestions

INDEPENDENT ACTIVITY

(*Student Reference Book,* p. 74H)

Children discuss the order of operations and share *Student Reference Book,* page 74H with family members. Children and family members determine whether their home calculators follow the conventional order of operations.

Algorithm 1 Project

U.S. Traditional Addition

Objective To introduce U.S. traditional addition.

Technology Resources www.everydaymathonline.com

eToolkit

Algorithms Practice

EM Facts Workshop Game™

Family Letters

Assessment Management

Common Core State Standards

Curriculum Focal Points

Interactive Teacher's Lesson Guide

1 Doing the Project

CCSS
Mathematical Practices
SMP1, SMP2, SMP3, SMP4, SMP5, SMP6, SMP7
Content Standards
3.OA.8, 3.NBT.2

Recommended Use After Lesson 2•7

Key Concepts and Skills

- Identify places in whole numbers and the values of the digits in those places. [Number and Numeration Goal 1]
- Use addition facts to find sums of multidigit whole numbers. [Operations and Computation Goal 1]
- Add multidigit whole numbers. [Operations and Computation Goal 2]
- Write and solve addition number stories. [Operations and Computation Goal 6]

Key Activities
Children explore and practice U.S. traditional addition with multidigit whole numbers.

Key Vocabulary
U.S. traditional addition

Materials
- *Math Journal 1* or *2,* pp. 1P–4P
- *Student Reference Book,* p. 74A
- base-10 blocks (optional)

2 Extending the Project

Children solve multidigit addition problems, first using the focus algorithm (partial-sums addition) and then using any algorithm they choose.

Materials
- Online Additional Practice, pp. 4A–4D
- *Student Reference Book,* pp. 57–59 and 74A

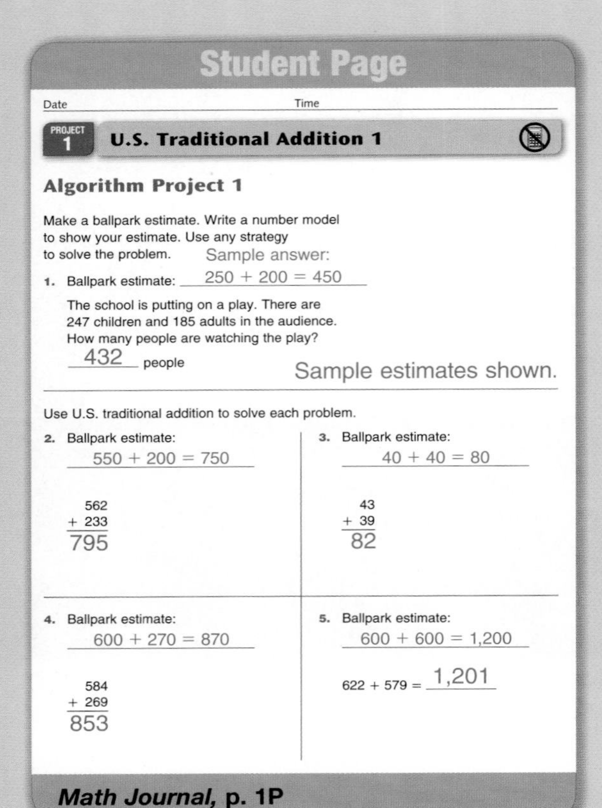
Student Page

Date Time

PROJECT 1 **U.S. Traditional Addition 1**

Algorithm Project 1

Make a ballpark estimate. Write a number model to show your estimate. Use any strategy to solve the problem. Sample answer:

1. Ballpark estimate: 250 + 200 = 450

The school is putting on a play. There are 247 children and 185 adults in the audience. How many people are watching the play?

432 people

Sample estimates shown.

Use U.S. traditional addition to solve each problem.

2. Ballpark estimate: 550 + 200 = 750

562 + 233 = 795

3. Ballpark estimate: 40 + 40 = 80

43 + 39 = 82

4. Ballpark estimate: 600 + 270 = 870

584 + 269 = 853

5. Ballpark estimate: 600 + 600 = 1,200

622 + 579 = 1,201

Math Journal, p. 1P

1 Doing the Project

▶ Solving an Addition Problem

INDEPENDENT ACTIVITY

(*Math Journal,* p. 1P)

Ask children to solve Problem 1 on journal page 1P. Tell them they may use base-10 blocks, paper and pencil, or any other tools they wish, except calculators.

▶ Discussing Solutions

WHOLE-CLASS ACTIVITY

(*Math Journal,* p. 1P)

Discuss children's solutions to Problem 1 on journal page 1P. 247 + 185 = 432 people Expect that children will use several different methods, including modeling with base-10 blocks, counting on, and using partial-sums addition. Some children may also use U.S. traditional addition. *Possible strategies:*

▷ Modeling with base-10 blocks

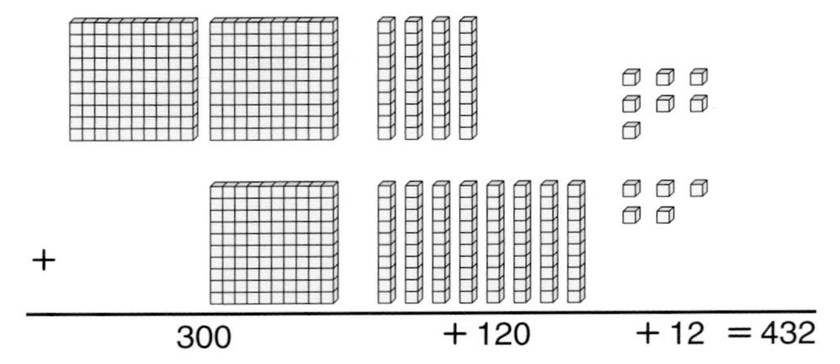

▷ Counting on

247 + 185 =

Count on by 100s:	247, 347
Count on by 10s:	347, 357, 367, 377, 387, 397, 407, 417, 427
Count on by 1s:	427, 428, 429, 430, 431, 432

247 + 185 = 432

▷ Using partial-sums addition

		247
		+ 185
Add the 100s.	200 + 100 →	300
Add the 10s.	40 + 80 →	120
Add the 1s.	7 + 5 →	12
Add the partial sums.	300 + 120 + 12 →	**432**

▷ Using U.S. traditional addition

```
  1 1
  2 4 7
+ 1 8 5
-------
  4 3 2
```

▶ Introducing U.S. Traditional Addition

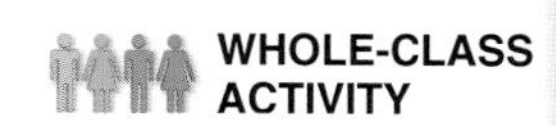

WHOLE-CLASS ACTIVITY

After you have discussed children's solutions, and even if one or more children used **U.S. traditional addition,** demonstrate it as described below.

Example 1: 247 + 185

Step 1:

Add the 1s: 7 + 5 = 12.
12 = 1 ten + 2 ones
Write 2 in the 1s place below the line.
Write 1 above the numbers in the 10s place.

```
   1
  247
+ 185
-----
    2
```

Step 2:

Add the 10s: 1 + 4 + 8 = 13.
13 tens = 1 hundred + 3 tens
Write 3 in the 10s place below the line.
Write 1 above the numbers in the 100s place.

```
  11
  247
+ 185
-----
   32
```

Step 3:

Add the 100s: 1 + 2 + 1 = 4.
Write 4 in the 100s place below the line.

```
  11
  247
+ 185
-----
  432
```

247 + 185 = 432
There are 432 people watching the play.

NOTE Throughout the discussion of U.S. traditional addition, be sure that children understand the values of the digits. For instance, in Step 2 of Example 1, 1 + 4 + 8 = 13 means 1 ten + 4 tens + 8 tens = 13 tens (1 hundred + 3 tens), or 10 + 40 + 80 = 130.

Example 2: 676 + 589

Step 1:

Add the 1s: 6 + 9 = 15.
15 = 1 ten + 5 ones
Write 5 in the 1s place below the line.
Write 1 above the numbers in the 10s place.

```
   1
  676
+ 589
-----
    5
```

Step 2:

Add the 10s: 1 + 7 + 8 = 16.
16 tens = 1 hundred + 6 tens
Write 6 in the 10s place below the line.
Write 1 above the numbers in the 100s place.

```
  11
  676
+ 589
-----
   65
```

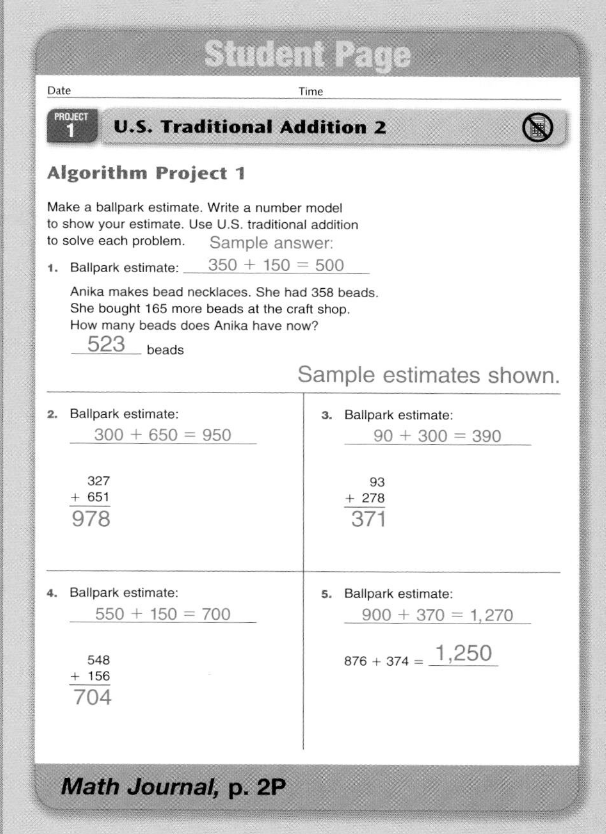

Student Page

Date Time

PROJECT 1 **U.S. Traditional Addition 2**

Algorithm Project 1

Make a ballpark estimate. Write a number model to show your estimate. Use U.S. traditional addition to solve each problem. Sample answer:

1. Ballpark estimate: 350 + 150 = 500

Anika makes bead necklaces. She had 358 beads. She bought 165 more beads at the craft shop. How many beads does Anika have now?

523 beads

Sample estimates shown.

2. Ballpark estimate: 300 + 650 = 950

327 + 651 = 978

3. Ballpark estimate: 90 + 300 = 390

93 + 278 = 371

4. Ballpark estimate: 550 + 150 = 700

548 + 156 = 704

5. Ballpark estimate: 900 + 370 = 1,270

876 + 374 = 1,250

Math Journal, p. 2P

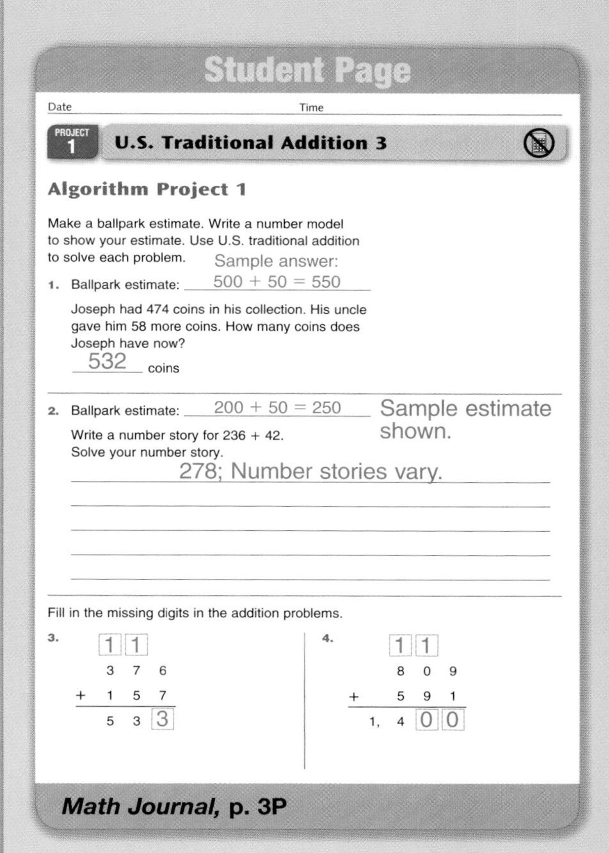

Student Page

Date Time

PROJECT 1 **U.S. Traditional Addition 3**

Algorithm Project 1

Make a ballpark estimate. Write a number model to show your estimate. Use U.S. traditional addition to solve each problem. Sample answer:

1. Ballpark estimate: 500 + 50 = 550

Joseph had 474 coins in his collection. His uncle gave him 58 more coins. How many coins does Joseph have now?

532 coins

2. Ballpark estimate: 200 + 50 = 250 Sample estimate shown.

Write a number story for 236 + 42. Solve your number story.

278; Number stories vary.

Fill in the missing digits in the addition problems.

3.
```
  11
  376
+ 157
-----
  533
```

4.
```
   11
   809
+  591
------
 1,400
```

Math Journal, p. 3P

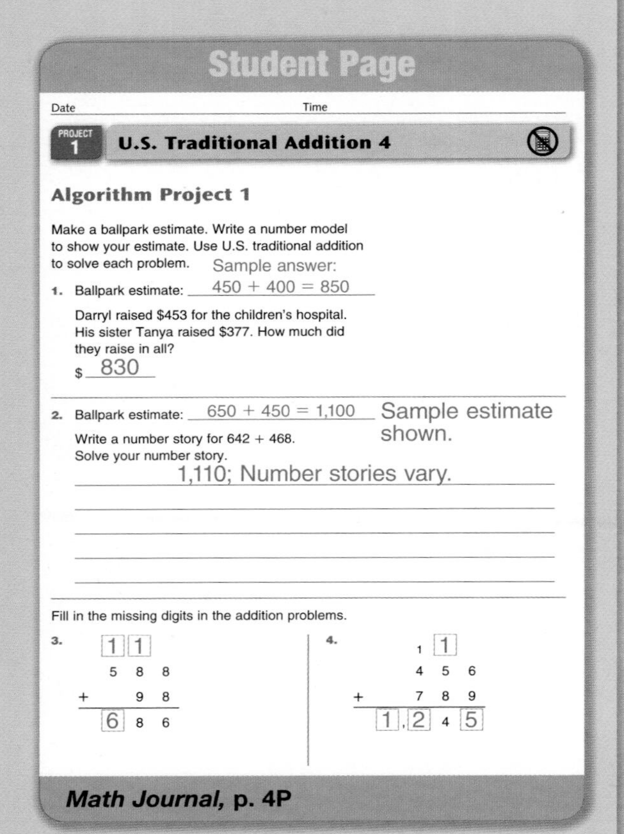
Student Page

Date Time

PROJECT 1 **U.S. Traditional Addition 4**

Algorithm Project 1

Make a ballpark estimate. Write a number model to show your estimate. Use U.S. traditional addition to solve each problem. Sample answer:

1. Ballpark estimate: 450 + 400 = 850

Darryl raised \$453 for the children's hospital. His sister Tanya raised \$377. How much did they raise in all?

\$ 830

2. Ballpark estimate: 650 + 450 = 1,100 Sample estimate shown.

Write a number story for 642 + 468. Solve your number story.

1,110; Number stories vary.

Fill in the missing digits in the addition problems.

3.
```
  1 1
  5 8 8
+   9 8
  6 8 6
```

4.
```
    1 1
    4 5 6
+   7 8 9
  1,2 4 5
```

Math Journal, p. 4P

Go to www.everydaymathonline.com to access the additional practice pages.

Online Master

Name Date Time

PROJECT 1 **Partial-Sums Addition** Online Additional Practice

Algorithm Project 1

Make a ballpark estimate. Write a number model to show your estimate. Use partial-sums addition to solve each problem.

1. Ballpark estimate: Sample answer: 240 + 80 = 320

Ji Young had \$243 in her bank account. She deposited \$78 more. How much money is in Ji Young's bank account now?

\$ 321

Sample estimates shown.

2. Ballpark estimate: 720 + 280 = 1,000

716 + 282 = 998

3. Ballpark estimate: 60 + 60 = 120

56 + 65 = 121

4. Ballpark estimate: 290 + 300 = 590

286 + 296 = 582

5. Ballpark estimate: 850 + 760 = 1,610

848 + 756 = 1,604

Online Additional Practice, p. 4A

Step 3:

Add the 100s: 1 + 6 + 5 = 12.
12 hundreds = 1 thousand + 2 hundreds
Write 2 in the hundreds place below the line.
Write 1 in the 1,000s place below the line.

```
   1 1
   6 7 6
 + 5 8 9
 1 2 6 5
```

676 + 589 = 1,265

You may want to work several more examples with the whole class.

Suggestions:

- ▷ 47 + 84 = ? 131
- ▷ 355 + 48 = ? 403
- ▷ 449 + 292 = ? 741
- ▷ 403 + 526 = ? 929
- ▷ 677 + 353 = ? 1,030
- ▷ 179 + 886 = ? 1,065

▶ Practicing U.S. Traditional Addition

(*Math Journal,* pp. 1P–4P; *Student Reference Book,* p. 74A)

When children are ready, have them solve Problems 2–5 on journal page 1P. They may find the example on *Student Reference Book,* page 74A helpful.

Journal pages 2P–4P provide children with additional practice using U.S. traditional addition. Use these journal pages as necessary.

2 Extending the Project

▶ Solving Multidigit Addition Problems

(Online Additional Practice, pp. 4A–4D; *Student Reference Book,* pp. 57–59 and 74A)

Online practice pages 4A–4D provide children with additional practice solving multidigit addition problems. Use these pages as necessary.

Encourage children to use the focus algorithm (partial-sums addition) to solve the problems on practice page 4A. Invite them to use any algorithm they wish to solve the problems on the remaining pages.

Children may find the examples on *Student Reference Book,* pages 57–59 and 74A helpful.

Algorithm 2 Project

U.S. Traditional Subtraction

Objective To introduce U.S. traditional subtraction.

Technology Resources www.everydaymathonline.com

eToolkit

Algorithms Practice

EM Facts Workshop Game™

Family Letters

Assessment Management

Common Core State Standards

Curriculum Focal Points

Interactive Teacher's Lesson Guide

1 Doing the Project

CCSS

Mathematical Practices
SMP1, SMP2, SMP3, SMP4, SMP5, SMP6, SMP7

Content Standards
3.OA.8, 3.NBT.2

Recommended Use After Lesson 2•8

Key Concepts and Skills

- Identify places in whole numbers and the values of the digits in those places.
  [Number and Numeration Goal 1]
- Use subtraction facts to find differences of multidigit whole numbers.
  [Operations and Computation Goal 1]
- Subtract multidigit numbers.
  [Operations and Computation Goal 2]
- Write and solve subtraction number stories.
  [Operations and Computation Goal 6]

Key Activities
Children explore and practice U.S. traditional subtraction with multidigit whole numbers.

Key Vocabulary
U.S. traditional subtraction

Materials
- *Math Journal 1* or *2,* pp. 5P–8P
- *Student Reference Book,* p. 74B
- $1, $10, $100 bills (*Math Masters,* pp. 399–402; optional)
- base-10 blocks (optional)

2 Extending the Project

Children solve multidigit subtraction problems, first using the focus algorithm (trade-first subtraction) and then using any algorithm they choose.

Materials
- Online Additional Practice, pp. 8A–8D
- *Student Reference Book,* pp. 60–63 and 74B

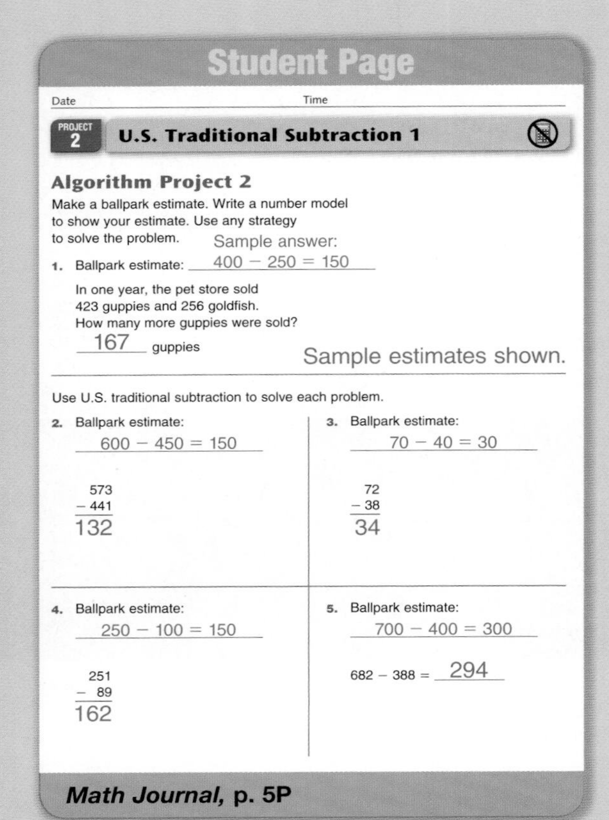
Student Page

Date Time

PROJECT 2 **U.S. Traditional Subtraction 1**

Algorithm Project 2

Make a ballpark estimate. Write a number model to show your estimate. Use any strategy to solve the problem.

1. Ballpark estimate: Sample answer: 400 − 250 = 150

In one year, the pet store sold 423 guppies and 256 goldfish. How many more guppies were sold?

167 guppies

Sample estimates shown.

Use U.S. traditional subtraction to solve each problem.

2. Ballpark estimate: 600 − 450 = 150

573 − 441 = 132

3. Ballpark estimate: 70 − 40 = 30

72 − 38 = 34

4. Ballpark estimate: 250 − 100 = 150

251 − 89 = 162

5. Ballpark estimate: 700 − 400 = 300

682 − 388 = 294

Math Journal, p. 5P

1 Doing the Project

▶ Solving a Subtraction Problem

INDEPENDENT ACTIVITY

(*Math Journal,* p. 5P)

Ask children to solve Problem 1 on journal page 5P. Tell them they may use base-10 blocks, play money, paper and pencil, or any other tools they wish, except calculators.

▶ Discussing Solutions

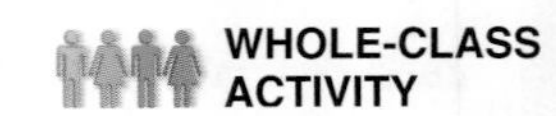
WHOLE-CLASS ACTIVITY

(*Math Journal,* p. 5P)

Discuss children's solutions to Problem 1 on journal page 5P. 423 − 256 = 167 guppies Expect that children will use several different methods, which may include modeling with base-10 blocks or other manipulatives, applying various paper-and-pencil methods such as counting up, and using trade-first subtraction. Some children may also use U.S. traditional subtraction. *Possible strategies:*

▷ Modeling with base-10 blocks

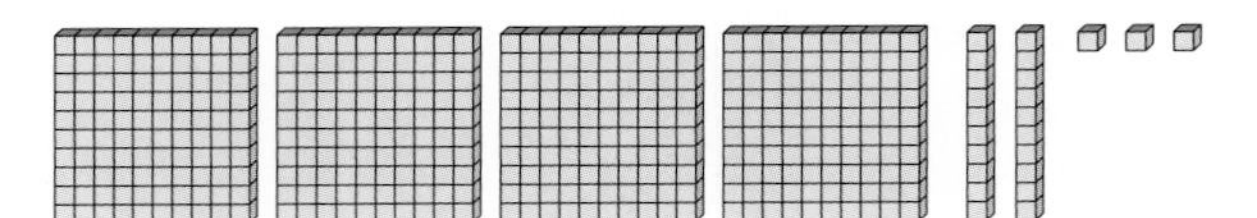

Show 423 with 4 hundreds, 2 tens, and 3 ones.

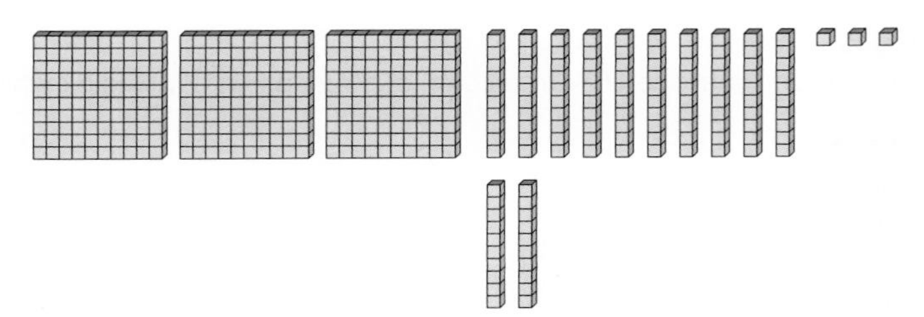

Trade 1 hundred for 10 tens.

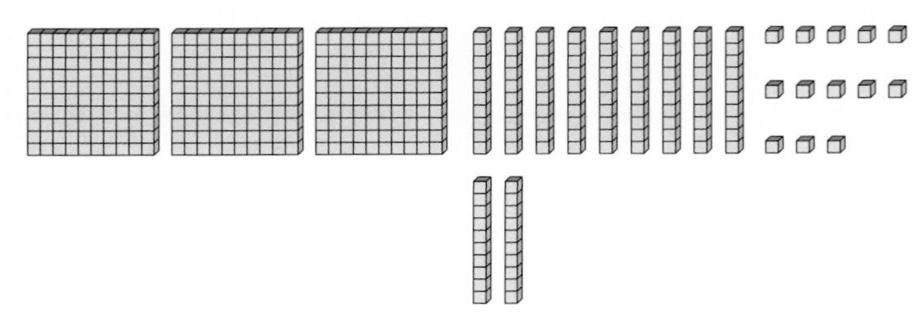

Trade 1 ten for 10 ones.

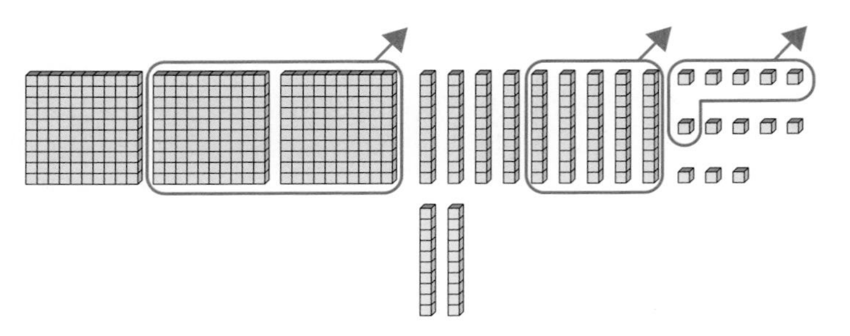

Subtract 256 by removing 2 hundreds, 5 tens, and 6 ones. 167 (1 hundred, 6 tens, and 7 ones) remains.

▷ Counting up

$$256 \xrightarrow{+4} 260 \xrightarrow{+40} 300 \xrightarrow{+100} 400 \xrightarrow{+20} 420 \xrightarrow{+3} 423$$

$256 + 4 = 260$
$260 + 40 = 300$
$300 + 100 = 400$
$400 + 20 = 420$
$420 + 3 = 423$

$4 + 40 + 100 + 20 + 3 = 167$
$423 - 256 = 167$

▷ Using trade-first subtraction

		11	
	3	~~1~~	13
	~~4~~	~~2~~	~~3~~
−	2	5	6
	1	6	7

▷ Using U.S. traditional subtraction

		11	
	3	~~1~~	13
	~~4~~	~~2~~	~~3~~
−	2	5	6
	1	6	7

NOTE Trade-first subtraction resembles U.S. traditional subtraction, except that in trade-first subtraction, as the name implies, all the trading is done before any subtractions are carried out, allowing the person to concentrate on one task at a time.

▶ Introducing U.S. Traditional Subtraction

After you have discussed children's solutions, and even if one or more children used **U.S. traditional subtraction,** demonstrate it again as described below.

Example 1: 423 – 256

Step 1:

Start with the 1s.

Since 6 > 3, you need to regroup.

Trade 1 ten for 10 ones:
423 = 4 hundreds + 1 ten + 13 ones.

Subtract the 1s: 13 – 6 = 7.

		1	**13**
	4	~~**2**~~	~~**3**~~
−	2	5	**6**
			7

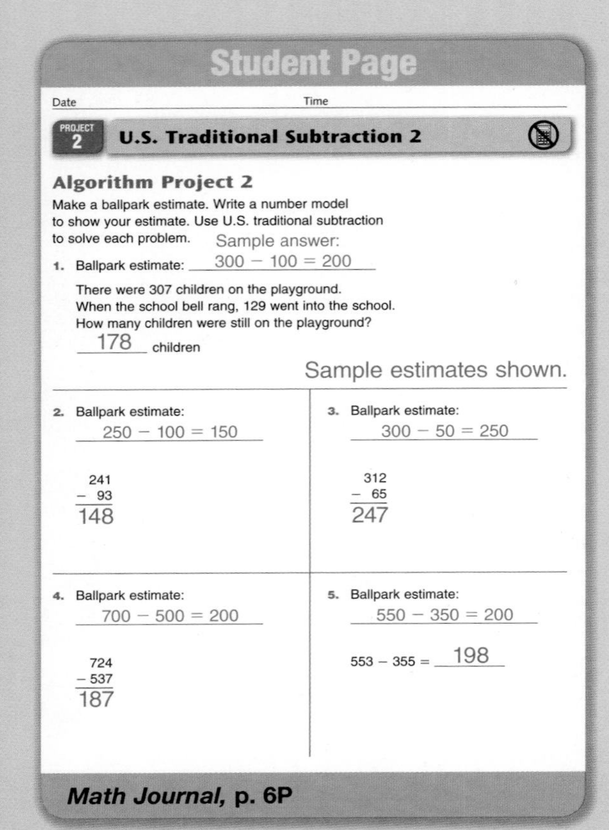
Student Page

Date Time

PROJECT 2 **U.S. Traditional Subtraction 2**

Algorithm Project 2

Make a ballpark estimate. Write a number model to show your estimate. Use U.S. traditional subtraction to solve each problem. Sample answer:

1. Ballpark estimate: 300 − 100 = 200

There were 307 children on the playground. When the school bell rang, 129 went into the school. How many children were still on the playground?

178 children

Sample estimates shown.

2. Ballpark estimate: 250 − 100 = 150

	241
−	93
	148

3. Ballpark estimate: 300 − 50 = 250

	312
−	65
	247

4. Ballpark estimate: 700 − 500 = 200

	724
−	537
	187

5. Ballpark estimate: 550 − 350 = 200

553 − 355 = 198

Math Journal, p. 6P

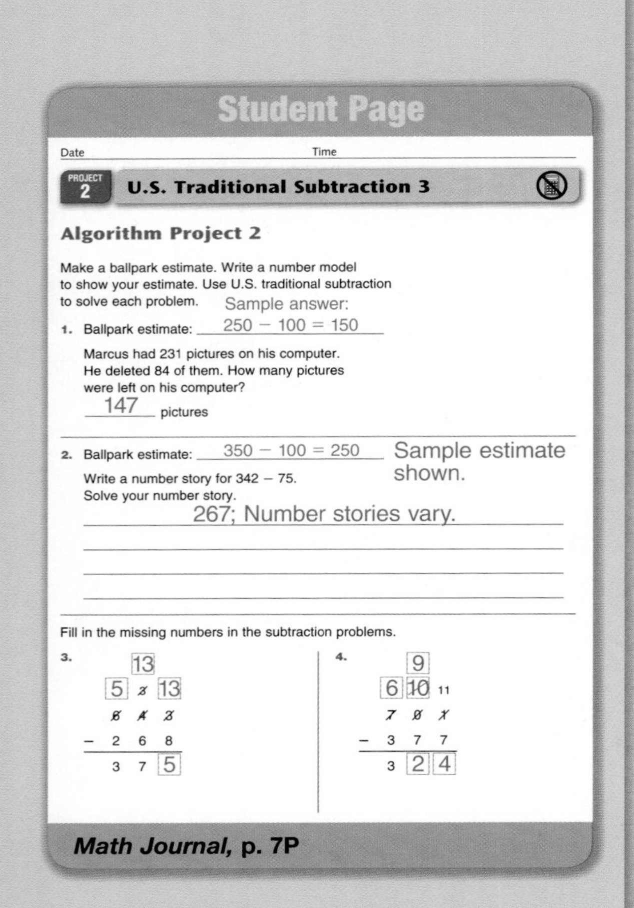
Student Page

Date Time

PROJECT 2 **U.S. Traditional Subtraction 3**

Algorithm Project 2

Make a ballpark estimate. Write a number model to show your estimate. Use U.S. traditional subtraction to solve each problem. Sample answer:

1. Ballpark estimate: 250 − 100 = 150

Marcus had 231 pictures on his computer. He deleted 84 of them. How many pictures were left on his computer?

147 pictures

2. Ballpark estimate: 350 − 100 = 250 Sample estimate shown.

Write a number story for 342 − 75. Solve your number story.

267; Number stories vary.

Fill in the missing numbers in the subtraction problems.

3.

		13	
	5	~~3~~	13
	~~6~~	~~4~~	~~3~~
−	2	6	8
	3	7	5

4.

		9	
	6	10	11
	~~7~~	~~0~~	~~1~~
−	3	7	7
	3	2	4

Math Journal, p. 7P

Step 2:

Go to the 10s.

Since 5 > 1, you need to regroup.

Trade 1 hundred for 10 tens:
423 = 3 hundreds + 11 tens + 13 ones.

Subtract the 10s: 11 − 5 = 6.

		11	
	3	~~1~~	13
	~~4~~	~~2~~	~~3~~
−	2	**5**	6
		6	7

Step 3:

Go to the 100s. You don't need to regroup.

Subtract the 100s: 3 − 2 = 1.

		11	
	3	~~1~~	13
	~~4~~	~~2~~	~~3~~
−	**2**	5	6
	1	6	7

423 − 256 = 167

167 more guppies than goldfish were sold.

Example 2: 604 − 288

Step 1:

Start with the 1s.

Since 8 > 4, you need to regroup.

There are no tens in 604, so trade 1 hundred for 10 tens and then trade 1 ten for 10 ones:
604 = 5 hundreds + 9 tens + 14 ones.

Subtract the 1s: 14 − 8 = 6.

		9	
	5	**~~10~~**	**14**
	~~6~~	**~~0~~**	**~~4~~**
−	2	8	**8**
			6

Step 2:

Go to the 10s. You don't need to regroup.

Subtract the 10s: 9 − 8 = 1.

		9	
	5	~~10~~	14
	~~6~~	~~0~~	~~4~~
−	2	**8**	8
		1	6

Step 3:

Go to the 100s. You don't need to regroup.

Subtract the 100s: 5 − 2 = 3.

		9	
	5	~~10~~	14
	~~6~~	~~0~~	~~4~~
−	**2**	8	8
	3	1	6

604 − 288 = 316

You may want to work several more examples with the whole class.

Suggestions:

▷ 46 − 18 = ? 28

▷ 529 − 313 = ? 216

▷ 131 − 56 = ? 75

▷ 944 − 576 = ? 368

▷ 730 − 237 = ? 493

▷ 302 − 124 = ? 178

Practicing U.S. Traditional Subtraction

PARTNER ACTIVITY

(*Math Journal,* pp. 5P–8P; *Student Reference Book,* p. 74B)

When children are ready, have them solve Problems 2–5 on journal page 5P. They may find the example on *Student Reference Book,* page 74B helpful.

Journal pages 6P–8P provide children with additional practice using U.S. traditional subtraction. Use these journal pages as necessary.

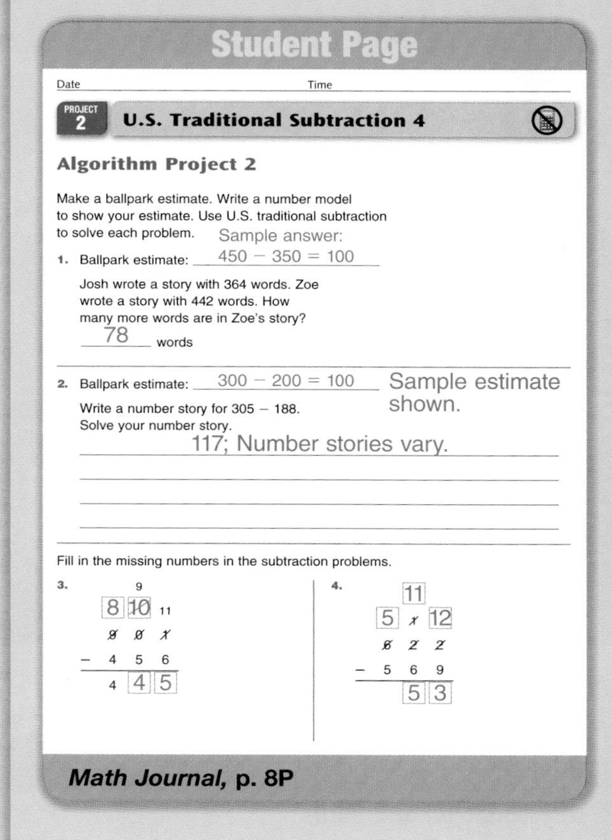
Student Page

Date ______ Time ______

PROJECT 2 **U.S. Traditional Subtraction 4**

Algorithm Project 2

Make a ballpark estimate. Write a number model to show your estimate. Use U.S. traditional subtraction to solve each problem.

1. Ballpark estimate: Sample answer: 450 – 350 = 100

Josh wrote a story with 364 words. Zoe wrote a story with 442 words. How many more words are in Zoe's story?

78 words

2. Ballpark estimate: 300 – 200 = 100 Sample estimate shown.

Write a number story for 305 – 188. Solve your number story.

117; Number stories vary.

Fill in the missing numbers in the subtraction problems.

3.
```
   9
 8 10 11
 9  1  1
-4  5  6
 4  4  5
```

4.
```
   11
 5  1 12
 6  2  2
-5  6  9
    5  3
```

Math Journal, p. 8P

2 Extending the Project

Solving Multidigit Subtraction Problems

INDEPENDENT ACTIVITY

(Online Additional Practice, pp. 8A–8D; *Student Reference Book,* pp. 60–63 and 74B)

Online practice pages 8A–8D provide children with additional practice solving multidigit subtraction problems. Use these pages as necessary.

Encourage children to use the focus algorithm (trade-first subtraction) to solve the problems on practice page 8A. Invite them to use any algorithm they wish to solve the problems on the remaining pages.

Children may find the examples on *Student Reference Book,* pages 60–63 and 74B helpful.

Go to www.everydaymathonline.com to access the additional practice pages.

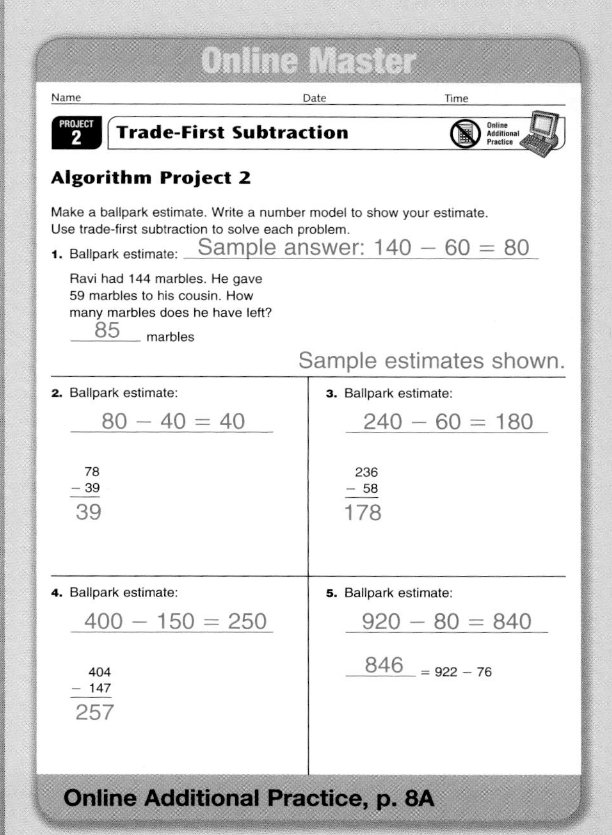
Online Master

Name ______ Date ______ Time ______

PROJECT 2 **Trade-First Subtraction**

Algorithm Project 2

Make a ballpark estimate. Write a number model to show your estimate. Use trade-first subtraction to solve each problem.

1. Ballpark estimate: Sample answer: 140 – 60 = 80

Ravi had 144 marbles. He gave 59 marbles to his cousin. How many marbles does he have left?

85 marbles

Sample estimates shown.

2. Ballpark estimate: 80 – 40 = 40

78 – 39 = 39

3. Ballpark estimate: 240 – 60 = 180

236 – 58 = 178

4. Ballpark estimate: 400 – 150 = 250

404 – 147 = 257

5. Ballpark estimate: 920 – 80 = 840

846 = 922 – 76

Online Additional Practice, p. 8A

Algorithm 3 Project

U.S. Traditional Multiplication

Objective To introduce U.S. traditional multiplication.

Technology Resources www.everydaymathonline.com

eToolkit

Algorithms Practice

EM Facts Workshop Game™

Family Letters

Assessment Management

Common Core State Standards

Curriculum Focal Points

Interactive Teacher's Lesson Guide

1 Doing the Project

CCSS

Mathematical Practices
SMP1, SMP2, SMP3, SMP4, SMP5, SMP6

Content Standards
3.OA.1

Recommended Use After Lesson 9•12

Key Concepts and Skills

- Identify places in whole numbers and the values of the digits in those places. [Number and Numeration Goal 1]
- Use multiplication facts to find products of multidigit whole numbers. [Operations and Computation Goal 3]
- Multiply multidigit whole numbers. [Operations and Computation Goal 4]
- Write and solve multiplication number stories. [Operations and Computation Goal 6]

Key Activities

Children explore and practice U.S. traditional multiplication with multidigit whole numbers.

Key Vocabulary

U.S. traditional multiplication

Materials

- *Math Journal 1* or *2,* pp. 9P–12P
- *Student Reference Book,* pp. 74C and 74D
- base-10 blocks (optional)

2 Extending the Project

Children solve multidigit multiplication problems, first using the focus algorithm (partial-products multiplication) and then using any algorithm they choose.

Materials

- Online Additional Practice, pp. 12A–12D
- *Student Reference Book,* pp. 68–72, 74C, and 74D

1 Doing the Project

Solving a Multiplication Problem

INDEPENDENT ACTIVITY

(*Math Journal,* p. 9P)

Ask children to solve Problem 1 on journal page 9P. Tell them they may use base-10 blocks, paper and pencil, or any other tools they wish, except calculators.

Discussing Solutions

WHOLE-CLASS ACTIVITY

(*Math Journal,* p. 9P)

Discuss children's solutions to Problem 1 on journal page 9P. $5 \times 64 = 320$ seeds Expect that children will use several different methods, including partial-products multiplication, lattice multiplication, arrays, mental math, and base-10 blocks or other manipulatives. Some children may also use U.S. traditional multiplication. *Possible strategies:*

▷ Using partial-products multiplication

$$\begin{array}{rr} & \mathbf{6\,4} \\ & \times \quad \mathbf{5} \\ \hline 5 \times 60 \rightarrow & 3\,0\,0 \\ 5 \times 4 \rightarrow & +\quad 2\,0 \\ \hline 300 + 20 \rightarrow & \mathbf{3\,2\,0} \end{array}$$

▷ Using lattice multiplication

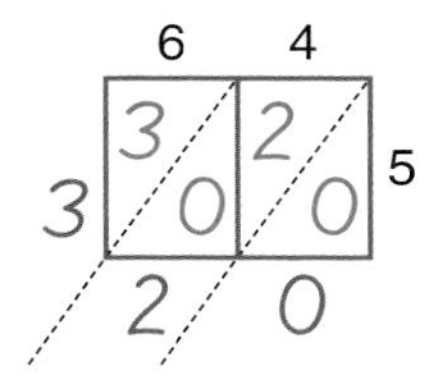

▷ Using U.S. traditional multiplication

$$\begin{array}{r} {}^{2} \\ 6\,4 \\ \times \quad 5 \\ \hline 3\,2\,0 \end{array}$$

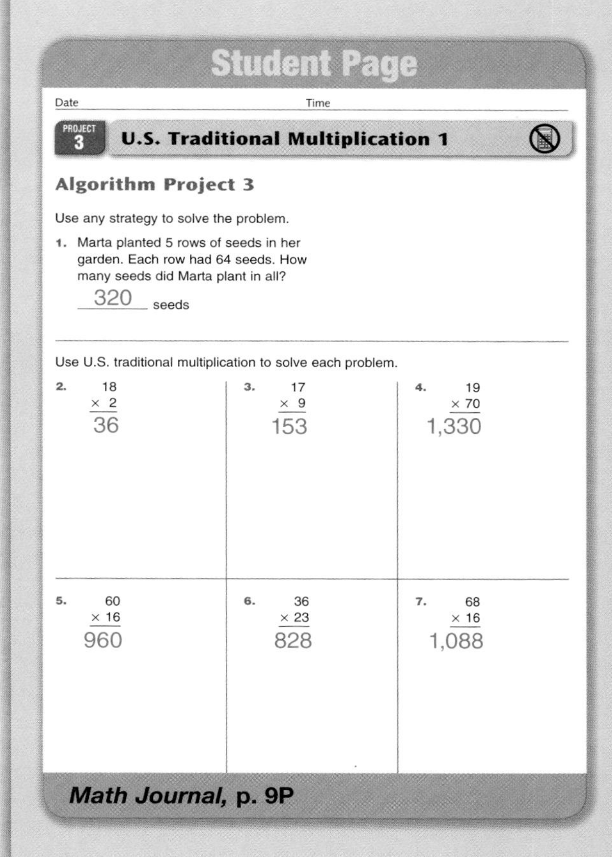

Student Page

Date Time

PROJECT 3 U.S. Traditional Multiplication 1

Algorithm Project 3

Use any strategy to solve the problem.

1. Marta planted 5 rows of seeds in her garden. Each row had 64 seeds. How many seeds did Marta plant in all?
320 seeds

Use U.S. traditional multiplication to solve each problem.

2. $18 \times 2 = 36$

3. $17 \times 9 = 153$

4. $19 \times 70 = 1{,}330$

5. $60 \times 16 = 960$

6. $36 \times 23 = 828$

7. $68 \times 16 = 1{,}088$

Math Journal, p. 9P

▶ Introducing U.S. Traditional Multiplication

After you have discussed children's solutions, and even if one or more children used **U.S. traditional multiplication,** demonstrate it again as described below.

Example 1: 5×64

Step 1:

Multiply the ones.
5×4 ones = 20 ones = 2 tens + 0 ones
Write 0 in the 1s place below the line.
Write 2 above the 6 in the 10s place.

$$\begin{array}{r} ^{2}\;\; \\ 64 \\ \times\;\; 5 \\ \hline 0 \end{array}$$

Step 2:

Multiply the tens.
5×6 tens = 30 tens
Remember the 2 tens from Step 1.
30 tens + 2 tens = 32 tens in all
32 tens = 3 hundreds + 2 tens
Write 2 in the 10s place below the line.
Write 3 in the 100s place below the line.

$$\begin{array}{r} ^{2}\;\; \\ 64 \\ \times\;\; 5 \\ \hline 320 \end{array}$$

$5 \times 64 = 320$

Marta planted 320 seeds.

NOTE U.S. traditional multiplication is so familiar that the details of its working may appear more meaningful than they are. Consider the following example:

$$\begin{array}{r} 1\,2\;\, \\ 3\,5\;\, \\ 1\,4\,7 \\ \times\quad 3\,8 \\ \hline 1\,1\,7\,6 \\ +\,4\,4\,1\,0 \\ \hline 5\,5\,8\,6 \end{array}$$

Many people, when asked why the "2" carried from "3×7" is written in the 10s place, will explain that it stands for "2 tens." But this "2" really means "2 hundreds" since the "3" is really "3 tens." U.S. traditional multiplication is efficient—though not as efficient as a calculator—but it is not, despite its familiarity, conceptually transparent.

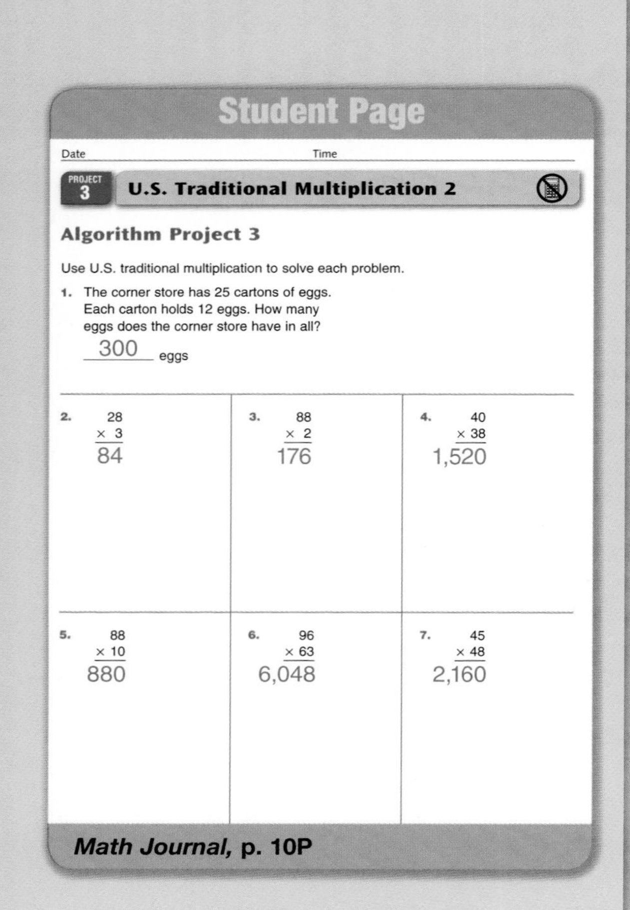
Student Page

Date Time

PROJECT 3 U.S. Traditional Multiplication 2

Algorithm Project 3

Use U.S. traditional multiplication to solve each problem.

1. The corner store has 25 cartons of eggs. Each carton holds 12 eggs. How many eggs does the corner store have in all?
300 eggs

2. 28×3 = 84
3. 88×2 = 176
4. 40×38 = 1,520
5. 88×10 = 880
6. 96×63 = 6,048
7. 45×48 = 2,160

Math Journal, p. 10P

Example 2: 32 × 78

Step 1:

Multiply 78 by the 2 in 32, as if the problem were 2 × 78.

```
   1
  78
× 32
 156  ← The partial product
        2 × 78 = 156
```

Step 2:

Multiply 78 by the 3 in 32, as if the problem were 3 × 78.

The 3 in 32 stands for 3 tens, so write the partial product one place to the left.

Write a 0 in the 1s place to show you are multiplying by tens.

Write the new carry above the old carry.

```
    2
    1
   78
×  32
  156
 2340  ← 30 × 78 = 2,340
```

Step 3:

Add the two partial products to get the final answer.

```
     2
     1
    78
 ×  32
   156
+ 2340
  2496  ← 32 × 78 = 2,496
```

32 × 78 = 2,496

You may want to work several more examples with the whole class.

Suggestions:

▷ 9 × 28 = ? 252

▷ 46 × 50 = ? 2,300

▷ 73 × 94 = ? 6,862

▷ 18 × 3 = ? 54

▷ 20 × 89 = ? 1,780

▷ 67 × 42 = ? 2,814

▶ Practicing U.S. Traditional Multiplication

PARTNER ACTIVITY

(*Math Journal,* pp. 9P–12P; *Student Reference Book,* pp. 74C and 74D)

When children are ready, have them solve Problems 2–7 on journal page 9P. They may find the examples on *Student Reference Book,* pages 74C and 74D helpful.

Journal pages 10P–12P provide children with additional practice using U.S. traditional multiplication. Use these journal pages as necessary.

Student Page

Date Time

PROJECT 3 **U.S. Traditional Multiplication 3**

Algorithm Project 3

Use U.S. traditional multiplication to solve each problem.

1. Corey can type 54 words per minute. How many words can Corey type in 9 minutes?
   486 words

2. Write a number story for 18 × 47. Solve your number story.
   846; Number stories vary.

Fill in the missing digits in the multiplication problems.

```
3.   6         4.    1          5.      1
     57             23                  4
  ×   9          ×  15                 46
  5 1 3           1 1 5              ×  28
                + 2 3 0               3 6 8
                  3 4 5             + 9 2 0
                                    1,2 8 8
```

Math Journal, p. 11P

Student Page

Date Time

PROJECT 3 **U.S. Traditional Multiplication 4**

Algorithm Project 3

Use U.S. traditional multiplication to solve each problem.

1. Samir babysat for 34 hours this month. He was paid $13 per hour. How much money did Samir earn this month?
   $ 442

2. Write a number story for 55 × 6. Solve your number story.
   330; Number stories vary.

Fill in the missing digits in the multiplication problems.

```
3.   4         4.       3        5.      1
    86                 38                6
  ×  7              ×  41               28
  6 0 2                3 8           ×  28
                  + 1 5 2 0          2 2 4
                    1,5 5 8        + 5 6 0
                                     7 8 4
```

Math Journal, p. 12P

Online Master

Name Date Time

PROJECT 3 **Partial-Products Multiplication** Online Additional Practice

Algorithm Project 3

Use partial-products multiplication to solve each problem.

1. Devon's bookshelf has 7 shelves. Each shelf can hold 48 paperback books. How many paperback books can the bookshelf hold in all?

 336 paperback books

2.	3.	4.
$19 \times 2 = 38$	$68 \times 6 = 408$	$62 \times 30 = 1,860$

5.	6.	7.
$28 \times 49 = 1,372$	$61 \times 19 = 1,159$	$86 \times 47 = 4,042$

Online Additional Practice, p. 12A

Go to www.everydaymathonline.com to access the additional practice pages.

2 Extending the Project

▶ Solving Multidigit Multiplication Problems

(Online Additional Practice, pp. 12A–12D; *Student Reference Book,* pp. 68–72, 74C, and 74D)

Online practice pages 12A–12D provide children with additional practice solving multidigit multiplication problems. Use these pages as necessary.

Encourage children to use the focus algorithm (partial-products multiplication) to solve the problems on practice page 12A. Invite them to use any algorithm they wish to solve the problems on the remaining pages.

Children may find the examples on *Student Reference Book,* pages 68–72, 74C, and 74D helpful.

Algorithm

Project

U.S. Traditional Multiplication: Decimals

Objective To introduce U.S. traditional multiplication for decimals in a money context.

Technology Resources www.everydaymathonline.com

eToolkit

Algorithms Practice

EM Facts Workshop Game™

Family Letters

Assessment Management

Common Core State Standards

Curriculum Focal Points

Interactive Teacher's Lesson Guide

1 Doing the Project

CCSS Mathematical Practices
SMP1, SMP2, SMP3, SMP4, SMP5, SMP6

Recommended Use
As Enrichment after Lesson 9•5

Key Concepts and Skills

- Identify places in whole numbers and decimals and the values of the digits in those places.
  [Number and Numeration Goal 1]
- Use multiplication facts to calculate products of decimals in a money context and 1-digit multipliers.
  [Operations and Computation Goal 3]
- Write and solve multiplication number stories with decimals in a money context.
  [Operations and Computation Goal 4]

Key Activities
Children explore and practice U.S. traditional multiplication with decimals in a money context.

Materials
- *Math Journal 1* or *2,* pp. 13P–16P
- *Student Reference Book,* pp. 74E and 74F
- \$1, \$10 bills (*Math Masters,* pp. 399–402)
- dimes, pennies

2 Extending the Project

Children solve decimal multiplication problems, first using the focus algorithm (partial-products multiplication) and then using any algorithm they choose.

Materials
- Online Additional Practice, pp. 16A–16D
- *Student Reference Book,* pp. 69A, 69B, 74E, and 74F

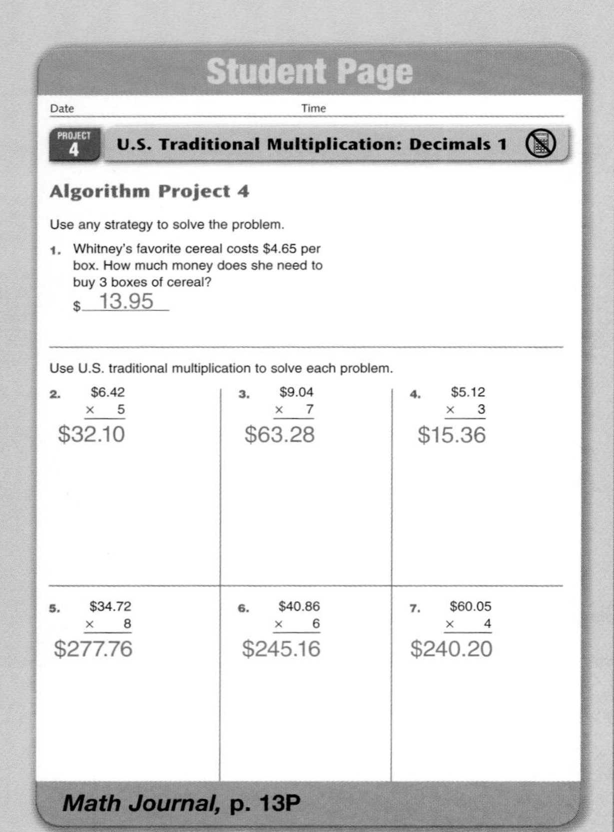

Student Page

Date Time

PROJECT 4 **U.S. Traditional Multiplication: Decimals 1**

Algorithm Project 4

Use any strategy to solve the problem.

1. Whitney's favorite cereal costs \$4.65 per box. How much money does she need to buy 3 boxes of cereal?
   \$ 13.95

Use U.S. traditional multiplication to solve each problem.

2. \$6.42 × 5 = \$32.10	3. \$9.04 × 7 = \$63.28	4. \$5.12 × 3 = \$15.36
5. \$34.72 × 8 = \$277.76	6. \$40.86 × 6 = \$245.16	7. \$60.05 × 4 = \$240.20

Math Journal, **p. 13P**

1 Doing the Project

▶ Solving a Decimal Multiplication Problem

INDEPENDENT ACTIVITY

(*Math Journal,* p. 13P)

Ask children to solve Problem 1 on journal page 13P. Tell them they may use play money, paper and pencil, or any other tools they wish, except calculators.

▶ Discussing Solutions

WHOLE-CLASS ACTIVITY

(*Math Journal,* p. 13P)

Discuss children's solutions to Problem 1 on journal page 13P. \$4.65 × 3 = \$13.95 Expect that children will use several different methods, which may include modeling with play money, using repeated addition, and using partial-products multiplication. Some children may also use U.S. traditional multiplication. *Possible strategies:*

▷ Modeling with play money

\$1 \$1 \$1 \$1	\$1 \$1 \$1 \$1	\$1 \$1 \$1 \$1
Ⓓ Ⓓ Ⓓ Ⓓ Ⓓ Ⓓ	Ⓓ Ⓓ Ⓓ Ⓓ Ⓓ Ⓓ	Ⓓ Ⓓ Ⓓ Ⓓ Ⓓ Ⓓ
Ⓟ Ⓟ Ⓟ Ⓟ Ⓟ	Ⓟ Ⓟ Ⓟ Ⓟ Ⓟ	Ⓟ Ⓟ Ⓟ Ⓟ Ⓟ

Use play money to show the cost of 3 boxes of cereal.

4 [\$1] + 4 [\$1] + 4 [\$1] = 12 [\$1] or 1 [\$10] and 2 [\$1]

Combine the bills.

6 Ⓓ + 6 Ⓓ + 6 Ⓓ = 18 Ⓓ or 1 [\$1] and 8 Ⓓ

Combine the dimes.

5 Ⓟ + 5 Ⓟ + 5 Ⓟ = 15 Ⓟ or 1 Ⓓ and 5 Ⓟ

Combine the pennies.

1 [\$10] + 2 [\$1] + 1 [\$1] + 8 Ⓓ + 1 Ⓓ + 5 Ⓟ = \$13.95

Combine the bills and coins.

▷ Using repeated addition

$$\begin{array}{r} \$4.65 \\ +\ \$4.65 \\ \hline \$8.00 \\ \$1.20 \\ +\ \$0.10 \\ \hline \$9.30 \end{array} \qquad \begin{array}{r} \$9.30 \\ +\ \$4.65 \\ \hline \$13.00 \\ \$0.90 \\ +\ \$0.05 \\ \hline \$13.95 \end{array}$$

▷ Using partial-products multiplication

$$\begin{array}{rr} & \$4\,.\,6\,5 \\ & \times \quad\quad 3 \\ \hline 3\ [\$4.00\text{s}] \rightarrow & 1\,2\,.\,0\,0 \\ 3\ [\$0.60\text{s}] \rightarrow & 1\,.\,8\,0 \\ 3\ [\$0.05\text{s}] \rightarrow & +\ 0\,.\,1\,5 \\ \hline & \$1\,3\,.\,9\,5 \end{array}$$

▷ Using U.S. traditional multiplication

$$\begin{array}{r} {\scriptstyle 1\ \ 1}\quad \\ \$4.\,6\,5 \\ \times \quad\quad 3 \\ \hline \$1\,3.\,9\,5 \end{array}$$

▶ Introducing U.S. Traditional Multiplication for Decimals

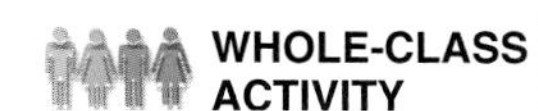

WHOLE-CLASS ACTIVITY

After you have discussed children's solutions, and even if one or more children used U.S. traditional multiplication, demonstrate it again as described below.

Example 1: $4.65 × 3

Step 1:

Start with the pennies.

3 × 5 pennies = 15 pennies

15 pennies = 1 dime + 5 pennies

$$\begin{array}{r} {\scriptstyle 1} \\ 4\,.\,6\,\mathbf{5} \\ \times \quad\quad \mathbf{3} \\ \hline \mathbf{5} \end{array}$$

Step 2:

Multiply the dimes: 3 × 6 dimes = 18 dimes.

Remember the 1 dime from Step 1.

18 dimes + 1 dime = 19 dimes in all

19 dimes = $1 + 9 dimes

$$\begin{array}{r} {\scriptstyle 1\ \ 1}\ \ \\ 4\,.\,\mathbf{6}\,5 \\ \times \quad\quad \mathbf{3} \\ \hline \mathbf{9}\,5 \end{array}$$

Step 3:

Multiply the dollars: 3 × $4 = $12.

Remember the $1 from Step 2.

$12 + $1 = $13 in all

$13 = 1 [$10] + 3 [$1]s

Remember to include the decimal point.

$$\begin{array}{r} {\scriptstyle 1\ \ 1}\ \ \ \ \\ \mathbf{4}\,.\,6\,5 \\ \times \quad\quad \mathbf{3} \\ \hline \mathbf{1\,3\,.}\,9\,5 \end{array}$$

$4.65 × 3 = $13.95

Whitney needs $13.95 to buy 3 boxes of cereal.

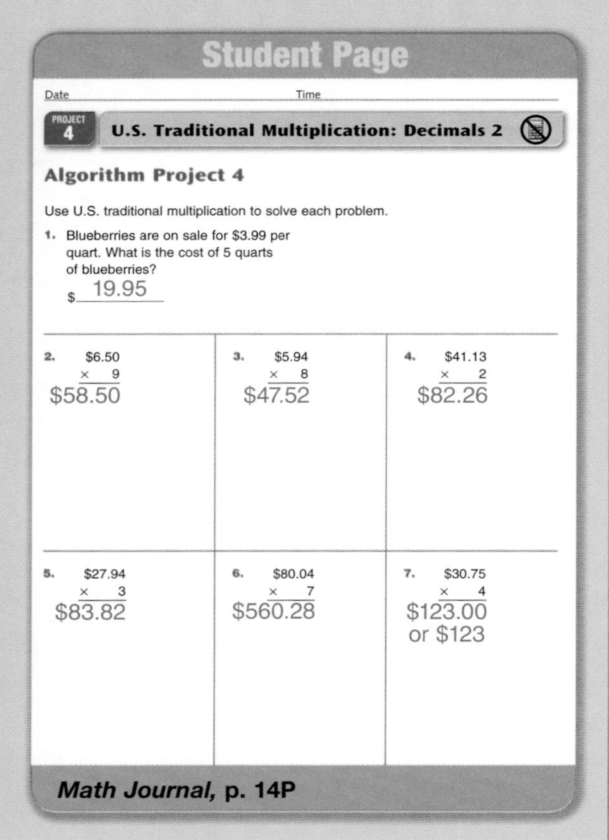
Student Page

Date Time

PROJECT 4 **U.S. Traditional Multiplication: Decimals 2**

Algorithm Project 4

Use U.S. traditional multiplication to solve each problem.

1. Blueberries are on sale for \$3.99 per quart. What is the cost of 5 quarts of blueberries?
   \$ 19.95

2. \$6.50 × 9	3. \$5.94 × 8	4. \$41.13 × 2
\$58.50	\$47.52	\$82.26

5. \$27.94 × 3	6. \$80.04 × 7	7. \$30.75 × 4
\$83.82	\$560.28	\$123.00 or \$123

Math Journal, p. 14P

Student Page

Date Time

PROJECT 4 **U.S. Traditional Multiplication: Decimals 3**

Algorithm Project 4

Use U.S. traditional multiplication to solve each problem.

1. Nida bought 4 sets of finger puppets for her friends. A set of finger puppets costs \$6.95. How much money did Nida spend?
   \$ 27.80

2. Write a number story for \$27.64 × 3. Solve your number story.
   \$82.92; Number stories vary.

Fill in the missing numbers in the multiplication problems.

3. carries: 3 4
   \$4 0 . 5 8
   × 6
   \$2 4 3 . 4 8

4. carries: 6 4
   \$9 . 8 6
   × 7
   \$6 9 . 0 2

5. carry: 3
   \$7 . 1 6
   × 5
   \$3 5 . 8 0

6. carries: 1 3
   \$7 2 . 4 9
   × 4
   \$2 8 9 . 9 6

Math Journal, p. 15P

Example 2: \$7.08 × 6

Step 1:

Start with the pennies.
6 × 8 pennies = 48 pennies
48 pennies = 4 dimes + 8 pennies

$$\begin{array}{r} 4 \\ 7.08 \\ \times \quad 6 \\ \hline 8 \end{array}$$

Step 2:

Multiply the dimes: 6 × 0 dimes = 0 dimes.
Remember the 4 dimes from Step 1.
0 dimes + 4 dimes = 4 dimes in all

$$\begin{array}{r} 4 \\ 7.08 \\ \times \quad 6 \\ \hline 48 \end{array}$$

Step 3:

Multiply the dollars: 6 × \$7 = \$42.
There are no dollars from Step 2.
\$42 = 4 [\$10]s + 2 [\$1]s
Remember to include the decimal point.

$$\begin{array}{r} 4 \\ 7.08 \\ \times \quad 6 \\ \hline 42.48 \end{array}$$

\$7.08 × 6 = \$42.48

Example 3: 5 × \$23.78

Step 1:

Start with the pennies.
5 × 8 pennies = 40 pennies
40 pennies = 4 dimes + 0 pennies

$$\begin{array}{r} 4 \\ 23.78 \\ \times \quad 5 \\ \hline 0 \end{array}$$

Step 2:

Multiply the dimes: 5 × 7 dimes = 35 dimes.
Remember the 4 dimes from Step 1.
35 dimes + 4 dimes = 39 dimes in all
39 dimes = \$3 + 9 dimes

$$\begin{array}{r} 3\ 4 \\ 23.78 \\ \times \quad 5 \\ \hline 90 \end{array}$$

Step 3:

Multiply the dollars: 5 × \$3 = \$15.
Remember the \$3 from Step 2.
\$15 + \$3 = \$18 in all
\$18 = 1 [\$10] + 8 [\$1]s

$$\begin{array}{r} 1\,3\ 4 \\ 23.78 \\ \times \quad 5 \\ \hline 8\ 90 \end{array}$$

Step 4:

Multiply the ten-dollar bills:
5 × 2 [\$10]s = 10 [\$10]s.
Remember the \$10 bill from Step 3.
10 [\$10]s + 1 [\$10] = 11 [\$10]s
11 [\$10]s = 1 [\$100] + 1 [\$10]
Remember to include the decimal point.

$$\begin{array}{r} 1\,3\ 4 \\ 23.78 \\ \times \quad 5 \\ \hline 118.90 \end{array}$$

5 × \$23.78 = \$118.90

You may want to work several more examples with the whole class.

Suggestions:

- ▷ $4.73 × 6 = ? $28.38
- ▷ 7 × $6.40 = ? $44.80
- ▷ $8.34 × 2 = ? $16.68
- ▷ 8 × $30.76 = ? $246.08
- ▷ 4 × $30.09 = ? $120.36
- ▷ $43.12 × 3 = ? $129.36

▶ Practicing U.S. Traditional Multiplication for Decimals

PARTNER ACTIVITY

(*Math Journal,* pp. 13P–16P; *Student Reference Book,* pp. 74E and 74F)

When children are ready, have them solve Problems 2–7 on journal page 13P. They may find the examples on *Student Reference Book,* pages 74E and 74F helpful.

Journal pages 14P–16P provide children with additional practice using U.S. traditional multiplication. Use these journal pages as necessary.

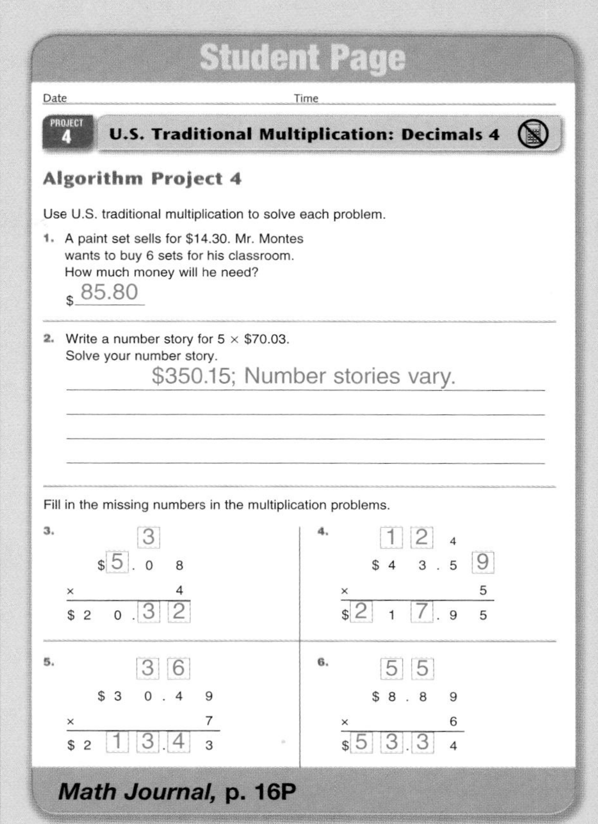

Student Page

Date Time

PROJECT 4 **U.S. Traditional Multiplication: Decimals 4**

Algorithm Project 4

Use U.S. traditional multiplication to solve each problem.

1. A paint set sells for $14.30. Mr. Montes wants to buy 6 sets for his classroom. How much money will he need?
$ 85.80

2. Write a number story for 5 × $70.03. Solve your number story.
$350.15; Number stories vary.

Fill in the missing numbers in the multiplication problems.

3. (carry 3) $ 5 . 0 8 × 4 = $ 2 0 . 3 2

4. (carries 1 2 4) $ 4 3 . 5 9 × 5 = $ 2 1 7 . 9 5

5. (carries 3 6) $ 3 0 . 4 9 × 7 = $ 2 1 3 . 4 3

6. (carries 5 5) $ 8 . 8 9 × 6 = $ 5 3 . 3 4

Math Journal, p. 16P

Go to www.everydaymathonline.com to access the additional practice pages.

2 Extending the Project

▶ Solving Decimal Multiplication Problems

INDEPENDENT ACTIVITY

(Online Additional Practice, pp. 16A–16D; *Student Reference Book,* pp. 69A, 69B, 74E, and 74F)

Online practice pages 16A–16D provide children with additional practice solving decimal multiplication problems. Use these pages as necessary.

Encourage children to use the focus algorithm (partial-products multiplication) to solve the problems on practice page 16A. Invite them to use any algorithm they wish to solve the problems on the remaining pages.

Children may find the examples on *Student Reference Book,* pages 69A, 69B, 74E, and 74F helpful.

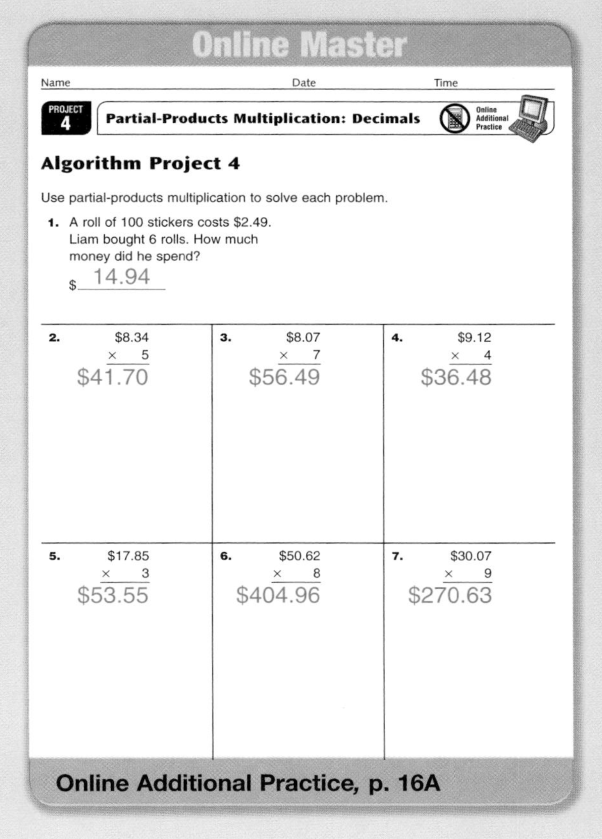

Online Master

Name Date Time

PROJECT 4 **Partial-Products Multiplication: Decimals**

Algorithm Project 4

Use partial-products multiplication to solve each problem.

1. A roll of 100 stickers costs $2.49. Liam bought 6 rolls. How much money did he spend?
$ 14.94

2. $8.34 × 5 = $41.70	3. $8.07 × 7 = $56.49	4. $9.12 × 4 = $36.48
5. $17.85 × 3 = $53.55	6. $50.62 × 8 = $404.96	7. $30.07 × 9 = $270.63

Online Additional Practice, p. 16A

Third Grade Key Vocabulary

For a more extensive glossary that includes additional illustrations and references, please refer to the *Teacher's Reference Manual.*

NOTE: In a definition, terms in italics are defined elsewhere in the glossary.

A

addend Any one of a *set* of numbers that are added. For example, in 5 + 3 + 1, the addends are 5, 3, and 1.

adjacent sides (1) Two *sides* of a *polygon* with a common *vertex.* (2) Two sides of a *polyhedron* with a common *edge.*

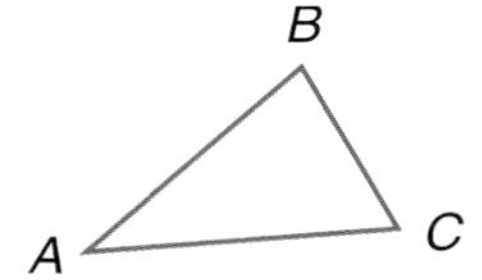

Sides *AB* and *BC*, *BC* and *CA*, and *CA* and *BA* are pairs of adjacent sides.

algorithm A *set* of step-by-step instructions for doing something, such as carrying out a computation or solving a problem. The most common algorithms are those for basic arithmetic computation, but there are many others. Some mathematicians and many computer scientists spend a great deal of time trying to find more efficient algorithms for solving problems.

angle A figure formed by two *rays* or two *line segments* with a common *endpoint* called the *vertex* of the angle. The rays or segments are called the *sides* of the angle. An angle is measured in *degrees* between 0 and 360. One side of an angle is the *rotation* image of the other side through a number of degrees. Angles are named after their vertex point alone as in $\angle A$ below; or by three points, one on each side and the vertex in the middle as in $\angle BCD$ below. See *right angle.*

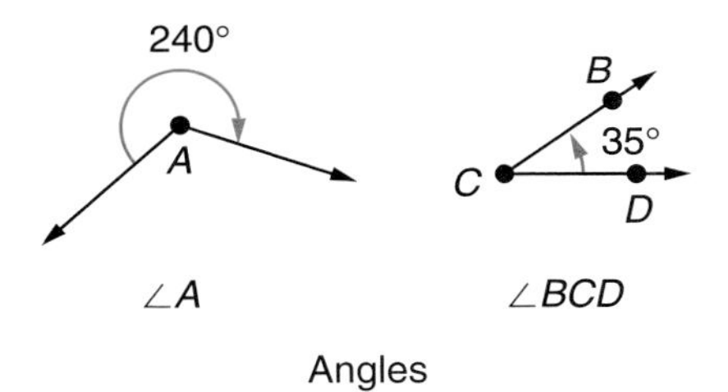

Angles

apex In a *pyramid* or *cone,* the *vertex* opposite the *base.* In a pyramid, all the nonbase *faces* meet at the apex.

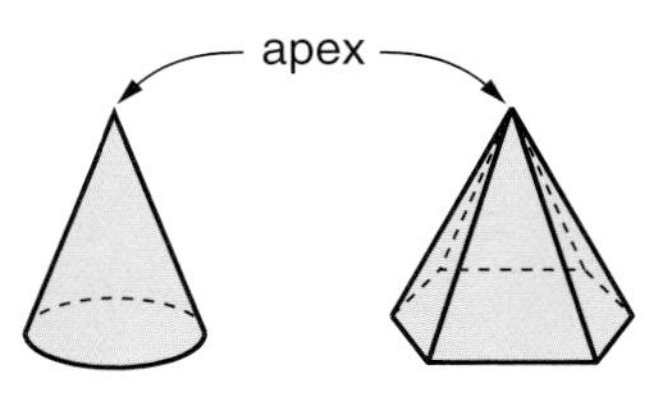

area The amount of surface inside a *2-dimensional figure.* The figure might be a *triangle* or *rectangle* in a *plane,* the curved surface of a *cylinder,* or a state or country on Earth's surface. Commonly, area is measured in *square units* such as square miles, square inches, or square centimeters.

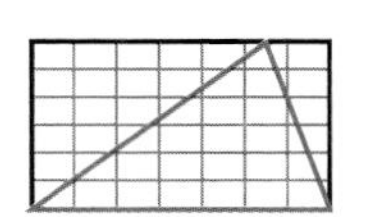

A triangle with area 21 square units

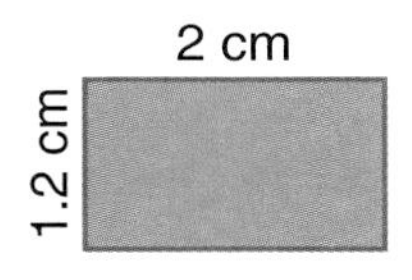

A rectangle with area 1.2 cm × 2 cm = 2.4 cm^2

The area of the United States is about 3,800,000 square miles

array (1) An arrangement of objects in a regular *pattern,* usually rows and columns. (2) A rectangular array. In *Everyday Mathematics,* an array is a rectangular array unless specified otherwise.

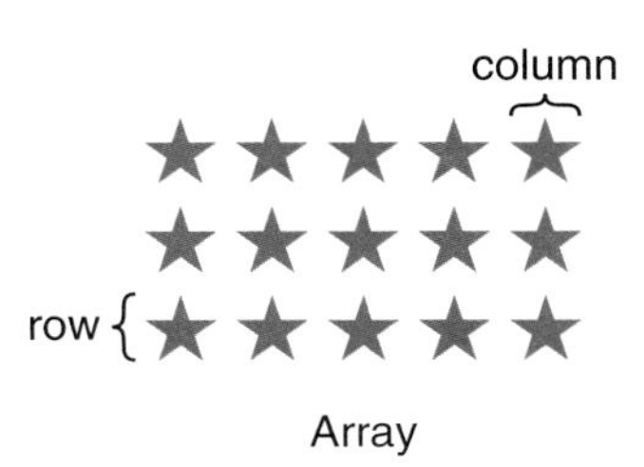

Array

arrow rule In *Everyday Mathematics,* an operation that determines the number that goes into the next frame in a *Frames-and-Arrows* diagram. There may be more than one arrow rule per diagram.

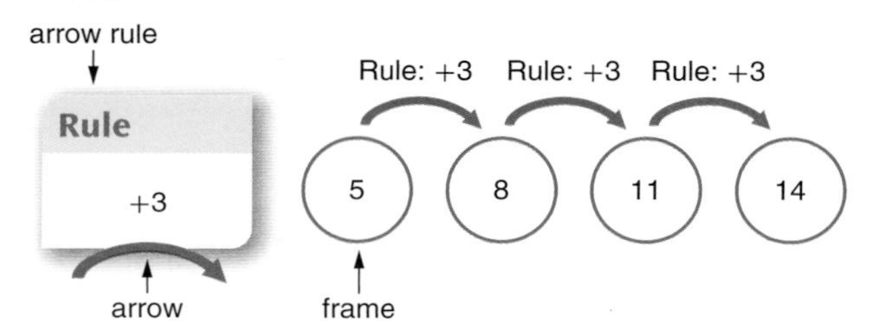

Associative Property of Addition A *property* of addition that three numbers can be added in any order without changing the sum. For example, $(4 + 3) + 7 = 4 + (3 + 7)$ because $7 + 7 = 4 + 10$. In symbols:

For any numbers a, b, and c,
$(a + b) + c = a + (b + c)$.

Subtraction is not associative. For example, $(4 - 3) + 7 \neq 4 - (3 + 7)$ because $8 \neq -6$.

Associative Property of Multiplication A *property* of multiplication that three numbers can be multiplied in any order without changing the *product.* For example, $(4 \times 3) \times 7 = 4\times (3 \times 7)$ because $12 \times 7 = 4 \times 21$. In symbols:

For any numbers a, b, and c,
$(a \times b) \times c = a \times (b \times c)$.

Division is not associative. For example, $(8 / 2) / 4 \neq 8 / (2 / 4)$ because $1 \neq 16$.

attribute A feature of an object or common feature of a *set* of objects. Examples of attributes include size, shape, color, and number of sides. Same as *property.*

autumnal equinox The first day of autumn, when the sun crosses the *plane* of Earth's equator and day and night are about 12 hours each. Equinox is from the Latin *aequi-* meaning equal and *nox* meaning night. Compare to *vernal equinox.*

average A typical value for a *set* of numbers. In everyday life, average usually refers to the *mean* of the set, found by adding all the numbers and dividing the sum by the number of numbers. In statistics, several different averages, or *landmarks*, are defined, including *mean, median,* and *mode.*

ballpark estimate A rough *estimate;* "in the ballpark." A ballpark estimate can serve as a check of the reasonableness of an answer obtained through some other procedure, or it can be made when an exact value is unnecessary or is impossible to obtain.

bar graph A graph with horizontal or vertical bars that represent *data.*

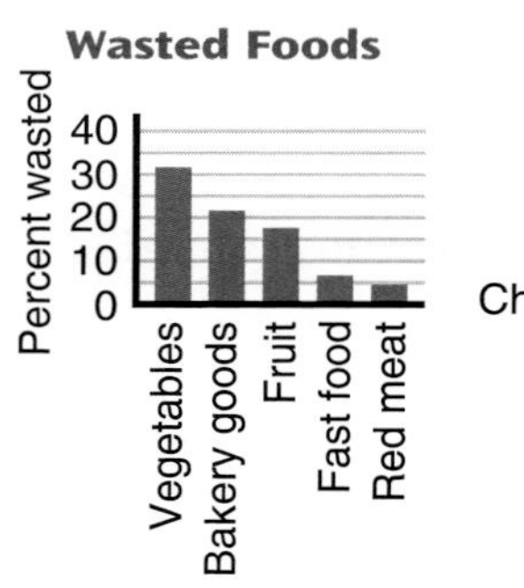

Source: The Garbage Product

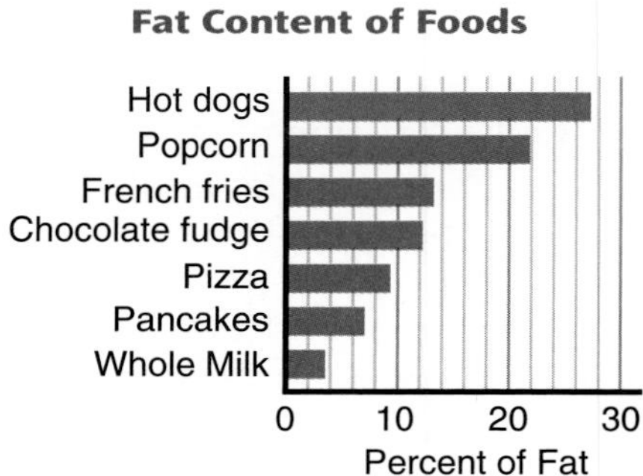

Source: The New York Public Library Desk Reference

base of a prism or cylinder Either of the two *parallel* and congruent *faces* that define the shape of a *prism* or *cylinder.* In a cylinder, the base is a circle.

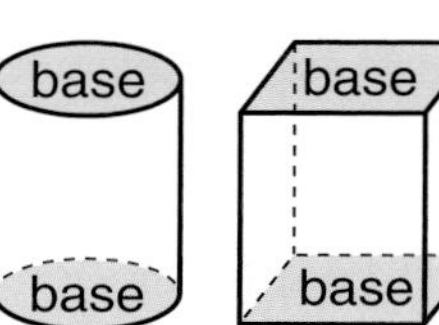

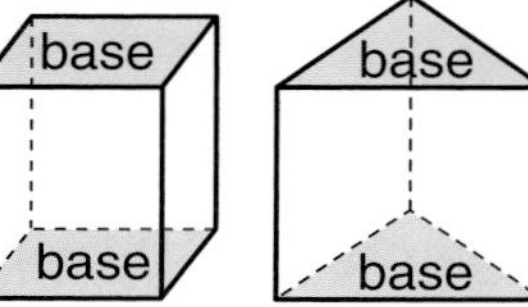

base of a pyramid or cone The *face* of a *pyramid* or *cone* that is opposite the *apex.* The base of a cone is a circle.

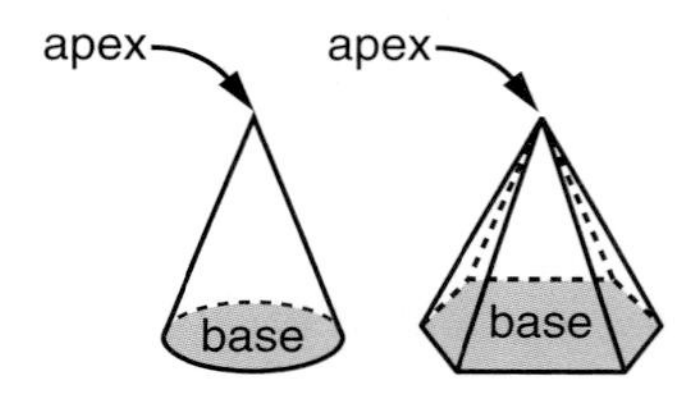

big cube In *Everyday Mathematics,* a base-10 block *cube* that measures 10 cm by 10 cm by 10 cm. A big cube consists of one thousand 1-cm cubes.

capacity (1) The amount of space occupied by a *3-dimensional figure.* Same as *volume.* (2) Less formally, the amount a container can hold.

Capacity is often measured in *units* such as *quarts, gallons, cups,* or *liters.* (3) The *maximum weight* a *scale* can measure.

capacity of a scale The *maximum weight* that a *scale* can measure.

Celsius A temperature *scale* on which pure water at sea level freezes at 0° and boils at 100°. The Celsius scale is used in the *metric system.* A less common name for this scale is centigrade, because there are 100 *units* between the freezing and boiling points of water. Compare to *Fahrenheit.*

census An official count of population and the recording of other demographic *data* such as age, gender, income, and education.

center of a circle The *point* in the *plane* of a circle equally distant from all points on the circle.

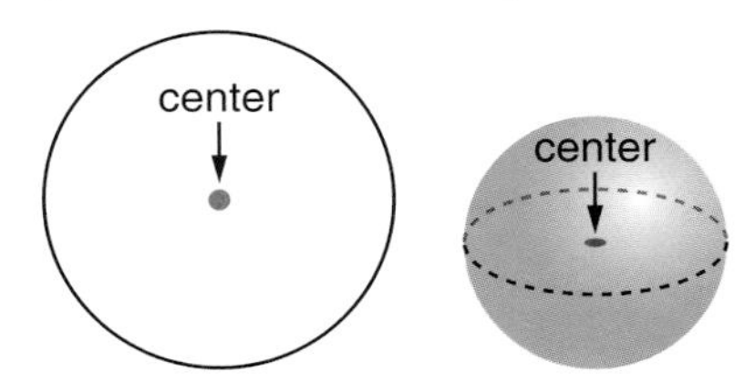

centimeter (cm) A metric *unit* of *length* equivalent to 10 *millimeters,* $\frac{1}{10}$ of a *decimeter,* and $\frac{1}{100}$ of a *meter.*

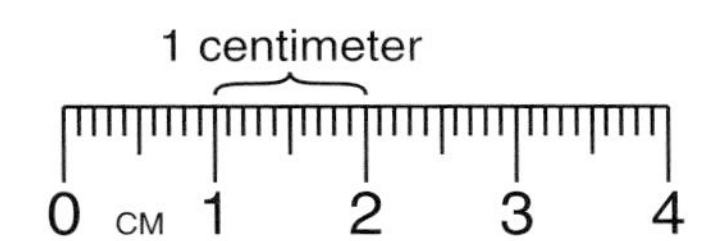

change diagram A diagram used in *Everyday Mathematics* to model situations in which quantities are either increased or decreased by addition or subtraction. The diagram includes a starting quantity, an ending quantity, and an amount of change.

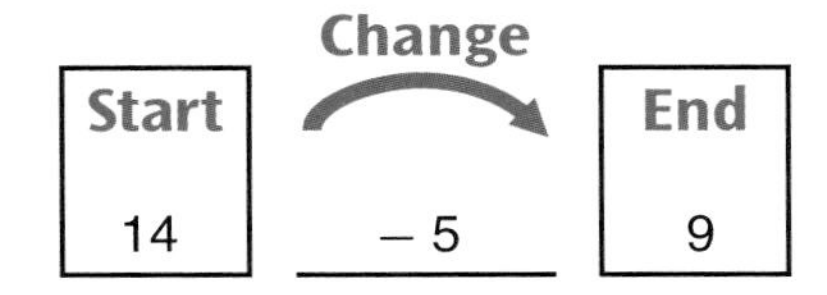

A change diagram for 14 – 5 = 9

circumference The distance around a circle; its *perimeter.* The circumference of a *sphere* is the circumference of a circle on the sphere with the same center as the sphere.

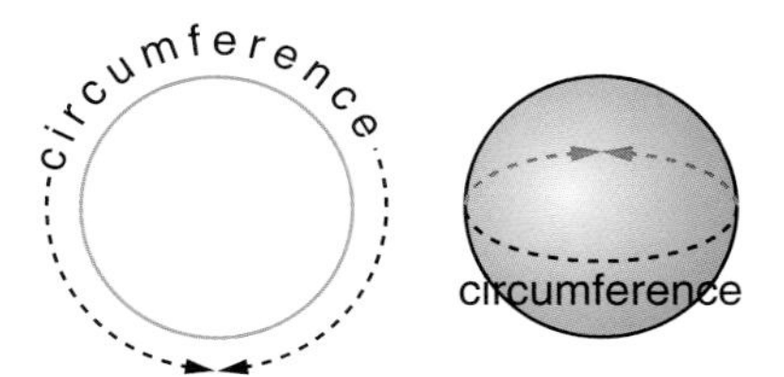

Class Data Pad In *Everyday Mathematics,* a large pad of paper used to store and recall *data* collected throughout the year. The data can be used for analysis, graphing, and generating *number stories.*

clockwise rotation The direction in which the hands move on a typical analog clock; a turn to the right.

Commutative Property of Addition A *property* of addition that two numbers can be added in either order without changing the sum. For example, $5 + 10 = 10 + 5$. In *Everyday Mathematics,* this is called a turn-around fact, and the two Commutative Properties are called turn-around rules. In symbols:

For any numbers a and b, $a + b = b + a$.

Subtraction is not commutative. For example, $8 - 5 \neq 5 - 8$ because $3 \neq -3$.

Commutative Property of Multiplication A *property* of multiplication that two numbers can be multiplied in either order without changing the product. For example, $5 \times 10 = 10 \times 5$. In *Everyday Mathematics,* this is called a turn-around fact, and the two Commutative Properties are called turn-around rules. In symbols:

For any numbers a and b, $a \times b = b \times a$.

Division is not commutative. For example, $10 / 5 \neq 5 / 10$ because $2 \neq \frac{1}{2}$.

comparison diagram A diagram used in *Everyday Mathematics* to model situations in which two quantities are compared by addition or subtraction. The diagram contains two quantities and their difference.

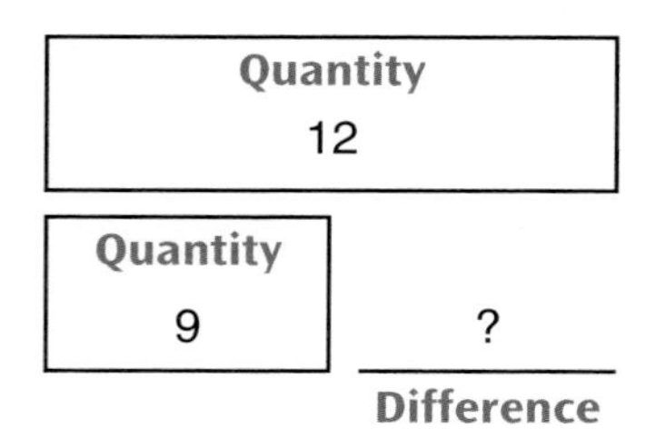

A comparison diagram for $12 = 9 + ?$

complement of a number *n* (1) In *Everyday Mathematics,* the difference between n and the next multiple of 10. For example, the complement of 4 is $10 - 4 = 6$ and the complement of 73 is $80 - 73 = 7$. (2) The difference between n and the next higher power of 10. In this definition, the complement of 73 is $100 - 73 = 27$.

cone A *geometric solid* with a circular *base,* a *vertex* (*apex*) not in the *plane* of the base, and all of the *line segments* with one *endpoint* at the apex and the other endpoint on the *circumference* of the base.

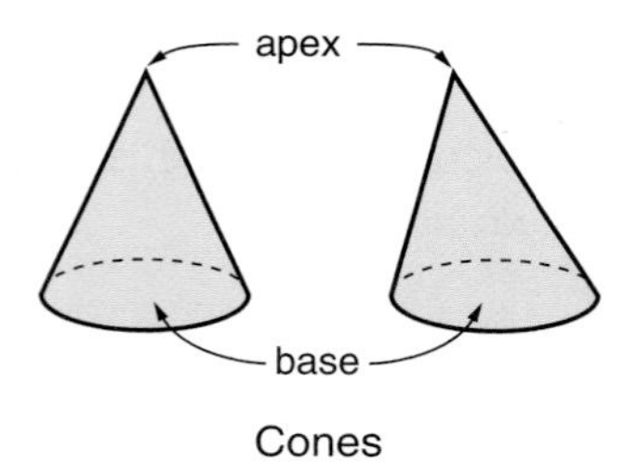

Cones

congruent figures (≅) Figures having the same size and shape. Two figures are congruent if they match exactly when one is placed on top of the other after a combination of slides, flips, and/or turns. In diagrams of congruent figures, the corresponding congruent sides may be marked with the same number of hash marks. The symbol ≅ means "is congruent to."

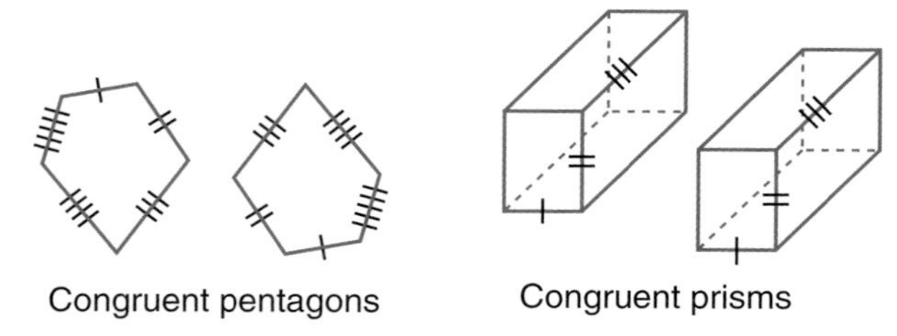

Congruent pentagons Congruent prisms

coordinate (1) A number used to locate a point on a *number line;* a point's distance from an origin. (2) One of the numbers in an *ordered pair* or triple that locates a point on a *coordinate grid* or in coordinate space, respectively.

coordinate grid (rectangular coordinate grid) A reference frame for locating points in a *plane* by means of *ordered pairs* of numbers. A rectangular coordinate grid is formed by two *number lines* that intersect at *right angles* at their zero points.

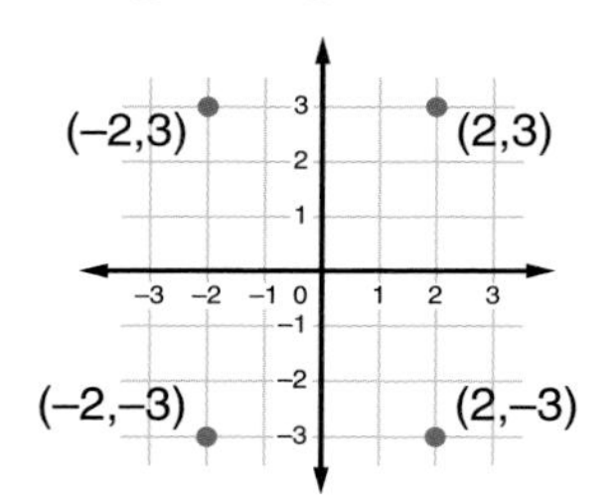

Coordinate grid

counterclockwise rotation Opposite the direction in which the hands move on a typical analog clock; a turn to the left.

counting numbers The numbers used to count things. The *set* of counting numbers is {1, 2, 3, 4, . . .}. Sometimes 0 is included, but not in *Everyday Mathematics.* Counting numbers are in the sets of *whole numbers,* integers, rational numbers, and real numbers, but each of these sets include numbers that are not counting numbers.

cube (1) A *regular polyhedron* with 6 square *faces.* A cube has 8 *vertices* and 12 edges.

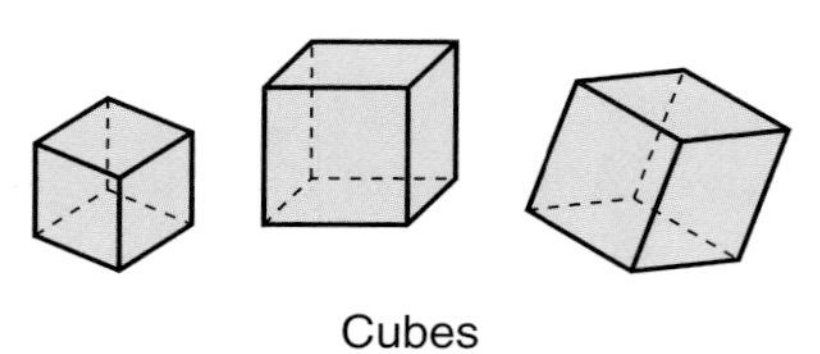

Cubes

(2) In *Everyday Mathematics,* the smaller cube of the base-10 blocks, measuring 1 cm on each edge.

cubic centimeter (cc or cm³) A metric *unit* of *volume* or *capacity* equal to the volume of a *cube* with 1-cm *edges.* $1 \text{ cm}^3 = 1$ milliliter (mL).

cubic unit A unit such as cubic centimeters, cubic inches, cubic feet, and cubic meters used to measure *volume* or *capacity.*

cup (c) A U.S. customary *unit* of *volume* or *capacity* equal to 8 fluid ounces or $\frac{1}{2}$ *pint.*

customary system of measurement In *Everyday Mathematics,* the same as *U.S. customary system* of measurement.

cylinder A *geometric solid* with two congruent, *parallel* circular regions for *bases* and a curved *face* formed by all the segments with an *endpoint* on each circle that are parallel to a segment with endpoints at the centers of the circles. Also called a circular cylinder.

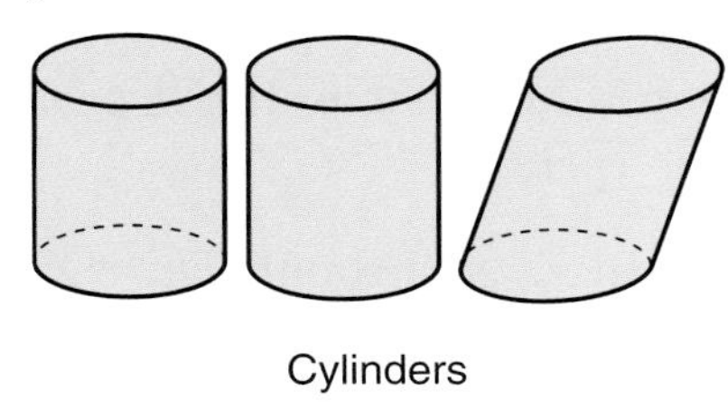

Cylinders

data Information that is gathered by counting, measuring, questioning, or observing. Strictly, data is the plural of datum, but data is often used as a singular word.

data bank (1) In *Third Grade Everyday Mathematics,* a collection of data sets presented in posters, tables, graphs and maps. (2) In general, any established data set or database.

deca- A prefix meaning ten.

decagon A 10-sided *polygon.*

decimal (1) In *Everyday Mathematics,* a number written in standard base-10 notation containing a decimal point, such as 2.54. (2) Any number written in standard base-10 notation.

decimal point A mark used to separate the ones and tenths places in *decimals.* A decimal point separates dollars from cents in dollars-and-cents notation. The mark is a dot in the *U.S. customary system* and a comma in Europe and some other countries.

decimeter (dm) A metric *unit* of length equivalent to $\frac{1}{10}$ *meter* or 10 *centimeters.*

degree (°) (1) A *unit* of measure for *angles* based on dividing a circle into 360 equal parts. Lines of latitude and longitude are measured in degrees, and these degrees are based on angle measures. (2) A unit for measuring temperature. See *Celsius* and *Fahrenheit.* The symbol ° means degrees of any type.

denominator The nonzero *divisor b* in a *fraction* $\frac{a}{b}$ and a / b. In a part-whole fraction, the denominator is the number of equal parts into which the *whole,* or *ONE,* has been divided. Compare to *numerator.*

diameter (1) A *line segment* that passes through the center of a circle or *sphere* and has *endpoints* on the circle or sphere. (2) The length of such a segment. The diameter of a circle or sphere is twice the *length* of the radius.

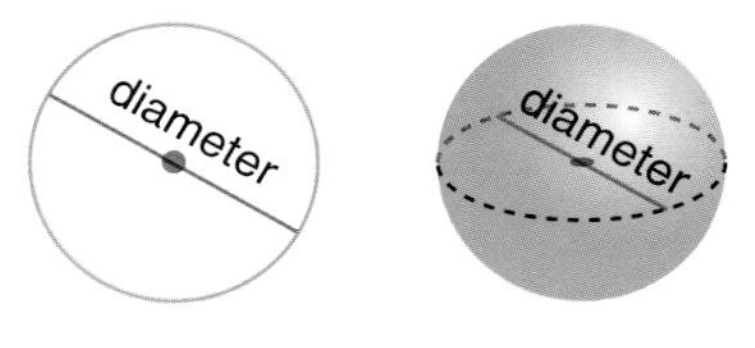

Diameter

difference The result of subtracting one number from another. For example, the difference of 12 and 5 is 7, $12 - 5 = 7$.

digit (1) Any one of the symbols 0, 1, 2, 3, 4, 5, 6, 7, 8, and 9 in the base-10 numeration system. For example, the numeral 145 is made up of the digits 1, 4, and 5. (2) Any one of the symbols in any number system. For example, A, B, C, D, E, and F are digits along with 0 through 9 in the base-16 notation used in some computer programming.

Distributive Property of Multiplication over Addition A property relating multiplication to a sum of numbers by distributing a *factor* over the terms in the sum. For example,
$2 \times (5 + 3) = (2 \times 5) + (2 \times 3) = 10 + 6 = 16$.

In symbols:

For any numbers a, b, and c:
$a \times (b + c) = (a \times b) + (a \times c)$

or $a(b + c) = ab + ac$

dividend The number in division that is being divided. For example, in $35 / 5 = 7$, the dividend is 35.

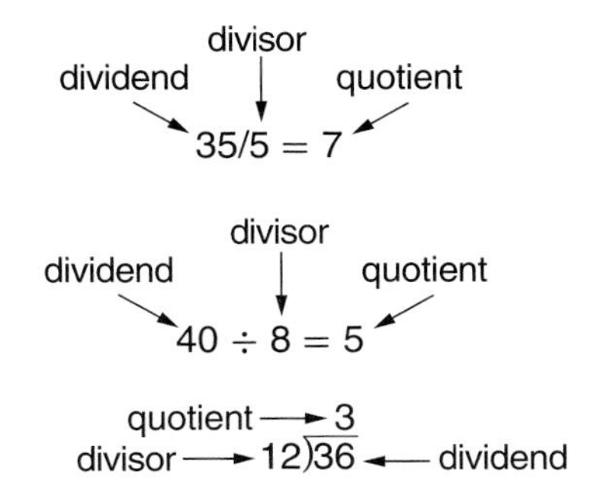

divisor In division, the number that divides another number, the *dividend.* For example, in 35 / 5 = 7, the divisor is 5. See the diagram under the definition of *dividend.*

edge (1) Any side of a polyhedron's faces. (2) A line segment or curve where two surfaces of a geometric solid meet.

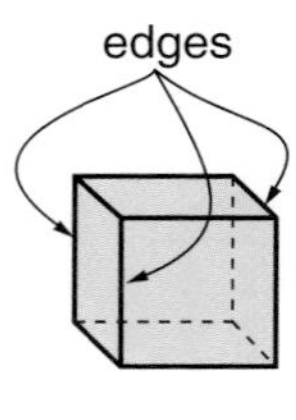

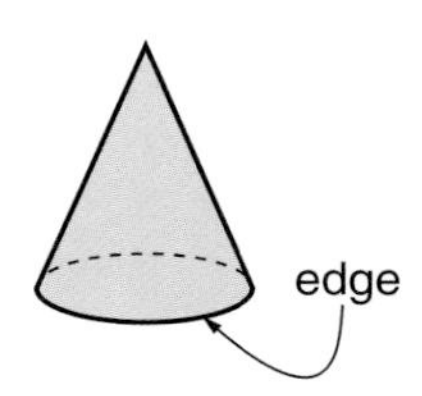

endpoint A point at the end of a *line segment, ray,* or arc. These shapes are usually named using their endpoints. For example, the segment shown is segment *TL* or segment *LT.*

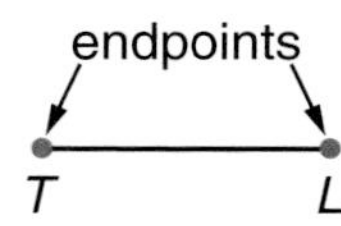

equal groups *Sets* with the same number of elements, such as cars with 5 passengers each, rows with 6 chairs each, and boxes containing 100 paper clips each.

equilateral triangle A *triangle* with all three *sides* equal in length. Each angle of an equilateral triangle measures 60°, so it is also called an equiangular triangle.

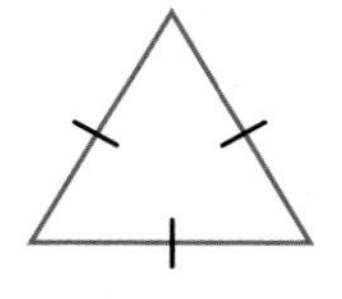

Equilateral triangle

equivalent fractions *Fractions* with different *denominators* that name the same number.

equivalent names Different ways of naming the same number. For example, 2 + 6, 4 + 4, 12 – 4, 18 – 10, 100 – 92, 5 + 2 + 1, eight, VIII, and ~~////~~ /// are all equivalent names for 8. See *name-collection box.*

estimate (1) An answer close to, or approximating, an exact answer. (2) To make an estimate.

even number (1) A *counting number* that is divisible by 2. (2) An integer that is divisible by 2. Compare to *odd number.*

event A set of possible *outcomes* to an experiment. For example, in an experiment flipping two coins, getting 2 HEADS is an event, as is getting 1 HEAD and 1 TAIL. The *probability* of an event is the chance that the event will happen. For example, the probability that a fair coin will land HEADS up is $\frac{1}{2}$. If the probability of an event is 0, the event is impossible. If the probability is 1, the event is certain.

Explorations In *First* through *Third Grade Everyday Mathematics,* independent or small-group activities that focus on one or more of the following: concept development, manipulatives, data collection, problem solving, games, and skill reviews.

face (1) In *Everyday Mathematics,* a flat surface on a *3-dimensional figure*. Some special faces are called *bases.* (2) More generally, any 2-dimensional surface on a 3-dimensional figure.

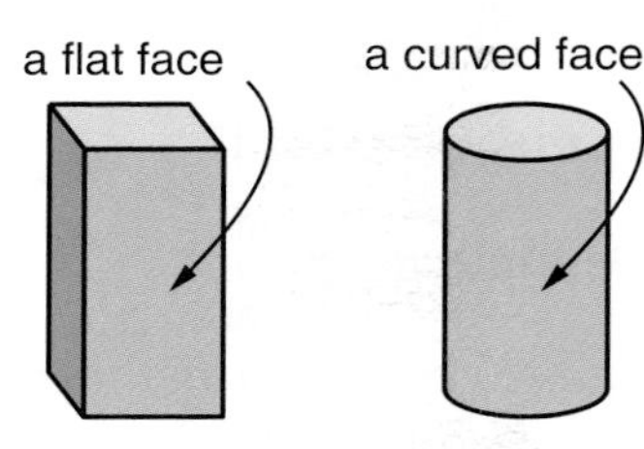

fact extensions Calculations with larger numbers using knowledge of basic arithmetic facts. For example, knowing the addition fact 5 + 8 = 13 makes it easier to solve problems such as 50 + 80 = ? and 65 + ? = 73. Fact extensions apply to all four basic arithmetic operations.

fact family A *set* of related arithmetic facts linking two inverse operations. For example,

$$5 + 6 = 11 \qquad 6 + 5 = 11$$
$$11 - 5 = 6 \qquad 11 - 6 = 5$$

are an addition/subtraction fact family. Similarly,

$$5 \times 7 = 35 \qquad 7 \times 5 = 35$$
$$35 \div 7 = 5 \qquad 35 \div 5 = 7$$

are a multiplication/division fact family. Same as *number family.*

fact power In *Everyday Mathematics,* the ability to automatically recall basic arithmetic facts. Knowing the facts automatically is as important to arithmetic as knowing words by sight is to reading.

Fact Triangle In *Everyday Mathematics,* a triangular flash card labeled with the numbers of a *fact family* that students can use to practice addition/subtraction and multiplication/division facts. The two 1-digit numbers and their sum or *product* (marked with a dot) appear in the corners of each triangle.

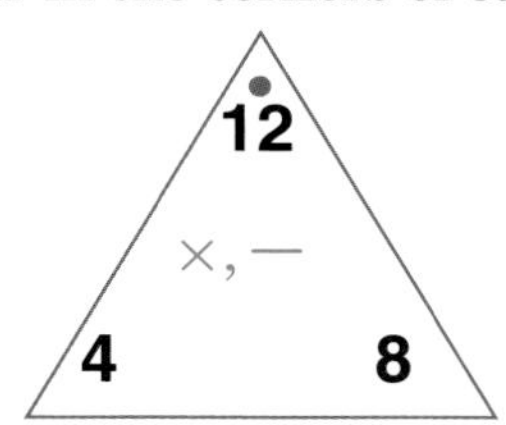

factor of a counting number n A *counting number* whose product with some other counting number equals n. For example, 2 and 3 are factors of 6 because $2 \times 3 = 6$. But 4 is not a factor of 6 because $4 \times 1.5 = 6$, and 1.5 is not a counting number.

Fahrenheit A temperature *scale* on which pure water at sea level freezes at 32° and boils at 212°. The Fahrenheit scale is widely used in the U.S. but in few other places. Compare to *Celsius*.

fair Free from bias. Each side of a fair die or coin will land up about equally often. Each region of a fair spinner will be landed on in proportion to its *area*.

fair game A game in which every player has the same chance of winning.

flat In *Everyday Mathematics,* the base-10 block consisting of one hundred 1-cm *cubes*.

A flat

foot (ft) A U.S. customary *unit* of length equivalent to 12 *inches* or $\frac{1}{3}$ of a *yard*.

fraction A number in the form $\frac{a}{b}$ or a/b, where a and b are *whole numbers* and b is not 0. A fraction may be used to name part of an object or part of a collection of objects, to compare two quantities, or to represent division. For example, $\frac{12}{6}$ might mean 12 eggs divided into 6 groups of 2 eggs each, a ratio of 12 to 6, or 12 divided by 6.

Frames and Arrows In *Everyday Mathematics,* diagrams consisting of frames connected by arrows used to represent number sequences. Each frame contains a number, and each arrow represents a rule that determines which number goes in the next frame. There may be more than one rule, represented by different-color arrows. Frames-and-Arrows diagrams are also called chains.

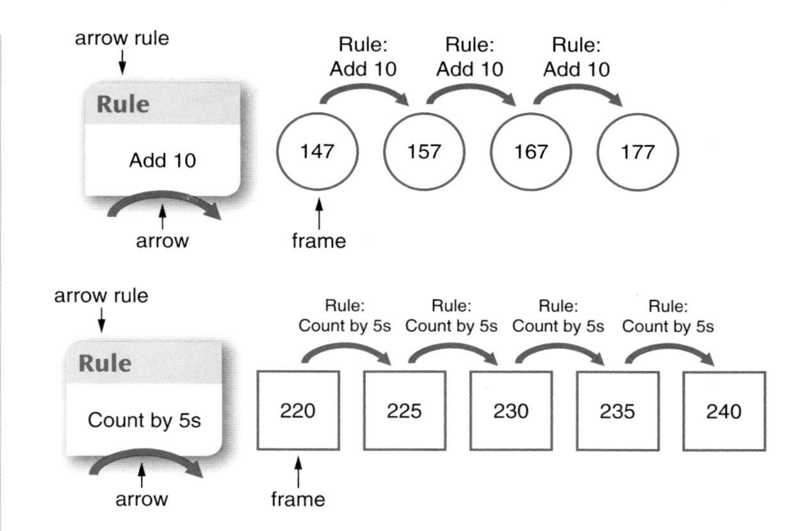

frequency (1) The number of times a value occurs in a *set* of *data*. (2) A number of repetitions per *unit* of time. For example, the vibrations per second in a sound wave.

frequency graph A graph showing how often each value occurs in a *data* set.

Colors in a Bag of Gumdrops

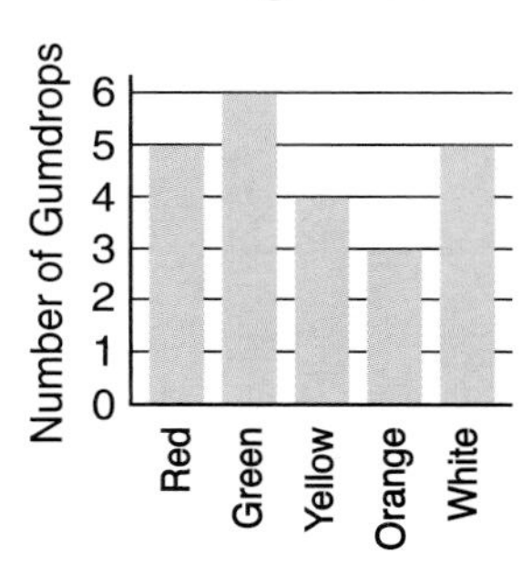

frequency table A table in which *data* are tallied and organized, often as a first step toward making a *frequency graph*.

Color	Number of Gumdrops
red	~~////~~
green	~~////~~ /
yellow	////
orange	///
white	~~////~~

function machine In *Everyday Mathematics,* an imaginary device that receives *inputs* and pairs them with *outputs.* For example, the function machine below pairs an input number with its double.

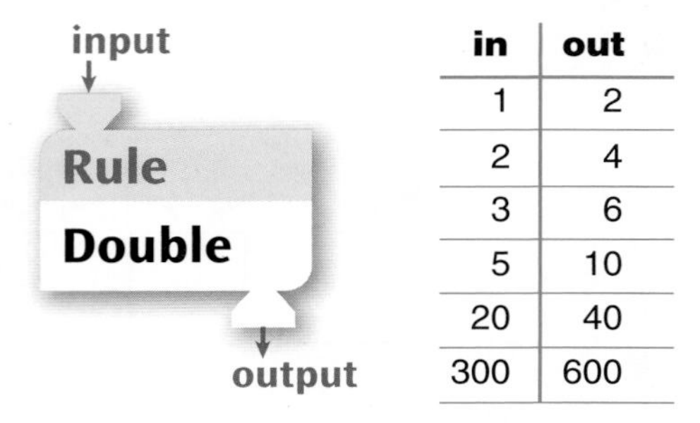

in	out
1	2
2	4
3	6
5	10
20	40
300	600

A function machine and function table

G

gallon (gal) A U.S. customary *unit* of *volume* or *capacity* equal to 4 *quarts.*

geometric solid The surface or surfaces that make up a *3-dimensional figure* such as a *prism, pyramid, cylinder, cone,* or *sphere.* Despite its name, a geometric solid is hollow, that is, it does not include the points in its interior. Informally, and in some dictionaries, a solid is defined as both the surface and its interior.

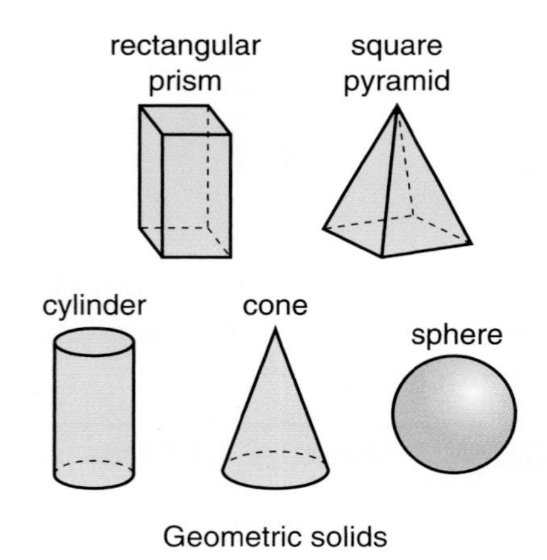

Geometric solids

-gon A suffix meaning *angle.* For example, a *hexagon* is a *plane figure* with six angles.

gram (g) A metric *unit* of mass equal to $\frac{1}{1000}$ of a *kilogram.*

H

hepta- A prefix meaning seven.

heptagon A 7-sided *polygon.*

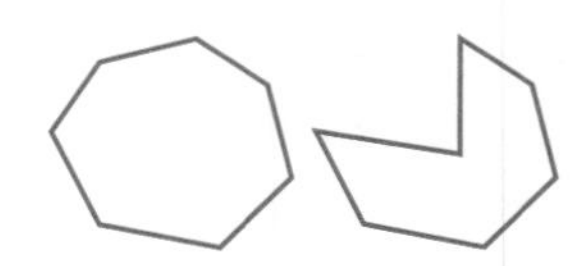

Heptagons

hexa- A prefix meaning six.

hexagon A 6-sided *polygon.*

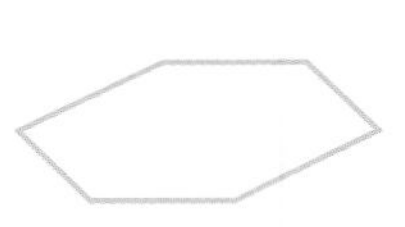

A hexagon

Home Link In *First* through *Third Grade Everyday Mathematics,* a suggested follow-up or enrichment activity to be done at home.

horizontal In a left-to-right orientation. *Parallel* to the horizon.

I

inch (in.) A U.S. customary *unit* of length equal to $\frac{1}{12}$ of a *foot* and 2.54 *centimeters.*

input (1) A number inserted into an imaginary *function machine,* which applies a rule to pair the input with an *output.* (2) Numbers or other information entered into a calculator or computer.

intersect To share a common *point* or points.

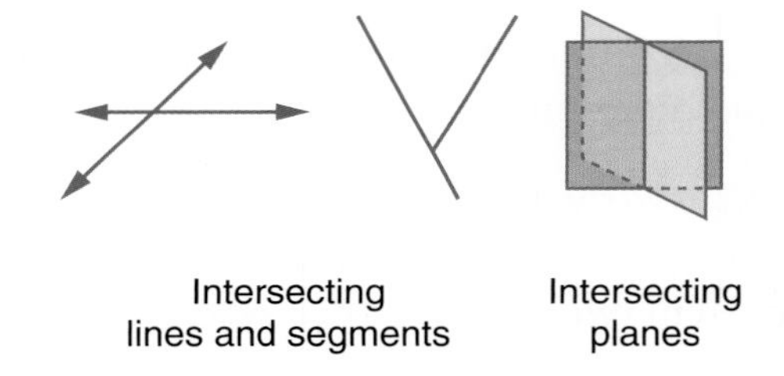

Intersecting lines and segments   Intersecting planes

K

kilogram A metric *unit* of mass equal to 1,000 *grams.* The international standard kilogram is a 39 mm *diameter,* 39 mm high *cylinder* of platinum and iridium kept in the International Bureau of Weights and Measures in Sévres, France. A kilogram is about 2.2 *pounds.*

kilometer A metric *unit* of *length* equal to 1,000 *meters.* A kilometer is about 0.62 mile.

kite A *quadrilateral* with two distinct pairs of *adjacent sides* of equal length. In *Everyday Mathematics,* the four sides cannot all have equal length; that is, a *rhombus* is not a kite. The diagonals of a kite are perpendicular.

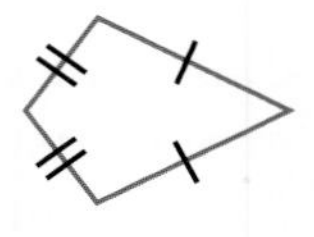

A kite

landmark In *Everyday Mathematics,* a notable feature of a *data* set. Landmarks include the *median, mode, mean, maximum, minimum,* and *range.*

lattice multiplication A very old *algorithm* for multiplying multidigit numbers that requires only basic multiplication facts and addition of 1-digit numbers in a lattice diagram.

length The distance between two points on a 1-dimensional figure. The figure might be a line segment, arc, or curve on a map modeling a hiking path. Length is measured in *units* such as *inches,* kilometers, and miles.

length of a rectangle Typically, but not necessarily, the longer dimension of a *rectangle.*

line In *Everyday Mathematics,* a 1-dimensional straight path that extends forever in opposite directions. A line is named using two *points* on it or with a single, italicized lower-case letter such as *l*. In formal Euclidean geometry, a line is an undefined geometric term.

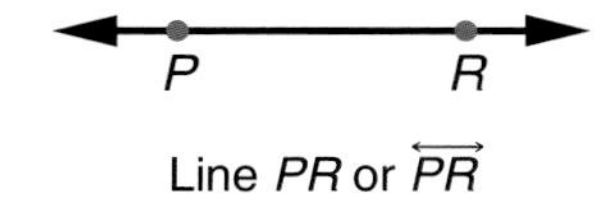

Line *PR* or $\overleftrightarrow{PR}$

line graph A graph in which *data* points are connected by *line segments.*

line of symmetry A line that divides a figure into two parts that are reflection images of each other. A figure may have zero, one, or more lines of symmetry. For example, the numeral 2 has no lines of symmetry, a *square* has four lines of symmetry, and a circle has infinitely many lines of symmetry. Also called a symmetry line.

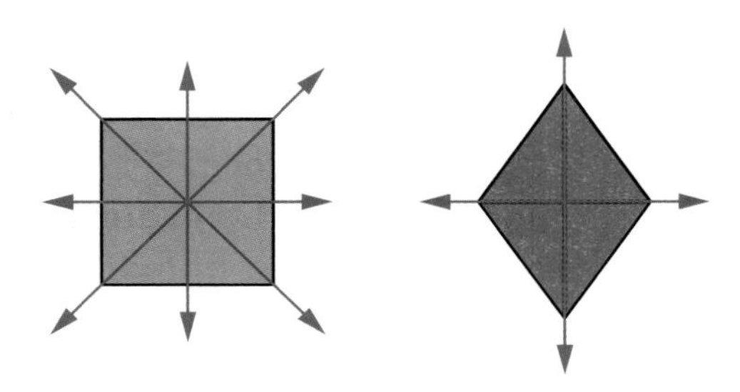

Lines of symmetry are shown in blue.

line plot A sketch of *data* in which check marks, Xs, or other symbols above a labeled line show the *frequency* of each value.

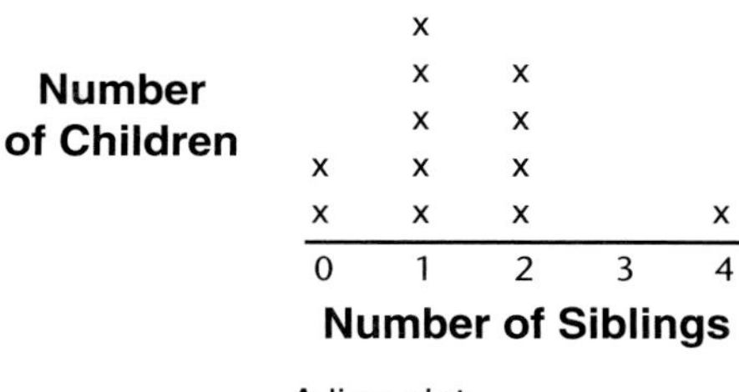

A line plot

line segment A part of a *line* between and including two *points,* called *endpoints* of the segment. A line segment is often named by its endpoints.

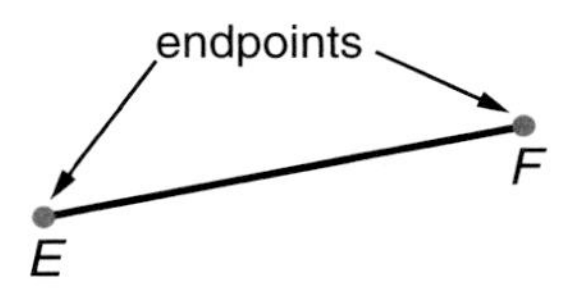

Segment *EF* or $\overline{EF}$

line symmetry A figure has line symmetry if a line can be drawn that divides it into two parts that are reflection images of each other.

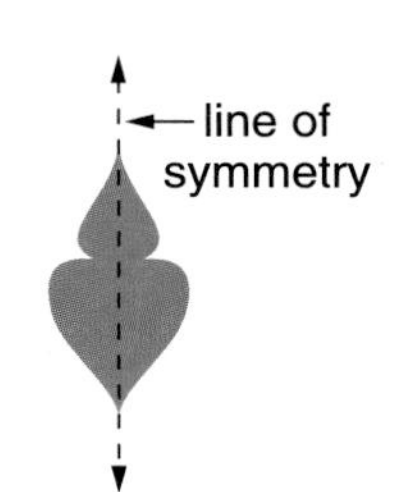

liter (L) A metric unit of *volume* or *capacity* equal to the volume of a *cube* with 10-cm-long *edges.* 1 L = 1,000 mL = 1,000 cm^3. A liter is a little larger than a *quart.*

long In *Everyday Mathematics,* the base-10 block consisting of ten 1-cm *cubes.* Sometimes called a rod.

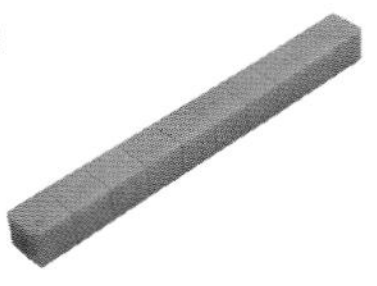

map scale The ratio of a distance on a map, globe, or drawing to an actual distance. For example, 1 *inch* on a map might correspond to 1 real-world mile. A map scale may be shown on a segment of a *number line,* given as a ratio of distances such as $\frac{1}{63,360}$ or 1:63,360 when an inch represents a mile, or by an informal use of the = symbol such as 1 inch = 1 mile.

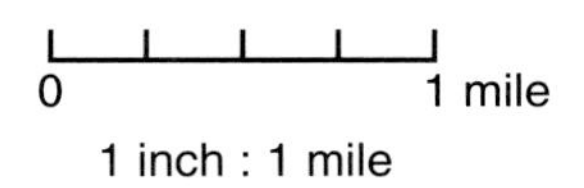

1 inch : 1 mile

mass A measure of the amount of matter in an object. Mass is not affected by gravity, so it is the same on Earth, the moon, or anywhere else in space. Mass is usually measured in grams, kilograms, and other metric units. Compare to *weight.*

Math Boxes In *Everyday Mathematics,* a collection of problems to practice skills. Math Boxes for each lesson are in the *Math Journal.*

Math Journal In *Everyday Mathematics,* a place for students to record their mathematical discoveries and experiences. Journal pages give models for conceptual understanding, problems to solve, and directions for individual and small-group activities.

Math Master In *Everyday Mathematics,* a page ready for duplicating. Most masters support children in carrying out suggested activities. Some masters are used more than once during the school year.

Math Message In *Everyday Mathematics,* an introductory activity to the day's lesson that children complete before the lesson starts. Messages may include problems to solve, directions to follow, sentences to complete or correct, review exercises, or reading assignments.

maximum The largest amount; the greatest number in a *set* of *data.* Compare to minimum.

mean For a *set* of numbers, their sum divided by the number of numbers. Often called the *average* value of the set. Compare to the other data *landmarks median* and *mode.*

median The middle value in a *set* of *data* when the data are listed in order from smallest to largest or vice versa. If there is an even number of data points, the median is the *mean* of the two middle values. Compare to other data *landmarks mean* and *mode.*

memory in a calculator Where numbers are stored in a calculator for use in later calculations. Most calculators have both a short-term memory and a long-term memory.

Mental Math and Reflexes In *Everyday Mathematics,* exercises at three levels of difficulty at the beginning of lessons for students to get ready to think about math, warm up skills they need for the lesson, continually build mental-arithmetic skills, and help you assess individual strengths and weaknesses.

meter (m) The basic metric *unit* of *length* from which other metric units of length are derived. Originally, the meter was defined as $\frac{1}{10,000,000}$ of the distance from the North Pole to the equator along a meridian passing through Paris. From 1960 to 1983, the meter was redefined as 1,630,763.73 wavelengths of orange-red light from the element krypton. Today, the meter is defined as the distance light travels in a vacuum in $\frac{1}{299,792,458}$ second. One meter is equal to 10 *decimeters,* 100 *centimeters,* or 1,000 *millimeters.*

metric system A measurement system based on the base-10 (decimal) numeration system and used in most countries and by virtually all scientists around the world. *Units* for *length* include *millimeter, centimeter, meter,* and *kilometer;* units for mass and *weight* include *gram* and *kilogram;* units for *volume* and *capacity* include milliliter and *liter;* and the unit for temperature change is *degrees Celsius.*

middle value Same as *median.*

millimeter (mm) A metric *unit* of length equal to $\frac{1}{10}$ of a *centimeter,* or $\frac{1}{1000}$ of a *meter.*

minimum The smallest amount; the smallest number in a *set* of *data.* Compare to *maximum.*

mixed number A number that is written using both a *whole number* and a *fraction.* For example, $2\frac{1}{4}$ is a mixed number equal to $2 + \frac{1}{4}$.

mode The value or values that occur most often in a *set* of *data.* Compare to other *landmarks median* and *mean.*

multiple of a number *n* (1) A *product* of *n* and a *counting number.* For example, the multiples of 7 are 7, 14, 21, 28, ... (2) A product of *n* and an integer. For example, the multiples of 7 are . . . , −21, −14, −7, 0, 7, 14, 21, ...

multiplication/division diagram A diagram used in *Everyday Mathematics* to model situations in which a total number is made up of equal-size groups. The diagram contains a number of groups, a number in each group, and a total number. Also called a multiplication diagram for short.

rows	chairs per row	total chairs
15	25	?

A multiplication/division diagram

name-collection box In *Everyday Mathematics,* a diagram that is used for collecting *equivalent* names for a number.

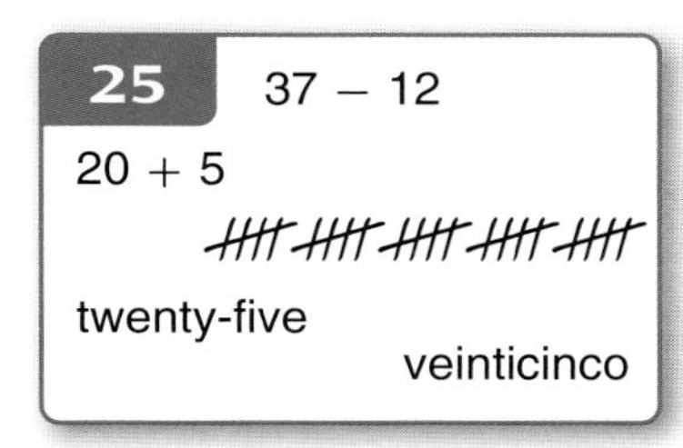

nona- A prefix meaning nine.

nonagon A 9-sided *polygon.*

number family Same as *fact family.*

number grid In *Everyday Mathematics,* a table in which consecutive numbers are arranged in rows, usually 10 columns per row. A move from one number to the next within a row is a change of 1; a move from one number to the next within a column is a change of 10.

–9	–8	–7	–6	–5	–4	–3	–2	–1	0
1	2	3	4	5	6	7	8	9	10
11	12	13	14	15	16	17	18	19	20
21	22	23	24	25	26	27	28	29	30
31	32	33	34	35	36	37	38	39	40
41	42	43	44	45	46	47	48	49	50
51	52	53	54	55	56	57	58	59	60
61	62	63	64	65	66	67	68	69	70
71	72	73	74	75	76	77	78	79	80
81	82	83	84	85	86	87	88	89	90
91	92	93	94	95	96	97	98	99	100
101	102	103	104	105	106	107	108	109	110

A number grid

number-grid puzzle In *Everyday Mathematics,* a piece of a *number grid* in which some, but not all, of the numbers are missing. Students use number-grid puzzles to practice place-value concepts.

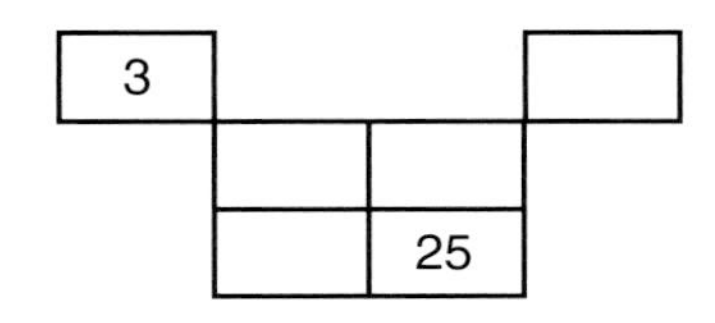

A number-grid puzzle

number line A line on which points are indicated by tick marks that are usually at regularly spaced intervals from a starting point called the origin, the zero point, or simply 0. Numbers are associated with the tick marks on a *scale* defined by the unit interval from 0 to 1.

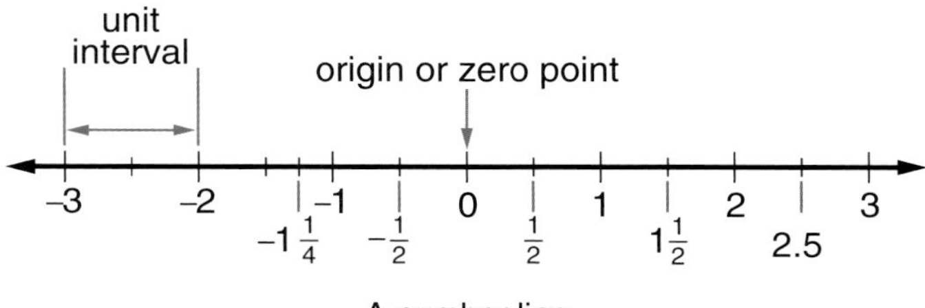

A number line

number model A number sentence, expression, or other representation that models a *number story* or situation. For example, the story *Sally had $5, and then she earned $8* can be modeled as the number sentence 5 + 8 = 13, as the expression 5 + 8, or by

$$\begin{array}{r} 5 \\ +\,8 \\ \hline 13 \end{array}$$

number sequence A list of numbers, often generated by a rule. In *Everyday Mathematics,* students explore number sequences using *Frames-and-Arrows* diagrams.

1, 2, 3, 4, 5, . . .   1, 4, 9, 16, 25, . . .

1, 2, 1, 2, 1, . . .   1, 3, 5, 7, 9, . . .

Number sequences

number story A story that involves numbers and one or more explicit or implicit questions. For example, *I have 7 crayons in my desk. Carrie gave me 8 more crayons. Now I have 15 crayons in all* is a number story.

numerator The *dividend a* in a *fraction* $\frac{a}{b}$ or *a*/*b*. In a part-whole fraction, in which the *whole* (the *ONE* or unit whole) is divided into a number of equal parts, the numerator is the number of equal parts being considered. Compare to *denominator.*

octa- A prefix meaning eight.

octagon An 8-sided *polygon.*

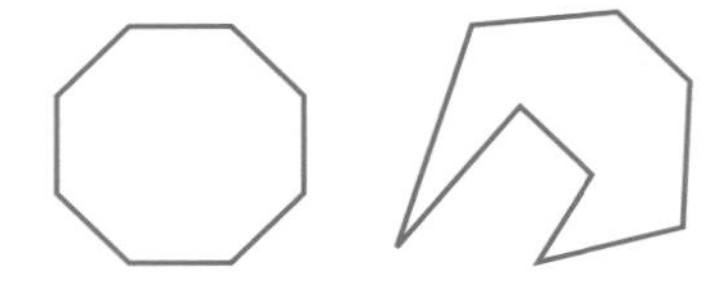

Octagons

odd number A *counting number* that is not divisible by 2. Compare to *even number.*

ONE In *Everyday Mathematics,* same as *whole.*

order of operations Rules that tell the order in which operations in an expression should be carried out. The conventional order of operations is:

1. Do operations inside grouping symbols. Work from the innermost set of grouping symbols outward. Inside grouping symbols, follow Rules 2–4.
2. Calculate all expressions with exponents.
3. Multiply and divide in order from left to right.
4. Add and subtract in order from left to right.

For example:

$$\begin{aligned} 5^2 + (3 \times 4 - 2) \div 5 &= 5^2 + (12 - 2) \div 5 \\ &= 5^2 + 10 \div 5 \\ &= 25 + 10 \div 5 \\ &= 25 + 2 \\ &= 27 \end{aligned}$$

Same as *algebraic order of operations.*

ordered pair (1) Two numbers, or *coordinates,* used to locate a point on a rectangular *coordinate grid.* The first coordinate x gives the position along the horizontal axis of the grid, and the second coordinate y gives the position along the vertical axis. The pair is written (x,y). (2) Any pair of objects or numbers in a particular order.

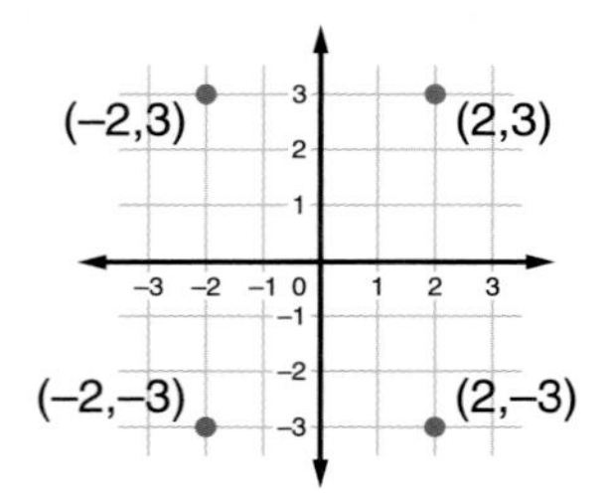

Ordered pairs

ounce (oz) A U.S. customary *unit* of *weight* equal to $\frac{1}{16}$ of a *pound* or about 28.35 *grams.*

outcome A possible result of a chance experiment or situation. For example, HEADS and TAILS are the two possible outcomes of flipping a coin. See *event.*

output (1) A number paired to an *input* by an imaginary *function machine* applying a rule. (2) Numbers or other information displayed by calculator or computer.

parallel *Lines* in a *plane* that never meet. Two parallel lines are always the same distance apart.

Line segments or *rays* on parallel lines are parallel to each other.

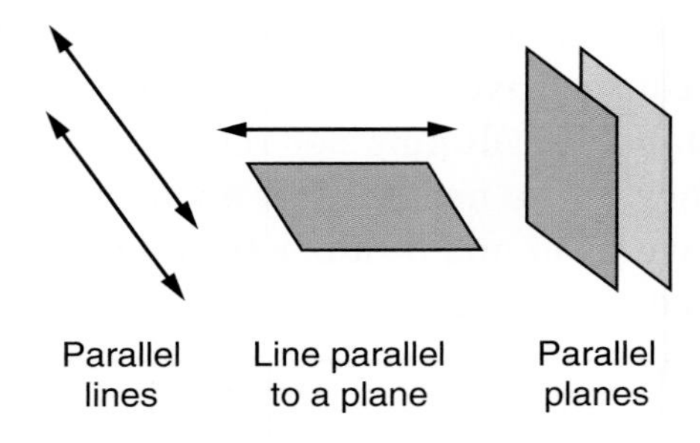

Parallel lines | Line parallel to a plane | Parallel planes

parallelogram A *quadrilateral* with two pairs of *parallel sides.* Opposite sides of a parallelogram have the same length and opposite *angles* have the same measure. All *rectangles* are parallelograms, but not all parallelograms are rectangles because parallelograms do not necessarily have *right angles.*

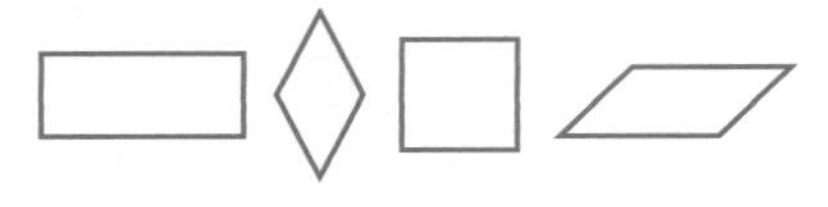

Parallelograms

parentheses ( ) Grouping symbols used to indicate which parts of an expression should be done first.

parts-and-total diagram In *Everyday Mathematics,* a diagram used to model problems in which two or more quantities (parts) are combined to get a total quantity.

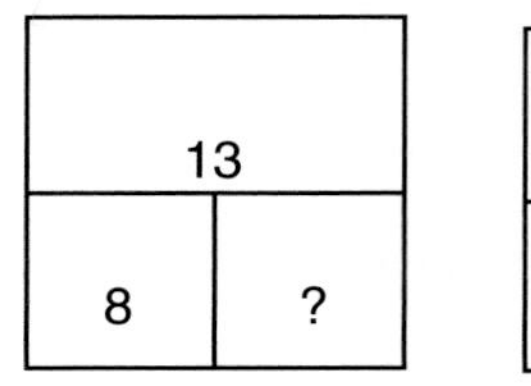

Total	
13	
Part 8	Part ?

Parts-and-total diagrams for 13 = 8 + ?

pattern A repetitive order or arrangement. In *Everyday Mathematics,* students mainly explore visual and number patterns in which elements are arranged so that what comes next can be predicted.

Pattern-Block Template In *First* through *Third Grade Everyday Mathematics,* a sheet of plastic with geometric shapes cut out, used to draw *patterns* and designs.

penta- A prefix meaning five.

pentagon A 5-sided *polygon.*

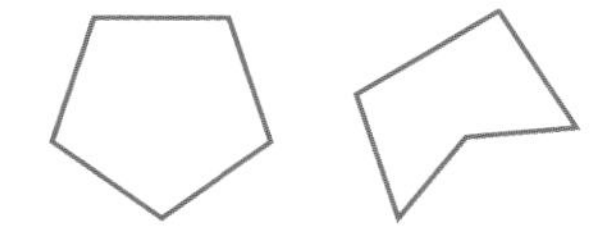

Pentagons

per For each, as in *ten chairs per row* or *six tickets per family.*

percent (%) Per hundred, for each hundred, or out of a hundred. $1\% = \frac{1}{100} = 0.01$. For example, *48% of the students in the school are boys* means that, on average, 48 of every 100 children in the school are boys.

perimeter The distance around the boundary of a *2-dimensional figure.* The perimeter of a circle is called its *circumference.* A formula for the perimeter P of a *rectangle* with length l and width w is $P = 2 \times (l + w)$. Perimeter comes from the Greek words for around measure.

pictograph A graph constructed with pictures or symbols.

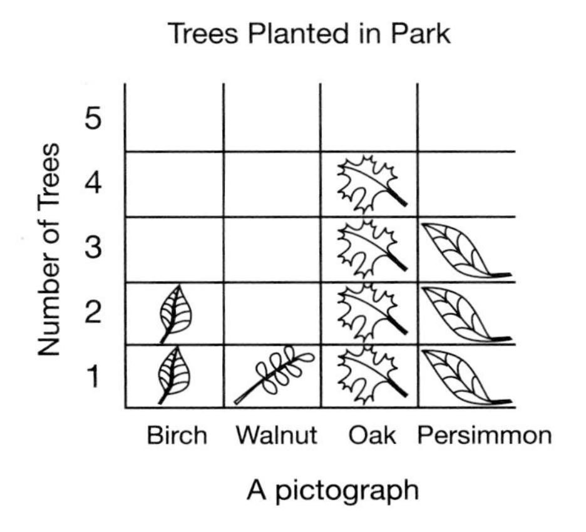

A pictograph

pint (pt) A U.S. customary *unit* of *volume* or *capacity* equal to 2 *cups* or 16 fluid *ounces.* A handy saying to remember is *A pint's a pound the world around,* meaning that a pint of water weighs about 1 *pound.*

plane In *Everyday Mathematics,* a 2-dimensional flat surface that extends forever in all directions. In formal Euclidean geometry, plane is an undefined geometric term.

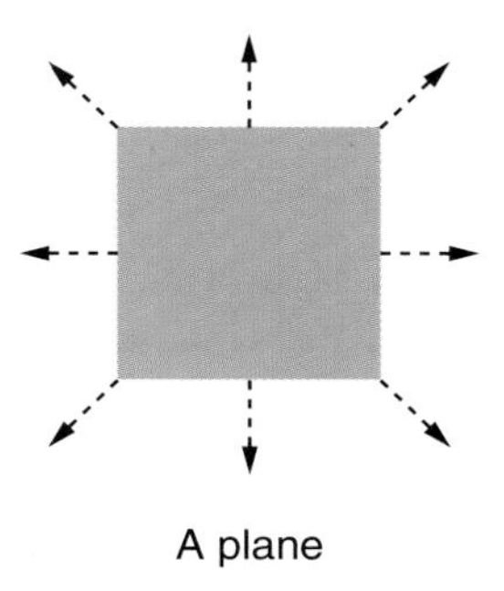

A plane

plane figure A *2-dimensional figure* that is entirely contained in a single *plane.* For example, *triangles, squares, pentagons,* circles, and parabolas are plane figures; *lines, rays, cones, cubes,* and *prisms* are not.

point In *Everyday Mathematics,* an exact location in space. Points are usually labeled with capital letters. In formal Euclidean geometry, a point is an undefined geometric term.

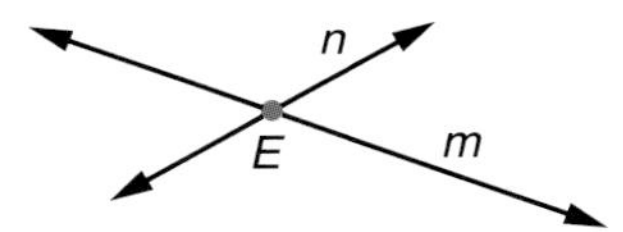

Lines m and n intersect at point E.

poly- A prefix meaning many.

polygon A *2-dimensional figure* formed by three or more *line segments* (*sides*) that meet only at their *endpoints* (*vertices*) to make a closed path. The sides may not cross one another.

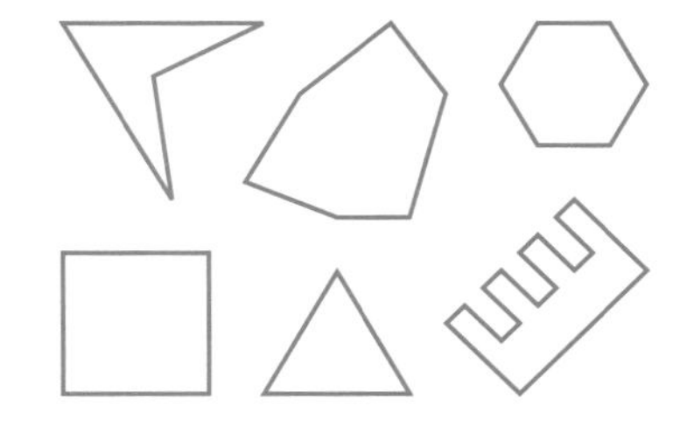

Polygons

polyhedron A *3-dimensional figure* formed by *polygons* with their interiors (*faces*) and having no holes. Plural is polyhedrons or polyhedra.

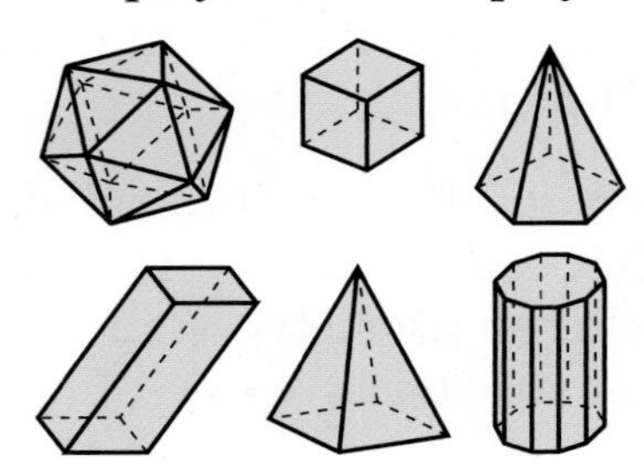

Polyhedrons

pound (lb) A U.S. customary *unit* of *weight* equal to 16 *ounces* and defined as 0.45359237 *kilograms.*

precipitation Condensed atmospheric moisture that falls to the ground, including rain, snow, and hail. In the United States, rainfall is typically measured in *inches.* Snow and hail are first melted and then measured like rain.

precise Exact or accurate.

prime number A *counting number* greater than 1 that has exactly two whole-number factors, 1 and itself. For example, 7 is a prime number because its only factors are 1 and 7. The first five prime numbers are 2, 3, 5, 7, and 11. Also simply called primes.

prism A *polyhedron* with two *parallel* and congruent polygonal regions for *bases* and lateral *faces* formed by all the *line segments* with *endpoints* on corresponding edges of the bases. The lateral faces are all *parallelograms.* Lateral faces intersect at lateral *edges.* In a right prism, the lateral faces are rectangular. Prisms get their names from the shape of their bases.

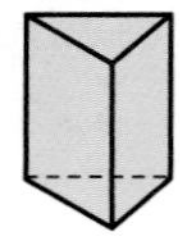
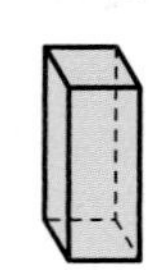
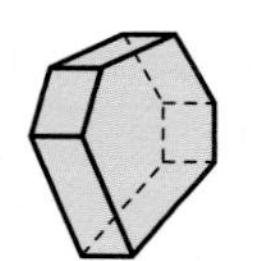

A triangular prism | A rectangular prism | A hexagonal prism

probability A number from 0 through 1 giving the likelihood that an *event* will happen. The closer a probability is to 1, the more likely the event is to happen. The closer a probability is to 0, the less likely the event is to happen. For example, the probability that a fair coin will show heads is $\frac{1}{2}$.

product The result of multiplying two numbers, called factors. For example, in $4 \times 3 = 12$, the product is 12.

Project In *Everyday Mathematics,* a thematic activity to be completed in one or more days by small groups or by a whole class. Projects often involve collecting and analyzing *data* and are usually cross-curricular in nature.

property (1) A generalized statement about a mathematical relationship such as the Commutative Property of Addition. (2) Same as *attribute.*

pyramid A *polyhedron* made up of any polygonal region for a *base,* a point (*apex*) not in the *plane* of the base, and all of the *line segments* with one *endpoint* at the apex and the other on an *edge* of the base. All *faces* except the base are triangular. Pyramids get their name from the shape of their base.

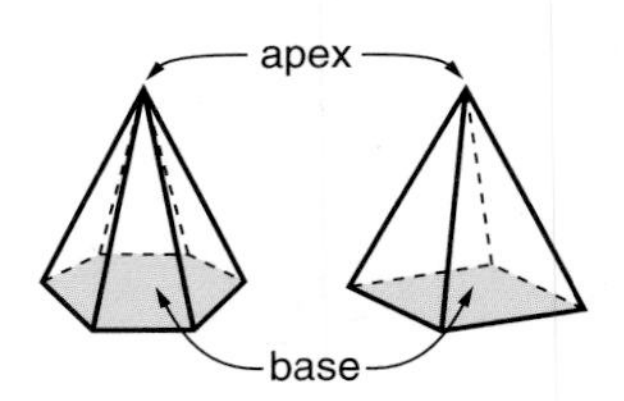

A hexagonal pyramid | A square pyramid

Q

quad A prefix meaning four.

quadrangle Same as *quadrilateral.*

quadrilateral A 4-sided *polygon.* See *square, rectangle, parallelogram, rhombus, kite,* and *trapezoid.*

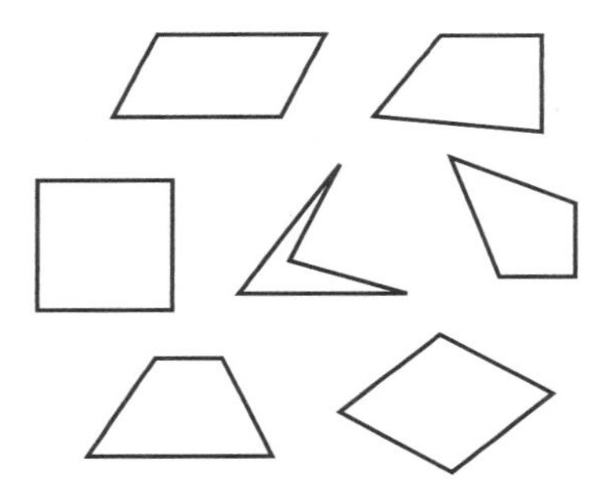

Quadrilaterals

quart A U.S. customary *unit* of *volume* or *capacity* equal to 32 fluid ounces, 2 *pints,* or 4 *cups.*

quotient The result of dividing one number by another number. For example, in 35 / 5 = 7, the quotient is 7.

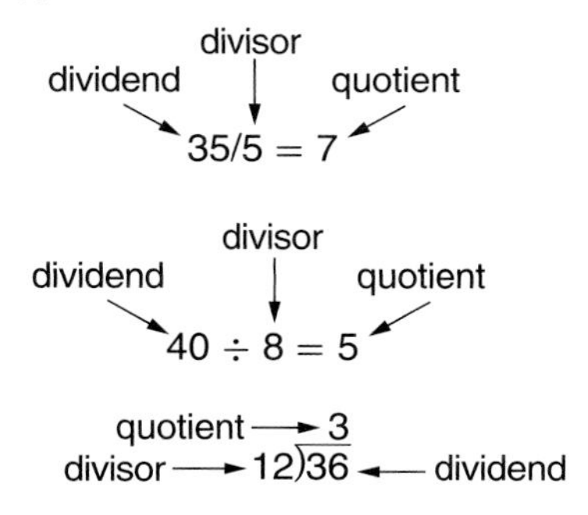

random draw Taking an object from a *set* of objects in which each object has an equally likely chance of being chosen. For example, drawing a card from a deck or drawing a domino from a bag of dominos are random draws.

random sample A *sample* that gives all members of the population the same chance of being selected.

range The *difference* between the *maximum* and the *minimum* in a set of *data*. Used as a measure of the spread of the data.

ray A part of a *line* starting at the ray's *endpoint* and continuing forever in one direction. A ray is often named by its endpoint and another *point* on it.

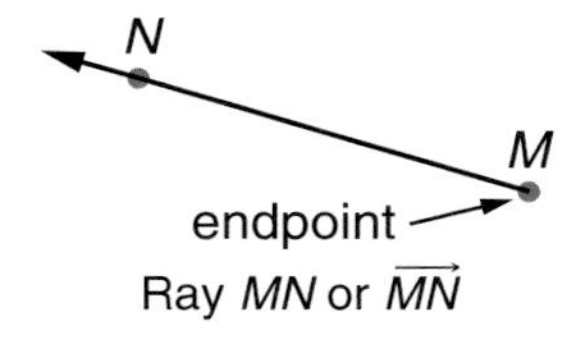

Ray *MN* or $\overrightarrow{MN}$

***r*-by-*c* array** A rectangular arrangement of elements with *r* rows and *c* elements per row. Among other things, an *r*-by-*c* array models *r sets* with *c* objects per set. Although listing rows before columns is arbitrary, it is in keeping with the order used in matrix notation, which students will study later.

rectangle A *parallelogram* with all *right angles.*

rectangular prism A *prism* with rectangular *bases.* The four *faces* that are not bases are either *rectangles* or *parallelograms.* For example, a shoe box models a rectangular prism in which all *sides* are rectangles.

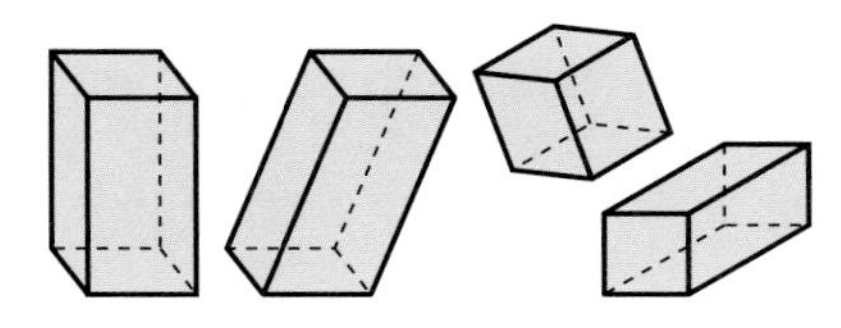

Rectangular prisms

rectangular pyramid A *pyramid* with a rectangular *base.*

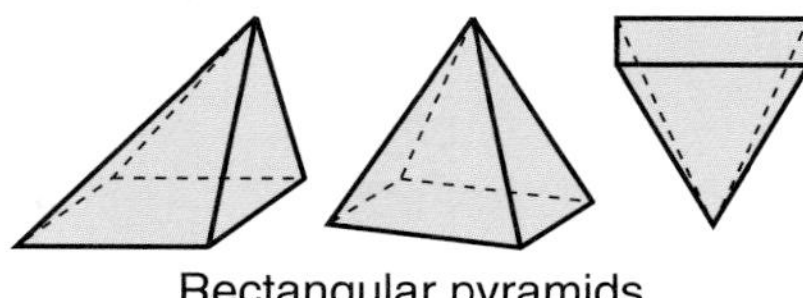

Rectangular pyramids

rectilinear figure (1) *In Everyday Mathematics,* a closed *2-dimensional* shape having *line segments* for *sides* and only 90° or 270° angles. (2) Any shape made up of line segments.

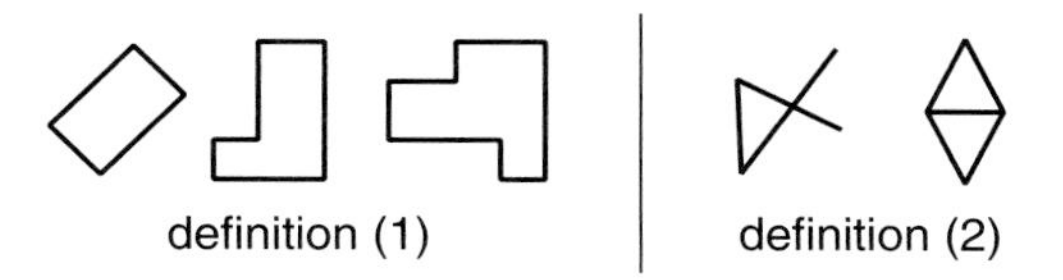

Rectilinear figures

regular polygon A *polygon* in which all *sides* are the same length and all *angles* have the same measure.

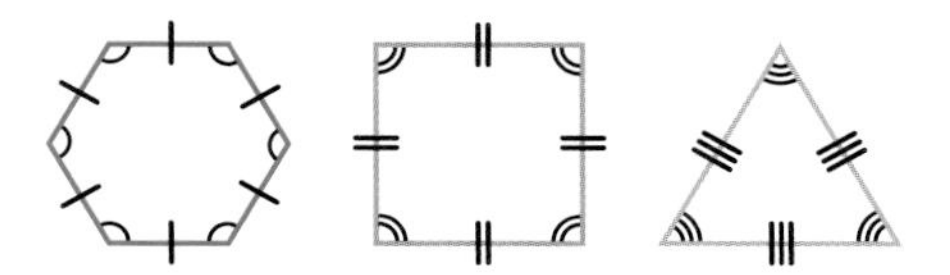

Regular polygons

regular polyhedron A *polyhedron* whose *faces* are all congruent *regular polygons* and in which the same number of faces meet at each *vertex.* The five regular polyhedrons, known as the Platonic solids, are shown below.

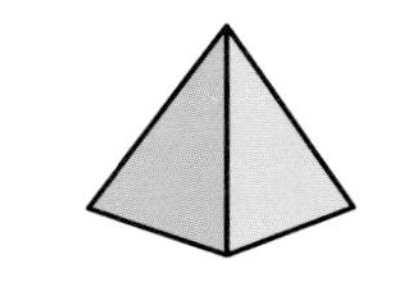

Tetrahedron
(4 equilateral triangles)

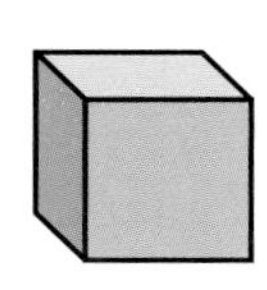

Cube
(6 squares)

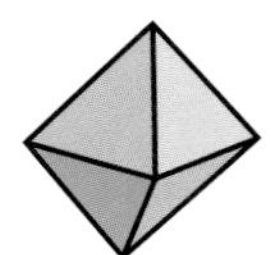

Octahedron
(8 equilateral triangles)

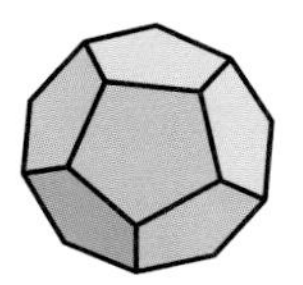

Dodecahedron
(12 regular pentagons)

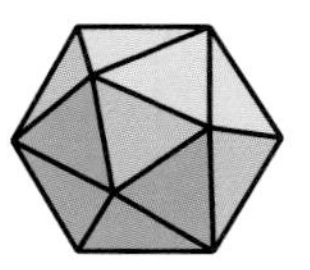

Icosahedron
(20 equilateral triangles)

relation symbol A symbol used to express a relationship between two quantities.

Relation	Meaning
$=$	is equal to
$\neq$	is not equal to
$<$	is less than
$>$	is greater than
$\leq$	is less than or equal to
$\geq$	is greater than or equal to
$\approx$	is approximately equal to

remainder An amount left over when one number is divided by another number. For example, in 16 / 3 → 5 R1, the *quotient* is 5 and the remainder R is 1.

rhombus A *parallelogram* with all *sides* the same length. All rhombuses are parallelograms. Every *square* is a rhombus, but not all rhombuses are squares. Also called a diamond. Plural is rhombuses or rhombi.

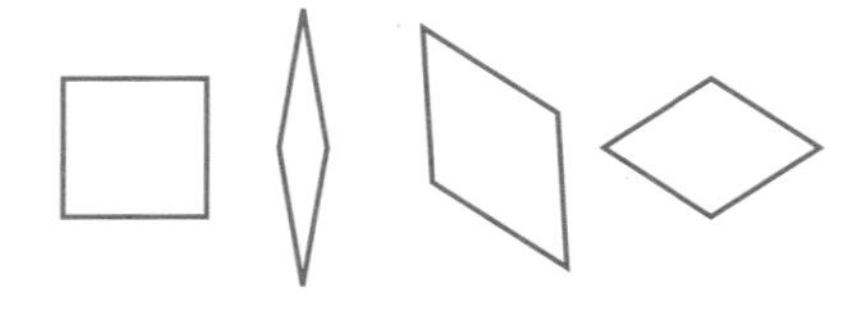

Rhombuses

right angle A 90° *angle*.

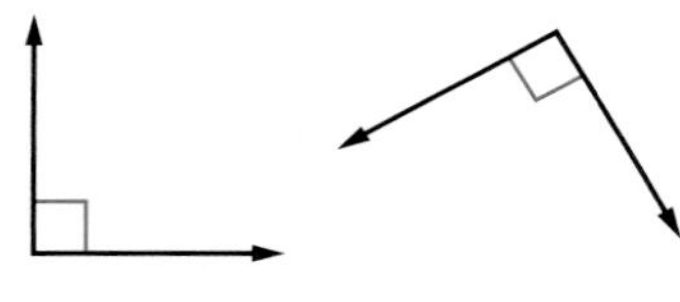

Right angles

S

sample A part of a population intended to represent the whole population. See *random sample*.

scale (1) The relative size of something. (2) Same as *scale factor*. (3) A tool for measuring *weight*.

scale factor (1) The ratio of lengths on an image and corresponding lengths on a preimage in a size change. (2) The ratio of lengths in a scale drawing or scale model to the corresponding lengths in the object being drawn or modeled.

set A collection or group of objects, numbers, or other items.

side (1) One of the *line segments* that make up a *polygon*. (2) One of the *rays* or segments that form an *angle*. (3) One of the *faces* of a *polyhedron*.

similar figures Figures that have the same shape, but not necessarily the same size. Compare to *congruent figures*.

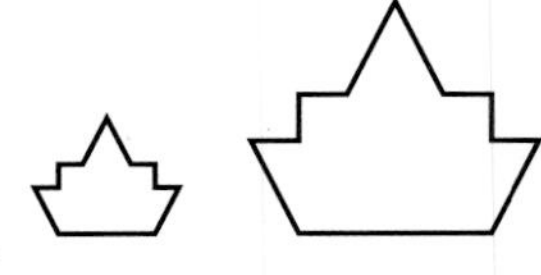

Similar Polygons

slate A lap-size (about 8-inch by 11-inch) chalkboard or whiteboard that children use in *Everyday Mathematics* for recording responses during group exercises and informal group assessments.

sphere The *set* of all *points* in space that are an equal distance from a fixed point called the center of the sphere. The distance from the center to the sphere is the radius of the sphere. The *diameter* of a sphere is twice its radius. Points inside a sphere are not part of the sphere.

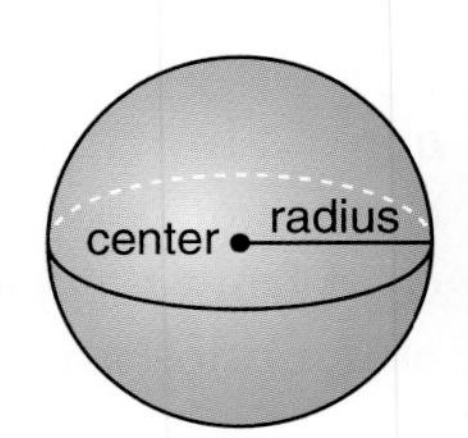

A sphere

square A *rectangle* with all *sides* of equal length. All *angles* in a square are *right angles*.

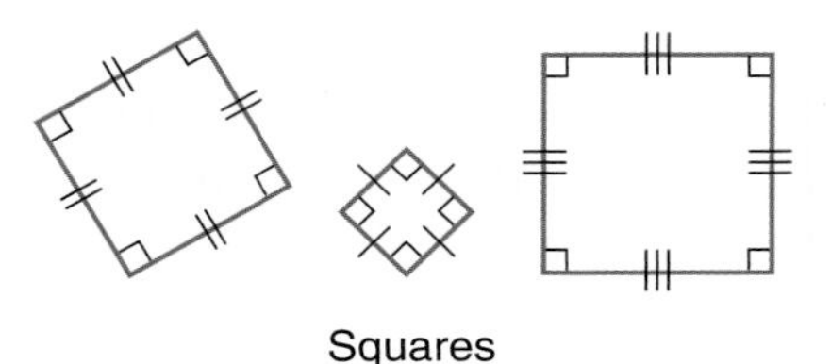

Squares

square numbers Figurate numbers that are the product of a *counting number* and itself. For example, 25 is a square number because $25 = 5 \times 5$. A square number can be represented by a square *array* and as a number squared, such as $25 = 5^2$.

square of a number *n* The product of n and itself, commonly written n^2. For example, $81 = 9 \times 9 = 9^2$ and $3.5^2 = 3.5 \times 3.5 = 12.25$.

square pyramid A *pyramid* with a square *base*.

square unit A *unit* to measure *area*. A model of a square unit is a square with each side a related unit of *length*. For example, a square inch is the area of a *square* with 1-inch sides. Square units are often labeled as the length unit squared. For example, 1 cm² is read "1 square centimeter" or "1 centimeter squared."

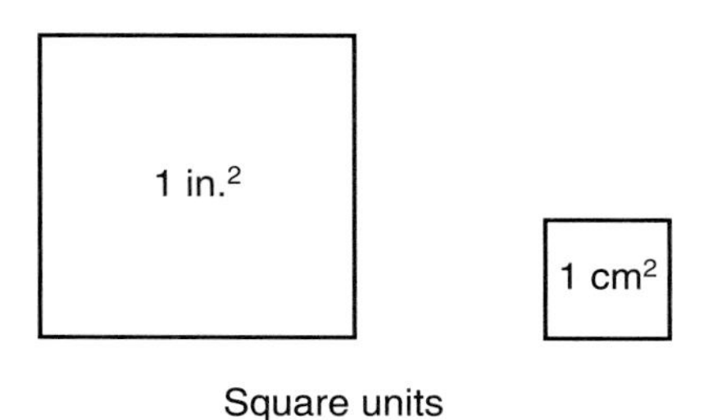

Square units

summer solstice The longest day of the year, when the sun is farthest north of Earth's equator. The number of hours of daylight depends on the latitude of a location. In Colorado, the summer solstice averages a little less than 16 hours of daylight. Compare to *winter solstice.*

survey A study that collects *data.* Surveys are commonly used to study demographics such as people's characteristics, behaviors, interests, and opinions.

symmetry The balanced distribution of *points* over a *line* or around a point in a symmetric figure. See *line symmetry.*

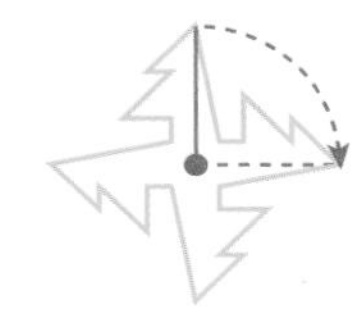

A figure with line symmetry A figure with rotation symmetry

tetrahedron A *polyhedron* with 4 *faces.* A tetrahedron is a *triangular pyramid.*

3-dimensional (3-D) figure A figure whose *points* are not all in a single *plane.* Examples include *prisms, pyramids,* and *spheres,* all of which have *length,* width, and *height.*

tiling A pattern of shapes that covers a surface completely without overlaps or gaps.

tool kit In *First* through *Third Grade Everyday Mathematics,* a bag or a box containing a calculator, measuring tools, and manipulatives often used by children in the program.

trapezoid A *quadrilateral* that has exactly one pair of *parallel sides.* In *Everyday Mathematics,* both pairs of *sides* cannot be parallel; that is, a *parallelogram* is not a trapezoid.

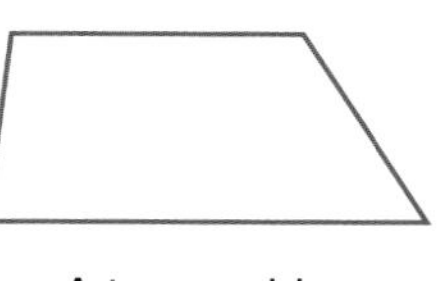

A trapezoid

triangle A 3-sided *polygon.* See *equilateral triangle.*

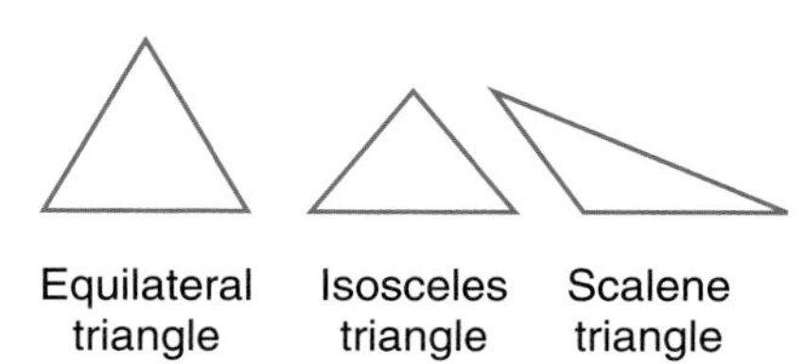

Equilateral triangle Isosceles triangle Scalene triangle

triangular prism A *prism* whose *bases* are *triangles.*

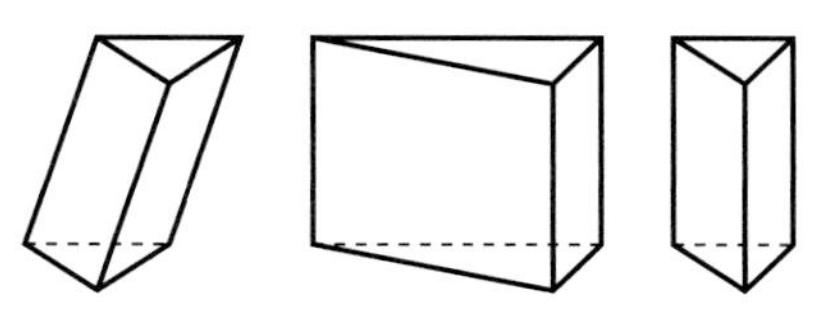

Triangular prisms

triangular pyramid A *pyramid* in which all *faces* are *triangles,* any one of which is the *base.* A regular tetrahedron has four *equilateral triangles* for faces and is one of the five *regular polyhedrons.*

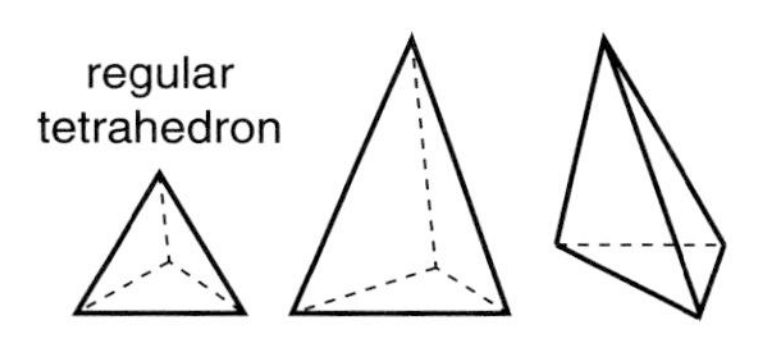

Triangular Pyramids

2-dimensional (2-D) figure A figure whose *points* are all in one *plane* but not all on one *line.* Examples include *polygons* and circles, all of which have length and width but no *height.*

unit A label used to put a number in context. In measuring *length,* for example, *inches* and *centimeters* are units. In a problem about 5 apples, apple is the unit. In *Everyday Mathematics,* students keep track of units in *unit boxes.*

unit box In *Everyday Mathematics,* a box displaying the *unit* for the numbers in the problems at hand.

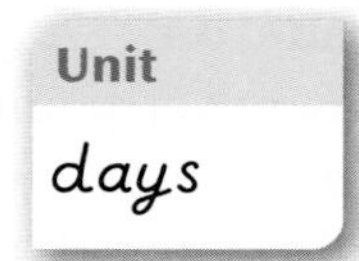

A unit box

unit fraction A *fraction* whose *numerator* is 1. For example, $\frac{1}{2}$, $\frac{1}{3}$, $\frac{1}{8}$, $\frac{1}{12}$, and $\frac{1}{20}$, are unit fractions. Unit fractions are especially useful in converting among *units* within measurement systems. For example, because 1 *foot* = 12 *inches* you can multiply a number of inches by $\frac{1}{12}$ to convert to feet.

U.S. customary system The measuring system used most often in the United States. *Units* for length include *inch, foot, yard,* and mile; units for *weight* include *ounce* and *pound;* units for *volume* or *capacity* include *cup, pint, quart,* gallon and *cubic units;* and the main unit for temperature change is *degrees Fahrenheit.*

vernal equinox The first day of spring, when the sun crosses the *plane* of Earth's equator and day and night are about 12 hours each. Equinox is from the Latin *aequi-* meaning equal and *nox* meaning night. Compare to *autumnal equinox.*

vertex The *point* at which the *rays* of an *angle,* the *sides* of a *polygon,* or the edges of a *polyhedron* meet. Plural is vertexes or vertices. In *Everyday Mathematics,* same as corner.

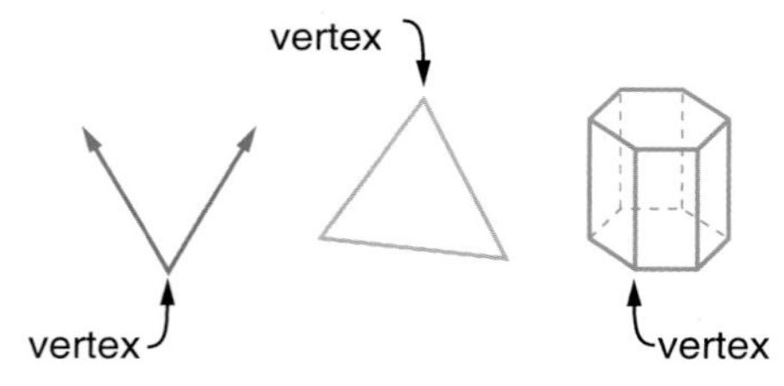

vertical Upright; perpendicular to the horizon. Compare to *horizontal.*

volume (1) The amount of space occupied by a *3-dimensional figure.* Same as *capacity.* (2) The amount a container can hold. Volume is often measured in cubic units, such as cm^3, cubic inches, or cubic feet.

weight A measure of how heavy something is; the force of gravity on an object. An object's mass is constant, but it weighs less in weak gravity than in strong gravity. For example, a person who weighs 150 *pounds* in San Diego weighs about 23 pounds on the moon.

"What's My Rule?" problem In *Everyday Mathematics,* a problem in which two of the three parts of a function (*input, output,* and rule) are known, and the third is to be found out.

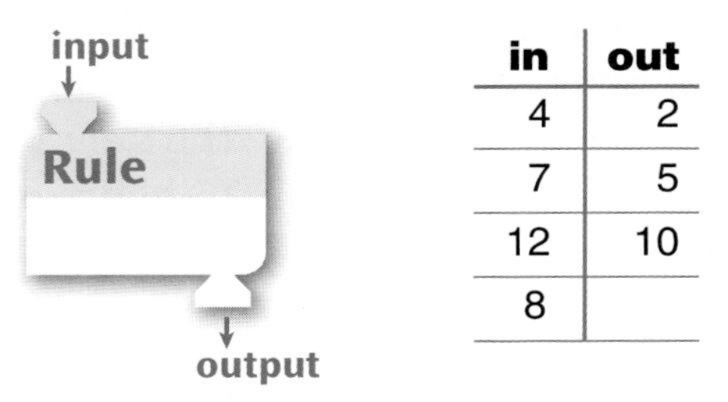

in	out
4	2
7	5
12	10
8	

A "What's My Rule?" problem

whole An entire object, collection of objects, or quantity being considered in a problem situation; 100%. Same as *ONE.*

whole numbers The counting numbers and 0. The set of whole numbers is (0, 1, 2, 3 . . .).

width of a rectangle The *length* of one *side* of a *rectangle* or rectangular object, typically the shorter side.

winter solstice The shortest day of the year, when the sun is farthest south of Earth's equator. The number of hours of daylight depends on the latitude of a location. In Colorado, the winter solstice averages a little more than 9 hours of daylight. Compare to *summer solstice.*

yard (yd) A U.S. customary *unit* of *length* equal to 3 *feet* or 36 *inches.* To Henry I of England, a yard was the distance from the tip of the nose to the tip of the middle finger. In *Everyday Mathematics,* it is from the center of the chest to the tip of the middle finger.

Grade-Level Goals

Everyday Mathematics organizes content through Program Goals and Grade-Level Goals. The Grade-Level Goals Chart shows the units in which goal content is taught and then practiced and applied. For more information, see the *Assessment Handbook.*

The Grade-Level Goals are divided according to the content strands below.

Content Strands

Pages

How to Read the Grade-Level Goals Chart

Each section of the chart includes Grade-Level Goals organized by content strand. The three grade-level columns divided into units indicate in which units the goals are addressed.

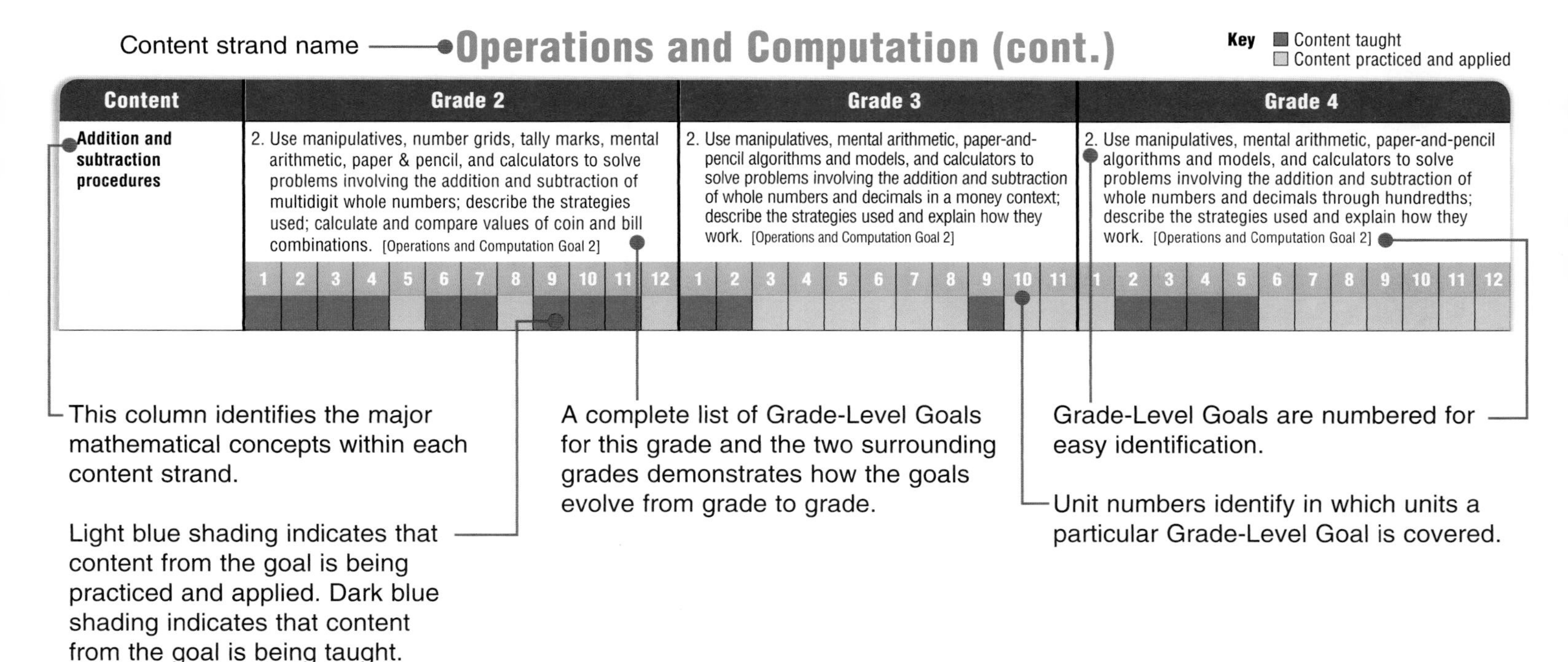

Content strand name
Operations and Computation (cont.)
Key
Content taught
Content practiced and applied
Content
Grade 2
Grade 3
Grade 4
Addition and subtraction procedures
2. Use manipulatives, number grids, tally marks, mental arithmetic, paper & pencil, and calculators to solve problems involving the addition and subtraction of multidigit whole numbers; describe the strategies used; calculate and compare values of coin and bill combinations. [Operations and Computation Goal 2]
2. Use manipulatives, mental arithmetic, paper-and-pencil algorithms and models, and calculators to solve problems involving the addition and subtraction of whole numbers and decimals in a money context; describe the strategies used and explain how they work. [Operations and Computation Goal 2]
2. Use manipulatives, mental arithmetic, paper-and-pencil algorithms and models, and calculators to solve problems involving the addition and subtraction of whole numbers and decimals through hundredths; describe the strategies used and explain how they work. [Operations and Computation Goal 2]
1 2 3 4 5 6 7 8 9 10 11 12
1 2 3 4 5 6 7 8 9 10 11
1 2 3 4 5 6 7 8 9 10 11 12
This column identifies the major mathematical concepts within each content strand.
Light blue shading indicates that content from the goal is being practiced and applied. Dark blue shading indicates that content from the goal is being taught.
A complete list of Grade-Level Goals for this grade and the two surrounding grades demonstrates how the goals evolve from grade to grade.
Grade-Level Goals are numbered for easy identification.
Unit numbers identify in which units a particular Grade-Level Goal is covered.

Number and Numeration

Key
- Content taught
- Content practiced and applied

Content	Grade 2	Grade 3	Grade 4
Rote counting	1. Count on by 1s, 2s, 5s, 10s, 25s, and 100s past 1,000 and back by 1s, 10s, and 100s from any number less than 1,000 with and without number grids, number lines, and calculators. [Number and Numeration Goal 1]		
Place value and notation	2. Read, write, and model with manipulatives whole numbers up to 10,000; identify places in such numbers and the values of the digits in those places; read and write money amounts in dollars-and-cents notation. [Number and Numeration Goal 2]	1. Read and write whole numbers up to 1,000,000; read, write, and model with manipulatives decimals through hundredths; identify places in such numbers and the values of the digits in those places; translate between whole numbers and decimals represented in words, in base-10 notation, and with manipulatives. [Number and Numeration Goal 1]	1. Read and write whole numbers up to 1,000,000,000 and decimals through thousandths; identify places in such numbers and the values of the digits in those places; translate between whole numbers and decimals represented in words and in base-10 notation. [Number and Numeration Goal 1]
Meanings and uses of fractions	3. Use manipulatives and drawings to model fractions as equal parts of a region or a collection; describe the models and name the fractions. [Number and Numeration Goal 3]	2. Read, write, and model fractions; solve problems involving fractional parts of a region or a collection; describe strategies used. [Number and Numeration Goal 2]	2. Read, write, and model fractions; solve problems involving fractional parts of a region or a collection; describe and explain strategies used; given a fractional part of a region or a collection, identify the unit whole. [Number and Numeration Goal 2]
Number theory	4. Recognize numbers as odd or even. [Number and Numeration Goal 4]	3. Find multiples of 2, 5, and 10. [Number and Numeration Goal 3]	3. Find multiples of whole numbers less than 10; identify prime and composite numbers; find whole-number factors of numbers. [Number and Numeration Goal 3]

Content	Grade 2	Grade 3	Grade 4
Equivalent names for whole numbers	5. Use tally marks, arrays, and numerical expressions involving addition and subtraction to give equivalent names for whole numbers. [Number and Numeration Goal 5]	4. Use numerical expressions involving one or more of the basic four arithmetic operations to give equivalent names for whole numbers. [Number and Numeration Goal 4]	4. Use numerical expressions involving one or more of the basic four arithmetic operations and grouping symbols to give equivalent names for whole numbers. [Number and Numeration Goal 4]
Equivalent names for fractions, decimals, and percents	6. Use manipulatives and drawings to model equivalent names for $\frac{1}{2}$. [Number and Numeration Goal 6]	5. Use manipulatives and drawings to find and represent equivalent names for fractions; use manipulatives to generate equivalent fractions. [Number and Numeration Goal 5]	5. Use numerical expressions to find and represent equivalent names for fractions and decimals; use and explain a multiplication rule to find equivalent fractions; rename fourths, fifths, tenths, and hundredths as decimals and percents. [Number and Numeration Goal 5]
Comparing and ordering numbers	7. Compare and order whole numbers up to 10,000; use area models to compare fractions. [Number and Numeration Goal 7]	6. Compare and order whole numbers up to 1,000,000; use manipulatives to order decimals through hundredths; use area models and benchmark fractions to compare and order fractions. [Number and Numeration Goal 6]	6. Compare and order whole numbers up to 1,000,000,000 and decimals through thousandths; compare and order integers between –100 and 0; use area models, benchmark fractions, and analyses of numerators and denominators to compare and order fractions. [Number and Numeration Goal 6]

Operations and Computation

Key
- Content taught
- Content practiced and applied

Content	Grade 2	Grade 3	Grade 4
Addition and subtraction facts	1. Demonstrate automaticity with all addition facts through 10 + 10 and fluency with the related subtraction facts. [Operations and Computation Goal 1]	1. Demonstrate automaticity with all addition and subtraction facts through 10 + 10; use basic facts to compute fact extensions such as 80 + 70. [Operations and Computation Goal 1]	1. Demonstrate automaticity with addition and subtraction fact extensions. [Operations and Computation Goal 1]

Operations and Computation (cont.)

Key Content taught / Content practiced and applied

Content	Grade 2	Grade 3	Grade 4
Addition and subtraction procedures	2. Use manipulatives, number grids, tally marks, mental arithmetic, paper & pencil, and calculators to solve problems involving the addition and subtraction of multidigit whole numbers; describe the strategies used; calculate and compare values of coin and bill combinations. [Operations and Computation Goal 2]	2. Use manipulatives, mental arithmetic, paper-and-pencil algorithms and models, and calculators to solve problems involving the addition and subtraction of whole numbers and decimals in a money context; describe the strategies used and explain how they work. [Operations and Computation Goal 2]	2. Use manipulatives, mental arithmetic, paper-and-pencil algorithms and models, and calculators to solve problems involving the addition and subtraction of whole numbers and decimals through hundredths; describe the strategies used and explain how they work. [Operations and Computation Goal 2]
Multiplication and division facts		3. Demonstrate automaticity with multiplication facts through 10×10. [Operations and Computation Goal 3]	3. Demonstrate automaticity with multiplication facts through $10 * 10$ and proficiency with related division facts; use basic facts to compute fact extensions such as $30 * 60$. [Operations and Computation Goal 3]
Multiplication and division procedures		4. Use arrays, mental arithmetic, paper-and-pencil algorithms and models, and calculators to solve problems involving the multiplication of 2- and 3-digit whole numbers by 1-digit whole numbers; describe the strategies used. [Operations and Computation Goal 4]	4. Use manipulatives, mental arithmetic, paper-and-pencil algorithms and models, and calculators to solve problems involving the multiplication of multidigit whole numbers by 2-digit whole numbers and the division of multidigit whole numbers by 1-digit whole numbers; describe the strategies used and explain how they work. [Operations and Computation Goal 4]
Procedures for addition and subtraction of fractions			5. Use manipulatives, mental arithmetic, and calculators to solve problems involving the addition and subtraction of fractions and mixed numbers; describe the strategies used. [Operations and Computation Goal 5]

Content	Grade 2	Grade 3	Grade 4
Computational estimation	3. Make reasonable estimates for whole number addition and subtraction problems; explain how the estimates were obtained. [Operations and Computation Goal 3]	5. Make reasonable estimates for whole number addition, subtraction, multiplication, and division problems; explain how the estimates were obtained. [Operations and Computation Goal 5]	6. Make reasonable estimates for whole number and decimal addition and subtraction problems, and whole number multiplication and division problems; explain how the estimates were obtained. [Operations and Computation Goal 6]
	1 2 3 4 5 6 7 8 9 10 11 12	1 2 3 4 5 6 7 8 9 10 11	1 2 3 4 5 6 7 8 9 10 11 12
Models for the operations	4. Identify and describe change, comparison, and parts-and-total situations; use repeated addition, arrays, and skip counting to model multiplication; use equal sharing and equal grouping to model division. [Operations and Computation Goal 4]	6. Recognize and describe change, comparison, and parts-and-total situations; use repeated addition, arrays, and skip counting to model multiplication; use equal sharing and equal grouping to model division. [Operations and Computation Goal 6]	7. Use repeated addition, skip counting, arrays, area, and scaling to model multiplication and division. [Operations and Computation Goal 7]
	1 2 3 4 5 6 7 8 9 10 11 12	1 2 3 4 5 6 7 8 9 10 11	1 2 3 4 5 6 7 8 9 10 11 12

Data and Chance

Key
- Content taught
- Content practiced and applied

Content	Grade 2	Grade 3	Grade 4
Data collection and representation	1. Collect and organize data or use given data to create tally charts, tables, graphs, and line plots. [Data and Chance Goal 1]	1. Collect and organize data or use given data to create charts, tables, graphs, and line plots. [Data and Chance Goal 1]	1. Collect and organize data or use given data to create charts, tables, graphs, and line plots. [Data and Chance Goal 1]
	1 2 3 4 5 6 7 8 9 10 11 12	1 2 3 4 5 6 7 8 9 10 11	1 2 3 4 5 6 7 8 9 10 11 12
Data analysis	2. Use graphs to ask and answer simple questions and draw conclusions; find the maximum, minimum, mode, and median of a data set. [Data and Chance Goal 2]	2. Use graphs to ask and answer simple questions and draw conclusions; find the maximum, minimum, range, mode, and median of a data set. [Data and Chance Goal 2]	2. Use the maximum, minimum, range, median, mode, and graphs to ask and answer questions, draw conclusions, and make predictions. [Data and Chance Goal 2]
	1 2 3 4 5 6 7 8 9 10 11 12	1 2 3 4 5 6 7 8 9 10 11	1 2 3 4 5 6 7 8 9 10 11 12

Data and Chance (cont.)

Key ■ Content taught ■ Content practiced and applied

Content	Grade 2	Grade 3	Grade 4
Qualitative probability	3. Describe events using *certain, likely, unlikely, impossible* and other basic probability terms; explain the choice of language. [Data and Chance Goal 3]	3. Describe events using *certain, very likely, likely, unlikely, very unlikely, impossible,* and other basic probability terms; explain the choice of language. [Data and Chance Goal 3]	3. Describe events using *certain, very likely, likely, unlikely, very unlikely, impossible,* and other basic probability terms; use *more likely, equally likely, same chance, 50-50, less likely,* and other basic probability terms to compare events; explain the choice of language. [Data and Chance Goal 3]
Quantitative probability		4. Predict the outcomes of simple experiments and test the predictions using manipulatives; express the probability of an event by using "______ out of ______" language. [Data and Chance Goal 4]	4. Predict the outcomes of experiments and test the predictions using manipulatives; summarize the results and use them to predict future events; express the probability of an event as a fraction. [Data and Chance Goal 4]

Measurement and Reference Frames

Content	Grade 2	Grade 3	Grade 4
Length, weight, and angles	1. Estimate length with and without tools; measure length to the nearest inch and centimeter; use standard and nonstandard tools to measure and estimate weight. [Measurement and Reference Frames Goal 1]	1. Estimate length with and without tools; measure length to the nearest $\frac{1}{2}$ inch and $\frac{1}{2}$ centimeter; draw and describe angles as records of rotations. [Measurement and Reference Frames Goal 1]	1. Estimate length with and without tools; measure length to the nearest $\frac{1}{4}$ inch and $\frac{1}{2}$ centimeter; use tools to measure and draw angles; estimate the size of angles without tools. [Measurement and Reference Frames Goal 1]
Area, perimeter, volume, and capacity	2. Partition rectangles into unit squares and count unit squares to find areas. [Measurement and Reference Frames Goal 2]	2. Describe and use strategies to measure the perimeter of polygons; find the areas of rectangles. [Measurement and Reference Frames Goal 2]	2. Describe and use strategies to measure the perimeter and area of polygons, to estimate the area of irregular shapes, and to find the volume of rectangular prisms. [Measurement and Reference Frames Goal 2]

Key
- ■ Content taught
- □ Content practiced and applied

Content	Grade 2	Grade 3	Grade 4
Units and systems of measurement	3. Describe relationships between days in a week and hours in a day. [Measurement and Reference Frames Goal 3]	3. Describe relationships among inches, feet, and yards; describe relationships between minutes in an hour, hours in a day, days in a week. [Measurement and Reference Frames Goal 3]	3. Describe relationships among U.S. customary units of measure and among metric units of measure. [Measurement and Reference Frames Goal 3]
Money	4. Make exchanges between coins and bills. [Measurement and Reference Frames Goal 4]		
Temperature	5. Read temperature on both the Fahrenheit and Celsius scales. [Measurement and Reference Frames Goal 5]		
Time	6. Tell and show time to the nearest five minutes on an analog clock; tell and write time in digital notation.* [Measurement and Reference Frames Goal 6]	4. Tell and show time to the nearest minute on an analog clock; tell and write time in digital notation.* [Measurement and Reference Frames Goal 4]	
Coordinate systems			4. Use ordered pairs of numbers to name, locate, and plot points in the first quadrant of a coordinate grid. [Measurement and Reference Frames Goal 4]

* Children record their start time at the top of journal pages on a daily basis.

Geometry

Key
- Content taught
- Content practiced and applied

Content	Grade 2	Grade 3	Grade 4
Lines and angles	1. Draw line segments and identify parallel line segments. [Geometry Goal 1]	1. Identify and draw points, intersecting and parallel line segments and lines, rays, and right angles. [Geometry Goal 1]	1. Identify, draw, and describe points, intersecting and parallel line segments and lines, rays, and right, acute, and obtuse angles. [Geometry Goal 1]
Plane and solid figures	2. Identify, describe, and model plane and solid figures including circles, triangles, squares, rectangles, hexagons, trapezoids, rhombuses, spheres, cylinders, rectangular prisms, pyramids, cones, and cubes. [Geometry Goal 2]	2. Identify, describe, model, and compare plane and solid figures including circles, polygons, spheres, cylinders, rectangular prisms, pyramids, cones, and cubes using appropriate geometric terms including the terms *face, edge, vertex,* and *base.* [Geometry Goal 2]	2. Describe, compare, and classify plane and solid figures, including polygons, circles, spheres, cylinders, rectangular prisms, cones, cubes, and pyramids, using appropriate geometric terms including *vertex, base, face, edge,* and *congruent.* [Geometry Goal 2]
Transformations and symmetry	3. Create and complete two-dimensional symmetric shapes or designs. [Geometry Goal 3]	3. Create and complete two-dimensional symmetric shapes or designs; locate multiple lines of symmetry in a two-dimensional shape. [Geometry Goal 3]	3. Identify, describe, and sketch examples of reflections; identify and describe examples of translations and rotations. [Geometry Goal 3]

Patterns, Functions, and Algebra

Content	Grade 2	Grade 3	Grade 4
Patterns and functions	1. Extend, describe, and create numeric, visual, and concrete patterns; describe rules for patterns and use them to solve problems; use words and symbols to describe and write rules for functions involving addition and subtraction and use those rules to solve problems. [Patterns, Functions, and Algebra Goal 1]	1. Extend, describe, and create numeric patterns; describe rules for patterns and use them to solve problems; use words and symbols to describe and write rules for functions involving addition, subtraction, and multiplication and use those rules to solve problems. [Patterns, Functions, and Algebra Goal 1]	1. Extend, describe, and create numeric patterns; describe rules for patterns and use them to solve problems; use words and symbols to describe and write rules for functions that involve the four basic arithmetic operations and use those rules to solve problems. [Patterns, Functions, and Algebra Goal 1]

Key ■ Content taught □ Content practiced and applied

Content	Grade 2	Grade 3	Grade 4
Algebraic notation and solving number sentences	2. Read, write, and explain expressions and number sentences using the symbols $+$, $-$, $=$, $>$, and $<$; solve number sentences involving addition and subtraction; write expressions and number sentences to model number stories. [Patterns, Functions, and Algebra Goal 2]	2. Read, write, and explain number sentences using the symbols $+$, $-$, $\times$, $\div$, $=$, $>$, and $<$; solve number sentences; write expressions and number sentences to model number stories. [Patterns, Functions, and Algebra Goal 2]	2. Use conventional notation to write expressions and number sentences using the four basic arithmetic operations; determine whether number sentences are true or false; solve open sentences and explain the solutions; write expressions and number sentences to model number stories. [Patterns, Functions, and Algebra Goal 2]
Order of operations		3. Recognize that numeric expressions can have different values depending on the order in which operations are carried out; understand that grouping symbols can be used to affect the order in which operations are carried out. [Patterns, Functions, and Algebra Goal 3]	3. Evaluate numeric expressions containing grouping symbols; insert grouping symbols to make number sentences true. [Patterns, Functions, and Algebra Goal 3]
Properties of the arithmetic operations	3. Describe the Commutative and Associative Properties of Addition and the Additive Identity and apply them to mental arithmetic problems. [Patterns, Functions, and Algebra Goal 3]	4. Describe and apply the Commutative and Associative Properties of Addition and Multiplication and the Multiplicative Identity; apply the Distributive Property of Multiplication over Addition. [Patterns, Functions, and Algebra Goal 4]	4. Describe and apply the Distributive Property of Multiplication over Addition. [Patterns, Functions, and Algebra Goal 4]

Scope and Sequence Chart

Throughout *Everyday Mathematics*, children repeatedly encounter skills in each of the content strands. Each exposure builds on and extends children's understanding. They study important concepts over consecutive years through a variety of formats. The Scope and Sequence Chart shows the units in which these exposures occur. The symbol ● indicates that the skill is introduced or taught. The symbol ■ indicates that the skill is revisited, practiced, or extended. These levels refer to unit content within the *K–6 Everyday Mathematics* curriculum.

The skills are divided according to the content strands below.

Content Strands — Pages

How to Read the Scope and Sequence Chart

Each section of the chart includes a content strand title, three grade-level columns divided by units or sections, and a list of specific skills grouped by major concepts.

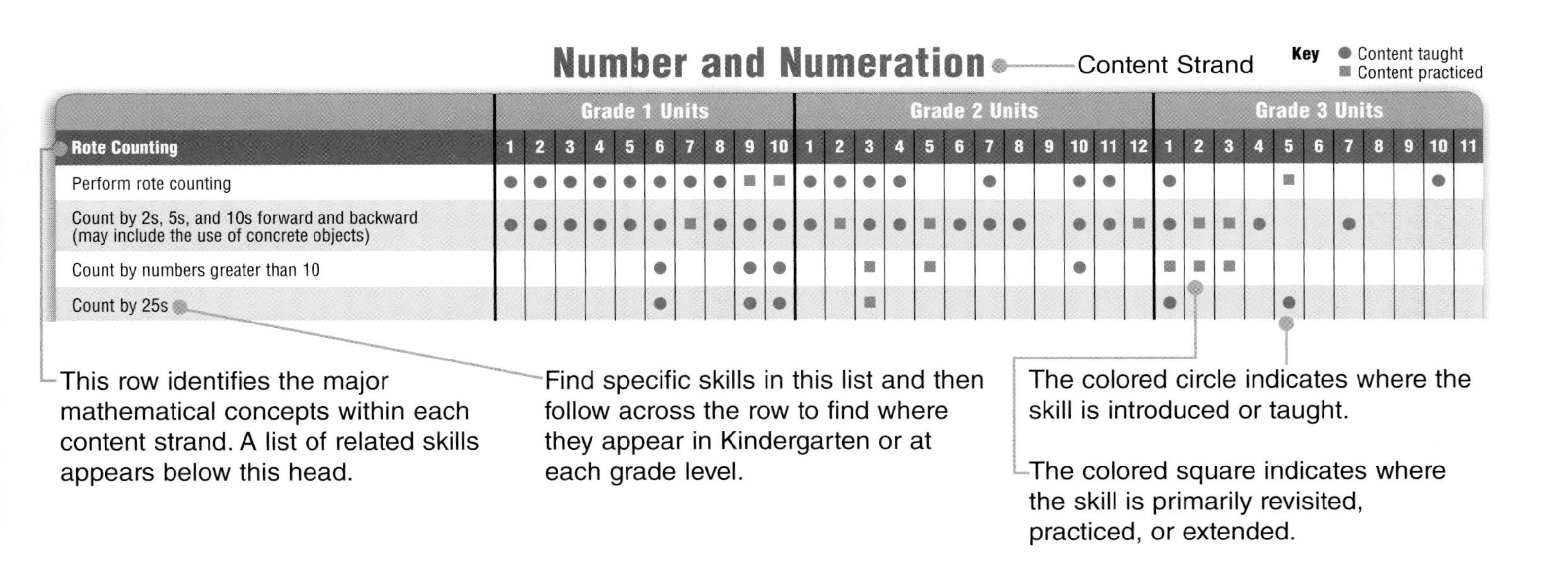

Number and Numeration — Content Strand

Key: ● Content taught ■ Content practiced

	Grade 1 Units										Grade 2 Units												Grade 3 Units										
Rote Counting	1	2	3	4	5	6	7	8	9	10	1	2	3	4	5	6	7	8	9	10	11	12	1	2	3	4	5	6	7	8	9	10	11
Perform rote counting	●	●	●	●	●	●	●	●	■	■	●	●	●	●			●			●	●		●				■					●	
Count by 2s, 5s, and 10s forward and backward (may include the use of concrete objects)	●	●	●	●	●	●	■	●	●	●	●	■	●	●	■	●	●	●		●	●	■	●	■	■	●			●				
Count by numbers greater than 10						●			●	●			■		■					●			■	■	■								
Count by 25s						●			●	●			■										●				●						

This row identifies the major mathematical concepts within each content strand. A list of related skills appears below this head.

Find specific skills in this list and then follow across the row to find where they appear in Kindergarten or at each grade level.

The colored circle indicates where the skill is introduced or taught.

The colored square indicates where the skill is primarily revisited, practiced, or extended.

Number and Numeration

Key ● Content taught ■ Content practiced

	Grade 1 Units										Grade 2 Units												Grade 3 Units										
Rote Counting	1	2	3	4	5	6	7	8	9	10	1	2	3	4	5	6	7	8	9	10	11	12	1	2	3	4	5	6	7	8	9	10	11
Perform rote counting	●	●	●	●	●	●	●	●	●	■	●	●	●	●			●			●	●		●				■					●	
Count by 2s, 5s, and 10s forward and backward (may include the use of concrete objects)	●	●	●	●	●	●	■	●	●	●	●	■	■	■	■	■	●	●		●	●	■	●	■	■	●			●				
Count by numbers greater than 10						●			●	●	■	■	■		■					●			■	■	■								
Count by 25s						●			●	●			■										●				●						
Count by 100s									●	●	●	■	■	■				●		●	●	■	■	■		■	■		■	■			■
Count up and back on a number grid		■	■	●	●		■	■	●		■	■				●	■	■	■	■			●	■		■		■					
Locate numbers on a number line; count up and back on a number line; complete a number line	●	■	●	●					■		●	■		■		■							●			■							
Count using a calculator or calculator repeat key			●			●		●		■	●	■	■			■	●			●	■	■	●			■							
Count back past zero																								●	●	●	●	■			●		
Count by tenths																											●	■					
Count by thousandths																											●	■					
Rational Counting	1	2	3	4	5	6	7	8	9	10	1	2	3	4	5	6	7	8	9	10	11	12	1	2	3	4	5	6	7	8	9	10	11
Perform rational counting	●	●	●	●	●	●	●	■	●	●	●	●	●	●	●	●	●	■	●	●	●		■	●	■	●	■	●	●	●	●	●	●
Estimate quantities of objects			■	■	●			●															●	●	■	■	●		●		●		■
Place Value and Notation	1	2	3	4	5	6	7	8	9	10	1	2	3	4	5	6	7	8	9	10	11	12	1	2	3	4	5	6	7	8	9	10	11
Read and write numbers to 20	●	●	●	●	●	●	●				●	●	■										●	●		●	●		●				
Read and write 2-digit numbers					●	■	●	●			●	●	●	●		●				●	●		●	●			●		●		●		
Read and write 3-digit numbers					●		●	●	■	●	●		●	■	■	■				●			●	●			●		●		●		
Read and write 4- and 5-digit numbers										●	●		●	●						●	●		●				●	■					
Read and write 6- and 7-digit numbers																											●	●	■	■	■		
Display and read numbers on a calculator		●	●		●	●		●		■	●	■	■			■				●			●	■	■		■					●	
Read, write, or use ordinal numbers						●					■	■				■				●													
Explore place value using a number grid			■		●				●		●									●			●				●						
Identify place value in 2-digit numbers			●		●	■		■	●	●	■		●	●		●				●	●			●		●	●				●		■

Key ● Content taught ■ Content practiced

Place Value and Notation (cont.)	1	2	3	4	5	6	7	8	9	10	1	2	3	4	5	6	7	8	9	10	11	12	1	2	3	4	5	6	7	8	9	10	11
Identify place value in 3-digit numbers								●		●	●	■	●	●	■	■		■		●		■				●	●		■		●		■
Identify place value in 4-digit numbers								●		●								■		●	■	■	■	■		●	●		●	●	●		■
Identify place value in larger numbers													●					■	■	●							●				■		■
Make exchanges among place values					●			●			●		●	●						●	●			●	■	■	●		■				
Make least and greatest numbers with randomly selected digits											■					■											■	■	■				
Write numbers in expanded notation									■				■							●				■		■	■				■		
Use cents notation		●	●		■	■		■			●		●	■		●				●			●	■	■	■	■	■	■	■			
Use dollars-and-cents notation		●	●		■	■	●	●					●	●		●			■	●	●		●				■	■	■		■		
Use calculator to count/compute money amounts								■				■								●									●				
Explore uses for decimals								●												●			●				■	■				■	
Model decimals with base-l0 materials																											●	●					
Read and write 1- and 2-digit decimals																							●				●	●		●	●	●	
Read and write 3-digit decimals																											●	■					
Identify place value in decimals through thousandths																											●	■		■		■	
Write decimals with expanded notation																											●	■		■		■	
Meanings and Uses of Fractions	**1**	**2**	**3**	**4**	**5**	**6**	**7**	**8**	**9**	**10**	**1**	**2**	**3**	**4**	**5**	**6**	**7**	**8**	**9**	**10**	**11**	**12**	**1**	**2**	**3**	**4**	**5**	**6**	**7**	**8**	**9**	**10**	**11**
Understand the meaning or uses of fractions							■	●	●	■								●	●	■	■				●	●			■	●	■	■	■
Construct concrete models of fractions and equivalent fractions; identify fractions on a number line								●	●									●	■	■					■	●			■	●	■		
Identify pennies and dimes as fractional parts of a dollar																●	■	●		●		■					■				■		
Identify numerator and denominator								●	●									●												●	●	●	■
Shade and identify fractional parts of a region							■	●	●	■							■	●		■							●		■	●	●		■
Shade and identify fractional parts of a set								●	■								■	●	●			■							■	●		■	●
Understand that the amount represented by a fraction depends on the size of the whole (ONE)								■										●		●	■						■		■	●			■
Identify and name mixed numbers																														●	■		

Number and Numeration (cont.)

Key ● Content taught ■ Content practiced

	Grade 1 Units										Grade 2 Units												Grade 3 Units										
Meanings and Uses of Fractions (cont.)	1	2	3	4	5	6	7	8	9	10	1	2	3	4	5	6	7	8	9	10	11	12	1	2	3	4	5	6	7	8	9	10	11
Identify and name whole numbers as fractions																														●			
Write fraction words																														●			
Use fractions in number stories									■	■								●	■	■	■									●	■	■	■
Demonstrate the concept of percent																															■		
Number Theory	1	2	3	4	5	6	7	8	9	10	1	2	3	4	5	6	7	8	9	10	11	12	1	2	3	4	5	6	7	8	9	10	11
Explore or identify even and odd numbers			●	■	■	■	■		■		●	●	■	●	■		●		■				●	●		●					■		
Equivalent Names for Whole Numbers	1	2	3	4	5	6	7	8	9	10	1	2	3	4	5	6	7	8	9	10	11	12	1	2	3	4	5	6	7	8	9	10	11
Find equivalent names for numbers	●	●	■	■	●	●	■	■	■		●	●	●	●	■				●	●	●	■	●						●	●	■		
Use Roman numerals											■																						
Equivalent Names for Fractions, Decimals, and Percents	1	2	3	4	5	6	7	8	9	10	1	2	3	4	5	6	7	8	9	10	11	12	1	2	3	4	5	6	7	8	9	10	11
Find equivalent fractions									●								■	●	●	●		■								●	■	■	■
Convert between mixed numbers and fractions																														●			
Comparing and Ordering Numbers	1	2	3	4	5	6	7	8	9	10	1	2	3	4	5	6	7	8	9	10	11	12	1	2	3	4	5	6	7	8	9	10	11
Compare and order numbers to 20	●	●	●	●	●	●				■	●		■		●		●		●				●										
Compare and order 2-digit numbers		●		●	●	●	■	■	■	●	●		■				●			●		●	●			■	●	■					
Compare and order 3-digit numbers				●	●		■	■	■	●	●		●							●			■			■	●	■					
Compare and order 4- or 5-digit numbers		■									●									●			■				●	■					
Compare and order larger numbers																				●		●	●			■	●	■	■				
Compare numbers using the symbols <, >, and =					●	■	■	■	●	■	●	■	●	■		■	■		■	■	■	■	●		■	■	■	■					
Explore magnitude of numbers																											●	■			●		
Compare and order fractions; use manipulatives to identify/compare fractions									●	■								●	●	●										●	■	■	
Compare fractions less than one																		●			■	■						■		●	■	■	
Compare and order decimals																							●				●	■				■	
Explore uses for positive and negative numbers (integers)																															●	■	
Explore zero as a reference point																															●		

Operations and Computation

Key ● Content taught ■ Content practiced

	Grade 1 Units										Grade 2 Units												Grade 3 Units										
Addition and Subtraction Facts	1	2	3	4	5	6	7	8	9	10	1	2	3	4	5	6	7	8	9	10	11	12	1	2	3	4	5	6	7	8	9	10	11
Find/use complements of 10		●	■	■	■	■					●						■	●	■					■	●	■	■			●		●	
Practice basic facts; know +/− fact families	●	●	■	●	●	●	●	■	■	■	●	●	■	■	■	●	■	■	■	●	■	●	●	●	●	■	■	■				●	●
Practice extensions of basic facts									■					■									●	●		●	■		■			■	●
Make and solve number-grid puzzles				●					●	●	■	●											■	●		■		■	■				
Addition and Subtraction Procedures	1	2	3	4	5	6	7	8	9	10	1	2	3	4	5	6	7	8	9	10	11	12	1	2	3	4	5	6	7	8	9	10	11
Understand meaning of addition/subtraction; model addition/subtraction using concrete objects	●	●	●	●	●			■	●		●	■	●	●	●	●	●				●		●	●			●		●	■			
Investigate the inverse relationships between addition and subtraction		●		●	●	●		●		■	●	●		●							■			●			■						
Use mental arithmetic or fact strategies to add/subtract	●	●	●	●	●	●	●	●	■	■	●	●	■	●	■	●	■	■	■	■	■	■	■	●					■		■	●	●
Use addition to find the total number of objects in rectangular arrays														■	●			■			●												
Use addition/subtraction algorithms																●	■	■	■	■	●	■		●	■						■		
Explore calculator functions					●	●		■	■		●	■	■	■									■	●			■	■	■		●	■	
Make up and/or solve 1- or 2-step addition/subtraction number stories; determine operation needed to solve a problem	●	●	●	●	●	●	●	●	●	●	■	●	■	●	■	●	●		■	●	●	●	■	●			■		●	■	●		
Use an Addition/Subtraction Facts Table					●	●						●												●									
Determine the value of the unknown number in an addition or subtraction problem			●	●	●	●						●	■	●	■	●				●				●	■								
Add/subtract using a number grid	●		■		●	■			●	■	●	■		■		●	●			■	■		●	●									
Add/subtract using a number line	●		●		■						●	●	■	●	●	●	●				■	●	●										●
Add/subtract using a calculator					●	●		■	■		●	●	■		■		●			■			●	●	■		■		●			●	
Add/subtract multiples of 10									●	●	●	■		■		■				●						■	■		■				
Add 3 or more 1-digit numbers		●	●			●		●								●	■			■		●				■	■						
Add/subtract 2-digit numbers					●	●		●	●	●	●			●	■	●	●	■	■	■	●	●		●	■	■			■				
Add 3 or more 2-digit numbers																●						●		●	■	■			■		■		
Add/subtract 3- and 4-digit numbers														●		●	■		●		●	●				■	■		■		■		■

Operations and Computation (cont.)

Key ● Content taught ■ Content practiced

	Grade 1 Units										Grade 2 Units												Grade 3 Units										
Addition and Subtraction Procedures (cont.)	1	2	3	4	5	6	7	8	9	10	1	2	3	4	5	6	7	8	9	10	11	12	1	2	3	4	5	6	7	8	9	10	11
Add/subtract money amounts/decimals; make change						●		●	●	●	●		●	●		●	●			●	●	■	●	■	■		■		●		■		
Solve money number stories					●	●		●	●	●				■		■			■	●	●	■	●	●	■	●	■			●	●		
Make change								●	■	●		■		■	■				■	●	●	■	●	■	■						■		
Use positive and negative numbers (integers) in number stories																															●		
Multiplication and Division Facts	1	2	3	4	5	6	7	8	9	10	1	2	3	4	5	6	7	8	9	10	11	12	1	2	3	4	5	6	7	8	9	10	11
Practice multiplication/division facts																					●	●				●	■	■	●	■	●	●	■
Find complements for multiples of 10																	●										●		●			■	
Recognize and know square products																										■			●	■			
Multiplication and Division Procedures	1	2	3	4	5	6	7	8	9	10	1	2	3	4	5	6	7	8	9	10	11	12	1	2	3	4	5	6	7	8	9	10	11
Use manipulatives, drawings/arrays, number sentences, repeated addition, or story problems to explain and demonstrate the meaning of multiplication/division				●				●							■	●	■	●		■	●	●			■	●	■	■	●	■	●	■	
Understand meaning of multiplication/division and related vocabulary															●	●	●				●					●		■		■	●		
Make up and/or solve multiplication/division number stories																●	●				●	●				●	■	■	●	■	●	■	
Investigate relationships between multiplication and division																●					●					●	■	■	●	■	■	■	
Multiply/divide using a number line or number grid																■					●					■			●				
Explore square numbers																					■							■	●				
Interpret a remainder in division number stories																											■	■			●		
Solve multistep multiplication/division number stories																													●	■	●		
Make difference and ratio comparisons																											●		●				
Multiply/divide with 2-digit numbers																															●	■	■
Use a calculator to multiply or divide																					●						■	■	■		●		
Use a Multiplication/Division Facts Table																					●					●			●				
Use mental arithmetic to multiply/divide																					●	■			■			■	●		●		

Key ● Content taught ■ Content practiced

Multiplication and Division Procedures (cont.)	1	2	3	4	5	6	7	8	9	10	1	2	3	4	5	6	7	8	9	10	11	12	1	2	3	4	5	6	7	8	9	10	11
Multiply/divide multiples of 10, 100, and 1,000 by 1-digit numbers																					■			●		●			●	■	●	●	
Use multiplication/division algorithms																										●	■	■			●	■	
Multiply multidigit numbers by 1- or 2-digit numbers																										●					●	■	■
Multiply/divide money amounts																										■			●	■	●	■	■
Identify factors of a number																					●					●	■	■			●	■	
Procedures for Addition and Subtraction of Fractions	**1**	**2**	**3**	**4**	**5**	**6**	**7**	**8**	**9**	**10**	**1**	**2**	**3**	**4**	**5**	**6**	**7**	**8**	**9**	**10**	**11**	**12**	**1**	**2**	**3**	**4**	**5**	**6**	**7**	**8**	**9**	**10**	**11**
Add/subtract positive and negative numbers, fractions, and decimals																							■	●		■				●	●		■
Computational Estimation	**1**	**2**	**3**	**4**	**5**	**6**	**7**	**8**	**9**	**10**	**1**	**2**	**3**	**4**	**5**	**6**	**7**	**8**	**9**	**10**	**11**	**12**	**1**	**2**	**3**	**4**	**5**	**6**	**7**	**8**	**9**	**10**	**11**
Estimate reasonableness of answers to basic facts			●		■	■		■	●	■				■						■			■	■									
Use estimation strategies to add/subtract; make ballpark estimates			●							●				●		■	■			●	●		●	●	■	■	■		■		■		■
Round whole numbers to the nearest ten					●		●	●	●											■				●			●		■				
Use estimation to multiply/divide																										●		■	●		●		■
Estimate costs						■		■						●						●	●							■	●		■		
Models for Operations	**1**	**2**	**3**	**4**	**5**	**6**	**7**	**8**	**9**	**10**	**1**	**2**	**3**	**4**	**5**	**6**	**7**	**8**	**9**	**10**	**11**	**12**	**1**	**2**	**3**	**4**	**5**	**6**	**7**	**8**	**9**	**10**	**11**
Solve change-to-more and change-to-less number stories/diagrams		●	●						●			●	●	●		●				■	●			●	■	■	■						
Solve parts-and-total number stories/diagrams			●	●	●	●		●					●	●		●		■	■	■				●	■	■	■		■				
Solve comparison number stories/diagrams								●		●		●			■	●				●	●	■		●	■		●	■					
Solve missing factor number models												■	■	■	■			■												■	●	●	
Solve equal-grouping and equal-sharing division problems															■					■	■					●	■	■	●	■	●		

Data and Chance

Key ● Content taught ■ Content practiced

	Grade 1 Units										Grade 2 Units												Grade 3 Units										
Data Collection and Representation	1	2	3	4	5	6	7	8	9	10	1	2	3	4	5	6	7	8	9	10	11	12	1	2	3	4	5	6	7	8	9	10	11
Collect data by counting	■							■		■			■			●	●					●	●		●	●					●		
Collect data by interviewing										■						■							●										■
Collect data by measuring				●						●							●		■	●							●		■		●	●	
Collect data from print sources and/or posters																■			■	■		●					●		■			■	●
Collect data from a map																			●								●						
Use a weather map										●														●			●						●
Conduct a survey						■										●																	●
Make a tally chart or frequency table	●	●	●		●	●	■	■			■		●			●	●					■	●	●								■	●
Record data in a table/chart	●					●				●			●		■	●	●			■	■	●	●		■	●				■	●	●	●
Record days/events on a timeline				●											■							●					■						
Create/interpret a bar graph, pictograph (picture graph), or Venn diagram				●	●	●	■	■	■	■			●		■	●	●					●	●	■		■	●	■		■		●	●
Create/interpret a line plot			●	●	■	■		■	■	●							●		■	●	●	●	■		■		●	■	■	■	■	■	■
Explore graphing software to make a bar graph or line plot			●	●		●				●						●												■				●	
Data Analysis	1	2	3	4	5	6	7	8	9	10	1	2	3	4	5	6	7	8	9	10	11	12	1	2	3	4	5	6	7	8	9	10	11
Read tables, graphs, and maps (including map scale, scale drawing)	●	●	●		●	●	■		■	●	●	●	●		■	●	●	■	●	■	■	●	●	■		●	●					●	●
Use a scale drawing																											■					●	
Summarize and interpret data	●	●	●	●	●	●	■	●	●	●					■	●	●					●	●			●	■					●	●
Compare two sets of data; use calculator to compare data										●						●	■				■	●		■								■	■
Make predictions about data	●	●				■							●			●							■							●		■	■
Compare quantities from a bar graph			●		■	●						■						■					●				●						
Find the minimum/maximum of a data set						●		■	■	■		■					●			■	■	●	●	●	●		●		■		■	■	●
Find the range						●		■	■	■			●				●			■	■	●		●	●		●		■		■	■	●
Find the median				●				■	■	●		■	●			■	●		■	■	■	●	■		●		●				■	●	●
Find the mode				●						●						■	■	■		■	■	●			●		●				■	●	■

Key ● Content taught ■ Content practiced

Data Analysis (cont.)	1	2	3	4	5	6	7	8	9	10	1	2	3	4	5	6	7	8	9	10	11	12	1	2	3	4	5	6	7	8	9	10	11
Find the mean																									●							●	■
Use data in problem solving		●	●	●		●						■				●	●			■	■	●			●							●	●
Qualitative and Quantitative Probability	**1**	**2**	**3**	**4**	**5**	**6**	**7**	**8**	**9**	**10**	**1**	**2**	**3**	**4**	**5**	**6**	**7**	**8**	**9**	**10**	**11**	**12**	**1**	**2**	**3**	**4**	**5**	**6**	**7**	**8**	**9**	**10**	**11**
Understand and use the language of probability to discuss likelihood of a given situation (using words such as *certain, likely, unlikely, always, maybe, sometimes, never, possible, impossible*)		■	■	■	●	■		■		■	■	■	■	■		■	■	■	■				●		●	■		■		■	■	■	●
Explore equal-chance events					●	●		■																		■				●	■	■	
Explore fair and unfair games																										●					■		●
Classify events																							●										●
Predict outcomes; solve problems involving chance outcomes	●	●	■	■	■	■							●				■						●		●	●				●	■	●	●
Conduct experiments; test predictions using concrete objects	●																■								●	●				●		●	●
Use fractions to record probabilities of events																																	●
Find combinations (Cartesian products)								■									■	■												●			
Understand area model of probability and solve simple spinner problems																																■	●
Explore random sampling																									●					●		■	●

Measurement and Reference Frames

Key ● Content taught ■ Content practiced

	Grade 1 Units										Grade 2 Units												Grade 3 Units										
Length, Weight, and Angles	1	2	3	4	5	6	7	8	9	10	1	2	3	4	5	6	7	8	9	10	11	12	1	2	3	4	5	6	7	8	9	10	11
Name tools used to measure length		●		●										●			■		●					■	■						■	■	
Estimate, compare, and order lengths/heights of objects		●	■	●		●			●	●						■	●		●	■				■	●	■	■					■	
Compare lengths indirectly				●		●													■														
Measure lengths with nonstandard units				●										■					●						●							●	
Measure to the nearest foot				●															●						●								
Measure to the nearest inch				●	■				●					●			●	■	●				●	■	●						■		
Measure to the nearest $\frac{1}{2}$ inch				●															●					■	●	■	■				●	●	
Measure to the nearest $\frac{1}{4}$ inch																									●	■				●	●		
Measure to the nearest $\frac{1}{8}$ inch																										■					■		
Investigate the yard																			●						●								
Measure to the nearest yard																			●						●								
Measure to the nearest centimeter						●								●	■	■	●	■	●	■	■		●	■	●	■							
Measure to the nearest $\frac{1}{2}$ centimeter																			●						●		■				●	●	
Measure to the nearest millimeter																									●							■	
Investigate the meter						●													●						■								
Measure to the nearest meter and/or decimeter																			●						●							●	
Relate decimals to metric measurement																											●					■	
Solve length/height number stories																●	●	■	■		■				●	■			■	■	■		
Investigate the mile and/or kilometer																			●		■					●					■	■	
Estimate and compare distances																		■	●						●	●					■	●	
Read measurement to the nearest mile																							■										
Solve distance number stories																			●		■											■	
Estimate, compare, and order weights									■			■		■			■	■	●													●	
Name tools used to measure weight																			●													●	
Order objects by weight																		■														●	

Key ● Content taught ■ Content practiced

Length, Weight, and Angles (cont.)	1	2	3	4	5	6	7	8	9	10	1	2	3	4	5	6	7	8	9	10	11	12	1	2	3	4	5	6	7	8	9	10	11
Use a pan balance					●	●					●	●																				●	
Use a bath scale									■					■			●		●													●	
Use a spring scale												●							●												●	●	
Choose the appropriate scale																			●													●	
Solve weight number stories														■			■		●													●	
Measure angles with nonstandard units																												●					
Draw angles to record rotations																												●			■		
Area, Perimeter, Volume, and Capacity	**1**	**2**	**3**	**4**	**5**	**6**	**7**	**8**	**9**	**10**	**1**	**2**	**3**	**4**	**5**	**6**	**7**	**8**	**9**	**10**	**11**	**12**	**1**	**2**	**3**	**4**	**5**	**6**	**7**	**8**	**9**	**10**	**11**
Investigate area					●	●								●					●						●	■	■	■	■		■	■	■
Find the area of regular shapes concretely					●	●												■	●			■			■	■					●	■	
Find the perimeter of regular shapes concretely, graphically, or with pictorial models																		■	●		■	■		■	●	■	●	●	●		■	■	
Find the area of a rectangular region divided into square units														■					●	●					●	■	■				●	●	
Partition rectangles into same-size squares; count to find the total														■					●	●													
Find the area of irregular shapes concretely																		■	●	●					●			■			■		
Find the perimeter of irregular shapes concretely, graphically, or with pictorial models																		■	●		■				●	■		■			■	■	
Estimate area																			●						●	■							
Estimate perimeter																			■									●					
Compare perimeter and area																			●						■			■					
Name tools used to measure area																			●						●	●					■		
Estimate volume/capacity									●									●														■	
Name tools used to measure volume and/or capacity																			●													●	
Find volume																		●														■	■
Measure capacities of irregular containers																			■													■	
Compare and order the capacities of containers									●										●													■	

Measurement and Reference Frames (cont.)

Key ● Content taught ■ Content practiced

	Grade 1 Units										Grade 2 Units												Grade 3 Units										
Area, Perimeter, Volume, and Capacity (cont.)	1	2	3	4	5	6	7	8	9	10	1	2	3	4	5	6	7	8	9	10	11	12	1	2	3	4	5	6	7	8	9	10	11
Order objects by volume																																●	
Investigate the relationship between volume and weight																																■	
Find mass																																●	
Explore the relationship between diameter and circumference; measure diameter and circumference																									●								
Units and Systems of Measurement	1	2	3	4	5	6	7	8	9	10	1	2	3	4	5	6	7	8	9	10	11	12	1	2	3	4	5	6	7	8	9	10	11
Select and use appropriate nonstandard units to measure time		●																	■														
Estimate the duration of a minute		●																															
Investigate the duration of an hour		●																															
Investigate 1-minute intervals																					■	■	■										■
Identify equivalent customary units of length																			●						●	■	■			■		●	
Identify equivalent metric units of length																			●						●	■	■					●	
Identify customary and/or metric units of weight																			●													●	
Identify equivalent customary units of weight																			●													●	
Identify customary and/or metric units of capacity									●										●													●	
Identify equivalent customary/metric units of capacity																			●													●	
Choose the appropriate unit of measure																			●						●	■	●					●	
Money	1	2	3	4	5	6	7	8	9	10	1	2	3	4	5	6	7	8	9	10	11	12	1	2	3	4	5	6	7	8	9	10	11
Recognize pennies and nickels		●	■		■			■			●	■	■	●	■	■	■	■	■	■	■	■											
Recognize dimes			●	●			■	●	●		●	■	■	●	■	■	■	■	■	■	■	■											
Recognize quarters						●	■	●			●	■	■	●					■	■		■											
Recognize dollars								●			●	■		■				■	■	■		■											
Calculate the value of coin combinations		●	●		■	●	●	●	■	●	●	■	●	●		■		■	■	●			●		■		■				●		
Calculate the value of bill combinations											●	■					■			●					■		■				●		
Calculate the value of coins/bills			●					●			●	■	●	●			●		■	●	■	■	■		■		■			■	●		

Key ● Content taught ■ Content practiced

Money (cont.)	1	2	3	4	5	6	7	8	9	10	1	2	3	4	5	6	7	8	9	10	11	12	1	2	3	4	5	6	7	8	9	10	11
Compare values of sets of coins or money amounts using <, >, and = symbols		■	■	■	●	■		■	■	■						■	■			●			●			■			●				
Identify equivalencies and make coin exchanges	●	●	●	■	●	●	■	●		■	■		●			●										■	■				■		
Identify equivalencies and make coin/bill exchanges								●	■	■			■			●	●		■	●			■				■				■		
Temperature	**1**	**2**	**3**	**4**	**5**	**6**	**7**	**8**	**9**	**10**	**1**	**2**	**3**	**4**	**5**	**6**	**7**	**8**	**9**	**10**	**11**	**12**	**1**	**2**	**3**	**4**	**5**	**6**	**7**	**8**	**9**	**10**	**11**
Use a thermometer	●		■	●	■				■	■	●	■	●	●		■															●		
Use the Fahrenheit temperature scale	●		■	●	■				■	●	●	■	●	●		■	■			■											●		
Use the Celsius temperature scale										●			●	●						■											●		
Solve temperature number stories				●						●	●			●		■			■												■		
Time	**1**	**2**	**3**	**4**	**5**	**6**	**7**	**8**	**9**	**10**	**1**	**2**	**3**	**4**	**5**	**6**	**7**	**8**	**9**	**10**	**11**	**12**	**1**	**2**	**3**	**4**	**5**	**6**	**7**	**8**	**9**	**10**	**11**
Demonstrate an understanding of the concepts of time; estimates and measures the passage of time using words like *before, after; yesterday, today, tomorrow, morning, afternoon, hour, half-hour*	●	●		●							●			■								●	■				■				■		■
Order or compare events according to duration; calculate elapsed time		●		■						●	■		■				■	■				●	●				■						■
Name tools used to measure time											●		■									■											■
Relates past events to future events						●																											
Investigate A.M. and P.M.		●									●	■	●	■	■	■	■	■	■	■	■	●	■										■
Use the calendar; identify today's date	●	■	■								●					■						●	■				■					■	
Number and name the months in a year or days in the week	●	■	■	■						■	●					■		■		■		●	■				■						
Investigate the second hand; compare the hour and minute hands		●	●								●		●										●					●				■	■
Use an analog or digital clock to tell time on the hour		■	●	■		■		■		●	●	■	●	■	●	■	■			■													■
Tell time on the half-hour			●	●	●	●	■	■		●	■	■	●	■	●					■			●										■
Tell time on the quarter-hour				●	●	●	■	■		●		■	●	■			■			■			●										■
Tell time to the nearest 5 minutes						●		■	●	●		■	●			■						●		■									■
Use digital notation*						●	■	■		●	■	■	●	■	●	■	■	■	■	■	■	■	●	■	■	■	■	■	■	■	■	■	■
Tell time to the nearest minute*										●	■	■	●	■	■	■	■	■	■	■	■	■	■	■	■	■	■	■	■	■	■	■	■

*In Grades 2 and 3, children record their start time at the top of journal pages on a daily basis. In Grade 2, they use A.M. and P.M.

Measurement and Reference Frames (cont.)

Key ● Content taught ■ Content practiced

	Grade 1 Units										Grade 2 Units												Grade 3 Units										
Time (cont.)	1	2	3	4	5	6	7	8	9	10	1	2	3	4	5	6	7	8	9	10	11	12	1	2	3	4	5	6	7	8	9	10	11
Read time in different ways and/or identify time equivalencies						■												■				●					■					■	
Solve time number stories												■	●	■		■							●										●
Coordinate Systems	1	2	3	4	5	6	7	8	9	10	1	2	3	4	5	6	7	8	9	10	11	12	1	2	3	4	5	6	7	8	9	10	11
Find and name locations with simple relationships on a coordinate system									■																							●	
Identify, locate, and plot ordered pairs on a graph																																●	

Geometry

	Grade 1 Units										Grade 2 Units												Grade 3 Units										
Lines and Angles	1	2	3	4	5	6	7	8	9	10	1	2	3	4	5	6	7	8	9	10	11	12	1	2	3	4	5	6	7	8	9	10	11
Identify and name line segments															●						■							●	■			●	
Draw line segments with a straightedge						●									●		■	■										●	■				
Draw line segments to a specified length						■								■				■	■									●		●			
Draw designs with line segments						■										■											●					●	
Identify and name points															●													●				●	
Model parallel lines on a geoboard															●																		
Draw parallel lines with a straightedge															●													●	■				
Identify and name lines																												●	■				
Identify, name, and/or model intersecting lines using concrete objects																												●	●				
Identify parallel, nonparallel, and intersecting line segments															●				■									●	■				
Identify and name rays																												●	■				
Draw lines and rays																												●	●		■		
Identify parts of an angle and name angles																												●			■		

Key ● Content taught ■ Content practiced

Lines and Angles (cont.)	1	2	3	4	5	6	7	8	9	10	1	2	3	4	5	6	7	8	9	10	11	12	1	2	3	4	5	6	7	8	9	10	11
Model line segments, rays, and angles																												●			■		
Measure angles with degree units																												●			■		●
Solve degree problems																																	●
Plane and Solid Figures	**1**	**2**	**3**	**4**	**5**	**6**	**7**	**8**	**9**	**10**	**1**	**2**	**3**	**4**	**5**	**6**	**7**	**8**	**9**	**10**	**11**	**12**	**1**	**2**	**3**	**4**	**5**	**6**	**7**	**8**	**9**	**10**	**11**
Explore shape relationships	●	■										■			●				●	■	■	■			●			●			■		
Recognizes open and closed figures							■				■	■		■														■			■		
Identify characteristics of 2-dimensional shapes; sort shapes by attributes	●					●	●	■	■	●	■	●		■	●							■						■	■	●			
Explore 2-dimensional shapes utilizing technology or multimedia resources							●																					■					
Identify characteristics and use appropriate vocabulary to describe properties of 2-dimensional shapes	■	●			●	■	●			●					●										●			●	■		■		
Construct models of polygons using manipulatives such as straws, geoboards	■			●		●		●		●			●		●					●					●			●	●		●	■	
Draw 2-dimensional shapes (such as triangles and quadrilaterals); draw/describe objects in the environment that depict geometric figures	●	■				●	●		●	●		■		■	●			■	■	●	■	■			●		■	●		■			
Create/extend designs with 2-dimensional shapes	■	■	●	■	■	■	●		■		●				●				■			■					■	●					
Combine shapes and take them apart to form other shapes			●				●		■	●					●			●		●									●	●	●		
Record shapes or designs				●									●												■		■	■				■	
Identify and draw congruent or similar shapes							●	■	■										■						●		●	●	●				
Classify and name polygons	●		■	■		●									●							■					■	●	●		■		
Compare 2-dimensional shapes	●	■					●	●							●							■			●			●	■				
Compare polygons and non-polygons							■								●													●					
Solve 2-dimensional-shapes problems												■		■	■										■		■	●	●				
Decompose shapes into shares								●	●	■								●		■													
Identify/compare 3-dimensional shapes; sort shapes and/or describe attributes of each group	●					■	●	■	■	●				■	●		■			■	■	■					■	●	■	■	■		

Geometry (cont.)

Key ● Content taught ■ Content practiced

	Grade 1 Units										Grade 2 Units												Grade 3 Units										
Plane and Solid Figures (cont.)	1	2	3	4	5	6	7	8	9	10	1	2	3	4	5	6	7	8	9	10	11	12	1	2	3	4	5	6	7	8	9	10	11
Construct 3-dimensional shapes										●					●				●									●				●	
Identify the number of faces, edges, vertices, and bases of prisms and pyramids															●													●	●	■	■	●	
Identify the shapes of faces							■										■											●	■			●	
Explore slanted 3-dimensional shapes																	■											●				■	
Transformations and Symmetry	1	2	3	4	5	6	7	8	9	10	1	2	3	4	5	6	7	8	9	10	11	12	1	2	3	4	5	6	7	8	9	10	11
Identify symmetrical figures or symmetry in the environment							●	■	●					■	●													●		●			
Fold and cut symmetrical shapes							●	■							●													●					
Create/complete a symmetrical design/shape using concrete models, geoboard, and/or technology							●		●						●	■		■										●	■	■			
Identify lines of symmetry							●		●						●	■	■		■	■							■	●	■	■			
Use objects to explore slides, flips, and turns; predict the results of changing a shape's position or orientation using slides, flips, and turns			●												■													■					
Model clockwise and counterclockwise turns/rotations																												●					●
Spatial	1	2	3	4	5	6	7	8	9	10	1	2	3	4	5	6	7	8	9	10	11	12	1	2	3	4	5	6	7	8	9	10	11
Recognize that the quantity remains the same when the spatial arrangement changes		●																										●		■			
Arrange or describe objects by proximity, position, or direction using words such as *over, under, above, below, inside, outside, beside, in front of, behind*			●				●																					●					
Give or follow directions for finding a place or object							■		●											■								●					
Identify structures from different views or match views of the same structures portrayed from different perspectives						●								■														●					

Patterns, Functions, and Algebra

Key ● Content taught ■ Content practiced

	Grade 1 Units										Grade 2 Units												Grade 3 Units										
Patterns and Functions	1	2	3	4	5	6	7	8	9	10	1	2	3	4	5	6	7	8	9	10	11	12	1	2	3	4	5	6	7	8	9	10	11
Explore and extend visual patterns		■	●	■	■	●	●					■				■	●							●		■			■				
Find patterns and common attributes in objects and people in the real world		■		●	●	■						■		●	●	■												●					●
Create and complete patterns with 2-dimensional shapes	■	■	●	■	■	■	■		■		■					■	●	●		●							●			■			
Identify and use patterns on a number grid			■	●	●				●	●	■	■		■	■		●			■			●	■		●	●	■					
Add and subtract using a number grid									●		●	■			■					■	■		■	■		■		■					
Investigate even and odd number patterns; create, describe, extend simple number patterns/sequences			●	■							●	●	■										●			■				■			
Explore counting patterns using a calculator			●								●					■	●							■		■							
Solve "What's My Rule?" (function machine) problems					●	●		■	■	■		●	■	●			●			■	●	■		●		●		■	●		●		
Solve Frames-and-Arrows problems with one or two rules			●	■	■	■			■	■	■	■	●	■		■		■	■	■	■		●	■	■	●		■	■	■	■		
Find patterns in addition and subtraction facts					●	●		●	■			■	●							■	■		●	●	■	■		■	●				
Explore patterns in doubling or halving numbers					●							●				■	●			■	■				■	■							
Find patterns in multiplication and division facts																	■				●	●				●			●	■	■	■	■
Find patterns in multiples of 10, 100, and 1,000													■							■	●						■		●	●	●	●	●
Investigate square numbers																					■					■			■				
Find number patterns that describe the relationship between similar figures																									●				■	■		■	■
Identify and/or use number patterns in data or to solve problems																							●	●			■		●		●	■	■
Algebraic Notation and Solving Number Sentences	1	2	3	4	5	6	7	8	9	10	1	2	3	4	5	6	7	8	9	10	11	12	1	2	3	4	5	6	7	8	9	10	11
Determine whether equations are true or false			●	■	●			■																									
Use symbols ×, ÷, =																●	●				●	●				●	■	■	●	■	●	■	
Use symbols +, −, =; pictures; manipulatives; and models to organize, record, and communicate mathematical ideas		●	●	■	●	●	●	●	●	●	●	■	●	●	■	■	■		●	●	●		●	●	■	■	■		■	■			
Use a symbol or letter to represent the unknown number														●		●								●		●	■	■	●	■	●		
Compare numbers using <, > symbols					●	■		■		■	●	■	●	■		■	■		■	■	■	■	●			■	●						

Patterns, Functions, and Algebra (cont.)

Key ● Content taught ■ Content practiced

	Grade 1 Units										Grade 2 Units												Grade 3 Units										
Algebraic Notation and Solving Number Sentences	1	2	3	4	5	6	7	8	9	10	1	2	3	4	5	6	7	8	9	10	11	12	1	2	3	4	5	6	7	8	9	10	11
Write/solve addition and subtraction number sentences		●					●	●	●	■	●	■	●	●	■	■	■		●	●	●		●	●	■	■			●	■			
Write/solve number sentences with missing addends					●							●				■	■		●	●	●			●	■	■			■				
Write/solve multiplication number sentences																●	●				●	●				●	■	■	●	■	●	■	
Write/solve division number sentences																					●	●				●				■	■		
Write/solve number sentences with missing factors; know that symbols can be used to represent missing or unknown quantities														●		●					●	●		●		●	■	■	●	■	●		
Order of Operations	1	2	3	4	5	6	7	8	9	10	1	2	3	4	5	6	7	8	9	10	11	12	1	2	3	4	5	6	7	8	9	10	11
Make up and/or solve number sentences involving parentheses																				●									●	■	●		
Add/subtract 2-digit numbers in number sentences containing parentheses																													●	■	●	■	■
Properties of Arithmetic Operations	1	2	3	4	5	6	7	8	9	10	1	2	3	4	5	6	7	8	9	10	11	12	1	2	3	4	5	6	7	8	9	10	11
Investigate properties of addition/subtraction		●	●	●	●	●						●												●	■		●		●				
Investigate properties of multiplication/division																					●	●				●			●	■	●	●	
Explore number properties (commutative, zero, and identity)					■																		■	●		●	■	■	●				

Index

C

G

H

I

L

O

P

Z

Notes

Notes

Notes

otes